Intermediate Logic

TEACHER

Meet the Canon Logic Series:

Introductory Logic	ITEM#	*Intermediate Logic*	ITEM#
Student Text	N-160	Student Text	N-162
Teacher Edition	N-161	Teacher Edition	N-163
Test and Quiz Packet	N-164	Test and Quiz Packet	N-165
DVD Course	DVD-N160	DVD Course	DVD-N162

The Amazing Dr. Ransom's Bestiary of Adorable Fallacies	
Student Edition with Answer Key	N-903
Adorable Fallacy Flashcards	N-904
Fallacy Flashcards (Classroom)	N-904LG

Free fallacy tests at www.canonpress.com/fallacies

Intermediate Logic: Mastering Propositional Arguments, Teacher
Third edition, revised and expanded. First edition 1996, revised 2002. Second edition, revised and expanded, 2006. Third edition, revised and expanded, 2014.

Published by Canon Press
P. O. Box 8729, Moscow, Idaho 83843
800-488-2034 | www.canonpress.com

Cover design by David Dalbey. Cover illustration by Forrest Dickison.
Interior design by Laura Storm and Jared Miller. Interior layout by Valerie Anne Bost.
Thanks to Leta Sundet for her help with constructing the teaching notes.
Printed in the United States of America.

ISBN-13: 978-1-59128-168-9
ISBN-10: 1-59128-168-7

Library of Congress Cataloging-in-Publication Data is available at www.canonpress.com.

20 21 9 8 7

INTERMEDIATE LOGIC

Mastering Propositional Arguments

TEACHER: THIRD EDITION

Canon Logic Series

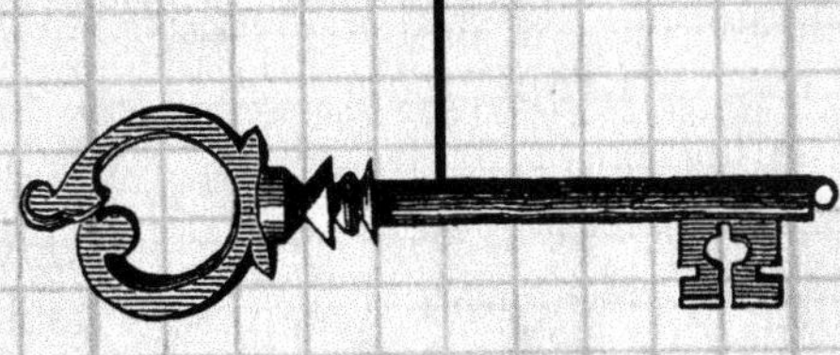

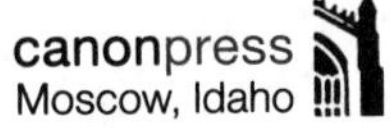

PUBLISHER'S NOTE from CANON PRESS

SCHEDULES

It's up to you to choose the pace for working through *Intermediate Logic*. If you're comfortable with moving at a quick pace, and can schedule three to five classes per week, you can work through the course in one semester. Those who prefer a more leisurely pace can plan to complete the course in a year with one to three class meetings per week. On the following pages, we have provided four sample schedules—one semester or a full year, including or not including the optional Unit 5. Use these as a guideline, and adapt as needed to meet the needs of your class or homeschool. Just cover the material listed for each week in as many days as you have, and you'll finish on time. Or tighten or expand either schedule to suit your students' pace and the time you have allotted for the course.

PAGE NUMBERS

This Teacher text contains the entire Student version as well—with the same page numbers as the students you'll be teaching. The Arabic numerals (on single-columned pages) are the same in both texts. Your teacher notes (double-columned pages) are numbered with Roman numerals.

DAILY LESSON PLANS

Each student lesson in the Teacher edition is accompanied by double-columned teaching notes: objectives, step-by-step teaching instructions, assignments, and more. You can decide whether you want to read through the lesson with the students out loud, have the students read through it alone and then teach through it, teach through it without reading it...whatever suits your personal teaching style best.

GRADING

This Teacher Edition contains all the answers you need for all exercises, quizzes, and tests. For many lessons, answers may vary depending on the imagination and creativity of your students. Expect this; you'll still be able to grade the differing answers fairly if you, as teacher, thoroughly understand the principles involved. We've included point values for each quiz or exercise question to help with this. Consider giving partial credit for incorrect answers that have a piece of the final answer right. If you mark an answer wrong, but a student thinks it is *not* wrong, consider allowing them to try to argue the point back, in writing. This gives them practice arguing, and they just might be right.

DVD COURSE

If you can take advantage of the fantastic DVD course companion, we'd suggest that you watch the day's lesson first (let our teacher's years of experience do the hard work), and then you can answer any questions as your students work on the exercises. The DVD works through every "Form B" Test, so the DVD can be especially helpful for practice tests.

As always, if you've got questions, ideas, or just want to get in touch, call 208-892-8074 or find us online at www.canonpress.com. We'd love to help you as you teach the mastery of propositional arguments.

SCHEDULE OPTION 1A: ONE SEMESTER (NOT INCLUDING UNIT 5)

This schedule will allow you to cover the contents of *Intermediate Logic* meeting daily over the course a sixteen-week semester. Adapt as needed if you meet fewer days per week.

Week	Day	Text	Assignment
1	Mon	Lesson 1	Exercise 1
	Tues	Lesson 2	Exercise 2
	Wed	Quiz Day	*Quiz One*
	Thur	Lesson 3	Exercise 3, 1–3
	Fri		Exercise 3, 4–15
2	Mon	Lesson 4	Exercise 4, 1–2
	Tues		Exercise 4, 3–15
	Wed	Quiz Day	*Quiz Two*
	Thur	Review for Test	Review Questions
	Fri	Test Day	*Test One*
3	Mon	Lesson 5	Exercise 5
	Tues	Lesson 6	Exercise 6
	Wed	Quiz Day	*Quiz Three*
	Thur	Lesson 7	Exercise 7a, 1–10
	Fri		Exercise 7a, 11–14
4	Mon		Exercise 7b
	Tues	Quiz Day	*Quiz Four*
	Wed	Review for Test	Review Questions
	Thur	Test Day	*Test Two*
	Fri	Lesson 8	Exercise 8, 1–6
5	Mon		Exercise 8, 7–12
	Tues	Lessons 9	Exercise 9
	Wed	Quiz Day	*Quiz Five*
	Thur	Lesson 10	Exercise 10
	Fri	Lesson 11	Exercise 11
6	Mon	Lesson 12	Exercise 12
	Tues	Quiz Day	*Quiz Six*
	Wed	Review for Test	Review Questions
	Thur	Test Day	*Test Three*
	Fri	Lesson 13	Exercise 13
7	Mon	Lesson 14	Exercise 14a, 1–9
	Tues		Exercise 14a, 10–16
	Wed	Quiz Day	*Quiz Seven*
	Thur		Exercise 14b
	Fri	Lesson 15	Exercise 15a, 1–6
8	Mon		Exercise 15a, 7–16
	Tues	Quiz Day	*Quiz Eight*
	Wed		Exercise 15b
	Thur	Review for Test	Review Questions
	Fri	Test Day	*Test Four*
9	Mon	Lesson 16	Exercise 16, 1–10
	Tues		Exercise 16, 11–18
	Wed	Quiz Day	*Quiz Nine*
	Thur	Lesson 17	Exercise 17a, 1–6
	Fri		Exercise 17a, 7–9
10	Mon		Lesson 17a, 10–14
	Tues		Exercise 17b
	Wed	Quiz Day	*Quiz Ten*
	Thur	Review for Test	Review Questions
	Fri	Test Day	*Test Five*
11	Mon	Lesson 18	Exercise 18, 1–4
	Tues		Exercise 18, 5–9
	Wed	Lesson 19	Exercise 29
	Thur	Quiz Day	*Quiz Eleven*
	Fri	Lesson 20	Exercise 20, 1–2
12	Mon		Exercise 20, 3–7
	Tues	Lesson 29	Exercise 21
	Wed	Quiz Day	*Quiz Twelve*
	Thur	Review for Test	Review Questions
	Fri	Test Day	*Test Six*
13	Mon	Lesson 22	Exercise 22
	Tues	Lesson 23	Exercise 23
	Wed	Lesson 24	Exercise 24
	Thur	Quiz Day	*Quiz Thirteen*
	Fri	Lesson 25	Exercise 25
14	Mon	Lesson 26	Exercise 26
	Tues	Lesson 27	Exercise 27
	Wed	Quiz Day	*Quiz Fourteen*
	Thur	Review for Test	Review Questions
	Fri	Test Day	*Test Seven*
15	Mon	Lesson 28	Exercise 28a
	Tues		Exercise 28b
	Wed		Exercise 28c, 1–4
	Thur		Exercise 28c, 5–9
	Fri	Quiz Day	*Quiz Fifteen*
16	Mon	Review for Comprehensive Exam	
	Tues	Review for Comprehensive Exam	
	Wed	Exam	*Comprehensive Exam*

SCHEDULE OPTION 1B: ONE SEMESTER (INCLUDING UNIT 5)

This schedule will allow you to cover the contents of *Intermediate Logic* meeting daily over the course a twenty-week semester. Adapt as needed if you meet fewer days per week.

Week	Day	Text	Assignment
1	Mon	Lesson 1	Exercise 1
	Tues	Lesson 2	Exercise 2
	Wed	Quiz Day	*Quiz One*
	Thur	Lesson 3	Exercise 3, 1–3
	Fri		Exercise 3, 4–15
2	Mon	Lesson 4	Exercise 4, 1–2
	Tues		Exercise 4, 3–15
	Wed	Quiz Day	*Quiz Two*
	Thur	Review for Test	Review Questions
	Fri	Test Day	*Test One*
3	Mon	Lesson 5	Exercise 5
	Tues	Lesson 6	Exercise 6
	Wed	Quiz Day	*Quiz Three*
	Thur	Lesson 7	Exercise 7a, 1–10
	Fri		Exercise 7a, 11–14
4	Mon		Exercise 7b
	Tues	Quiz Day	*Quiz Four*
	Wed	Review for Test	Review Questions
	Thur	Test Day	*Test Two*
	Fri	Lesson 8	Exercise 8, 1–6
5	Mon		Exercise 8, 7–12
	Tues	Lessons 9	Exercise 9
	Wed	Quiz Day	*Quiz Five*
	Thur	Lesson 10	Exercise 10
	Fri	Lesson 11	Exercise 11
6	Mon	Lesson 12	Exercise 12
	Tues	Quiz Day	*Quiz Six*
	Wed	Review for Test	Review Questions
	Thur	Test Day	*Test Three*
	Fri	Lesson 13	Exercise 13
7	Mon	Lesson 14	Exercise 14a, 1–9
	Tues		Exercise 14a, 10–16
	Wed	Quiz Day	*Quiz Seven*
	Thur		Exercise 14b
	Fri	Lesson 15	Exercise 15a, 1–6
8	Mon		Exercise 15a, 7–16
	Tues	Quiz Day	*Quiz Eight*
	Wed		Exercise 15b
	Thur	Review for Test	Review Questions
	Fri	Test Day	*Test Four*
9	Mon	Lesson 16	Exercise 16, 1–10
	Tues		Exercise 16, 11–18
	Wed	Quiz Day	*Quiz Nine*
	Thur	Lesson 17	Exercise 17a, 1–6
	Fri		Exercise 17a, 7–9
10	Mon		Lesson 17a, 10–14
	Tues		Exercise 17b
	Wed	Quiz Day	*Quiz Ten*
	Thur	Review for Test	Review Questions
	Fri	Test Day	*Test Five*

Week	Day	Text	Assignment
11	Mon	Lesson 18	Exercise 18, 1–4
	Tues		Exercise 18, 5–9
	Wed	Lesson 19	Exercise 29
	Thur	Quiz Day	*Quiz Eleven*
	Fri	Lesson 20	Exercise 20, 1–2
12	Mon		Exercise 20, 3–7
	Tues	Lesson 29	Exercise 21
	Wed	Quiz Day	*Quiz Twelve*
	Thur	Review for Test	Review Questions
	Fri	Test Day	*Test Six*
13	Mon	Lesson 22	Exercise 22
	Tues	Lesson 23	Exercise 23
	Wed	Lesson 24	Exercise 24
	Thur	Quiz Day	*Quiz Thirteen*
	Fri	Lesson 25	Exercise 25
14	Mon	Lesson 26	Exercise 26
	Tues	Lesson 27	Exercise 27
	Wed	Quiz Day	*Quiz Fourteen*
	Thur	Review for Test	Review Questions
	Fri	Test Day	*Test Seven*
15	Mon	Lesson 28	Exercise 28a
	Tues		Exercise 28b
	Wed		Exercise 28c, 1–4
	Thur		Exercise 28c, 5–9
	Fri	Quiz Day	*Quiz Fifteen*
16	Mon	Lesson 29	Exercise 29
	Tues	Lesson 30	Exercise 30
	Wed	Lesson 31	Exercise 31
	Thur	Quiz Day	*Quiz Sixteen*
	Fri	Lesson 32	Exercise 32
17	Mon	Lesson 33	Exercise 33
	Tues	Lesson 34	Exercise 34
	Wed	Lesson 35	Exercise 35
	Thur	Quiz Day	*Quiz Seventeen*
	Fri	Lesson 36	Exercise 36
18	Mon	Lesson 37	Exercise 37, 1–3
	Tues		Exercise 37, 4–6
	Wed	Lesson 38	Exercise 38
	Thur	Quiz Day	*Quiz Eighteen*
	Fri	Lesson 39	Exercise 39
19	Mon	Lesson 40	Exercise 40a
	Tues	Quiz Day	*Quiz Nineteen*
	Wed		Exercise 40b
	Thur		Exercise 40b continued
	Fri		Exercise 40b continued
20	Mon	Review for Test	Review Questions
	Tues	Test Day	*Test Eight*
	Wed	Review for Comprehensive Exam	
	Thur	Review for Comprehensive Exam	
	Fri	Exam	*Comprehensive Exam*

SCHEDULE OPTION 2A: FULL YEAR (NOT INCLUDING UNIT 5)

This schedule will allow you to cover the contents of *Intermediate Logic* meeting three days per week over the course a thirty-week school year. Adapt as needed if you meet fewer days per week.

Week	Day	Text	Assignment
1	1	Lesson 1	Exercise 1
	2	Lesson 2	Exercise 2
	3	Quiz Day	*Quiz One*
2	4	Lesson 3	Exercise 3, 1–3
	5		Exercise 3, 4–15
	6	Lesson 4	Exercise 4, 1–2
3	7		Exercise 4, 3–15
	8	Finish Exercises and Review	
	9	Quiz Day	*Quiz Two*
4	10	Review for Test	Review Questions
	11	Practice Test	*Test 1a*
	12	Test	*Test 1b*
5	13	Lesson 5	Exercise 5
	14	Lesson 6	Exercise 6
	15	Quiz Day	*Quiz Three*
6	16	Lesson 7	Exercise 7a, 1–10
	17		Exercise 7a, 11–14
	18		Exercise 7b
7	19	Quiz/Test Review	*Quiz Four*
	20	Practice Test	*Test 2a*
	21	Test Day	*Test 2b*
8	22	Lesson 8	Exercise 8, 1–6
	23		Exercise 8, 7–12
	24	Lesson 9	Exercise 9
9	25	Quiz Day	*Quiz Five*
	26	Lesson 10	Exercise 10
	27	Lesson 11	Exercise 11
10	28	Lesson 12	Exercise 12
	29	Finish Exercises and Review	
	30	Quiz Day	*Quiz Six*
11	31	Review for Test	Review Questions
	32	Practice Test	*Test 3a*
	33	Test Day	*Test 3b*
12	34	Lesson 13	Exercise 13
	35	Lesson 14	Exercise 14a, 1–9
	36		Exercise 14a, 10–16
13	37	Quiz Day	*Quiz Seven*
	38		Exercise 14b
	39	Lesson 15	Exercise 15a, 1–6
14	40		Exercise 15a, 7–16
	41	Quiz Day	*Quiz Eight*
	42		Exercise 15b
15	43	Review for Test	Review Questions
	44	Practice Test	*Test 4a*
	45	Test Day	*Test 4b*

Week	Day	Text	Assignment
16	46	Lesson 16	Exercise 16, 1–10
	47		Exercise 16, 11–18
	48	Quiz Day	*Quiz Nine*
17	49	Lesson 17	Exercise 17a, 1–6
	50		Exercise 17a, 7–9
	51		Exercise 17a, 10–14
18	52		Exercise 17b
	53	Finish Exercises and Review	
	54	Quiz Day	*Quiz Ten*
19	55	Review for Test	Review Questions
	56	Practice Test	*Test 5a*
	57	Test Day	*Test 5b*
20	58	Lesson 18	Exercise 18, 1–4
	59		Exercise 18, 5–9
	60	Lesson 19	Exercise 19
21	61	Quiz Day	*Quiz Eleven*
	62	Lesson 20	Exercise 20, 1–2
	63		Exercise 20, 3–7
22	64	Lesson 21	Exercise 21
	65	Finish Exercises and Review	
	66	Quiz Day	*Quiz Twelve*
23	67	Review for Test	Review Questions
	68	Practice Test	*Test 6a*
	69	Test Day	*Test 6b*
24	70	Lesson 22	Exercise 22
	71	Lesson 23	Exercise 23
	72	Finish exercises	
25	73	Lesson 24	Exercise 24
	74	Quiz Day	*Quiz Thirteen*
	75	Lesson 25	Exercise 25
26	76	Lesson 26	Exercise 26
	77	Lesson 27	Exercise 27
	78	Quiz Day	*Quiz Fourteen*
27	79	Review for Test	Review Questions
	80	Practice Test	*Test 7a*
	81	Test Day	*Test 7b*
28	82	Lesson 28	Exercise 28a
	83		Exercise 28b
	84	Finish exercises	
29	85		Exercise 28c, 1–4
	86		Exercise 28c, 5–9
	87	Quiz Day	*Quiz Fifteen*
30	88	Review for Comprehensive Exam	
	89	Review for Comprehensive Exam	
	90	Exam	*Comprehensive Exam*

SCHEDULE OPTION 2B: FULL YEAR (INCLUDING UNIT 5)

This schedule will allow you to cover the contents of *Intermediate Logic* meeting three days per week over the course a thirty-seven-week school year. Adapt as needed if you meet fewer days per week.

Week	Day	Text	Assignment
1	1	Lesson 1	Exercise 1
	2	Lesson 2	Exercise 2
	3	Quiz Day	*Quiz One*
2	4	Lesson 3	Exercise 3, 1–3
	5		Exercise 3, 4–15
	6	Lesson 4	Exercise 4, 1–2
3	7		Exercise 4, 3–15
	8	Finish Exercises and Review	
	9	Quiz Day	*Quiz Two*
4	10	Review for Test	Review Questions
	11	Practice Test	*Test 1a*
	12	Test	*Test 1b*
5	13	Lesson 5	Exercise 5
	14	Lesson 6	Exercise 6
	15	Quiz Day	*Quiz Three*
6	16	Lesson 7	Exercise 7a, 1–10
	17		Exercise 7a, 11–14
	18		Exercise 7b
7	19	Quiz/Test Review	*Quiz Four*
	20	Practice Test	*Test 2a*
	21	Test Day	*Test 2b*
8	22	Lesson 8	Exercise 8, 1–6
	23		Exercise 8, 7–12
	24	Lesson 9	Exercise 9
9	25	Quiz Day	*Quiz Five*
	26	Lesson 10	Exercise 10
	27	Lesson 11	Exercise 11
10	28	Lesson 12	Exercise 12
	29	Finish Exercises and Review	
	30	Quiz Day	*Quiz Six*
11	31	Review for Test	Review Questions
	32	Practice Test	*Test 3a*
	33	Test Day	*Test 3b*
12	34	Lesson 13	Exercise 13
	35	Lesson 14	Exercise 14a, 1–9
	36		Exercise 14a, 10–16
13	37	Quiz Day	*Quiz Seven*
	38		Exercise 14b
	39	Lesson 15	Exercise 15a, 1–6
14	40		Exercise 15a, 7–16
	41	Quiz Day	*Quiz Eight*
	42		Exercise 15b
15	43	Review for Test	Review Questions
	44	Practice Test	*Test 4a*
	45	Test Day	*Test 4b*
16	46	Lesson 16	Exercise 16, 1–10
	47		Exercise 16, 11–18
	48	Quiz Day	*Quiz Nine*
17	49	Lesson 17	Exercise 17a, 1–6
	50		Exercise 17a, 7–9
	51		Exercise 17a, 10–14
18	52		Exercise 17b
	53	Finish Exercises and Review	
	54	Quiz Day	*Quiz Ten*
19	55	Review for Test	Review Questions
	56	Practice Test	*Test 5a*
	57	Test Day	*Test 5b*
20	58	Lesson 18	Exercise 18, 1–4
	59		Exercise 18, 5–9
	60	Lesson 19	Exercise 19
21	61	Quiz Day	*Quiz Eleven*
	62	Lesson 20	Exercise 20, 1–2
	63		Exercise 20, 3–7
22	64	Lesson 21	Exercise 21
	65	Finish Exercises and Review	
	66	Quiz Day	*Quiz Twelve*
23	67	Review for Test	Review Questions
	68	Practice Test	*Test 6a*
	69	Test Day	*Test 6b*
24	70	Lesson 22	Exercise 22
	71	Lesson 23	Exercise 23
	72	Finish exercises	
25	73	Lesson 24	Exercise 24
	74	Quiz Day	*Quiz Thirteen*
	75	Lesson 25	Exercise 25
26	76	Lesson 26	Exercise 26
	77	Lesson 27	Exercise 27
	78	Quiz Day	*Quiz Fourteen*
27	79	Review for Test	Review Questions
	80	Practice Test	*Test 7a*
	81	Test Day	*Test 7b*
28	82	Lesson 28	Exercise 28a
	83		Exercise 28b
	84	Finish exercises	
29	85		Exercise 28c, 1–4
	86		Exercise 28c, 5–9
	87	Quiz Day	*Quiz Fifteen*
30	88	Lesson 29	Exercise 29
	89	Lesson 30	Exercise 30
	90	Lesson 31	Exercise 31
31	91	Quiz Day	*Quiz Sixteen*
	92	Lesson 32	Exercise 32
	93	Lesson 33	Exercise 33
32	94	Lesson 34	Exercise 34
	95	Lesson 35	Exercise 35
	96	Quiz Day	*Quiz Seventeen*
33	97	Lesson 36	Exercise 36
	98	Lesson 37	Exercise 37
	99	Lesson 38	Exercise 38
34	100	Quiz Day	*Quiz Eighteen*
	101	Lesson 39	Exercise 39
	102	Lesson 40	Exercise 40a
35	103	Quiz Day	*Quiz Nineteen*
	104	Project	Exercise 40b
	105		Exercise 40b continued
36	106	Review for Test	Review Questions
	107	Practice Test	*Test 8a*
	108	Test Day	*Test 8b*
37	109	Review for Comprehensive Exam	
	110	Review for Comprehensive Exam	
	111	Exam	*Comprehensive Exam*

INTERMEDIATE LOGIC

CONTENTS

UNIT TWO: FORMAL PROOFS OF VALIDITY

UNIT THREE: TRUTH TREES

UNIT FOUR: APPLYING THE TOOLS TO ARGUMENTS

UNIT FIVE: DIGITAL LOGIC

APPENDICES

PREFACE to the FIRST EDITION

This text, *Intermediate Logic: Mastering Propositional Arguments,* is designed as a continuation to *Introductory Logic: The Fundamentals of Thinking Well.* Together, these two textbooks should provide sufficient material for a complete course in basic logic.

We have attempted to make this a useable workbook for the logic student. To that end we have included exercises for every lesson, each of which has been developed and used over many years of logic classes. The goal is to keep the text clear and complete, such that an adult could teach himself the fundamentals of logic.

A number of other logic texts were consulted throughout the writing of *Intermediate Logic.* Most helpful was Irving Copi's invaluable *Introduction To Logic* (Macmillan Publishing Co., 1978). While we did not lift material directly from it, of course, that book has so shaped our own understanding of this subject that *Intermediate Logic* undoubtedly echoes much of its format and contents. *Intermediate Logic* has also benefitted from *The Art of Reasoning* by David Kelley (W. W. Norton & Company, Inc., 1990) and *The Logic Book* by Bergmann, Moor, and Nelson (McGraw-Hill, Inc., 1990).

Although we cannot list them here, we are indebted to many people for the completion of this project. We give special credit to the students throughout the years who have been introduced to the beauty and practicality of the world of logic found in the pages of these textbooks. Good students always force teachers to re-evaluate their own understanding of a subject, and such students have contributed more to this book than we or they realize.

PREFACE to the SECOND EDITION

The subject of logic may be divided into two main branches: formal and informal. The definition of logic as "the science and the art of correct reasoning" allows us to distinguish these two branches. Formal logic deals *directly* with reasoning. Reasoning means "drawing conclusions from other information." Whenever we consider how to analyze and write logical arguments—in which conclusions are drawn from premises—we are working in the realm of formal logic. Informal logic, on the other hand, deals more *indirectly* with reasoning. When we argue, we often find ourselves defining terms, determining the truth values of statements, and detecting spurious informal fallacies. While in none of these activities do we concentrate on reasoning in a formal way, we do recognize that such activities are indirectly related to and support the process of reasoning, and are thus best included under informal logic.

With this in mind, several changes were made in 2006 to this second edition of *Intermediate Logic*. If it's of interest, those changes are listed below.

First, in order to present to the student a more logical progression of topics, the section on defining terms from the first edition has been entirely removed from this text and placed at the beginning of *Introductory Logic*, where it is taught along with other branches of informal logic and categorical logic. Consequently, this text now focuses solely on the branch of formal logic called propositional logic, of which formal proofs of validity and truth trees are subsets.

Second, review questions and review exercises have been added to each unit for every lesson in the text, effectively doubling the number of exercises for students to verify their knowledge and develop their understanding of the material. Additionally, some especially challenging problems which relate to the material have been included in the review exercises. Students who can correctly answer all of the review questions demonstrate a sufficient knowledge of the important concepts. Students who can correctly solve the review exercises demonstrate a sufficient understanding of how to apply those concepts.

Third, the definitions of important terms, key points made, and caution signs regarding common errors are now set apart in the margins of the text. This should help students to distinguish the most important topics, as well as aid in their review of the material.

Fourth, every lesson has been reviewed in detail with the goal of improving the clarity of the explanations and correcting several minor errors that were found in the first edition. To all logic students and teachers goes the credit for any improvements that have been made in this second edition; for those remaining errors and defects we take full responsibility.

PREFACE to the THIRD EDITION

Formal logic is a fascinating subject. Students are often intrigued by the concepts and methods of reasoning revealed in it. Truth tables, formal proofs, and other operations of propositional logic challenge their ability to think abstractly, and provide opportunities to practice and develop their puzzle solving skills. Pure logic is fun. But for students to learn how to reason properly, and through the process of reasoning to recognize and discover truth, they must learn how to apply these methods of formal logic to the world around them.

Many teachers and parents want logic to be practical. They want their logic students to be able to employ symbolic logic as a tool of thinking, a tool both powerful and flexible enough to use in many different ways and on many different media.

With these things in mind, in 2014 we added two important sections on the practical applications of propositional logic to the third edition.

First, a new lesson teaches students how to apply the tools that they have learned to actual arguments. Lesson 28 teaches students how to analyze chains of reasoning found in writings such as philosophy and theology. Though some new concepts are introduced, most of this lesson is aimed at teaching students to employ what they have learned in the previous 27 lessons. This one lesson therefore has three corresponding exercises, giving students the opportunity to work through small portions of three ancient texts: Boethius's *The Consolation of Philosophy*, the Apostle Paul's argument on the resurrection from 1 Corinthians 15, and a section on angelic will from Augustine's *City of God*. The additional exercises for this lesson also consider Deuteronomy 22, a portion from Martin Luther's sermon on John chapter 1, and a witty interchange that you may have seen in the 2008 action comedy *Get Smart*.

Second, a longer optional unit has been added on the useful and stimulating topic of digital logic. Unit 5 includes twelve new lessons that unlock the logic of electronic devices. These lessons work through the concepts of digital displays, binary numbers, and the design and simplification of digital logic circuits. Many of the lessons learned earlier in the text are given new and intriguing applications, as students learn how to employ propositional logic to understand the electronic gadgets that they see and use every day. The final exercise gives students the opportunity to design a complex circuit that can convert a binary input to a decimal display output. This unit has become a favorite of many logic students over the past decades.

It is our hope that these additions give students a vision of the power of propositional logic and fulfill teachers' and parents' desires to make propositional logic more practical.

INTRODUCTION

Logic has been defined both as the *science* and the *art* of correct reasoning. People who study different sciences observe a variety of things: biologists observe living organisms, astronomers observe the heavens, and so on. From their observations they seek to discover natural laws by which God governs His creation. The person who studies logic as a science observes the mind as it reasons—as it draws conclusions from premises—and from those observations discovers laws of reasoning which God has placed in the minds of people. Specifically, he seeks to discover the principles or laws which may be used to distinguish good reasoning from poor reasoning. In deductive logic, good reasoning is *valid* reasoning—in which the conclusions follow necessarily from the premises. Logic as a science discovers the principles of valid and invalid reasoning.

Logic as an *art* provides the student of this art with practical skills to construct arguments correctly as he writes, discusses, debates, and communicates. As an art logic also provides him with rules to judge what is spoken or written, in order to determine the validity of what he hears and reads. Logic as a science discovers rules. Logic as an art teaches us to apply those rules.

Logic may also be considered as a symbolic language which represents the reasoning inherent in other languages. It does so by breaking the language of arguments down into symbolic form, simplifying them such that the arrangement of the language, and thus the reasoning within it, becomes apparent. The outside, extraneous parts of arguments are removed like a biology student in the dissection lab removes the skin, muscles and organs of a frog, revealing the skeleton of bare reasoning inside. Thus revealed, the logical structure of an argument can be examined, judged and, if need be, corrected, using the rules of logic.

So logic is a symbolic language into which arguments in other languages may be translated. Now arguments are made up of propositions, which in turn are made up of terms. In categorical logic, symbols (usually capital letters) are used to represent terms. Thus "All men are sinners" is translated "All M are S." In propositional logic, the branch of logic with which this book primarily deals, letters are used to represent entire propositions. Other symbols are used to represent the logical operators which modify or relate those propositions. So the argument, "If I don't eat, then I will be hungry; I am not hungry, so I must have eaten" may appear as $\sim E \supset H, \sim H, \therefore E$.

Unit 1 of this book covers the translation and analysis of such propositional arguments, with the primary concern of determining the validity of those arguments. Unit 2 introduces a new kind of logical exercise: the writing of formal proofs of validity and related topics. Unit 3 completes propositional logic with a new technique for analyzing arguments: truth trees. Unit 4 considers how to apply these tools and techniques to arguments contained in real-life writings: philosophy, theology, and the Bible itself. Unit 5 introduces digital logic and helps students to unlock the logic of electronic devices.

UNIT 1

TRUTH TABLES

CONTENTS

TEACHER'S NOTES on LESSON 1

INTRODUCTION TO PROPOSITIONAL LOGIC

Intermediate Logic, pp. 9–11

STUDENT OBJECTIVES

1. Define "proposition," "logical operator," and "truth functional."
2. Distinguish between simple and compound propositions, and between propositional constants and variables.
3. Complete Exercise 1.

SPECIAL NOTES

1. It is up to you whether you read the chapter aloud with students prior to teaching the material, read through it in chunks and teach as you go, or teach straight through the lesson and have students read the chapter on their own later. The lesson plans are designed to stand alone; they cover all the material in the chapter, so you may find it redundant to read the chapter aloud as well. At some point, however, the students should read through the chapter on their own.
2. Before beginning the lesson, it may be good to refresh some memories. Ask the students a few questions: What are we studying when we study logic? How is logic a science? How is logic an art? Have them refer to the Introduction on p. 5 if they're clueless.

TEACHING INSTRUCTIONS

1. Write "languages" on the board. Have students shout out the names of as many different languages as they can think of (French, Latin, German, Russian, Swahili) and list them on the board. Tell them that there is one language that you don't expect them to think of. Some smarty-pants will probably eventually suggest "logic." Explain that logic is indeed a language: a symbolic language that arguments in every other language can be translated into.
2. Remind students that earlier they studied categorical logic, and in categorical logic they used symbols to represent terms (All M are S), because terms ("bird," "bat," "bandits") were the basic unit of thought. Explain that this semester they will be studying **propositional logic, a branch of logic in which the basic unit of thought is the proposition**. Have somebody take a stab at defining "proposition." Explain that **a proposition is simply a statement**. Write on the board the three sentences from Intermediate Logic p. 9: "God loves the world," "The world is loved by God," and "Deus mundum amat." Explain that even though these are three different sentences, they all have the same meaning, and they therefore represent the same proposition.
3. Explain that "propositional logic" is often called "symbolic logic," because in propositional logic we replace almost all the words with symbols. Letters are used to represent not terms but whole propositions. For example, the proposi-

tion "Women are humans" would be represented not by "All W are H" but just by "W."

4. Explain that propositional or symbolic logic deals with **truth-functional propositions, propositions in which the truth value of the proposition depends on the truth value of the component parts.** Reassure students that if that makes no sense to them yet, that's okay, it will soon. Write on the board "There are stars in the sky." Ask how many component parts (statements) this proposition has (one). Explain that **if a proposition has only one component part it is a simple proposition. If it has more than one component part, or is somehow modified, it is a compound proposition.** Ask students how they might turn the simple proposition on the board into a compound proposition (something like: "There are stars in the sky but there is no moon.") Write this compound proposition on the board. Circle the word "but." Tell students that **words like "and," "but," and "or," which combine or modify simple propositions to make compound propositions, are called logical operators.**
5. Explain that the new sentence on the board is a truth-functional compound proposition. It is truth-functional because whether or not it is true depends on whether or not the two statements inside it are true. If it is actually the case *both* that there are stars in the sky and that there is no moon, then the whole proposition is true as well. But if either of those statements are false—there aren't any stars out or there is in fact a moon—the whole proposition is false.
6. Go back to the simple proposition "There are stars in the sky." Explain that there is another logical operator we can add to this simple proposition to make it a compound proposition: "It is false that." Write "It is false that there are stars in the sky." Make sure students can see that this is in fact compound: it contains a statement that could stand alone ("There are stars in the sky"). Explain that this new proposition is also truth-functional; the truth value of "It is false that there are stars in the sky," depends on the truth value of "There are stars in the sky." Ask students what the truth value of the whole proposition is if "There are stars in the sky" is false. If it's true?
7. Write on the board "I believe that there are stars in the sky." Ask students if this statement is truth-functional. Does the truth or falsity of the component part ("There are stars in the sky") effect the truth or falsity of the whole? Make sure students can see that because "I believe that there are stars in the sky" is a self-report, it can be considered true whether or not the component part is true; it could be true that you believe there are stars even if its false that there are any. Thus, self-reports are not truth-functional.
8. Explain that just as in syllogisms we abbreviated terms to make them easier to work with, in compound propositions we abbreviate the component parts—the simple propositions—so that we can handle them more easily. Explain that **a propositional constant is an uppercase letter that represents a single, given proposition**. Usually we choose propositional constants that have some connection with the propositions they symbolize: i.e., "The walrus ate me" would probably be abbreviated "W," and "Stephanie ate a cookie" would be abbreviated "S." But if you had the propositions "Stephanie ate a cookie" along with "Stephanie drank milk," you would probably abbreviate them as "C" and "M," respectively. Emphasize that within one argument or compound proposition it is important to use the same propositional constant to represent the same proposition every time it appears. Make sure students understand that a simple proposition cannot be represented by more than one constant: you are abbreviating not the terms but the whole statement.

9. Explain to students that we only use uppercase letters when we are dealing with particular, known propositions. If we want to emphasize the form of an argument and not the content of it, we use **propositional variables: lowercase letters that represent any proposition.** Explain that using propositional variables in logic is a lot like using "x" and "y" in algebra: just like x and y represent an unlimited number of possible numbers, propositional variables represent any unlimited number of possible propositions. Explain that for some reason when using propositional variables, we usually begin with the letter "p" and continue from there (q, r, s, . . .). Who knows what those original logicians had against the first half of the alphabet.

10. Tell students to take a deep breath: you are about to make this all rather more complicated. While a simple proposition cannot be represented by more than one constant or variable, a compound proposition doesn't have to be represented by more than one. A compound proposition can be represented by one constant or variable. Write on the board "It is false that if the Walrus eats Stephanie, then, if Stephanie does not eat a cookie, then the Walrus will not get indigestion." Explain that you could abbreviate this very compound proposition as *~[S ⊃ (~C ⊃ ~I)].* Or you could abbreviate it simply as "F." Explain that how you decide to abbreviate a compound proposition depends on the context, and that students will learn how to do this in the next few lessons.

ASSIGNMENT

Have students complete Exercise 1, and go over it with them.

LESSON 1

INTRODUCTION TO PROPOSITIONAL LOGIC

Propositional logic is a branch of formal, deductive logic in which the basic unit of thought is the propositon. A **proposition** is a statement, a sentence which has a truth value. A single proposition can be expressed by many different sentences. The following sentences all represent the same proposition:

God loves the world.
The world is loved by God.
Deus mundum amat.

These sentences represent the same proposition because they all have the same meaning.

In propositional logic, letters are used as symbols to represent propositions. Other symbols are used to represent words which modify or combine propositions. Because so many symbols are used, propositional logic has also been called "symbolic logic." Symbolic logic deals with **truth-functional propositions**. A proposition is truth-functional when the truth value of the proposition depends upon the truth value of its component parts. If it has only one component part, it is a **simple proposition**. A categorical statement is a simple proposition. The proposition *God loves the world* is simple. If a proposition has more than one component part (or is modified in some other way), it is a **compound proposition**. Words which combine or modify simple propositions in order to form compound propositions (words such as *and* and *or*) are called **logical operators**.

For example, the proposition *God loves the world and God sent His Son* is a truth-functional, compound proposition. The word *and* is the logical operator. It is truth functional because its truth value depends upon the truth value of the two simple propositions which make it up. It is in fact a true proposition, since it is true that God

DEFINITIONS

Propositional logic is a branch of formal, deductive logic in which the basic unit of thought is the proposition. A ***proposition*** is a statement.

KEY POINT

One proposition may be expressed by many different sentences.

DEFINITIONS

A proposition is ***truth-functional*** when its truth value depends upon the truth values of its component parts.

If a proposition has only one component part, it is a ***simple proposition***. Otherwise, it is ***compound***.

DEFINITIONS

Logical operators are words that combine or modify simple propositions to make compound propositions.

A ***propositional constant*** is an uppercase letter that represents a single, given proposition.

A ***propositional variable*** is a lowercase letter that represents any proposition.

loves the world, and it is true that God sent His Son. Similarly, the proposition *It is false that God loves the world* is compound, the phrase *it is false that* being the logical operator. This proposition is also truth-functional, depending upon the truth value of the component *God loves the world* for its total truth value. If *God loves the world* is false, then the proposition *It is false that God loves the world* is true, and vice versa.

However, the proposition *Joe believes that God loves the world,* though compound (being modified by the phrase *Joe believes that),* is *not* truth-functional, because its truth value does not depend upon the truth value of the component part *God loves the world.* The proposition *Joe believes that God loves the world* is a self-report and can thus be considered true, regardless of whether or not *God loves the world* is true.

When a given proposition is analyzed as part of a compound proposition or argument, it is usually abbreviated by a capital letter, called a **propositional constant**. Propositional constants commonly have some connection with the propositions they symbolize, such as being the first letter of the first word, or some other distinctive word within the proposition. For example, the proposition *The mouse ran up the clock* could be abbreviated by the propositional constant M. On the other hand, *The mouse did not run up the clock* may be abbreviated *~M* (read as *not M*). Within one compound proposition or argument, the same propositional constant should be used to represent a given proposition. Note that a simple proposition cannot be represented by more than one constant.

When the *form* of a compound proposition or argument is being emphasized, we use **propositional variables**. It is customary to use lowercase letters as propositional variables, starting with the letter *p* and continuing through the alphabet (*q*, *r*, *s*, . . .). Whereas a propositional constant represents a single, given proposition, a propositional variable represents an unlimited number of propositions.

KEY POINT

A propositional constant or variable can represent a simple proposition or a compound proposition.

It is important to realize that a single constant or variable can represent not only a simple proposition but also a compound proposition. The variable *p* could represent *God loves the world* or it could represent *God loves the world but He hates sin.* The entire compound proposition *It is false that if the mouse ran up the clock, then, if the clock did not strike one, then the mouse would not run down* could be abbreviated by a single constant F, or it could be represented by symbolizing each part, such as ~(M ⊃ (~S ⊃ ~D)). The decision concerning how to abbreviate a compound proposition depends on the purpose for abbreviating it. We will learn how to abbreviate compound propositions in the next few lessons.

SUMMARY

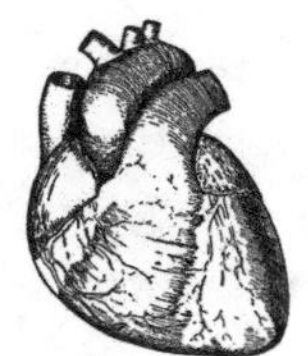

A proposition is a statement. Propositions are truth-functional when the truth value of the proposition depends upon the truth value of its component parts. Propositions are either simple or compound. They are compound if they are modified or combined with other propositions by means of logical operators. Propositional constants are capital letters which represent a single given proposition. Propositional variables are lower case letters which represent an unlimited number of propositions.

EXERCISE 1 (25 points)

What are two main differences between propositional constants and propositional variables? (2 each)

1. Constants represent one given proposition; variables represent any proposition

2. Constants are abbreviated by uppercase letters, variables by lowercase

Modify or add to the simple proposition *We have seen God* to create the following (2 each):

3. A truth-functional compound proposition:

   We have seen God but we will not die.

4. A proposition which is *not* truth-functional:

   I think we have seen God.

Circle S if the given proposition is simple. Circle C if it is compound. (1 each)

5. The Lord will cause your enemies to be defeated before your eyes. (S) C
6. There is a way that seems right to a man but in the end it leads to death. S (C)
7. The fear of the Lord is the beginning of wisdom. (S) C
8. If we confess our sins then He is faithful to forgive us our sins. S (C)
9. It is false that a good tree bears bad fruit and that a bad tree bears good fruit. S (C)
10. The Kingdom of God is not a matter of talk but of power. S (C)

Given that B means *The boys are bad* M means *The man is mad*
G means *The girls are glad* S means *The students are sad*

Translate the following compound propositions (2):

11. It is false that B. The boys are not bad. (2)
12. B or G. The boys are bad or the girls are glad. (2)
13. B and M. The boys are bad and the man is mad. (2)
14. If M then S. If the man is mad, then the students are sad. (2)
15. If not M and not S then G. If the man is not mad and the students are not sad, then the girls are glad. (3)

TEACHER'S NOTES on LESSON 2

NEGATION, CONJUNCTION, AND DISJUNCTION

Intermediate Logic, pp. 15–18

STUDENT OBJECTIVES

1. Provide the symbols, truth-tables, and English equivalents for the three basic logical operators.
2. Complete Exercise 2.

SPECIAL NOTE

Inform students that there will be a quiz next class over Lessons 1 and 2 (depending on which schedule you're following). Encourage them to study particularly the definitions and key points in the margins of their *Intermediate Logic* textbooks. Tell students about the new quiz/test schedule: every week (after this week) they will have a quiz on the lessons covered since the last quiz. Every other week or so, there will be a test on the material from the last two quizzes.

TEACHING INSTRUCTIONS

1. Remind students that they learned last class about logical operators; see if anyone can remember what they are. If they are all at a loss, explain that **logical operators are the words which combine or modify simple propositions to make compound propositions**. Have students give you some examples of these words ("and," "but," "or," "it is false that"). Explain that in this lesson they will be learning about three fundamental logical operators: negation, conjunction, and disjunction. In this lesson you will be asking and answering three questions for each logical operator (write them at the top of the board): What words in English are abbreviated by it? What is its symbol? How is the truth value of the compounds proposition affected by the truth values of the component parts?
2. Write **negation** on the board, and have students take a stab at guessing what words this logical operator represents ("not," "it is false that," or any other phrase that denies the proposition). See if anyone remembers what symbol represents negation and write it on the board (~). Explain that **negation is the logical operator that denies or contradicts a proposition**. Write a proposition on the board (i.e., "Everyone can read"). Have students abbreviate it (i.e., "E"). Write the negation (~E) and then have students translate it ("Not everyone can read" or "Some people cannot read").
3. Have students remember way back to *Introductory Logic* when they learned about contradictions. The contradiction of an A statement ("All S is P") is "Some S is not P" and vice versa. The contradiction of an E statement ("No S is P") is "Some S is P" and vice versa. Since the logical operator negation "contradicts" a proposition, what was true of contradictions is true of a proposition and its negation: if a proposition is true, its negation is false. If a proposition is false, its negation is true. Make sure that students can see this: if it's true that everyone can read, it must be false that some people can't. Explain

that we can express this relationship between the truth values of a proposition and its negation by making a **truth table**. Draw on the board the negation chart:

p	~p
T	F
F	T

Make sure students follow it: if "*p*" is true (T), "*~p*" (be sure to read it as "not p") must be false (F); if *p* is F, *~p* must be T. Explain that a **truth table** like the one that you have just drawn **is a listing of the possible truth values for a set of one or more propositions**. Explain that this negation truth table is called **a defining truth table,** because **it displays the truth values produced by a logical operator modifying a minimum number of variables**. When students look at you like you just spoke Greek, explain that, in other words, this truth table is the simplest truth table possible for negation.

4. Have students guess what words the logical operator **conjunction** represents ("and," "but," "still," or other similar words), and help them see that this makes sense because "conjunction" is when two things come together. Draw the symbol for conjunction, • (called, shockingly, a dot) on the board. Have students tell you how to abbreviate the compound proposition "It is snowing and I am cold" *(S • C)*. Explain that **conjunction is a logical operator that joins two propositions and is true if and only if both the propositions (conjuncts) are true**. If either conjunct is false, the whole thing is false.

5. Draw this (incomplete) truth table for conjunction on the board, leaving the third column (under *p* • *q*) empty for now:

p	q	p • q
T	T	
T	F	
F	T	
F	F	

Explain that the four rows represent all the possible combinations of truth and falsity for the two propositions: that both are true (i.e., it is true both that it is snowing and that I am cold because I am walking around outside), that the first is true and the second false (i.e., it is true that it is snowing, but it is false that I am cold, because I am inside wrapped in a fuzzy blanket), that the first is false and the second true (i.e., it is false that it is snowing, but it is true that I am cold because I am hiding in the fridge), and that both are false (i.e., it is false that it is snowing and it is false that I am cold, because it is summer and I am playing softball). Now walk students through where the T's and F's should go in the final column of the chart. If *p* is true and *q* is true, then of course the proposition *p* • *q* will be true as well. But if *p* is true and *q* is false, the compound proposition is tainted with falsity and the whole thing is false. So with the third row, and, of course, the fourth. The completed table should look like this:

p	q	p • q
T	T	T
T	F	F
F	T	F
F	F	F

6. Point out that in ordinary English the conjunction does not always appear between two distinct sentences; sometimes it's a little less obvious. "I am cold and wet" is still two separate propositions connected by a conjunction: "I am cold and I am wet." Have students symbolize this conjunction *(C • W)*. Then have them symbolize "You and I are both lost" *(Y • I)*.

7. Have students guess what words the logical operator **disjunction** represents. It's not as obvious: "or," as in "I got us lost or you got us lost." Draw the symbol for disjunction, ∨ (called, believe it or not, a "vee"), on the board. Have students symbolize "I got us lost or you got us lost" *(I ∨ Y)*.

8. Explain that in English, the word "or" is ambiguous: it has two different senses. It can mean "this or that, but not both," as in "We are either lost or not lost"; this is called the "exclusive or," because only one of these options can be true. On the other hand, "or" can also mean "this or that, or both," as in "Forest rangers look for the lost or injured." The rangers will look for you if you are lost, or if you are injured, or if you happen to be both lost and injured, they will look for you too. This is called the "inclusive or." Explain that Latin, clever language that it is, has two separate words for "or": "aut" is exclusive and "vel" is inclusive. Emphasize that **in Logic we always use the disjunction in the *inclusive* sense (this or that or both)**, and that is why we represent it as a "∨"—v for "vel." Explain that **disjunction**, then, **is the logical operator that joins two propositions and is true if and only if one or both of the propositions (disjuncts) is true**.

9. This time, have students tell you how to set up the truth table for disjunction, leaving out the third column for the moment:

p	q	p ∨ q
T	T	
T	F	
F	T	
F	F	

Explain that once again that first two columns represent all possible combinations of truth and falsity between the two propositions: True and true, true and false, false and true, and false and false. Walk students through determining the final column and fill it in as they figure it out: if p is true and q is true, $p \vee q$ must also be true, because "or" is inclusive. If p is true and q is false, $p \vee q$ is still true because one of the propositions at least is true; it is the same if p is false and q is true. But if both p and q are false, the whole compound proposition is, of course, false. The completed table should look like this:

p	q	p ∨ q
T	T	T
T	F	T
F	T	T
F	F	F

10. Explain that students may find themselves in a situation where they need to use an exclusive "or" instead of an inclusive "or," i.e., "Either the ranger is on his way or he has forgotten us." In that case they will have to symbolize the proposition in a much more complicated way: $(O \vee F) \bullet \sim(O \bullet F)$—that is, "Either the ranger is on his way or he is still at the fort, but he is not both on his way and at the fort." Tell students that they should always assume "or" to be *inclusive* unless otherwise instructed. Keep in mind that sometimes people use the word either to help indicate the exclusive sense of the disjunction, but other times "either p or q" is just a way of saying "p or q" with more words.

11. Write on the board $A \vee B \bullet C$. Ask students what the problem is with symbolizing the compound proposition this way. Hopefully someone will notice that it is ambiguous: it could mean "*A* or *B*, and *C*" or "*A*, or *B* and *C*." Explain that the way to remove this ambiguity in logic, as in math, is to use parentheses to distinguish which operation should be performed first. Tell students that **in a series of three or more connected propositions parentheses should be used**. Point out that the word "both" is often a good indicator of where to place the parentheses when dealing with conjunctions; in the compound proposition "*O* or *F*, but not both *O* and *F*," the word "both" tells you to place the parentheses around $O \bullet F$.

12. Explain that parentheses also help us make the small but **very important distinction between "not both" propositions and "both not" propositions**. Write on the board "Forest rangers and grizzly bears are not both friendly creatures." Explain that this is true and that

you would symbolize it as $\sim(F \bullet G)$, because the "not" (~) comes before the "both" (•). Now write on the board "Both forest rangers and grizzly bears are not friendly creatures." Explain that this does not mean the same thing at all; it is (for the most part) false, and you would symbolize it as $(\sim F \bullet \sim G)$, because the "both" comes before the "not."

13. Explain that when symbolizing compound propositions that use negation, we usually assume that whatever proposition the negation immediately precedes is the proposition it is negating. Write on the board $\sim p \vee q$ and explain that we just assume this to mean $(\sim p) \vee q$ because the tilde immediately precedes the p. Emphasize that $\sim p \vee q$ means something very different from $\sim(p \vee q)$, just as in math $-5 + 6 = 1$ and $-(5 + 6) = -11$. Make sure students understand that when they want to negate a single variable or constant they don't need parentheses, but if they are negating an entire compound proposition they do need them.

ASSIGNMENTS

1. Have students complete Exercise 2, and go over it with them.
2. Remind students to study for next class's quiz over Lessons 1 and 2.

NEGATION, CONJUNCTION, AND DISJUNCTION

We will begin our study of abbreviating and analyzing compound propositions by learning about three fundamental logical operators: *negation, conjunction,* and *disjunction.* As we do, we will be answering three questions for each logical operator: What words in English are abbreviated by it? What is its symbol? How is the truth value of the compound proposition affected by the truth values of the component parts?

KEY POINT

Three fundamental logical operators are **negation**, **conjunction**, and **disjunction**.

Negation

Negation is the logical operator representing the words *not, it is false that,* or any other phrase which denies or contradicts the proposition. As we have already seen, the symbol ~ (called a *tilde*) represents negation. If the proposition *All roads lead to Rome* is represented by the propositional constant *R*, then ~*R* means *Not all roads lead to Rome* or *It is false that all roads lead to Rome.* Note that the negation of a proposition is the contradiction of that proposition. Thus ~*R* could also be translated *Some roads do not lead to Rome.* If a proposition is true, its negation is false. If a proposition is false, its negation is true. This can be expressed by the following **truth table**, where T means *true* and F means *false*:

p	~p
T	F
F	T

Truth tables show how the truth value of a compound proposition is affected by the truth value of its component parts. The table above is called the **defining truth table** for negation because it completely defines its operations on a minimum number of variables (in this case, one). The defining truth table for an operator that joins two propositions would require two variables.

DEFINITIONS

Negation (~, *not*) is the logical operator that denies or contradicts a proposition.

A ***truth table*** is a listing of the possible truth values for a set of one or more propositions. A ***defining truth table*** displays the truth values produced by a logical operator modifying a minimum number of variables.

DEFINITIONS

Conjunction (•, *and*) is a logical operator that joins two propositions and is true if and only if both the propositions (*conjuncts*) are true.

Conjunction

When two propositions are joined by *and, but, still,* or other similar words, a **conjunction** is formed. The conjunction logical operator is symbolized by • (called, of course, a *dot*). If *Main Street leads to home* is represented by the constant *H*, then *All roads lead to Rome, but Main Street leads to home* could be represented by *R* • *H* (read as *R dot H,* or *R and H*).

The conjunction is true if and only if its components (called **conjuncts**) are both true. If either conjunct is false, the conjunction as a whole is false. The defining truth table for conjunction is therefore:

p	q	p • q
T	T	T
T	F	F
F	T	F
F	F	F

Thus if *All roads lead to Rome* is false and *Main Street leads to home* is true, then the entire conjunction *All roads lead to Rome but Main Street leads to home* is false, as seen on the third row down.

In ordinary English, the conjunction is not always placed between two distinct sentences. For example, *Paul and Apollos were apostles* could be symbolized *P* • *A*, where *P* means *Paul was an apostle* and A means *Apollos was an apostle.* Similarly, the proposition *Jesus is both God and man* could be represented by *G* • *M.*

DEFINITIONS

Disjunction (∨, *or*) is a logical operator that joins two propositions and is true if and only if one or both of the propositions (*disjuncts*) is true.

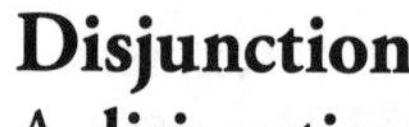

Disjunction

A **disjunction** is formed when two propositions are joined by the logical operator *or*, as in *Paul was an apostle or Apollos was an apostle.* The symbol for disjunction is ∨ (called a *vee*). The foregoing disjunction would thus be symbolized *P* ∨ *A* (read simply *P or A*).

In English, the word *or* is ambiguous. In one sense it can mean "this or that, but not both" (called the *exclusive or*). For example, in the sentence *The senator is either a believer or an unbeliever,* the word *or* must be taken in the exclusive sense; nobody could be both a believer and an unbeliever at the same time in the same way. However, the word *or* can also mean "this or that, or both" (called the *inclusive or*). This is how it should be taken in the sentence *Discounts are given to senior citizens or war veterans.* If you were a senior citizen or a war veteran *or both,* you would be allowed a discount.

In Latin, the ambiguity is taken care of by two separate words: *aut,* meaning the "exclusive *or,*" and *vel,* meaning the "inclusive *or.*" Although it may seem like the exclusive sense of the word *or* is the more natural sense, in logic the disjunction is always taken in the inclusive sense. This is seen in the fact that the symbol ∨ is derived from the Latin *vel.*

The defining truth table for disjunction is therefore:

p	q	p∨q
T	T	T
T	F	T
F	T	T
F	F	F

A disjunction is thus considered to be false if and only if both components (called **disjuncts**) are false. If either disjunct is true, the disjunction as a whole is true.

If the context of an argument requires that the word *or* be represented in the exclusive sense, as in *The senator is either a Republican or a Democrat,* it may be translated with the more complicated *(R ∨ D) • ~(R • D)*—that is, "The senator is either a Republican or a Democrat, but not both a Republican and a Democrat." However, you should assume that *or* is meant in the more simple inclusive sense unless instructed otherwise.

As you can see, logic may use parentheses in symbolizing complicated compound propositions. This is done to avoid ambiguity. The compound proposition *A ∨ B • C* could mean *A or B, and C* or it could mean *A, or B and C.* Parentheses remove the ambiguity, as in *(A ∨ B) • C,* which represents *A or B, and C.* This is similar to how parentheses are used in mathematics. Assuming there are no rules about which operation should be performed first, the mathematical expression 5 + 6 × 4 could equal either 44 or 29, depending on whether one adds first or multiplies first. But parentheses would make it clear, as in (5 + 6) × 4. Logic uses parentheses in the same way. Generally, in a series of three or more connected propositions, parentheses should be used.

KEY POINT

The logical operator for disjunction is always understood in the inclusive sense: "this or that, or both." If you intend the exclusive *or,* you must specify it explicitly.

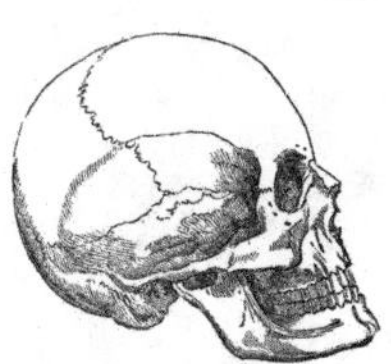

CAUTION

Though in English grammar the word *or* is called a conjunction, in logic only *and* (and equivalent words) is a conjunction. *Or* is always called a disjunction.

KEY POINT

Generally, in a series of three or more connected propositions, parentheses should be used to avoid ambiguity.

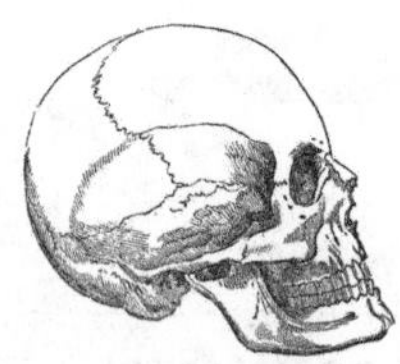

CAUTION

Do not confuse the propositional meaning of the phrases *not both* and *both not.* Use parentheses to distinguish between them.

KEY POINT

In the absence of parentheses, assume that negation attaches only to the proposition it immediately precedes.

The word *both* is often an indicator of how parentheses are to be placed when using conjunctions. The symbolized *exclusive or* in the paragraph above could be read *R or D, but not* ***both*** *R and D,* the word *both* telling us to place parentheses around $R \bullet D$.

A proper use of parentheses can also help us to distinguish between *not both* and *both not* propositions. For example, the proposition *Cats and snakes are not both mammals* (which is true) would be symbolized as $\sim(C \bullet S)$. The *not* comes before the *both,* so the tilde is placed before the parenthesis. However, *Both cats and snakes are not mammals* (which is false) would be symbolized as $(\sim C \bullet \sim S)$. Note that this second proposition could also be translated *Neither cats nor snakes are mammals.*

When symbolizing compound propositions which use negation, it is standard practice to assume that whatever variable, constant, or proposition in parentheses the tilde immediately precedes is the one negated. For example, the compound proposition $\sim p \vee q$ is understood to mean $(\sim p) \vee q$, because the tilde immediately precedes the variable p. This is different from $\sim(p \vee q)$. Negation is used in the same way that the negative sign is used in mathematics. The mathematical expression $-5 + 6$ means $(-5) + 6$, which equals 1. This is different from $-(5 + 6)$, which equals -11. So when negating a single variable or constant, you need not use parentheses. But when negating an entire compound proposition, place the tilde in front of the parentheses around the proposition.

SUMMARY

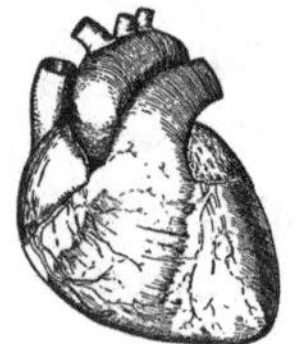

Three common logical operators are negation (*not,* symbolized ~), conjunction (*and,* symbolized •), and disjunction (*or,* symbolized ∨). These logical operators can be defined by means of truth tables. Negation reverses the truth value of a proposition, conjunction is true if and only if both conjuncts are true, and disjunction is false if and only if both disjuncts are false.

EXERCISE 2 (26 points)

Given: J means *Joseph went to Egypt* F means *There was a famine*
I means *Israel went to Egypt* S means *The sons of Israel became slaves*

Translate the symbolic propositions. (2 each)

1. F • I There was a famine and Israel went to Egypt.
2. ~J ∨ S Joseph did not go to Egypt or the sons of Israel became slaves.
3. ~(J ∨ I) It is false that Joseph or Israel went to Egypt.
4. J • ~S Joseph went to Egypt and the sons of Israel did not become slaves.

Symbolize the compound propositions .

5. Joseph and Israel went to Egypt. J•I (2)
6. Israel did not go to Egypt. ~I (2)
7. Israel went to Egypt, but his sons became slaves. I•S (2)
8. Either Joseph went to Egypt, or there was a famine. J∨F (2)
9. Joseph and Israel did not both go to Egypt. ~(J•I) (2)
10. Neither Joseph nor Israel went to Egypt. ~J•~I (2)
11. Joseph and Israel went to Egypt; however, there was a famine, and the sons of Israel became slaves. (J•I)•(F•S) (3)
12. Israel went to Egypt; but either Joseph did not go to Egypt, or there was a famine. I•(~J∨F) (3)

TEACHER'S NOTES

QUIZ 1 (LESSONS 1–2)

STUDENT OBJECTIVE

Complete Quiz 1.

TEACHING INSTRUCTIONS

1. Give the quiz. Allow 20 minutes for it. Grade quiz with students and spend time reviewing (maybe re-explaining) any problems they struggled with.
2. If you have the time (and the desire) to do so, introduce Lesson 3.

INTERMEDIATE LOGIC | QUIZ 1

Lessons 1–2 (25 points)

Name ____________________________________

1. How does *propositional logic* differ from *categorical logic*? (3) In categorical logic, the basic unit of thought is the term. In propositional logic, the basic unit of thought is the proposition.

2. What is a *proposition*? (1) A proposition is a statement.

3. What does it mean that a proposition is *truth functional*? (2) The truth value of the proposition depends upon the truth value of its component parts.

4. Give an example of a proposition that is *not* truth functional. (2)
   I think this is a hard question. (Any self-report, tautology, or self-contradiction).

5. Give an example of a *simple* proposition. (2)
   Jesus is Lord.

Problems 6-12: Given: **V** means *You eat your veggies.*
M means *You eat your meat.*
D means *You get dessert.*

Translate the following symbolic propositions into words.

6. ~ V (1) You do not eat your veggies.

7. M ∨ ~ D (2) You eat your meat or you do not get dessert.

8. ~ (V • M) (2) You do not eat both your veggies and your meat.

Translate the following propositions into symbols.

9. You eat neither your veggies nor your meat. (2) ~ (V ∨ M)

10. You eat your veggies but you do not get dessert. (2) V • ~D

11. You eat your meat or your veggies, but you don't eat both. (3) $(M \vee V) \bullet \sim(M \bullet V)$

12. Are the letters **V**, **M**, and **D** used above *constants* or *variables?* Explain how you know. (3)

They are constants, because they are capital letters that represent given propositions.

TRUTH TABLES FOR DETERMINING TRUTH VALUES

Intermediate Logic, pp. 21–23

STUDENT OBJECTIVES

1. Use truth tables to determine the truth values of truth-functional propositions.
2. Complete Exercise 3.

SPECIAL NOTE

Depending on which schedule you're following, you have two days to work through Lesson 3. Get through as much of the lesson as you can on the first day, and spend the second day tying up loose ends and working through Exercise 3 with students.

TEACHING INSTRUCTIONS

1. Remind students that in the last couple lessons we have used truth tables to help define logical operators. Have students tell you the three logical operators they defined with truth tables, and have some volunteers draw the completed tables on the board. Make sure everyone has a good grasp of these three tables. Remind them that conjunction is true if both parts are true, and disjunction is false if both parts are false.
2. Explain that truth tables also serve another purpose. **We use them to determine the truth value of compound propositions given the truth value of their component parts.** Write on the board the compound proposition $\sim p \vee (\sim q \bullet r)$. Ask them to think of a compound proposition in English that could be symbolized this way, for example: "I don't move my pawn, or I don't move my queen but I move my rook." Explain that you are going to spend the lesson learning the procedure for determining the truth values of this kind of proposition.
3. First have students briefly analyze the proposition. It is a disjunction, so in order to figure out its truth values, you need the truth values of its component parts, $\sim p$ and $(\sim q \bullet r)$. And in order to figure out the truth values of $(\sim q \bullet r)$ you need the truth values of $\sim q$ and r.
4. Explain that you start out by setting up the truth table exactly as you did for the truth tables defining the logical operators, except that now you have an extra variable: r. Explain that every time you add a new variable to the table, you double the number of rows, because there are twice as many combinations of true and false. Draw the following table on the board, and as you draw show students that in the column under the first variable, p, you label the first four rows T and the second four F; under the q column the first two rows T, the next two F, the next two T, and so on; and in the final column under r, you alternate between T and F all the way down. Show students that when you set the table up like this, every row has a different combination of truth values, and that these are all the combinations of true and false there can be for these three variables.

p	q	r
T	T	T
T	T	F
T	F	T
T	F	F
F	T	T
F	T	F
F	F	T
F	F	F

5. Ask students what they think is the next thing to add to this chart. Explain that **when completing a truth table, you start with the standard truth values for the variables (or constants)**, as you have just done, and **then find the truth values for the *negated* variables (or constants).** Ask students which variables are negated in the compound propositions you are analyzing (*p* and *q*). Place arrows over p and q to show that you are about to use these basic variables to build more complicated propositions on the right-hand side of the table.

6. Add *~p* and *~q* to the top row of the table, and have students walk you through inserting truth values in the rows underneath. Remind them that negation is simply contradiction, so whenever p is T, *~p* is F, and vice versa. The table should now look like this:

↓ p	↓ q	r	~p	~q
T	T	T	F	F
T	T	F	F	F
T	F	T	F	T
T	F	F	F	T
F	T	T	T	F
F	T	F	T	F
F	F	T	T	T
F	F	F	T	T

7. Make sure that everyone is keeping up. Explain that you now have all the individual parts you need to determine the truth value of the compound proposition *~p ∨ (~q • r)*.

Ask students which part of this proposition should be analyzed first. Explain that, just like in math, whatever is inside the parentheses should be completed before whatever is outside. Add *~q • r* to the top row of the table, and place arrows above *r* and *~q* to show that you are dealing with these two columns. Remind students that a conjunction is only true when both the component parts are true. So when there is a T in both the r and the *~q* column, *~q • r* will have a T as well; otherwise *~q • r* will be F. Have students walk you through inserting the truth values in the *~q • r* column. The table should now look like this:

p	q	↓ r	~p	↓ ~q	(~q • r)
T	T	T	F	F	F
T	T	F	F	F	F
T	F	T	F	T	T
T	F	F	F	T	F
F	T	T	T	F	F
F	T	F	T	F	F
F	F	T	T	T	T
F	F	F	T	T	F

8. Have students tell you what the last step is. Add the whole proposition *~p ∨ (~q • r)* to the top row, and ask students what two columns you will be using to figure out the truth values. Put arrows over these two columns (*~p* and *~q • r*). Show students that since you have the truth values of both these component parts, all you have to do is figure out the truth values for the disjunction. Remind students that a disjunction is true whenever either of its two disjuncts is true. So if either *~p* or *(~q • r)* is T the whole proposition *~p ∨ (~q • r)* is T as well; but if both are F the whole proposition is F. Have students walk you through inserting the truth values in the final column. The finished table should look like this:

p	q	r	↓ ~p	~q	↓ (~q • r)	~p ∨ (~q • r)
T	T	T	F	F	F	F
T	T	F	F	F	F	F
T	F	T	F	T	T	T
T	F	F	F	T	F	F
F	T	T	T	F	F	T
F	T	F	T	F	F	T
F	F	T	T	T	T	T
F	F	F	T	T	F	T

9. Have students review what you did: **to create a truth table (or the set of possible truth values) for the compound proposition *~p ∨ (~q • r)* you figured out truth tables for the component parts and then put them all together**. Explain that by looking at this truth table they can figure out what the truth value of the proposition will be if *p*, *q*, and *r* are all true, if they are all false, and so on.

10. Explain that the truth table you just created was a truth table of *variables*; sometimes you use constants (uppercase letters that represent particular statements) instead, and sometimes you already know the truth values of those constants. In that case, you only need one row to you table. Write on the board "Either aunts are pleasant people or uncles are jolly people, and cousins are not very nice." Abbreviate it to *(A ∨ X)* • *~Y*, and tell students to assume that *A* is true and *X* and *Y* are false. Have them create and fill in the table with you, using only one row. It should look like this:

A	X	Y	(A ∨ X)	~Y	(A ∨ X) • ~Y
T	F	F	T	T	T

ASSIGNMENT

Have students complete Exercise 3, and go over it with them.

LESSON 3

TRUTH TABLES FOR DETERMINING TRUTH VALUES

So far we have seen that truth tables help define logical operators. Truth tables also serve other functions, one of which is to help us determine the truth value of compound propositions. The truth value of elementary negations, conjunctions and disjunctions can be immediately determined from their defining truth tables. But what about compound propositions like $\sim p \vee (\sim q \bullet r)$? To find the truth values for such complicated propositions, the following procedure may be followed:

KEY POINT

Truth tables help determine the truth value of compound propositions, given the truth value of their component parts.

1. Draw a line, and on the leftmost part of the line place the variables (or constants) which are used in the proposition. Under these, put all the possible combinations of true and false. This will require four rows for two variables, eight rows for three variables, and in general 2^n rows for n variables. Under the first variable, place a T for each of the first half of the rows, then an F for each of the second half. Under the next variable, place half again as many Ts, half again as many Fs, then repeat this. The final column should have alternating single Ts and Fs, as follows:

p	q	r
T	T	T
T	T	F
T	F	T
T	F	F
F	T	T
F	T	F
F	F	T
F	F	F

You can verify for yourself that all the possible combinations of true and false are found in these eight rows.

KEY POINT

When completing a truth table, start with the standard truth values for the variables (or constants), then find the truth values for the negated variables (or constants).

2. If any variables are negated, these should be added next, with the corresponding truth values under them (specifically, under the operator):

p ↓	q ↓	r	~p	~q
T	T	T	F	F
T	T	F	F	F
T	F	T	F	T
T	F	F	F	T
F	T	T	T	F
F	T	F	T	F
F	F	T	T	T
F	F	F	T	T

Here arrows are placed over *p* and *q* to show that those basic variables are being used to build more complicated propositions on the right-hand side of the table. Whenever *p* is true, *~p* is false, and vice versa, just as the defining truth table for negation shows. This is also the case for *q* and *~q*.

KEY POINT

After determining truth values for negations, complete the truth values for compound propositions within parentheses.

3. Continue to the next level of complexity in the proposition. As in mathematics, whatever is in parentheses should be completed before going outside the parentheses. In our example, the proposition in parentheses is *~q • r*. This is placed on the line, and whenever both *~q* and *r* are true, the conjunction *~q • r* is true, according to the defining truth table for conjunction. Thus we now have:

p	q	r ↓	~p	~q ↓	(~q • r)
T	T	T	F	F	F
T	T	F	F	F	F
T	F	T	F	T	T
T	F	F	F	T	F
F	T	T	T	F	F
F	T	F	T	F	F
F	F	T	T	T	T
F	F	F	T	T	F

4. Continue with the same procedure, adding on to the truth table until the entire compound proposition is filled out. In our example, the propositions *~p* and *(~q • r)* are disjuncts. Thus, whenever

either is true, the whole disjunction is true. We fill in those values and finish the truth table:

KEY POINT

Finish the truth table for a compound proposition by finding out the truth tables for all of its component parts and then putting them together.

p	q	r	~p ↓	~q	(~q • r) ↓	~p ∨ (~q • r)
T	T	T	F	F	F	F
T	T	F	F	F	F	F
T	F	T	F	T	T	T
T	F	F	F	T	F	F
F	T	T	T	F	F	T
F	T	F	T	F	F	T
F	F	T	T	T	T	T
F	F	F	T	T	F	T

We see from the first row that whenever *p*, *q*, and *r* are all true, the compound proposition *~p ∨ (~q • r)* is false, and so on down the truth table. As you get more familiar with this procedure, you will be able to dispense with the initial guide columns of true and false, working only with the compound proposition and placing the truth values directly beneath the variables in it.

KEY POINT

When you make a truth table for propositions that use only constants with known truth values, you need just one row.

Sometimes, the truth values of constants in a compound proposition are already known. In that case finding the truth value of the compound proposition requires only one row. For instance, assume that A is true, and X and Y are false. Finding the truth value of *(A ∨ X) • ~Y* requires this:

A	X	Y	(A ∨ X)	~Y	(A ∨ X) • ~Y
T	F	F	T	T	T

SUMMARY

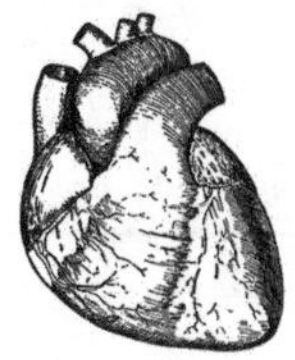

The truth values of a compound proposition may be determined by placing all possible combinations of true and false under the variables or constants, then using the definitions of the logical operators to determine the corresponding truth values of each component of the proposition.

EXERCISE 3 (26 points)

1. Fill in the following truth table to determine the truth values for the exclusive *or*. The truth values for *p* and *q* are filled out for you on this first one. (4)

p	q	(p∨q)	(p•q)	~(p•q)	(p∨q)•~(p•q)
T	T	T	T	F	F
T	F	T	F	T	T
F	T	T	F	T	T
F	F	F	F	T	F

2. Determine the truth values for *~(J • R)* and *~J • ~R* to prove that they are different propositions. The initial truth values of J and R should follow the same pattern as the truth values of *p* and *q* in Problem 1. (6)

J	R	~J	~R	(J•R)	~(J•R)	~J•~R
T	T	F	F	T	F	F
T	F	F	T	F	T	F
F	T	T	F	F	T	F
F	F	T	T	F	T	T

3. Write sentences in English (using *both* and *not*) corresponding to the two compound propositions in Problem 2, using *Joe is a student* for J and *Rachel is a student* for R. (4)

~(J • R) Joe and Rachel are not both students.

~J • ~R Both Joe and Rachel are not students.

Determine the truth value for the compound propositions. Assume that propositions A and B are true, while X and Y are false. Circle T if the entire compound proposition is true. Circle F if it is false. Use the space at the right for showing any work. (1 each)

4. ~A ∨ B (T) F

A	B	~A	~A∨B
T	T	F	T

5. X ∨ ~B T (F)

X	B	~B	X∨~B
F	T	F	F

6. ~(A ∨ B) T (F)

A	B	A∨B	~(A∨B)
T	T	T	F

7. (A • X) ∨ (B • Y) T (F)

A	X	B	Y	A•X	B•Y	(A•X)∨(B•Y)
T	F	T	F	F	F	F

8. ~[X ∨ (Y • ~A)] (T) F

X	Y	A	~A	Y•~A	X∨(Y•~A)	~[X∨(Y•~A)]
F	F	T	F	F	F	T

Continued on next page.

Identify the truth value of each sentence by circling T or F. (Note that Jonah, Isaiah, and Jeremiah were all prophets.) (1 each)

9. Jonah was a prophet or Isaiah was a prophet. (T) F

10. Jeremiah was not a prophet but Isaiah was a prophet. T (F)

11. It is not true that both Jeremiah was a prophet and Isaiah was not a prophet. (T) F

12. Jonah was not a prophet or both Jeremiah and Isaiah were not prophets. T (F)

13. A false proposition is not true. (T) F

14. It is false that a true proposition is not false. T (F)

15. It is true that it is false that a true proposition is not false. T (F)

TEACHER'S NOTES on LESSON 4

THE CONDITIONAL

Intermediate Logic, pp. 27–31

STUDENT OBJECTIVES

1. Provide the symbol, truth table, and English equivalents of the conditional.
2. Complete Exercise 4.

SPECIAL NOTE

Depending on which schedule you're following, you have two days to work through Lesson 4. Get through as much of the lesson as you can on the first day, and spend the second day tying up loose ends and working through Exercise 4 with students.

TEACHING INSTRUCTIONS

1. Write these five sentences (or similar ones) on the board: 1. If I make a face, the baby will laugh. 2. Everyone will be disappointed if I change my mind. 3. The fact that he goes to Harvard implies that he is smart. 4. When you finish shoveling the driveway I will give you fifty cents. 5. Decapitating my paper dolls is a sufficient condition for your death. Ask students what these sentences have in common. If everyone is clueless, explain that these sentences are all different forms of the logical operator called **the conditional**. Some other words for the conditional are **hypothetical** or **material implication**, but they all mean the same thing: an **if/then proposition**. Show how each of the above sentences can be translated into if/then form. (If I make a face, then the baby will laugh; if I change my mind, then everyone will be disappointed; if he goes to Harvard, then he is smart; if you shovel the driveway, then I will give you fifty cents; if you decapitate my paper dolls, then I will have every right to kill you.)
2. Explain that in a conditional, the proposition that follows the "if" is called the antecedent, and the proposition that follows the "then" is called the consequent. It shouldn't be hard to remember which is which; remind students that in Latin "ante" means before, so it makes sense that the "**ante**cedent" would come first, and the "consequence" of something is the result, so it makes sense that the "**consequent**" would come second. Have students determine the antecedents and consequents in the above sentences.
3. Draw the symbol for the conditional logical operator, $\supset$, (called a "horseshoe"), on the board. Have students help you symbolize "If I make a face, the baby will laugh" using this symbol $(M \supset L)$. Students may wonder why there isn't a symbol in front of the antecedent as well to symbolize the "if" part; tell them not to ask silly questions.
4. Explain that in a conditional proposition the antecedent *implies* the consequent; the consequent necessarily follows from the antecedent. So, in a true conditional, if the antecedent is true, the consequent must also be true. Let's assume that the conditional "If I make a face, the baby will laugh" is a true conditional; then if it is true that

I make a face, it must also be true that the baby laughs. On the other hand, if we know that the antecedent is true but the consequent is false, we know that we are dealing with a false conditional. For example, we know that "If God loves me, I can do whatever I want" is a false conditional, since the antecedent is obviously true and the consequent obviously false. The consequent thus does not follow from the antecedent.

5. Explain that, like the disjunction, the conditional is a somewhat ambiguous concept. Return to the five sentences on the board. The first is talking about the likelihood of someone's behavior given certain conditions: if I make a face, the baby will most likely feel inclined to laugh at me. The second is describing a cause/effect relationship: My changing my mind will *cause* everyone to be disappointed. The third sentence is implication by definition: students at Harvard are *by definition* smart, so if he goes to Harvard, he must also be smart. The fourth conditional is a promise: if you shovel the driveway, I promise to give you the vast reward of fifty cents. And the fifth sentence describes a sufficient condition: the fact that you decapitated my paper dolls is sufficient reason for me to decapitate you. But if there are so many different kinds of if/then statements, how can we come up with one truth table for them all? Explain that propositional logic deals with this ambiguity by noting that all of these examples do have one feature in common: they are all false conditionals when the antecedent is true and the consequent is false. If I make a face at the baby and she doesn't laugh, I know that the conditional was false, because even though the antecedent was true, the consequent did not follow from it. If you shovel the driveway (true antecedent) and I refuse to give you fifty cents (false consequent), my original conditional was a lie. And if you decapitate my paper dolls and Mom does not think this is sufficient reason for me to kill you, then my original conditional was erroneous. Emphasize that all other combinations of true and false (true antecedent and true consequent, false antecedent and true consequent, and even false antecedent and false consequent) result in a *true* conditional. Only conditionals with a true antecedent and false consequent are false.

6. Given all this, have students help you construct the truth table for the conditional $(p \supset q)$. It begins like every other truth table: with all the possible truth values of the component parts p and q. When both p and q are true, the conditional is true; when p (the antecedent) is true and q (the consequent) is false, the conditional is false. When p is false and q is true, the conditional is true, and when both are false the conditional is also true. The completed truth table should look like this:

p	q	p ⊃ q
T	T	T
T	F	F
F	T	T
F	F	T

7. At this point some students may be protesting loudly that it doesn't make sense for "if false then true" to be true and "if false then false" to be true. Tell them that they're asking a good question, although the answer may be hard for them to wrap their minds around. Write this example on the board: "If a cat is a rat, then a cat is an animal." False antecedent (a cat is not a rat), but true consequent (a cat is a animal). Write this second example: "If a cat is a rat, then a cat is a rodent." False antecedent and false conclusion. But have them consider: if a cat *really was* a rat, it *would* follow that a cat was an animal. And if a cat really was a rat, it would follow that the cat was a rodent. So these two conditionals are true.

8. While they are swallowing that, add this complication: it is possible to come up with "if false then true" and "if false then false" conditionals that are *false* conditionals. For example, you

could argue "If a cat is a rat, then a cat purrs." The antecedent is false (cats aren't rats), the consequent is true (cats do purr), but the consequent does not follow from the antecedent: even if it *were* true that cats were rats, it wouldn't follow that they could purr. Therefore the whole conditional is false. Similarly, you could argue "If a cat is a rat, then a cat is a balloon." Both antecedent and consequent are false, but the consequent does not follow at all from the antecedent, because being a rat would not make a cat a balloon. Thus the conditional is false.

9. Explain that what all this confusion means is that conditional propositions with false antecedents are *not truth-functional* in everyday English: the truth value of a conditional with a false antecedent does *not* always depend on the truth value of its component parts. Then what are we supposed to do with conditionals?

10. Return to the first sentence on the board "If I make a face, the baby will laugh." Explain that there is another, logically equivalent way of stating this proposition; you could say instead, "It is false that I make a face and the baby does not laugh." Make sure all the students understand that these two sentences mean the same thing. As another example: "The fact that he goes to Harvard implies that he is smart" is logically equivalent to "It is false that he both goes to Harvard and is stupid." Have students help you symbolize these equivalent restatements as $\sim(p \bullet \sim q)$. **$p \supset q$ is equivalent to $\sim(p \bullet \sim q)$.**

11. Have students help you make a truth table for $\sim(p \bullet \sim q)$. You will first determine the truth values of p and q, then of $\sim q$, then of $p \bullet \sim q$, then of $\sim(p \bullet \sim q)$. The completed table should look like this:

p	q	~q	(p • ~q)	~(p • ~q)
T	T	F	F	T
T	F	T	T	F
F	T	F	F	T
F	F	T	F	T

Make sure students see that the truth table for the equivalent proposition $\sim(p \bullet \sim q)$ is the same as the one we came up for for the conditional $p \supset q$: TFTT. Tell students that in the exercises they will see that there are other propositions equivalent to $p \supset q$ that also result in TFTT. They can thus be confident that the truth table for $p \supset q$ is indeed TFTT.

12. Give students a breather, encouragement, and maybe a milkshake. Then dive in again.

13. Explain that translating conditionals from ordinary English into propositional logic can be very tricky. Return to the second sentence on the board: "Everyone will be disappointed if I change my mind." Have students identify the antecedent and the consequent in it. It should be straightforward: "I change my mind" is the antecedent, and "everyone will be disappointed" is the consequent. Then write this sentence on the board: "A polygon is a square only if it has four sides." Warn students that translating this sentence is a bit trickier. It is *not* the same as "If a polygon has four sides, it is a square"; that tiny word "only" make a big difference. It is *not* true that if a polygon has four sides it is a square. (What about rectangles?) Help students see that the proper way to translate this sentence is "If a polygon is a square, then it has four sides." Explain and write on the board that **the proposition "p only if q" means "If p then q".**

14. Return to the third sentence on the board: "The fact that he goes to Harvard implies that he is smart." Have students translate this into an if/then statement; it shouldn't be hard: "If he goes to Harvard, then he is smart." Have them do the same with the fourth sentence, "When you finish shoveling the driveway I will give you fifty cents," which should also be easy: "If you shovel the driveway, I will give you fifty cents." Explain and write on the board that **both "p implies q" and "when p, q" mean "if p then q."**

15. Return to the fifth sentence on the board: "Decapitating my paper dolls is a sufficient condition for your death" and ask students how they would translate it into if/then form. If they get tripped up over "sufficient condition" tell them just to find the antecedent and the consequent and set it up accordingly; they should come up with "If you decapitate my paper dolls, you will die." Write on the board **"p is sufficient for q" is equivalent to "if p then q."** Now change the sentence to "decapitating my paper dolls is a *necessary* condition for you death." Asks students if they think that this has changed anything. They may think that this sentence means exactly the same thing, but it is subtly different: rather than saying "if you do this, you will die," it is saying, "the only way you can die is if you do this." Thus it would be translated "If you die, you decapitated my paper dolls." Write on the board **"p is a necessary condition for q" is equivalent to "if q then p."**

16. Write on the board the sentence, "You will fall unless you step away from the edge." Ask students how they would translate this into an if/then statement. Make sure students see that it does *not* mean "If you step away from the edge, you will not fall," because even if you did step away from the edge, you might fall off something else. Rather, it should be translated "If you do not step away from the edge, you will fall." Write on the board: **"p unless q" is equivalent to "if not q then p."** Make sure students also see that if, in the above sentence, you switched the antecedent and the consequent, putting "unless" at the beginning ("Unless you step away from the edge, you will fall"), the if/then statement would switch as well. Thus, **"unless p, q" is equivalent to "if not p, then q."**

17. Tell students that you have one final rule to give them, called the rule of transposition. Write on the board "If there is not a fire, then there is not smoke," and ask students to turn it into an if/then statement without any negatives. They may want to translate simply as "If there is a fire, then there is smoke," but explain that that doesn't follow necessarily from the sentence. Rather, it should be translated "if there is smoke, then there is a fire." **The rule of transposition says that "if p then q" is equivalent to "if not q then not p."**

18. Write this table of propositions and translations on the board, and explain that this table summarizes all of the info that you have just gone over:

proposition	translation
If p then q	$p \supset q$
p implies q	$p \supset q$
p only if q	$p \supset q$
When p, q	$p \supset q$
p is sufficient for q	$p \supset q$
p if q	$q \supset p$
p is necessary for q	$q \supset p$
p unless q	$\sim q \supset p$
Unless p, q	$\sim p \supset q$
Rule of transposition	$(p \supset q) \equiv (\sim q \supset \sim p)$

ASSIGNMENTS

1. Have students complete Exercise 4, and go over it with them.
2. Remind students to study for next class's quiz over Lessons 3 and 4.

LESSON 4

THE CONDITIONAL

A very useful logical operator is the **conditional** (also called **hypothetical** or **material implication**). The conditional is an *if/then*-type proposition: "If it is raining then I will take my umbrella." The proposition following the *if* is called the **antecedent**, and the proposition following the *then* is the **consequent**. In the preceding example, "It is raining" is the antecedent; "I will take my umbrella" is the consequent.

DEFINITIONS

The ***conditional*** operator (⊃, *if/then*) asserts that one component (the *antecedent*) implies the other (the *consequent*). It is false if and only if the antecedent is true and the consequent is false.

Conditionals can take many forms. All of the following propositions can be considered as conditionals, because they can all be translated into *if/then* form:

1. If I move my rook then he will put me in check.
2. The diode will light if the switch is closed.
3. Fido is a dog implies that Fido is a mammal.
4. When you finish your dinner I will give you dessert.
5. Cheating during a test is a sufficient condition for your suspension.

Can you determine the antecedent and the consequent for each of those statements?

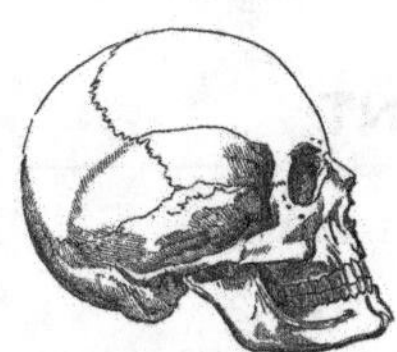

CAUTION

Conditionals can take many forms other than the basic "if x, then y" structure.

The symbol for the conditional logical operator is ⊃ (called a *horseshoe*). "If I move my rook then he will put me in check" could be symbolized $R \supset C$ (read as *If R then C*).

In a conditional proposition, the antecedent is said to *imply* the consequent. That is, for a true conditional, if the antecedent is considered to be true (whether or not it actually *is* true), then the consequent must also be true. Like the disjunction, the concept of implication is somewhat ambiguous. Example one above shows that it can apply to the likelihood of behavior. The person is stating the likelihood of his opponent's behavior when certain conditions are

KEY POINT

The conditional includes many types of implication: cause/effect, definition, promises, conditions, and so on.

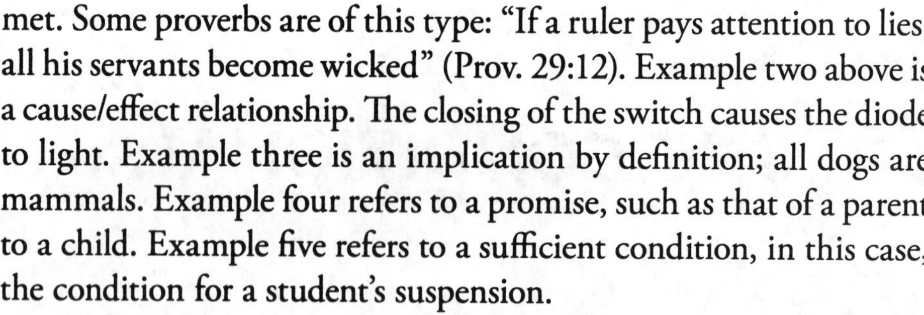

met. Some proverbs are of this type: "If a ruler pays attention to lies, all his servants become wicked" (Prov. 29:12). Example two above is a cause/effect relationship. The closing of the switch causes the diode to light. Example three is an implication by definition; all dogs are mammals. Example four refers to a promise, such as that of a parent to a child. Example five refers to a sufficient condition, in this case, the condition for a student's suspension.

Propositional logic deals with this ambiguity by recognizing that each of the given examples are false when the antecedent is true and the consequent is false. If he moves his rook but his opponent does not put him in check, example one is false. If the switch is closed and the diode doesn't light, example two is false, and so on. All other combinations of true and false in the conditional are considered to be true.

The defining truth table for the conditional is thus:

p	q	p⊃q
T	T	T
T	F	F
F	T	T
F	F	T

The last two rows may cause some problems. How can *if* FALSE *then* TRUE be considered true? Worse yet, how can *if* FALSE *then* FALSE be true? These are good questions to ask, though the answer may be hard to grasp. But consider the following examples of such propositions:

KEY POINT

Though it may seem counterintuitive, a conditional is always true if the antecedent is false.

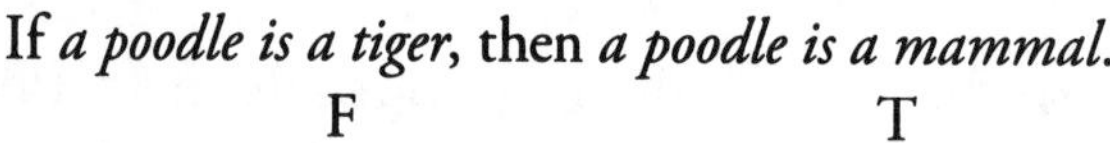

If *a poodle is a tiger*, then *a poodle is a mammal.*
F T

If *a poodle is a tiger*, then *a poodle is a feline.*
F F

Both of these conditional propositions are true. If a poodle really was a tiger (i.e., if the antecedent, though false, was *considered* to be true), then a poodle would be a mammal (which of course it is). You see that it is possible for an *if* FALSE *then* TRUE proposition to be true. Similarly, if a poodle really was a tiger, then it really would be a feline. This *if* FALSE *then* FALSE proposition is true.

Now, it is equally possible to develop *if FALSE then TRUE* conditionals and *if FALSE then FALSE* conditionals which are false. Try substituting "dog" for "mammal," and "lizard" for "feline" in the above conditionals. This gives us the following propositions:

If *a poodle is a tiger*, then *a poodle is a dog*.
F T

If *a poodle is a tiger*, then *a poodle is a lizard*.
F F

Those propositions are both false. This shows that conditional propositions, as they are commonly used in everyday English, are not really truth-functional when the antecedent is false. How then are we to understand conditionals?

Another way of thinking about this is to consider $p \supset q$ as meaning $\sim(p \bullet \sim q)$. So the proposition *If I move my rook then he puts me in check* is considered logically equivalent to *It is false that I move my rook and he does not put me in check*. Another example: *If you study then you will pass* is equivalent to *It is false that you study but you don't pass*. Consider these carefully and you should see how they are equivalent.

The following truth table development of $\sim(p \bullet \sim q)$ shows that it has the same pattern as $p \supset q$:

p	q	~q	(p•~q)	~(p•~q)
T	T	F	F	T
T	F	T	T	F
F	T	F	F	T
F	F	T	F	T

Other equivalent compound propositions could be developed which show this same T F T T pattern, as we shall see in the exercise.

As noted earlier, conditionals can take many forms. Let's look at how to best symbolize them.

First, the proposition *The diode will light if the switch is closed* places the antecedent after the consequent. This proposition means the same as *If the switch is closed then the diode will light*. In general, *p if q* means *If q then p*. However, the superficially similar proposition *p only if q* means the same as *If p then q*. This is not immediately obvious, so consider this true proposition as an example: *A polygon is a square only if it has four sides.* This proposition does not mean "If a polygon has four sides, then it is a square" (which is false), but rather "If a polygon is a square then it has four sides."

Second, *Fido is a dog implies that Fido is a mammal* is clearly just another way of saying that *If Fido is a dog then Fido is a mammal.* Similarly, *When you finish your dinner I will give you dessert* means *If you finish your dinner then I will give you dessert.* So both *p implies q* and *When p, q* are equivalent to *If p then q*.

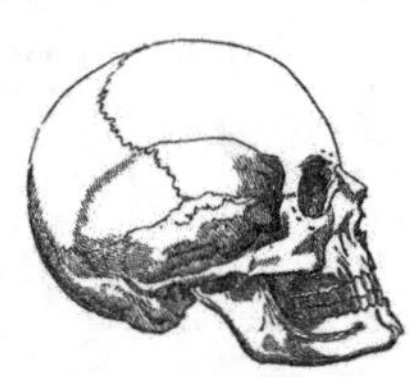

CAUTION

Translating conditionals can be tricky. The proposition *p only if q* means *If p then q*; *p is sufficient for q* is equivalent to *If p then q*; *p is a necessary condition for q* is equivalent to *If q then p*; and finally, *p unless q* means *If not q then* p.

Third, *Cheating during a test is a sufficient condition for your suspension* means that if one cheats during a test, then one will be suspended (since if one cheats during a test but is not suspended, then cheating during a test apparently is *not* sufficient). Thus, *p is sufficient for q* is equivalent to *If p then q*. On the other hand, *p is a necessary condition for q* is equivalent to *If q then p*. For example, *The presence of water is necessary for life to exist there* is best translated *If life exists there then water is present.*

Fourth, consider the proposition *p unless q*. How is this to be translated? Well, what does *You will starve unless you eat sometime* mean? A reasonable translation is "If you do not eat sometime, then you will starve." Note, however, that this proposition is not equivalent to *If you eat sometime then you will not starve* since a person could eat something, but still starve later. So *p unless q* should be translated as *If not q then p*. However, we must be careful: When the "unless" appears at the beginning of the sentence, the translated proposition gets turned around as well. *Unless you repent, you too will perish* means "If you do not repent, then you too will perish." So *unless p, q* is equivalent to *If not p then q*.

Finally, note that *If p then q* is equivalent to *If not q then not* p. This equivalence is called the **rule of transposition**, which we will see later. It is similar to the contrapositive of a categorical statement. So the proposition *If a whale is a mammal, then a whale breathes air* is logically equivalent to *If a whale does not breathe air, then a whale is not a mammal.*

KEY POINT

If *p* then *q* is equivalent to If not *q* then not *p*.

The following table summarizes the above information:

Proposition	Translation
If p then q	$p \supset q$
p implies q	$p \supset q$
p only if q	$p \supset q$
When p, q	$p \supset q$
p is sufficient for q	$p \supset q$
p if q	$q \supset p$
p is necessary for q	$q \supset p$
p unless q	$\sim q \supset p$
Unless p, q	$\sim p \supset q$

Rule of transposition: $(p \supset q) \equiv (\sim q \supset \sim p)$

SUMMARY

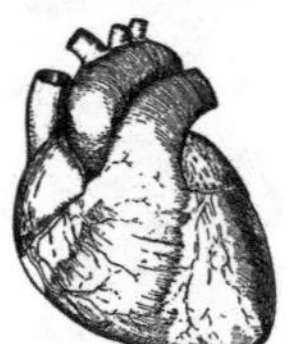

The conditional is an important logical operator. It represents *if/then* propositions and has the symbol $\supset$. The conditional is considered false if and only if the antecedent is true and the consequent is false. Thus, $p \supset q$ can be considered equivalent to $\sim(p \bullet \sim q)$. Many different propositions can be translated as conditional propositions. They are summarized in the table above.

EXERCISE 4 (16 points)

1. Develop the truth table for the compound proposition $\sim p \vee q$ on the line below. (2)

p	q	~p	~p∨q
T	T	F	T
T	F	F	F
F	T	T	T
F	F	T	T

2. What other compound proposition has the same truth table as $\sim p \vee q$? (1)

p ⊃ q

If A, B, and C represent true propositions and X, Y, and Z represent false propositions, determine whether each compound proposition is true or false, and circle the appropriate letter. (1 each)

3. A ⊃ B — (T) F
4. B ⊃ Z — T (F)
5. X ⊃ C — (T) F
6. (A ⊃ B) ⊃ Z — T (F)
7. X ⊃ (Y ⊃ Z) — (T) F
8. (A ⊃ Y) ∨ (B ⊃ ~C) — T (F)
9. [(X ⊃ Z) ⊃ C] ⊃ Z — T (F)
10. [(A • X) ⊃ Y] ⊃ [(X ⊃ ~Z) ∨ (A ⊃ Y)] — (T) F

If S represents *I will go swimming* and C represents *The water is cold,* symbolize each statement: (1 each)

11. If the water is not cold then I will go swimming. ~C ⊃ S
12. I will go swimming if the water is cold. C ⊃ S
13. I will go swimming unless the water is cold. ~C ⊃ S
14. I will go swimming only if the water is not cold. S ⊃ ~C
15. When the water is cold I will go swimming. C ⊃ S

QUIZ 2 (LESSONS 3–4)

STUDENT OBJECTIVE

Complete Quiz 2.

TEACHING INSTRUCTIONS

1. Give the quiz. Allow 20 minutes for it. Grade quiz with students and spend time reviewing (maybe re-explaining) any problems they struggled with.
2. If you have the time (and the desire) to do so, begin reviewing for Test 1.

INTERMEDIATE LOGIC | QUIZ 2

Lessons 3–4 (18 points)

Name ________________________________

1. Complete the truth table for the conditional logical operator (2):

p	q	p⊃q
T	T	T
T	F	F
F	T	T
F	F	T

Problems 2-7: Given the following: **K** means *The knight attacks the dragon.*
D means *The dragon devours the damsel.*
T means *The damsel is trapped in the tower.*

Translate the symbolic proposition into English.

2. T ⊃ D (2) If the damsel is trapped in the tower then the dragon devours the damsel.

3. D • ~ K (2) The dragon devours the damsel but the knight does not attack the dragon.

4. (T ∨ D) ⊃ K (3) If the damsel is trapped in the tower or the dragon devours the damsel, then the knight attacks the dragon.

Symbolize the proposition. (2 each)

5. The knight attacks the dragon if the damsel is trapped in the tower. T ⊃ K
6. The knight attacks the dragon only if the dragon devours the damsel. K ⊃ D
7. The damsel is trapped in the tower unless the dragon devours the damsel. ~D ⊃ T

Problems 8-10: If **A** and **B** are true propositions, and **X** and **Y** are false propositions, determine the truth value of the given compound proposition. Circle T for true, F for false. (1 each)

8. X ⊃ A (T) F
9. B ⊃ (~ X ⊃ Y) T (F)
10. Y ⊃ X (T) F

REVIEW FOR TEST 1 (LESSONS 1–4)

STUDENT OBJECTIVES

Complete the objectives from Lessons 1–4. Objectives are listed at the beginning of each lesson's teacher's notes.

TEACHING INSTRUCTIONS

1. Ask students the Review Questions for Lessons 1-4, starting on p. 79. Have them answer aloud or create the truth tables and show them to you. Allow them to look for the answers in their textbooks if they need to.
2. If you'd like, give students "Test 1: Form A" from the *Intermediate Logic Test and Quiz Packet* as a practice exam. Go over the answers together.
3. For additional practice, students can work through the Additional Exercises for Lessons 1–4 on pp. 83–88 of *Intermediate Logic.*

ASSIGNMENT

Have students study for Test 1.

TEST 1 (LESSONS 1–4)

STUDENT OBJECTIVE

Complete Test 1.

TEACHING INSTRUCTIONS

1. Give students "Test 1: Form B" from the *Intermediate Logic Test and Quiz Packet.* Allow one hour for it.
2. Grade tests. Have them ready to hand back to students within a week.

INTERMEDIATE LOGIC | Test 1, Form A

Lessons 1–4 (40 points)

Name ________________________________

1. What is another word for a *proposition*? (1) a statement.
2. Give an example of a truth-functional, compound proposition (in words, not symbols). (2)

   He is there, and he is not silent. (The proposition must use logical operators, and may not be a self-report, tautology, or self-contradiction.)
3. Explain the major differences between *simple propositions* and *compound propositions*. (3)

   Simple propositions have one component part, not modified by logical operators. Compound propositions may have many component parts, combined or modified by logical operators.
4. What are the differences between *propositional constants* and *propositional variables*? (3)

   Constants are upper case letters (usually the first letter of a key word) representing a single, given proposition. Variables are lower case letters (p, q, r...) which represent any proposition.

Problems 5-12: Symbolize the proposition using the given constants.

M means *We see a movie.* **P** means *We eat popcorn.*
C means *We eat candy.* **G** means *We play a game.*

5. We do not see a movie. (1) $\sim M$
6. We eat popcorn and candy. (1) $P \bullet C$
7. We see a movie or play a game. (1) $M \vee G$
8. We do not both see a movie and play a game. (2) $\sim(M \bullet G)$
9. We do not eat popcorn but we see a movie. (2) $\sim P \bullet M$
10. If we see a movie then we eat popcorn. (1) $M \supset P$
11. We play a game and eat candy, or we see a movie and eat popcorn. (2) $(G \bullet C) \vee (M \bullet P)$
12. If we see a movie then if we eat popcorn then we do not eat candy. (3) $M \supset (P \supset \sim C)$

13. Complete the truth table for each of the given compound propositions. (4)

p	q	~p	p ∨ q	p • q	p ⊃ q
T	T	F	T	T	T
T	F	F	T	F	F
F	T	T	T	F	T
F	F	T	F	F	T

Problems 14-15: Construct the truth table for the compound proposition on the line to the right.

14. ~(~p ∨ q) (4)

p	q	~p	~p ∨ q	~(~p ∨ q)
T	T	F	T	F
T	F	F	F	T
F	T	T	T	F
F	F	T	T	F

15. p ⊃ (q • r) (5)

p	q	r	q • r	p ⊃ (q • r)
T	T	T	T	T
T	T	F	F	F
T	F	T	F	F
T	F	F	F	F
F	T	T	T	T
F	T	F	F	T
F	F	T	F	T
F	F	F	F	T

Problems 16-20: Assume the propositions **A** and **B** are *true*, **X** and **Y** are *false*, and **P** and **Q** are an *unknown* truth value. Find the truth value of each compound proposition. If true circle T, if false circle F. If the truth value cannot be determined, circle ? (1 each)

16. A ∨ X (T) F ?

17. Y • P T (F) ?

18. B ⊃ Q T F (?)

19. X ⊃ Q (T) F ?

20. (A ∨ P) • X T (F) ?

INTERMEDIATE LOGIC | Test 1, Form B

Lessons 1–4 (41 points)

Name ______________________________

1. Give a synonym for the term *proposition.* (1) statement

2. What is a *logical operator*? (2) a word or phrase that modifies or combines simple propositions, making them compound.

3. What is a propositional *variable?* (2) a lower case letter (p, q, r...) that represents any proposition.

4. Give an example of a truth-functional, compound proposition (in words, not symbols). (2)

   Hatred stirs up conflict, but love covers over all wrongs. (The proposition must use logical operators, and may not be a self-report, tautology, or self-contradiction.)

Problems 5-13: **M** means *I listen to music.* **D** means *I like to dance.* **S** means *I like to sing along.* **P** means *I play an instrument.*

Symbolize the following propositions:

5. I do not play an instrument. (1) ~ P
6. If I listen to music, then I like to dance or sing along. (2) M ⊃ (D ∨ S)
7. I like to sing along unless I play an instrument. (2) ~ P ⊃ S
8. I neither listen to music nor play an instrument. (2) ~ (M ∨ P)
9. I do not like to both dance and sing along. (2) ~ (D • S)
10. I listen to music only if I like to sing along. (2) M ⊃ S

Translate the following symbolic propositions:

11. ~ S ∨ ~ P (2) I do not like to sing along or I do not play an instrument.
12. P • ~ S (2) I play an instrument but I do not like to sing along.
13. (M • ~ P) ⊃ S (3) If I listen to music but do not play an instrument, then I like to sing along.

14. Complete the truth table for each of the given compound propositions. (4)

p	q	~ p	p • q	p ∨ q	p ⊃ q
T	T	F	T	T	T
T	F	F	F	T	F
F	T	T	F	T	T
F	F	T	F	F	T

Problems 15-16: Construct the truth table for the compound proposition on the line to the right.

15. ~ p ⊃ q (3)

p	q	~ p	~ p ⊃ q
T	T	F	T
T	F	F	T
F	T	T	T
F	F	T	F

16. p • (q ∨ r) (5)

p	q	r	q ∨ r	p • (q ∨ r)
T	T	T	T	T
T	T	F	T	T
T	F	T	T	T
T	F	F	F	F
F	T	T	T	F
F	T	F	T	F
F	F	T	T	F
F	F	F	F	F

Problems 17-20: Assume the propositions **A** and **B** are *true*, **X** and **Y** are *false*, and **P** and **Q** are an *unknown* truth value. Find the truth value of each compound proposition. If true circle T, if false circle F. If the truth value cannot be determined, circle ? (1 each)

17. P • X T (F) ?

18. ~ (X ∨ Y) (T) F ?

19. ~ B ⊃ Q (T) F ?

20. P ⊃ (A • P) (T) F ?

TEACHER'S NOTES on LESSON 5

THE BICONDITIONAL

Intermediate Logic, pp. 35–36

STUDENT OBJECTIVES

1. Provide the symbol, truth table, and English equivalents of the biconditional.
2. Complete Exercise 5.

TEACHING INSTRUCTIONS

1. Write on the board the sentence "My parents will worry if I'm out late." Have students tell you how to symbolize this sentence (using p's and q's). They should come up with $q \supset p$. Next write on the board "My parents will worry only if I'm out late," and have students tell you how to symbolize it. They should come up with $p \supset q$. Now write on the board the sentence "My parents will worry if and only if I'm out late." Unless they are reading ahead in the chapter, students will probably have no idea how to symbolize this.
2. Explain that "if and only if" sentence like the one you just wrote on the board is called a **biconditional. "If and only if" is symbolized by three horizontal lines on top of each other (≡).** So the above sentence could be symbolized p≡q. Explain that a biconditional is actually pretty easy to understand: it is just a combination of the first two conditionals you wrote of the board: mixing "p *if* q" and "p *only if* q" together gives you "p if *and* only if q." Explain that since "p if q" is the same things as $q \supset p$ and "p only if q" is the same thing as $p \supset q$, the biconditional is therefore the conjunction of a conditional $(p \supset q)$ and its converse $(q \supset p)$. Write on the board **$p \equiv q$ is logically equivalent to $(p \supset q) \bullet (q \supset p)$.** This explains why it is called a biconditional: it is the combination of two conditionals.
3. Explain that we can use this equivalent proposition in order to develop a truth table for the biconditional. Draw this truth table on the board and have students help you fill in the columns. The completed table should look like this:

p	q	p ⊃ q	q ⊃ p	(p ⊃ q) • (q ⊃ p)
T	T	T	T	T
T	F	F	T	F
F	T	T	F	F
F	F	T	T	T

Then draw the simplified truth table for the biconditional:

p	q	p ≡ q
T	T	T
T	F	F
F	T	F
F	F	T

Explain that, as this truth table shows, **a biconditional is true if and only if the truth values of both parts are the same**; that is, if both propositions are true or both propositions are false. If the two propositions have different truth values, the biconditional is false.

ASSIGNMENT

Have students complete Exercise 5, and go over it with them.

LESSON 5

THE BICONDITIONAL

The final logical operator we will consider is the *biconditional.* Biconditionals represent *if and only if* propositions, such as *Skyscrapers are buildings if and only if it is false that skyscrapers are not buildings.* The symbol for biconditional is ≡. If *Skyscrapers are buildings* is represented by the constant B, the proposition could be symbolized as $B \equiv \sim\sim B$ (read as *B if and only if not not B*).

What does *if and only if* mean? Recall that *p only if q* means the same as *If p then q,* while *p if q* means *If q then* p. Putting these together, *p if and only if q* means *If p then q and if q then* p. The biconditional can thus be considered as the conjunction of a conditional and its converse. Taking $p \supset q$ as the conditional and $q \supset p$ as its converse, this means that $p \equiv q$ is logically equivalent to $(p \supset q) \bullet (q \supset p)$. You can see why it is called the biconditional. We can use this equivalent proposition to develop the defining truth table for the biconditional:

DEFINITIONS

The biconditional operator (≡, "if and only if") is true when both component propositions have the same truth value, and is false when their truth values differ.

p	q	p⊃q	q⊃p	(p⊃q)•(q⊃p)
T	T	T	T	T
T	F	F	T	F
F	T	T	F	F
F	F	T	T	T

Thus the biconditional is true when both parts are true or when both parts are false. In other words, the biconditional is true if and only if the truth values of both parts are the same.

We can simplify the defining truth table for the biconditional like this:

p	q	p≡q
T	T	T
T	F	F
F	T	F
F	F	T

SUMMARY

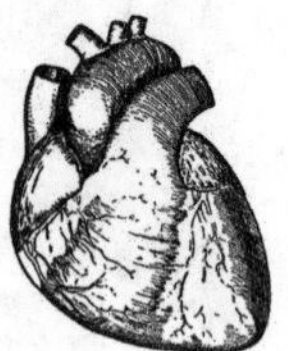

The biconditional represents *if and only if* propositions, and has the symbol ≡. The biconditional is true when both parts have the same truth value; otherwise it is false.

EXERCISE 5 (25 points)

Given: A means *Apples are fruit* | C means *Carrots are fruit*
B means *Bananas are fruit* | D means *They are delicious*

Translate each symbolic proposition

1. $A \bullet D$ Apples are fruit and they are delicious. (2)
2. $B \vee C$ Bananas are fruit or carrots are fruit. (2)
3. $\sim C \supset \sim D$ If carrots are not fruit, then they are not delicious. (2)
4. $A \equiv B$ Apples are fruit if and only if bananas are fruit. (2)
5. $(A \bullet B) \equiv \sim C$ Apples and bananas are both fruits if and only if carrots are not fruit. (3)

Symbolize each compound proposition.

6. Apples and bananas are both fruit, but carrots are not fruit. $(A \bullet B) \bullet \sim C$ (3)
7. Bananas are fruit implies that they are delicious. $B \supset D$ (2)
8. Carrots are fruit if and only if bananas are not fruit. $C \equiv \sim B$ (2)
9. Either bananas or carrots are fruit, but they are not both fruit. $(B \vee C) \bullet \sim(B \bullet C)$ (3)
10. Apples are not fruit if and only if it is false that apples are fruit. $\sim A \equiv \sim A$ (2)
11. Apples are fruit is a necessary and sufficient condition for bananas being fruit. $A \equiv B$ (2)

TEACHER'S NOTES on LESSON 6

LOGICAL EQUIVALENCE AND CONTRADICTION

Intermediate Logic, pp. 39–40

STUDENT OBJECTIVES

1. Use the biconditional to determine if two propositions are logically equivalent, contradictory, or neither.
2. Complete Exercise 6.

TEACHING INSTRUCTIONS

1. Have students shout out some things they learned about the biconditional yesterday (it is an "if and only if" proposition, it is the conjunction of a conditional and its converse, it is true only if both its parts have the same truth value, etc.). Explain that in this lesson students are going to learn another use for the biconditional besides translating "if and only if" propositions. It can also be used to test whether two statements are logically equivalent. **Two propositions are logically equivalent if and only if they have identical truth values.** Since a biconditional is only true whenever the truth values of the component parts are the same, we can use it to determine whether its component parts are logically equivalent.
2. Give students the biconditional "The wind is blowing if and only if it false that the wind is not blowing." Symbolize it on the board as $B \equiv \sim\sim B$. Have students walk you through creating a truth table for this biconditional. The completed table should look like this:

B	~B	~~B	B ≡ ~~B
T	F	T	T
F	T	F	T

Explain that because the biconditional $B \equiv \sim\sim B$ is always true, B and $\sim\sim B$ must always have the same truth value: when one is true, the other is true; when one is false, the other is false. Thus, B and $\sim\sim B$ are logically equivalent. This should make sense: remind students that a double negative always equals a positive (at least in English); "The wind is blowing" and "The wind is not not-blowing" mean the same thing.

3. Explain that a proposition like $B \equiv \sim\sim B$ which is true in every row of the truth table is called a tautology. **A tautology is a proposition that is always true due to its logical structure**. Tell students that a couple other important tautologies are $p \supset p$ and $p \vee \sim p$. They should be able to see that these are tautologies: if you have a p then you must necessarily have a p, and either p or ~p must be true. Make sure students understand that these statements cannot be false.
4. Have students help you form the truth table for the proposition $p \bullet \sim p$. The completed table should look like this:

p	~p	p • ~p
T	F	F
F	T	F

Point out that this proposition is the opposite of a tautology: it is false in every row of the truth table. Explain that a proposition that is false in every row of the truth table is called a self-contradiction; **a self-contradiction is a statement that is false by logical structure**, and in other words can never be true. Students should be able to see that there is no way to have both p and *~p*; *p* • *~p* is necessarily false.

5. Explain that we can test whether two statements are logically equivalent, contradictory, or neither, by putting the biconditional sign between them and solving the truth table for the biconditional. Write on the board the two propositions *p* ⊃ *q* and *p* • *~q*, along with their biconditional *(p* ⊃ *q)* ≡ *(p* • *~q)*. Explain that you are going to determine whether *p* ⊃ *q* and *p* • *~q* are equivalent, contradictory, or neither, by making a truth table for their biconditional. Have students guess beforehand which these two statements will be.

6. Set up the truth table as below and explain that from here on out you will be doing truth tables without the guide columns p and *q* at the beginning, simply putting the truth values immediately below the variables in the propositions. You will still start with the variables *p* and *q*, with the same familiar patterns of T and F for each. Then go on to the negation *(~q)*, then what's in parentheses, then finish. Have students walk you through assigning truth values. The completed table should look like this:

(p ⊃ q)	≡	(p • ~q)
T T T	F	T F FT
T F F	F	T T TF
F T T	F	F F FT
F T F	F	F F TF

Point out that in every single instance this biconditional is false. It is not possible for it to be true. Therefore these two propositions are (everybody all together now) contradictory.

ASSIGNMENTS

1. Have students complete Exercise 6, and go over it with them.
2. Remind students to study for next class's quiz over Lessons 6–8.

LESSON 6

LOGICAL EQUIVALENCE AND CONTRADICTION

The biconditional has another useful function beyond translating "if and only if" propositions. Since the biconditional is true whenever the truth values of the component parts are the same, the biconditional can be used to determine whether or not two propositions are **logically equivalent**; that is, it can show if two propositions have identical truth values.

Consider the example from the previous lesson, in which it was stated that $B \equiv {\sim}{\sim}B$. The truth table for this is:

B	~B	~~B	B ≡ ~~B
T	F	T	T
F	T	F	T

This biconditional is always true, so B and ${\sim}{\sim}B$ are seen to be logically equivalent.

A proposition that is true for every row in the truth table is called a **tautology**. In other words, tautologies are propositions that are true by logical structure. The compound proposition $B \equiv {\sim}{\sim}B$ is thus a tautology. Other important tautologies are $p \supset p$ and $p \vee {\sim}p$. So we can now say more briefly that the biconditional of logically equivalent propositions is a tautology.

When a proposition is false for every row in the truth table, you have a **self-contradiction**. Self-contradictions are propositions that are false by logical structure, such as $p \bullet {\sim}p$.

Consider the two propositions $p \supset q$ and $p \bullet {\sim}q$, along with their biconditional. We will do this truth table (and every one from now on) without guide columns, simply placing the truth values immediately below the variables p and q and working out the truth value of the compound propositions, finishing with the ≡ sign.

DEFINITION

Two propositions are ***logically equivalent*** if and only if they have identical truth values in a truth table.

A ***tautology*** is a proposition that is always true due to its logical structure.

A ***self-contradiction*** is a proposition that is false by logical structure.

KEY POINT

The biconditional can be used to test for equivalence. If the biconditional of two statements is a tautology, then the statements are equivalent.

KEY POINT

The biconditional can be used to test for contradiction. If the biconditional of two statements is a self-contradiction, then the statements are contradictory.

$(p \supset q)$	$\equiv$	$(p \bullet \sim q)$
T T T	F	T F F T
T F F	F	T T T F
F T T	F	F F F T
F T F	F	F F T F

Because this biconditional is a self-contradiction, we can say that $p \supset q$ contradicts $p \bullet \sim q$.

SUMMARY

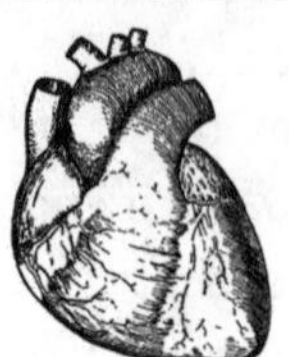

When the biconditional of two propositions is a tautology, the propositions are logically equivalent. When it is a self-contradiction, the propositions are contradictory. A tautology is a proposition that is true by logical structure. A self-contradiction is a proposition that is false by logical structure.

EXERCISE 6 (30 points)

Set up the biconditional between each pair of propositions (as in the lesson) to determine if they are *logically equivalent, contradictory,* or *neither.* In this exercise, do not use guide columns. Rather, place the truth values immediately beneath the variables and work through the proposition to determine its truth value. Problem 4 has three variables, so it will require eight rows.

1. $[\sim (p \lor q)] \equiv (\sim p \lor \sim q)$ (7)

F TTT T FTFFT
F TTF F FTTTF
F FTT F TFTFT
T FFF T TFTTF

NEITHER

2. $(p \supset q) \equiv (\sim q \supset \sim p)$ (6)

T T T T FT T FT
T F F T TF F FT
F T T T FT T TF
F T F T TF T TF

EQUIVALENT

3. $[\sim (\sim p \lor q)] \equiv (p \supset q)$ (6)

F FTTT F TTT
T FTFF F TFF
F TFTT F FTT
F TFTF F FTF

CONTRADICTORY

4. $[p \supset (q \supset r)] \equiv [(p \supset q) \supset r]$ (9)

TT TTT T TTT TT
TF TFF T TTT FF
TT FTT T TFF TT
TT FTF T TFF TF
FT TTT T FTT TT
FT TFF F FTT FF
FT FTT T FTF TT
FT FTF F FTF FF

NEITHER

5. Write a set of propositions in English which could be represented by the symbolic propositions in Problem 2. (2)

If a platypus is a mammal then it is warm-blooded.

If a platypus is not warm-blooded then it is not a mammal. (Answers will vary.)

TEACHER'S NOTES

QUIZ 3 (LESSONS 5–6)

STUDENT OBJECTIVE

Complete Quiz 3.

TEACHING INSTRUCTIONS

1. Give Quiz 3. Allow 20 minutes. Grade quiz with students.
2. If you have extra time, introduce Lesson 7 to get a head start on next class's material.

INTERMEDIATE LOGIC | Quiz 3

Lessons 5–6 (24 points)

Name ______________________________

1. What is a *tautology?* (2) a proposition that is true by logical structure.

2. Complete the defining truth table for *biconditional.* (2)

p	q	p ≡ q
T	T	T
T	F	F
F	T	F
F	F	T

Problems 3-6: **B** means *One believes in Christ.* **D** means *One is drawn by the Father.* **C** means *One comes to Christ.* **E** means *One has everlasting life.*

Translate the following symbolic propositions (2 each):

3. ~B ⊃ ~E If one does not believe in Christ then one does not have ever lasting life.

4. C ≡ D One comes to Christ if and only if one is drawn by the Father.

Symbolize the following propositions (2 each):

5. No one comes to Christ unless the Father draws him. ~ D ⊃ ~ C

6. One believes in Christ if and only if one has everlasting life. B ≡ E

Problems 7-8: Set up the biconditional between the pairs of propositions, and determine if they are logically equivalent, contradictory, or neither. (6 each)

7.

p • ~ q	≡	~ p ∨ q
TFFT	F	FTTT
TTTF	F	FTFF
FFFT	F	TFTT
FFTF	F	TFTF

CONTRADICTORY

8.

~ p ≡ q	≡	p ≡ ~ q
FTFT	T	TFFT
FTTF	T	TTTF
TFTT	T	FTFT
TFFF	T	FFTF

LOGICALLY EQUIVALENT

TEACHER'S NOTES on LESSON 7

TRUTH TABLES FOR DETERMINING VALIDITY

Intermediate Logic, pp. 43–46

STUDENT OBJECTIVES

1. Use truth tables to determine the validity of arguments in up to four variables.
2. Complete Exercises 7a and 7b.

SPECIAL NOTE

Depending on which schedule you're following, you have three days to work through Lesson 7. Get through as much of the lesson as you can on the first day, and spend the following days tying up loose ends and working through both parts of Exercise 7 with students.

TEACHING INSTRUCTIONS

1. Tell students that so far they have learned how to use truth tables for three things: defining logical operators (have someone give an example of this), determining the truth values of compound propositions (have someone give an example of this), and determining logical equivalence (have someone give an example of this). Explain that students are about to learn another use for truth tables (the most useful and the most interesting use): determining the *validity* of propositional arguments.
2. See if anyone remembers the definition of validity (glare more and more darkly at them until someone is frightened into remembering). Make sure everyone has fresh in their minds that **in a valid argument, if the premises are true, the conclusion must be true, and if the premises can be true and the conclusion false, the argument is invalid**. In other words, if an argument has true premises and a false conclusion, it is automatically invalid.
3. Explain that there are several steps to setting up a truth table to determine the validity of an argument. Write on the board this argument (or something similar): "If it rains, it pours. It rains. Therefore it pours." Explain that the first step is to determining this argument's validity is to translate it into a symbolic form. Have the students do this, using *p*'s and *q*'s. Inform them, if they do not already know, that **the symbol for "therefore," or the conclusion of the argument, is a triangle of three dots**: $\therefore$. They should come up with $p \supset q$, p, $\therefore q$. They should recognize it as *modus ponens*, and should know that it is valid, but ignore that for this moment. Write this symbolized argument on the board.
4. Draw a line underneath the symbolized argument, and explain that the next step is to set up the truth table for this argument just like the truth tables you have done before. Have students tell you what truth values to place below the propositions (it may be easier to start from the right and work left). The completed table should look like this:

p ⊃ q	p	∴ q
T	T	T
F	T	F
T	F	T
T	F	F

5. Ask students how they think that from looking at this table they can determine the validity of the argument. If they are lost, tell them that if the argument was invalid, there would be at least one row in which the premises were true and the conclusion false. Is there any row in which the premises are both T and the conclusion F? There is no such row in this truth table; therefore the argument $p \supset q$, p, ∴ q is valid. Emphasize that if there is just one row with true premises and a false conclusion, the whole argument is invalid, even if *other* rows have true premises and a true conclusion. Remind them that only one counterexample is needed to show an argument to be invalid.

6. Write on the board the argument $p \supset q$, $\sim p$, ∴ $\sim q$. Students should recognize this argument as the invalid "denying the antecedent" argument. Have students help you set up the truth table for it and determine the truth values. The completed table should look like this:

p ⊃ q	~p	∴ ~q	
T	F	F	
F	F	T	
T	T	F	←INVALID
T	T	T	

Have students look for the row with the true premises and the false conclusion (row 3) that makes this argument invalid, even though the row 4 has true premises with a true conclusion. It takes just one bad apple to spoil the whole barrel. To mark the argument as invalid, circle the row that makes it so and identify it with an arrow and the word "invalid."

7. Write on the board this argument: "The argument must be either valid or invalid. If it is invalid then there will be a row of true premises with a false conclusion. There is no row of true premises with a false conclusion. Therefore the argument is valid." To determine whether this argument is as valid as it claims to be, first have students symbolize it using the constants V, I, and R. They should come up with $V \vee I$, $I \supset R$, $\sim R$, ∴ V. Set up the truth table, and have them help you fill in the truth values under the three constants, *V*, *I*, and *R*. Remember that, because there are three constants, the truth table will have eight rows. The preliminary table should look like this:

V ∨ I	I ⊃ R	~R	∴ V
T T	T		
T T	F		
T F	T		
T F	F		
F T	T		
F T	F		
F F	T		
F F	F		

8. Next have students determine the other values until the entire argument is complete (it may be easiest for them to work from right to left). The completed table should look like this:

V ∨ I	I ⊃ R	~R	∴ V
T T T	T T T	F T	T
T T T	T F F	T F	T
T T F	F T T	F T	T
T T F	F T F	T F	T
F T T	T T T	F T	F
F T T	T F F	T F	F
F F F	F T T	F T	F
F F F	F T F	T F	F

Have students tell you which columns are unnecessary and can be erased for clarity, leaving only the truth values of the premises and conclusion.

V ∨ I	I ⊃ R	~R	∴ V	
T T T	T T T	F T	T	
T T T	T F F	T F	T	
T T F	F T T	F T	T	
T T F	F T F	T F	T	←VALID
F T T	T T T	F T	F	
F T T	T F F	F T	F	
F F F	F T T	F T	F	
F F F	F T F	T F	F	

By looking at this table, students should be able to see that there are no rows in which the premises are T and the conclusion F; the argument is therefore valid. Tell students that they can label an argument "valid" just as they labeled it "invalid," by circling the rows in which all true premises lead to a true conclusion and labeling it with an arrow and "valid."

9. Finally, write on the board this argument: "If we drink the poison then I will die. If we drink the poison then you will die. So either I will die, or you will." Before doing anything else, have students think for a moment and try to predict whether this argument will be valid or invalid (if its premises are true, must its conclusion be true as well?). Then have them symbolize it using the constants *P*, *I*, and *Y*. They should come up with $P \supset I$, $P \supset Y$, $\therefore I \vee Y$. Have them tell you how to set up and fill in the truth table for this argument. The completed table (with all intermediate steps erased) should look like this:

P ⊃ I	P ⊃ Y	∴ I ∨ Y
T	T	T
T	F	T
F	T	T
F	F	F
T	T	T
T	T	T
T	T	T
T	T	F

Have students search for the T T F line that makes the argument invalid (the last line). And if they haven't noted it already, make sure students see that this makes sense given the original argument: even if it's true that you or I will die if we drink poison, we don't *have* to drink the poison. So as long as we're not foolish, neither of us has to die.

10. Write on the board the following procedure for determining the validity of an argument using truth tables. Make sure students copy it down too, to solidify it in their memories.

The Truth Table Method for Validity

1. Write the argument in symbolic form on a line.

2. Under the variables, place the columns of T and F.

3. Determine the columns of T and F for the propositions following the defining truth tables.

4. Remove any unnecessary columns of T and F, leaving only the columns for the premises and conclusion.

5. Examine the rows. If any row has all true premises with a false conclusion, the argument is invalid. Otherwise it is valid. Mark the row(s) showing valid or invalid.

ASSIGNMENTS

1. Have students complete Exercises 7a and 7b, and go over them with them.
2. On the last day, remind students to study for next class's quiz over Lesson 7.

LESSON 7

TRUTH TABLES FOR DETERMINING VALIDITY

So far we have seen three uses for truth tables: determining the truth values of compound propositions, defining logical operators, and determining logical equivalence. Another use for truth tables, and perhaps the most practical (and thus the most interesting), is that of determining the validity of propositional arguments.

Before we look at how truth tables do this, we first need to consider what is meant by **validity**. When an argument is valid, the conclusion follows necessarily from the premises. In other words, *if the premises are assumed to be true,* then in a valid argument *the conclusion must also be true.* If an argument has true premises with a false conclusion, it is invalid.

To use truth tables to determine the validity of an argument, the argument is translated into symbolic form (if it is not already symbolic) then placed above a line, with the symbol ∴ (meaning "therefore") in front of the conclusion. Then the truth values are placed below the propositions, just like we have done before. These steps are completed for the *modus ponens* argument shown:

p⊃q	p	∴ q
T	T	T
F	T	F
T	F	T
T	F	F

Notice that p and q (and thus $p \supset q$) have the same pattern of T and F that we have seen up to this point.

Now consider again the definition of validity. How does the truth table show that this argument is valid? Well, the argument must be either valid or invalid. If it was invalid, there would be a horizontal

DEFINITIONS

Recall that in a ***valid*** argument, if the premises are true, the conclusion must be true. If the premises can be true and the conclusion false, the argument is ***invalid***.

KEY POINT

The symbol ∴ means "therefore" and signals the conclusion of an argument.

row which showed *true premises* with a *false conclusion*. No such row exists; the argument is not invalid. So it must be valid.

KEY POINT

If a truth table shows at least one row in which the premises of an argument are true but the conclusion is false, then the argument is invalid. Otherwise, it is valid.

Consider this another way. Look at each of the four rows for the above argument. For *every* row in which all the premises show T, does the conclusion also show T? Yes it does; the first row above is the only row with all true premises, and it also shows a true conclusion. The argument is thus valid. If *any* row showed premises with all Ts and a conclusion with F, it would be invalid, even if *other* rows had premises with all Ts and a conclusion with a T.

For an example of an argument shown to be invalid by truth table, consider the *denying the antecedent* argument here:

p⊃q	~p	∴~q	
T	F	F	
F	F	T	
T	T	F	← INVALID
T	T	T	

The truth values have been completed for the premises and conclusion (with the initial truth values for *p* and *q* removed for the sake of clarity). Now, notice that the third row has true premises with a false conclusion. This argument is thus invalid (even though the fourth row shows true premises with a true conclusion). To mark it as invalid, identify the row (or rows) with true premises and a false conclusion and write *Invalid* near it, as shown above.

Let's look at two more examples of truth tables for validity, one valid and one invalid. On the first one we will show the step-by-step procedure. Consider, just for fun, the argument above: "The argument must be either valid or invalid. If it is invalid then there will be a row of true premises with a false conclusion. There is no row of true premises with a false conclusion. Therefore the argument is valid." We symbolize this argument as *V*∨ *I*, *I*⊃ *R*, ~*R*,- ∴*V*, and complete the truth table. First, write out the argument in symbolic form, placing the truth values under the three constants *V*, *I*, and *R* in the same pattern as we used before:

V ∨ I		I ⊃ R	~R	∴V
T	T	T		
T	T	F		
T	F	T		
T	F	F		
F	T	T		
F	T	F		
F	F	T		
F	F	F		

From these truth values, determine the other values until the entire argument is completed. You may find it easier to start from the right and work your way left.

V ∨ I	I ⊃ R	~R	∴V
T T T	T T T	FT	T
T T T	T F F	TF	T
T T F	F T T	FT	T
T T F	F T F	TF	T
F T T	T T T	FT	F
F T T	T F F	TF	F
F F F	F T T	FT	F
F F F	F T F	TF	F

Then the unnecessary columns of T and F may be removed (by erasing or marking out), leaving only the patterns for the premises and the conclusion, as shown:

V ∨ I	I ⊃ R	~R	∴V	
T	T	F	T	
T	F	T	T	
T	T	F	T	
T	T	T	T	← VALID
T	T	F	F	
T	F	T	F	
F	T	F	F	
F	T	T	F	

The only row with all true premises is the fourth row down, and it also shows a true conclusion. Thus the argument is valid, as marked.

Now for one more example of an invalid argument before we go on to the assignment. "If we stop here then I will be lost. If we stop here then you will be lost. So either I will be lost, or you will." This can be symbolized $S \supset I$, $S \supset Y$, $\therefore I \lor Y$.

The truth table can be developed as before (you should do so on your own), resulting in the following patterns:

$S \supset I$	$S \supset Y$	$\therefore I \lor Y$	
T	T	T	
T	F	T	
F	T	T	
F	F	F	
T	T	T	
T	T	T	
T	T	T	
T	T	F	← INVALID

Although there are many rows which have true premises with a true conclusion (namely rows one, five, six and seven), the eighth row shows true premises with a false conclusion. Thus the entire argument has been shown to be invalid, and is marked as such.

We have the following procedure for determining the validity of arguments using truth tables.

SUMMARY

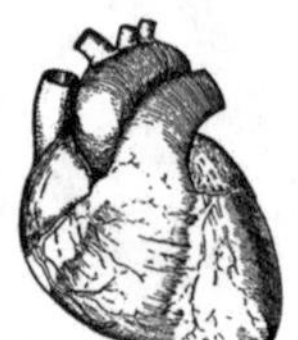

The Truth Table Method for Validity

1. Write the argument in symbolic form on a line.
2. Under the variables, place the columns of T and F.
3. Determine the columns of T and F for the propositions following the defining truth tables.
4. Remove any unnecessary columns of T and F, leaving only the columns for the premises and conclusion.
5. Examine the rows. If any row has all true premises with a false conclusion, the argument is invalid. Otherwise it is valid. Mark the row(s) showing valid or invalid.

EXERCISE 7a (48 points)

Determine the truth value of each compound proposition. Assume that propositions A and B are true, X and Y are false, and P and Q are unknown. Circle T if the proposition is true, F if it is false, and ? if the truth value cannot be determined. (Hint: There are two of each.) (1 each)

1. P ∨ ~P — (T) F ?
2. (P ⊃ P) ⊃ ~A — T (F) ?
3. (Y ⊃ P) ⊃ Q — T F (?)
4. P ≡ (X ∨ Y) — T F (?)
5. ~Q • [(P ∨ Q) • ~P] — T (F) ?
6. ~[P ∨ (B • Y)] ∨ [(P ∨ B) • (P ∨ Y)] — (T) F ?

Use truth tables to determine the validity of each argument. Identify each as either VALID or INVALID, and identify the rows that show this. (4 each)

7.

p ⊃ q	∴ p ⊃ (p • q)	
T	T	← Valid
F	F	
T	T	← Valid
T	T	← Valid

8.

p • q	∴ p ∨ q	
T	T	← Valid
F	T	
F	T	
F	F	

9.

p ≡ ~q	~q	∴ p	
F	F	T	
T	T	T	← Valid
T	F	F	
F	T	F	

10.

p ∨ q	~p	∴ q	
T	F	T	
T	F	F	
T	T	T	← Valid
F	T	F	

Continued on next page.

Translate the arguments into symbolic form using the given constants, and then use truth tables to determine their validity as in the previous problems.

11. If Jesus was John the Baptist raised from the dead, then He could do miracles. Jesus did miracles, so He was John the Baptist raised from the dead. (J means *Jesus was John the Baptist raised from the dead,* M means *He could do miracles.*) (5)

$J \supset M$	M	$\therefore J$	
T	T	T	
F	F	T	
T	T	F	← Invalid
T	F	F	

12. If Jeff studies then he will get good grades. If Jeff does not study then he will play. So Jeff will either get good grades or he will play. (S means *Jeff studies,* G means *He will get good grades, P* means *He will play.*) (7)

$S \supset G$	$\sim S \supset P$	$\therefore G \vee P$	
T	T	T	← Valid
T	T	T	← Valid
F	T	T	
F	T	F	
T	T	T	← Valid
T	F	T	
T	T	T	← Valid
T	F	F	

13. If Jesus is not God then He was a liar or He was insane. Jesus was clearly not a liar. He certainly was not insane. We conclude that Jesus is God. (G means *Jesus is God,* L means *He was a liar,* I means *He was insane.*) (7)

$\sim G \supset (L \vee I)$	$\sim L$	$\sim I$	$\therefore G$	
T	F	F	T	
T	F	T	T	
T	T	F	T	
T	T	T	T	← Valid
T	F	F	F	
T	F	T	F	
T	T	F	F	
F	T	T	F	

Continued on next page.

14. If taxes increase then the public will complain, but if the deficit increases then the public will complain. Either taxes or the deficit will increase. Thus the public is bound to complain. (T means *Taxes increase, P* means *The public will complain,* D means *The deficit increases.*) (7)

$T \supset P$	$D \supset P$	$T \vee D$	$\therefore P$	
T	T	T	T	← Valid
T	T	T	T	← Valid
F	F	T	F	
F	T	T	F	
T	T	T	T	← Valid
T	T	F	T	
T	F	T	F	
T	T	F	F	

EXERCISE 7b (30 points)

Use truth tables to determine the validity of the propositional arguments below. (Problems 4 and 5 require eight rows each; Problem 6 requires sixteen!)

1.

p	∴ ~p ∨ q (3)	
T	T	
T	F	← Invalid
F	T	
F	T	

2.

p ⊃ q	∴ ~q ⊃ ~p (3)	
T	T	← Valid
F	F	
T	T	← Valid
T	T	← Valid

3.

p ⊃ q	~q	∴ p ≡ q (4)	
T	F	T	
F	T	F	
T	F	F	
T	T	T	← Valid

4.

p ⊃ (q ⊃ r)	q	∴ r ⊃ p (5)	
T	T	T	
F	T	T	
T	F	T	
T	F	T	
T	T	F	← Invalid
T	T	T	
T	F	F	
T	F	T	

5.

p ⊃ (~q ⊃ r)	p	∴ ~r ⊃ q (6)	
T	T	T	← Valid
T	T	T	← Valid
T	T	T	← Valid
F	T	F	
T	F	T	
T	F	T	
T	F	T	
T	F	F	

6.

$(p \supset q) \bullet [(p \bullet q) \supset r]$	$p \supset (r \supset s)$	$\therefore p \supset s$	(9)
T	T	T	← Valid
T	F	F	
F	T	T	
F	T	F	
F	T	T	
F	F	F	
F	T	T	
F	T	F	
T	T	T	← Valid
T	T	T	← Valid
T	T	T	← Valid
T	T	T	← Valid
T	T	T	← Valid
T	T	T	← Valid
T	T	T	← Valid
T	T	T	← Valid

QUIZ 4 (LESSON 7)

STUDENT OBJECTIVE

Complete Quiz 4.

TEACHING INSTRUCTIONS

1. Give the quiz. Allow 30 minutes for it. Grade quiz with students.
2. If you have extra time, begin reviewing for Test 2.

INTERMEDIATE LOGIC | Quiz 4

Lesson 7 (35 points)

Name ______________________________

1. What does it mean that an argument is *valid?* (2) An argument is valid when the premises imply the conclusion./In a valid argument, if the premises are true, then the conclusion must be true.

Problems 2-3: Use a truth table to determine the validity of the given argument. Remember to write VALID or INVALID. If invalid, circle the row(s) which show invalidity. (5, 8)

2.

$\sim(p \bullet q)$	q	$\therefore \sim p$	
F	T	F	
T	F	F	
T	T	T	VALID
T	F	T	

3.

$p \equiv (q \vee r)$	$q \supset r$	$\therefore p \supset q$	
T	T	T	
T	F	T	
(T	T	F)	INVALID
F	T	F	
F	T	T	
F	F	T	
F	T	T	
T	T	T	

Problems 4-5: Translate the argument into symbolic form on the line using the given constants. Then use a truth table to determine the validity of the argument. Remember to write VALID or INVALID. If invalid, circle the row(s) which show invalidity. (10 each)

4. If a government becomes tyrannical, then it will take away the rights of citizens. A government takes away the rights of citizens if and only if the citizens are complacent. Thus, a government does not become tyrannical or the citizens are complacent. (**T**, **R**, **C**)

$T \supset R$	$R \equiv C$	$\therefore \sim T \vee C$	
T	T	T	
T	F	F	
F	F	T	
F	T	F	
T	T	T	VALID
T	F	T	
T	F	T	
T	T	T	

5. If you brush and floss regularly then you will have healthy teeth. You brush regularly but you do not floss regularly. Therefore you will not have healthy teeth. (**B**, **F**, **H**)

$(B \bullet F) \supset H$	$B \bullet {\sim}F$	$\therefore {\sim}H$	
T	F	F	
F	F	T	
T	T	F	INVALID
T	T	T	
T	F	F	
T	F	T	
T	F	F	
T	F	T	

REVIEW FOR TEST 2 (LESSONS 5–7)

STUDENT OBJECTIVES

Complete the objectives from Lessons 5–7. Objective's are listed at the beginning of each lesson's teacher's notes.

TEACHING INSTRUCTIONS

1. Ask students the Review Questions for Lessons 5-7 on p. 80. Have them answer aloud or create the truth tables. Allow them to look for the answers in their textbooks if they need to, but drill them until they don't need the books.
2. If you'd like, give students "Test 2: Form A" from the *Intermediate Logic Test and Quiz Packet* as a practice exam. Go over the answers together.
3. For additional practice, students can work through the other Additional Exercises for Lessons 5–7 on p. 89–91 of *Intermediate Logic.*

ASSIGNMENT

Have students study for Test 2.

TEACHER'S NOTES

TEST 2 (LESSONS 5–7)

STUDENT OBJECTIVE

Complete Test 2.

TEACHING INSTRUCTIONS

1. Give students Test 2: Form B from the *Intermediate Logic Test and Quiz Packet.* Allow one hour to complete it.
2. Grade tests. Have them ready to hand back to students within a week.

INTERMEDIATE LOGIC | Test 2, Form A

Lessons 5–7 (54 points)

Name ______________________________

1. What is a *tautology*? Give a symbolic example of a tautology. (3) A tautology is a compound proposition which is true due to its logical structure. Some symbolic examples are $p \supset p$, $p \vee {\sim}p$, ${\sim}(p \bullet {\sim}p)$.

Problems 2-3: Circle T if the statement is true, circle F if it is false. (1 each)

2. A biconditional is true if and only if both parts are true. T (F)
3. If the conclusion of a valid argument is false, one of the premises is false. (T) F

Problems 4-6: Symbolize the proposition using the given constants.

B means *You eat breakfast.* **L** means *You eat lunch.*
D means *You eat dinner.* **H** means *You are hungry.*

4. You eat lunch or dinner, but you don't eat breakfast. (3) $(L \vee D) \bullet {\sim} B$
5. You eat lunch only if you don't eat breakfast. (2) $L \supset {\sim}B$
6. You are not hungry if and only if you eat breakfast and dinner. (3) ${\sim} H \equiv (B \bullet D)$

Problems 7-9: Assume the propositions **A** and **B** are *true*, **X** and **Y** are *false*, and **P** and **Q** are an *unknown* truth value. Determine the truth value of each compound proposition. If true circle T, if false circle F. If the truth value cannot be determined, circle ? (1 each)

7. $(A \bullet {\sim} X) \equiv {\sim} B$ T (F) ?
8. ${\sim} P \supset (P \supset Y)$ (T) F ?
9. $(P \supset Q) \vee (Q \supset P)$ (T) F ?

10. Construct a truth table on the line below to determine if ${\sim} p \supset q$ is equivalent to $p \vee q$. (5)

$({\sim} p \supset q)$	$\equiv$	$(p \vee q)$
F T T T	T	T T T
F T T F	T	T T F
T F T T	T	F T T
T F F F	T	F F F

Are they equivalent? (Yes) No

11. Construct a truth table on the line below to determine if $p \equiv q$ contradicts $p \equiv \sim q$. (5)

(p ≡ q)	≡	(p ≡ ~ q)
T T T	F	T F F T
T F F	F	T T T F
F F T	F	F T F T
F T F	F	F F T F

Are they contradictory? (Yes) No

Problems 12-13: Use a longer truth table to determine the validity of the given argument. Remember to write VALID or INVALID. If invalid, circle the row(s) which show invalidity. (5 each)

12.

p ⊃ q	p	∴ p • q	
T	T	T	VALID
F	T	F	
T	F	F	
T	F	F	

13.

p ∨ q	~ p	∴ p ≡ q	
T	F	T	
T	F	F	
(T	T	F)	INVALID
F	T	T	

Problems 14-15: Translate the argument into symbolic form on the line using the given constants. Then use a longer truth table to determine the validity of the argument. Remember to write VALID or INVALID. If invalid, circle the row(s) which show invalidity.

14. He is a prince if and only if his mother is a queen. Either he is not a prince or his mother is not a queen. Thus, he is not a prince. (**P, Q**) (8)

P ≡ Q	~ P ∨ ~ Q	∴ ~ P	
T	F	F	
F	T	F	
F	T	T	
T	T	T	VALID

15. Scott and Rachel are not both students. Scott is a student or Luke is a student. Therefore, if Luke is a student then Rachel is not a student. (**S, R, L**) (10)

~ (S • R)	S ∨ L	∴ L ⊃ ~ R	
F	T	F	
F	T	T	
T	T	T	
T	T	T	
(T	T	F)	INVALID
T	F	T	
T	T	T	
T	F	T	

INTERMEDIATE LOGIC | Test 2, Form B

Lessons 5–7 (51 points)

Name ________________________________

1. Give a symbolic example of a self-contradiction. (2) p • ~ p Other possible answers: ~(p ∨ ~p), ~(p ⊃ p), ~(p ≡ p).

Problems 2-4: Circle T if the statement is true, circle F if it is false. (1 each)

2. The negation of any self-contradiction is a tautology. (T) F
3. If the antecedent of a conditional is false, the conditional is considered true. (T) F
4. An invalid argument can have true premises and a true conclusion.  (T) F

Problems 5-7: Symbolize the proposition using the given constants. (2 each)

B means *You read books.* **T** means *You travel.* **L** means *You will learn.*

5. If you read books or travel then you will learn. (B ∨ T) ⊃ L
6. You will not learn unless you read books. ~ B ⊃ ~ L
7. It is not the case that you travel but will not learn. ~ (T • ~L)

Problems 8-10: Assume the propositions **A** and **B** are *true*, **X** and **Y** are *false*, and **P** and **Q** are an *unknown* truth value. Determine the truth value of each compound proposition. If true circle T, if false circle F. If the truth value cannot be determined, circle ? (1 each)

8. ~ (A • X) (T) F ?
9. (P ∨ ~ P) ⊃ ~ B T (F) ?
10. Q ≡ (Y ⊃ Q) T F (?)

11. Construct a truth table on the line below to determine if p ∨ q is equivalent to ~ (p • q) (5)

(p ∨ q)	≡	~(p • q)
T T T	F	F T T T
T T F	T	T T F F
F T T	T	T F F T
F F F	F	T F F F

Are they equivalent? Yes (No)

 |

12. Construct a truth table on the line below to determine if p • q contradicts p ⊃ ~ q. (5)

(p • q) ≡ (p ⊃ ~ q)
TTT F TFFT
TFF F TTTF
FFT F FTFT
FFF F FTTF

Do they contradict? (Yes) No

Problems 13-14: Use a longer truth table to determine the validity of the given argument. Remember to write VALID or INVALID. If invalid, circle the row(s) which show invalidity. (5 each)

13.

p ∨ q	p	∴ ~ q	
(T	T	F)	INVALID
T	T	T	
T	F	F	
F	F	T	

14.

p ⊃ q	q ⊃ p	∴ p ≡ q	
T	T	T	
F	T	F	
T	F	F	
T	T	T	VALID

Problems 15-16: Translate the argument into symbolic form on the line using the given constants. Then use a longer truth table to determine the validity of the argument. Remember to write VALID or INVALID. If invalid, circle the row(s) which show invalidity.

15. He is a native if and only if he was born here. He was not born here. So he is not a native. (**N**, **B**) (7)

N ≡ B	~ B	∴ ~ N	
T	F	F	
F	T	F	
F	F	T	
T	T	T	VALID

16. The Seattle Symphony and Nirvana are not both great bands. The Seattle Symphony is a great band if the London Orchestra also is. Thus, if the London Orchestra is a great band then Nirvana is not. (**S, N, L**) (10)

~ (S • N)	L ⊃ S	∴ L ⊃ ~ N	
F	T	F	
F	T	T	
T	T	T	
T	T	T	
T	F	F	
T	T	T	
T	F	T	
T	T	T	VALID

TEACHER'S NOTES on LESSON 8

SHORTER TRUTH TABLES FOR DETERMINING VALIDITY

Intermediate Logic, pp. 53–56

STUDENT OBJECTIVES

1. Use shorter truth tables to determine the validity of propositional arguments.
2. Complete Exercise 8.

SPECIAL NOTE

Depending on which schedule you're following, you have two days to work through Lesson 8. Get through as much of the lesson as you can on the first day, and spend the second day tying up loose ends and working through Exercise 8 with students.

TEACHING INSTRUCTIONS

1. Students should breathe an enormous sigh of relief when they hear the title of this lesson. If they don't, remind them how many hundreds of Ts and Fs they had to write in the exercises for Lesson 7. Explain that each time a new variable is added to the truth table, the number of rows doubles; that means if someone asks you to create a truth table for an argument with six variables, you'll be writing sixty-four Ts and Fs under each variable, and you'll be toast. Explain that there *is* a shorter method for determining validity using truth tables. In fact, most truth tables can be compressed into just one row.
2. Have students remind you what makes an argument invalid (true premises and false conclusion). Explain that **in a shorter truth table, you assume that the argument is invalid; that is, you assume that the premises are true and the conclusion false. Then you work backwards, plugging in the truth values that follow from that assumption. If everything after the assumption works without creating any unavoidable contradictions, the argument is indeed invalid. But if the assumption results in an unavoidable contradiction, the argument is valid.**
3. Remind students of the argument you used in Lesson 7: "If we drink the poison then I will die. If we drink the poison then you will die. So either I will die, or you will." Have someone symbolize it for you again using *P*, *I*, and *Y* ($P \supset I$, $P \supset Y$, $\therefore I \vee Y$). Ask students what truth values you should assign to each proposition, assuming that the argument is invalid. The initial truth table should look like this:

P ⊃ I	P ⊃ Y	∴ I ∨ Y
T	T	F

Make sure students notes that the Ts and F are placed beneath the parts of the propositions that would be filled in *last* in a longer truth table.

4. Have students look at the conclusion. Assuming it is false, can we determine anything about the truth values of *I* and *Y*? Yes, because in order for the whole disjunction to be false, both the disjuncts must be false as well, according to the defining truth table for disjunction. So *I* and *Y* must both be false. But if *I* and *Y* are false in the

conclusion they must be false in the premises as well. The table should now look like this:

P ⊃ I	P ⊃ Y	∴ I ∨ Y
T F	T F	F F F

5. Now have students look at the premises. The two conditionals are true with false consequents. What must the truth value of their antecedent *P* be? Given the defining truth table for the conditional, *P* must be false as well in order for the whole conditional to be true. So we assign *P* an F value in both premises. The table now looks like this:

P ⊃ I	P ⊃ Y	∴ I ∨ Y	
F T F	F T F	F F F	←INVALID

Make sure students see that everything plugged in perfectly without contradiction when we assumed that the argument was invalid. Have them explain what that means (the argument is indeed invalid.)

6. Return to another argument from Lesson 7: "The argument must be either valid or invalid. If it is invalid then there will be a row of true premises with a false conclusion. There is no row of true premises with a false conclusion. Therefore the argument is valid." Have student symbolize it, using the constants V, I, and R. They should come up with *V ∨ I, I ⊃ R, ~R, ∴ V.* Have them help you set up the truth table, assuming that the argument is invalid. The table should look like this:

V ∨ I	I ⊃ R	~R	∴ V
T	T	T	F

7. Have students once again begin by looking at the conclusion. If V is false there, where else must it be false? Write in F under the *V* in the first premise. Look at the third premise and ask students what they can determine from it (if *~R* is true, *R* must be false in premise 2). Write F in under the *R*. The table should now look like this:

V ∨ I	I ⊃ R	~R	∴ V
F T	T F	T F	F

Have students look again at the second premise, and ask what truth values they can determine from it. As in the last example, in order for the conditional to be true with a false consequent, the antecedent I must also be false. Write F in under the *I* in both the first and second premises. The table should now look like this:

V ∨ I	I ⊃ R	~R	∴ V	
F T F	F T F	T F	F	←VALID
↑CONTRADICTION				

8. Ask students if everything is fine. They should see that it is not. In the first premise both V and I are false, but in that case, the whole disjunction should be false as well. But we made it true at the beginning. Explain that this contradiction means that it is impossible to make this argument invalid. Thus *V ∨ I, I ⊃ R, ~R, ∴ V* is a valid argument. Tell the students to identify the contradiction when they find a valid argument.

9. Have someone give you the symbols for the *modus tollens* argument (*p⊃q, ~q, ∴ ~p*), which students should already know is a valid argument. Have them walk you through setting up the truth table that assumes that *modus tollens* is invalid. It should look like this:

p ⊃ q	~q	∴ ~p
T	T	F

Students should be able to solve this one without your help. Remind them to start with the conclusion. If *~p* is false, *p* must be true. If *~q* is true, q must be false. The table should look like this:

p ⊃ q	~q	∴ ~p	
T T F	T F	F T	←VALID

But if *p* is true and *q* is false, then *p⊃q* should be false, and we labeled it true. There's a contradiction in the first premise; mark it as a contradiction and write "VALID" beside the table.

10. Now have someone give you the symbols for the "affirming the consequent" fallacy. Write the truth table on the board assuming its invalidity:

$p \supset q$	q	$\therefore p$
T	T	F

Have students go at it. They should come up with this table:

$p \supset q$	q	$\therefore p$	
F T T	T	F	←INVALID

They should conclude that, as there is no contradiction, "affirming the consequent" is indeed invalid.

11. Explain that when a shorter truth table is completed like this for an invalid argument, **the truth values you find for the variables or constants are the same truth values that you would find in a row in that longer truth table showing the argument to be invalid.** Since that row is really the only row you're concerned about in the longer truth table, the shorter truth table simply isolates that row and determines whether it actually exists or not. Write on the board beside the truth table you just did this longer truth table for "affirming the consequent" and compare the two:

$p \supset q$	q	$\therefore p$	
T	T	T	
F	F	T	
T	T	F	←INVALID
T	F	F	

Make sure students see that the third row of the longer truth table and the one row of the shorter truth table are the same.

12. Write on the board the procedure for determining validity with the shorter truth table, and make sure students copy it down as well.

The Shorter Truth Table Method for Validity

1. **Write the argument in symbolic form on a line.**
2. **Assume the argument is invalid by assigning the premises the value T and the conclusion the value F.**
3. **Work backwards along the argument, determining the remaining truth values to be T or F as necessary, avoiding the contradiction if possible.**
4. **If the truth values are completed without contradiction, then the argument is invalid as assumed.**
5. **If a contradiction is unavoidable, then the original assumption was wrong and the argument is valid.**

ASSIGNMENT

Have students complete Exercise 8, and go over it with them.

LESSON 8

SHORTER TRUTH TABLES FOR DETERMINING VALIDITY

In the last exercise, you found that you needed to write hundreds of Ts and Fs because of the number of variables. And each time a new variable is added, the size of the truth table doubles. With this level of complexity it is easy to get confused or make careless errors. Surely there must be a shorter method!

Fortunately, there is. All the work in a truth table can (for most arguments) be compressed into only one row. That's right, just one. In this lesson we will see how it works.

KEY POINT

The validity of most arguments can be determined with a truth table having only one row. Assume the conclusion is false and the premises true, then work backward looking for unavoidable contradictions.

Remember that an argument is proved invalid whenever the premises can be shown to be true and the conclusion false. With the shorter truth table, you start by *assuming the argument to be invalid.* You assume each premise is true and the conclusion is false. Then, you work backwards along the argument, trying to make this assumption work without any contradictions. If you succeed, you have proved the argument to be invalid. However, if assuming the argument to be invalid results in an unavoidable contradiction, then your assumption is wrong and the argument must be valid.

Take, for example, one of the arguments from the last chapter. We start by assigning the premises the value T and the conclusion the value F. Notice that the Ts and F are placed under those parts of the propositions which would be filled in last in the longer truth table.

$S \supset I$	$S \supset Y$	$\therefore I \vee Y$
T	T	F

Now, for the disjunction $I \vee Y$ to be false as assumed, both disjuncts must be false, according to the defining truth table. But if I and Y are false in the conclusion, they must be false in the premises. Thus we obtain this table:

$S \supset I$	$S \supset Y$	$\therefore I \vee Y$
T F	T F	F F F

A true conditional with a false consequent must also have a false antecedent (check the defining truth table for the conditional). Thus we assign the antecedents *S* in the above conditionals the value of F, as shown:

$S \supset I$	$S \supset Y$	$\therefore I \vee Y$	
F T F	F T F	F F F	INVALID

We are now finished. We assumed the argument was invalid, every truth value was determined, and no contradiction was found. Thus we conclude the argument is indeed invalid.

Now we will look at the valid argument from the last chapter. Again, we start by assuming the argument to be invalid (true premises, false conclusion), then work backward to see if we get a contradiction.

$V \vee I$	$I \supset R$	$\sim R$	$\therefore V$
T	T	T	F

If *V* is false in the conclusion, it must be false everywhere else. Write F under the *V* in the first premise. Also, if ~*R* is true, then *R* must be false. We write F under the *R*s and get

$V \vee I$	$I \supset R$	$\sim R$	$\therefore V$
F T	T F	T F	F

Now, look at $I \supset R$. For this conditional to be true with a false consequent, the antecedent *I* must be false. And if *I* is false there, then it is false in $V \vee I$. Filling these in gives us

$V \vee I$	$I \supset R$	$\sim R$	$\therefore V$	
F T F	F T F	T F	F	VALID
↑ CONTRADICTION				

We see that *V* and *I* are both found to be false. But this would imply the disjunction $V \vee I$ is false. However, we assigned it as a premise the value of true. This contradiction means that it is impossible to make the argument invalid. Thus it must be valid.

Now for two familiar examples. First, consider the *modus tollens* argument $p \supset q$, $\sim q$, $\therefore \sim p$. We will assume it to be invalid, like this:

$p \supset q$	$\sim q$	$\therefore \sim p$
T	T	F

Start with the conclusion. If $\sim p$ is false as assumed, then p is true. Filling that in gives us

$p \supset q$	$\sim q$	$\therefore \sim p$
T T	T	F T

But if $\sim q$ is true, q must be false:

$p \supset q$	$\sim q$	$\therefore \sim p$	
T T F	T F	F T	VALID
↑ CONTRADICTION			

We see the contradiction in the first premise, mark it as a contradiction and write "VALID."

For a final example, let's look at *affirming the consequent.* We assume it to be invalid:

$p \supset q$	q	$\therefore p$
T	T	F

We see that p is false and q is true, and write those values in.

$p \supset q$	q	$\therefore p$	
F T T	T	F	INVALID

There is no contradiction. The argument is invalid, with true premises and a false conclusion.

When a shorter truth table is completed for an invalid argument as above, you should discover that the truth values found for the variables (or constants) are the same truth values from one of the rows showing the argument invalid on the longer truth table. In this case, the argument was seen to be invalid when p is false and q is true. Compare this with the longer truth table:

KEY POINT

When a shorter truth table is completed for an invalid argument, the truth values found for the variables (or constants) are the same truth values from a row showing the argument to be invalid on the longer truth table.

$p \supset q$	q	$\therefore p$	
T	T	T	
F	F	T	
T	T	F	← INVALID
T	F	F	

We see that the longer truth table also shows the argument to be invalid when *p* is false and *q* is true.

Thus we have the following procedure for determining the validity of arguments using the shorter truth table:

SUMMARY

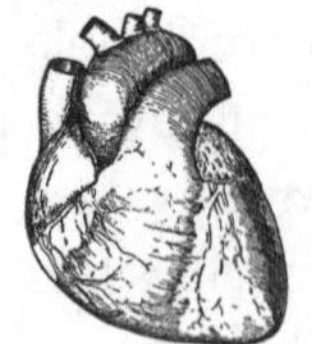

The Shorter Truth Table Method for Validity

1. Write the argument in symbolic form on a line.
2. Assume the argument is invalid by assigning the premises the value T and the conclusion the value F.
3. Work backwards along the argument, determining the remaining truth values to be T or F as necessary, avoiding contradiction if possible.
4. If the truth values are completed without contradiction, then the argument is invalid as assumed.
5. If a contradiction is unavoidable, then the original assumption was wrong and the argument is valid.

EXERCISE 8 (48 points)

Determine the validity of each argument using the shorter truth-table method. Use the constants given in order of appearance in the argument to symbolize each proposition.

1. If I study for my test tonight then I am sure to pass it, but if I watch TV then I will get to see my favorite show. So if I study for the test and watch TV, then I will either pass the test or I will see my favorite show. (S, P, W, F) (5)

S ⊃ P	W ⊃ F	∴ (S • W) ⊃ (P ∨ F)
T T F	T T F	T T T F F F F
↑	↑	

Valid

2. If Caesar had been a benevolent king, then all Romans would have received their full rights under the law. The Roman Christians were persecuted for their faith. If all Romans had received their full rights, then the Roman Christians would not have been persecuted. Therefore Caesar was not a benevolent king. (B, R, P) (5)

B ⊃ R	P	R ⊃ ~P	∴ ~B
T T F	T	F T F T	F T
↑			

Valid

3. If a composition has both meter and rhyme, then it is a poem. It is not the case that this composition has meter or rhyme. Therefore this composition is not a poem. (M, R, P) (5)

(M • R) ⊃ P	~(M ∨ R)	∴ ~P
F F F T T	T F F F	F T

Invalid

4. If the book of Hebrews is Scripture then it was written by Paul or Apollos. If Paul wrote anonymously to the Hebrews then he wrote anonymously in some of his letters. If Hebrews was written by Paul then he wrote anonymously to the Hebrews. Paul did not write anonymously in any of his letters. The book of Hebrews is Scripture. Therefore Hebrews was written by Apollos. (S, P, A, H, L) (6)

S ⊃ (P ∨ A)	H ⊃ L	P ⊃ H	~L	S	∴ A
T T F F F	F T F	F T F	T F	T	F
↑					

Valid

Continued on next page.

5. If you sin apart from the law then you will perish apart from the law, but if you sin under the law then you will be judged by the law. If you sin, then you either sin apart from the law or you sin under the law. You do sin. Therefore you will either perish apart from the law or you will be judged by the law. (A, P, U, J, S) (6)

$A \supset P$	$U \supset J$	$S \supset (A \vee U)$	S	$\therefore P \vee J$
F T F	F T F	T T F T F	T	F F F
		↑		

Valid

6. If you obey the law then you will not be condemned. You have not obeyed the law. Thus, you will be condemned. (O, C) (4)

$O \supset \sim C$	$\sim O$	$\therefore C$
F T T F	T F	F

Invalid

Determine the validity of each argument from Exercise 7b using the shorter truth-table method.

7. $p \quad \therefore \sim p \vee q$ (2)

p	$\therefore \sim p \vee q$
T	F T F F

Invalid

8. $p \supset q \quad \therefore \sim q \supset \sim p$ (2)

$p \supset q$	$\therefore \sim q \supset \sim p$
T T F	T F F F T
↑	

Valid

9. $p \supset q \quad \sim q \quad \therefore p \equiv q$ (3)

$p \supset q$	$\sim q$	$\therefore p \equiv q$
T T F	T F	T F F
↑		

Valid

10. $p \supset (q \supset r) \quad q \quad \therefore r \supset p$ (3)

$p \supset (q \supset r)$	q	$\therefore r \supset p$
F T T T T	T	T F F

Invalid

11. $p \supset (\sim q \supset r) \quad p \quad \therefore \sim r \supset q$ (3)

$p \supset (\sim q \supset r)$	p	$\therefore \sim r \supset q$
T T T F F	T	T F F F
↑		

Valid

12. $(p \supset q) \bullet [(p \bullet q) \supset r] \quad p \supset (r \supset s) \quad \therefore p \supset s$ (4)

$(p \supset q) \bullet [(p \bullet q) \supset r]$	$p \supset (r \supset s)$	$\therefore p \supset s$
T T F T T F F T F	T T F T F	T F F
↑		

Valid

USING ASSUMED TRUTH VALUES IN SHORTER TRUTH TABLES

Intermediate Logic, pp. 59–61

STUDENT OBJECTIVES

1. Determine the validity of arguments using shorter truth tables in which a truth value must be assumed.
2. Complete Exercise 9.

TEACHING INSTRUCTIONS

1. Most likely, students found Lesson 8 refreshingly easy. Explain that, unfortunately, that's not *quite* all there is to shorter truth tables. Write on the board this argument: "It is false that both policemen and pirates are criminals. Therefore neither policemen nor pirates are criminals." Have students symbolize the form of the argument, using *p*s and *q*s: $\sim(p \bullet q)$, $\therefore \sim(p \vee q)$. Have students try to use the shorter truth table to determine validity. They should get to here . . .

~(p • q)	∴~(p ∨ q)
T F	F T

. . . before they get stuck. We know that the conjunction $p \bullet q$ is false, but to make it false either p or q or both could be false. Which do we choose? And the conclusion doesn't help us out at all; to make $p \vee q$ true either p or q or both could be true. Explain that **sometimes we are faced with a choice in assigning truth values in a shorter truth table, and in that case we need to guess at truth values until we obtain the desired result.**

2. Have students guess that p is true, marking the T with an arrow and labeling it ***guess.*** Have them solve the rest of this truth table based on that guess. It should be smooth sailing after that, and the completed truth table should look like this:

~(p • q)	∴~(p ∨ q)	
T T F F	F T T F	←INVALID
	↑ GUESS	

Guessing that p was T allowed us to find a way to make the premises true and the conclusion false without creating a contradiction; the argument is therefore indeed invalid. Explain to students that since they have proved the argument invalid, they can stop right there; they don't have to explore the other possible truth values. But have them try a different guess before moving on (*p* is F); explain that for this particular argument, any guess would have worked to prove it invalid.

3. Warn students that some arguments aren't quite so straightforward. Write on the board the argument "There will be war if and only if the enemy attacks, and if the enemy attacks, we will fight back. Therefore, there will be war if and only if we fight back. Have students symbolize the form of this argument with *p*s, *q*s, and *r*s: $p \equiv q$, $q \supset r$, $\therefore p \equiv r$. Have students walk you through setting up a shorter truth table for it, which should look like this:

p ≡ q	q ⊃ r	∴p ≡ r
T	T	F

Students should see quickly that already they are stuck. There are two ways for the biconditional in the first premise to be true (both *p* and *q* are T or both *p* and *q* are F), three ways for the conditional in the second premise to be true (*q* and *r* are both T, F and T, or both F), and two ways for the biconditional in the second premise to be false (*p* and *r* are T and F or F and T).

4. Have the students once again guess that *p* is T, marking it with an arrow and labeling it "guess." As before, all the other truth values should follow easily after that, and the completed truth table should look like this:

p ≡ q	q ⊃ r	∴p ≡ r
T T F	F T F	T F F
↑ CONTRADICTION		↑ GUESS

Students should catch that they have run into a contradiction in the first premise (*p* is T and *q* is F, which should make $p \equiv q$ F, but the premise has to be T). Ask students what this seems to imply (that the argument is in fact valid). But explain that we can't know this for sure yet; we may simply have made a bad guess. It's possible that another guess will not lead to a contradiction.

5. Have students return to the original pre-guess truth table and this time assume that *p* is false, once again labeling the guess. The resulting table should look like this:

p ≡ q	q ⊃ r	∴p ≡ r	
F T F	F T T	F F T	←INVALID
		↑ GUESS	

Make sure students see that since the *second* guess produced no contradiction, there *is* an instance where this argument can have true premises and a false conclusion, and the argument is therefore invalid. This should make sense when student return to the original argument: it's true that there will be war if and only if the enemy attacks, and it's true that if the enemy attacks we will fight back, but it does not follow from those premises that our fighting back will cause the war.

6. Warn students not to assume that every argument in which they have to guess a truth value will end up being invalid. Write on the board the argument "If I tell a lie, you won't believe me, and if you don't believe me, I told a lie. Therefore I told a lie if and only if you don't believe me." Have students symbolize the form of the argument with *p*s and *q*s: $p \supset q$, $q \supset p$, $\therefore p \equiv q$. Then have them set up a shorter truth table for it, guessing that p is T. The completed table should look like this:

p ⊃ q	q ⊃ p	∴p ≡ q
T T F	F T T	T F F
↑ CONTRADICTION		↑ GUESS

7. Students should see the contradiction in the first premise. Have them tell you what to do next (guess instead that p is false). The resulting table should look like this:

p ⊃ q	q ⊃ p	∴p ≡ q
F T T	T T F	F F T
CONTRADICTION ↑		↑ GUESS

Students should see that this guess also leads to a contradiction in the second premise. Explain that since both possible guesses led to contradiction, the argument is in fact valid. When they return to the original argument, students should see that this makes sense.

8. Reassure students that with some practice, their guessing will become more and more educated, and they should be able to solve shorter truth tables more and more quickly.

ASSIGNMENTS

1. Have students complete Exercise 9, and go over it with them.
2. Remind students to study for next class's quiz over Lessons 8–9.

LESSON 9

USING ASSUMED TRUTH VALUES IN SHORTER TRUTH TABLES

The propositional arguments which have been examined so far have avoided one difficulty which may arise while using the shorter truth-table method. To understand what that difficulty is, we will analyze the following argument: "It is false that both reading and skiing are dangerous activities. Therefore neither reading nor skiing is dangerous." This argument follows the form $\sim(p \bullet q)$, $\therefore \sim(p \vee q)$. If we begin using the shorter truth table to determine validity we get to this point:

KEY POINT

In some cases, shorter truth tables may not be completed in only one row—you might be faced with a choice in assigning truth values. In this case, you must guess at truth values until you obtain the desired result.

~(p • q)	∴~(p ∨ q)
T F	F T

Now we are stuck. For the conjunction to be false, either *p* or *q* could be false, and for the disjunction to be true, either *p* or *q* could be true. For this situation, in which there are no "forced" truth values, we must *assume a truth value.* In other words, we need to guess. Looking at the conclusion, we will guess that *p* is true. Working this out leads us to this:

~(p • q)	∴~(p ∨ q)	
T T F F	F T T F	INVALID
	↑GUESS	

Our guess allowed us to find a way to make the premises true and the conclusion false, and thus determine that the argument is invalid, without having to go any further. In fact, any guess we could have made would have worked with this example. Try another guess before you go on.

Let's look at a different example. Consider this argument:

p ≡ q	q ⊃ r	∴ p ≡ r
T	T	F

After taking the first step we are already stuck. There are two ways the biconditional can be true, two ways it can be false, and three ways for the conditional to be true. So we must guess. Like before, we will guess that *p* is true. Following the procedure leads us to obtain this:

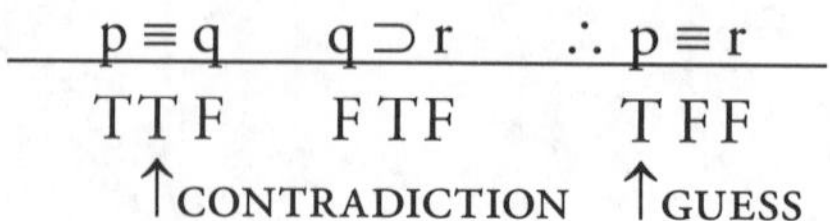

p ≡ q	q ⊃ r	∴ p ≡ r
TTF	FTF	TFF
↑CONTRADICTION		↑GUESS

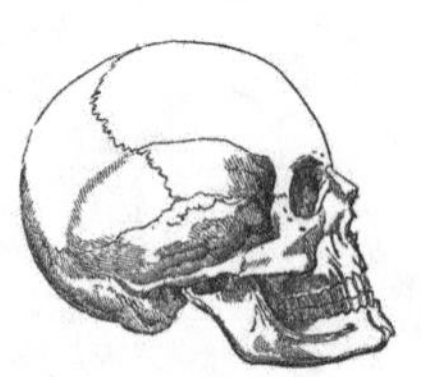

CAUTION

If you reach a contradiction after an initial guess, you still must try other possible guesses before concluding that an argument is valid.

We get a contradiction in the first premise, which appears to imply that the argument is valid. However, it may simply mean that we made a bad assumption. Whenever a contradiction is reached after the first guess, we must then try the other way. So we will now assume that *p* is false, which leads to us this:

p ≡ q	q ⊃ r	∴ p ≡ r	
FTF	FTT	FFT	INVALID
		↑GUESS	

This second guess gave us no contradiction. This means that, in fact, the argument *is* invalid. You see the importance of guessing both truth values for the variable if a contradiction is found the first time.

Since the examples in this section have been found invalid, you may get the mistaken notion that any time you have to guess a truth value, the argument is necessarily invalid. This is not true. Consider this argument: $p \supset q$, $q \supset p$, $\therefore p \equiv q$. The shorter truth table requires one to guess a truth value. Let's start by guessing that *p* is true. This leads to the following result:

p ⊃ q	q ⊃ p	∴ p ≡ q
TTF	FTT	TFF
↑CONTRADICTION		↑GUESS

The guess of *p* as true lead us to a contradiction. So we must try guessing that *p* is false. That leads to this result:

$p \supset q$	$q \supset p$	$\therefore p \equiv q$
F T T	T T F	F F T
CONTRADICTION↑		↑GUESS

After some experience with this method, you should find that your guesses become less random and more educated, and that you are able to determine invalid arguments to *be* invalid after the first guess. This may take some careful thought and practice, so don't get discouraged on the way.

SUMMARY

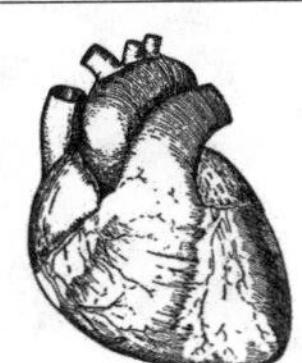

Sometimes when using the shorter truth-table method for validity, no forced truth values occur before you finish. When this happens, you must guess the truth value of one variable or constant, then continue with the same method. If no contradiction appears, the argument is invalid. If a contradiction does appear, you must guess the other truth value for that variable or constant.

EXERCISE 9 (20 points)

Use the shorter truth table method to determine the validity of the following arguments. Most of these (but not all) will require you to guess a truth value.

1. $p \equiv q \qquad q \equiv r \qquad \therefore p \equiv r$ (4)

   T T F   F T F   T F F

   ↑

   F T T   T T T   F F T

   ↑

   Valid

2. $p \vee q \qquad \therefore p \bullet q$ (3)

   T T F   T F F

   Invalid

3. $p \supset q \qquad q \equiv r \qquad \therefore p \supset r$ (3)

   T T F   F T F   T F F

   ↑

   Valid

4. $(p \supset q) \vee (r \supset s) \qquad p \vee r \qquad \therefore q \vee s$ (3)

   T F F T F T F   T T F   F F F

   Invalid

5. $p \vee q \qquad \sim[q \bullet (r \supset p)] \qquad \therefore \sim(p \equiv q)$ (4)

   T T T   T T F T T   F T T T

   ↑

   F T F   T F F F   F F T F

   ↑

   Valid

6. $p \supset (q \supset r) \qquad q \supset (p \supset r) \qquad \therefore (p \vee q) \supset r$ (3)

   T T F T F   F T T F F   T T F F F

   Invalid

TEACHER'S NOTES

QUIZ 5 (LESSONS 8–9)

STUDENT OBJECTIVE

Complete Quiz 5.

TEACHING INSTRUCTIONS

1. Give Quiz 5. Allow 20 minutes. Grade quiz with students.
2. If you have extra time, introduce Lesson 10 to get a head start on next class's material.

INTERMEDIATE LOGIC | Quiz 5

Lessons 8–9 (35 points)

Name ______________________________

1. Explain how a shorter truth table can show an argument to be *invalid.* (3)

   A shorter truth table assumes that the premises of an argument are true and the conclusion is false. If it is possible to complete the truth values of the component parts without contradiction, then the argument is invalid, as assumed.

Problems 2-4: Use a shorter truth table to determine the validity of the symbolic argument. Remember to write VALID or INVALID. Circle any guesses. (4, 4, 7))

2. $p \supset \sim q \quad p \bullet r \quad \therefore \sim (q \supset \sim r)$

   T T T   T T T   F F T F

   INVALID

3. $p \supset q \quad q \supset r \quad \sim r \quad \therefore \sim p$

   T T F   F T F   T   F
      F

   VALID

4. $p \vee q \quad p \supset r \quad q \supset \sim r \quad \therefore p \equiv r$

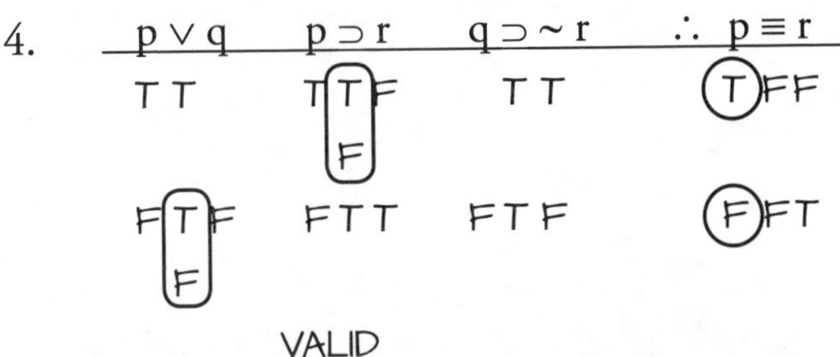

Problems 5-6: Translate the argument into symbolic form and use a shorter truth table to determine the validity of the symbolic argument. Remember to write VALID or INVALID. Circle any guesses.

5. If a number is rational then its digits repeat. A number is rational or its digits do not repeat. Thus, a number is rational if and only if its digits repeat. (**R**, **D**) (8)

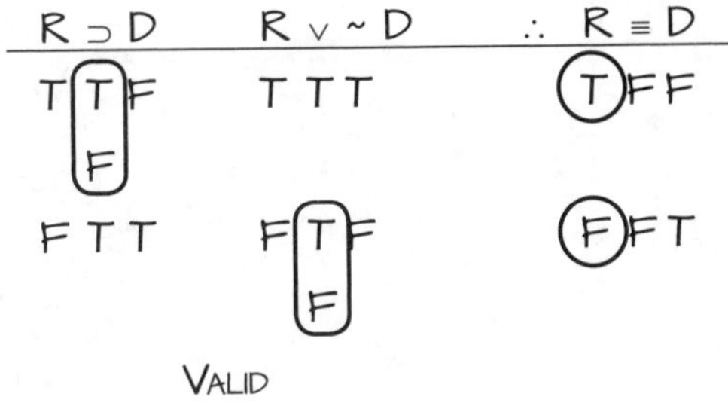

6. If Jesus has been given all authority, then Jesus is the ruler of this world. Either Jesus or Satan is the ruler of this world, but they are not both ruler of this world. If the Bible is true, then Jesus has been given all authority. The Bible is true. Therefore, Satan is not the ruler of this world. (**A**, **J**, **S**, **B**) (9)

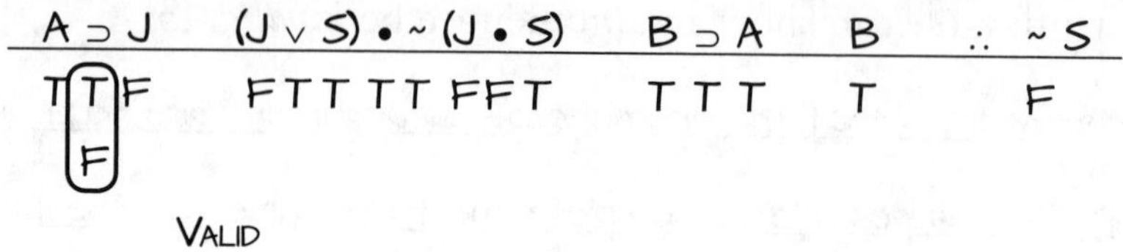

SHORTER TRUTH TABLES FOR CONSISTENCY

Intermediate Logic, pp. 65–66

STUDENT OBJECTIVES

1. Use shorter truth tables to determine if a set of propositions is consistent.
2. Complete Exercise 10.

TEACHING INSTRUCTIONS

1. Have students review what they have learned to use the shorter truth table for so far (determining the validity of an argument). Explain that there are a couple other uses for shorter truth tables, one of which is determining the consistency of a set of propositions.
2. Have a student explain what it means for two propositions to be "consistent" (**propositions are consistent if they can be true at the same time**). Ask students how they think we could use a shorter truth table to determine whether or not two propositions are consistent, whether or not they can be simultaneously true.
3. Write these two propositions on the board: 1."It is false that a warm winter implies that the sun is getting closer to the earth." 2."If the winter is not warm, then the sun is not getting closer to the earth." Ask students how we should set up a truth table to determine whether these two propositions are consistent.
4. Have students symbolize these two propositions using *W* and *S*: *~(W⊃ S)*, *~W⊃ ~S*. Explain, if they haven't figured it out all ready, that to determine whether they can both be true at the same time, we should *assume* that they are both true and see if it results in a contradiction. **If we reach a contradiction when we assume that they are both true, then they are not consistent.** The initial truth table should look like this:

~(W ⊃ S)	~W ⊃ ~S
T	T

5. Have the students walk you through assigning truth values. They should see that in this case it is not helpful to begin with the second proposition since there are three different ways a conditional can be true. But they should see that, in the premise, if the negation of the conditional is true, the conditional must be false. Since there is only one way for a conditional to be false, *W* must be T and *S* must be F. Inserting these truth values into the second proposition results in this table:

~(W ⊃ S)	~W ⊃ ~S
T T F F	F T T T F

Ask students what this table means. They should conclude that since assuming these two propositions were true resulted in no contradiction, the two propositions are indeed consistent. Return to the original two propositions, and this should make sense, since they do not obviously contradict each other.

6. Tell students that we can determine the consistency of more than two propositions. For

example, write on the board this (believable) series of statements. 1."I did not take the cookies." 2."My little brother took the cookies." 3."It is false that my little brother took the cookies if I did not take them." Have students imagine that they are the confused mother in this situation trying to figure out if her child is being honest. Can all of these statement be true? Have students symbolize the three propositions using *I* and *B*: *~I*, *B*, *~(~I ⊃ B)*. Have them set up the truth table. The initial truth table for consistency should look like this:

~I	B	~(~I ⊃ B)
T	T	T

7. Have students walk you through assigning truth values. No matter where you start, you will quickly run into a contradiction. The completed table should look something like this:

~I	B	~(~I ⊃ B)
T	T	TT TT
		↑

Note the contradiction in the conclusion. The three propositions cannot all be true; they are therefore inconsistent, and there is something fishy about the cookie story (as we all suspected). Remind students to be sure to mark the contradiction and label the truth table "inconsistent."

ASSIGNMENT

Have students complete Exercise 10, and go over it with them.

LESSON 10

SHORTER TRUTH TABLES FOR CONSISTENCY

We have seen that the shorter truth table is a powerful tool for quickly determining the validity of even relatively complex arguments. Shorter truth tables may also be used to determine the consistency of sets of propositions and the equivalence of two propositions. Let's look at consistency first.

To say that propositions are **consistent** simply means that they can be true at the same time. Assuming consistent propositions all to be true will result in no logical contradiction.

For example, consider these two propositions. "It is false that increasing inflation implies a thriving economy"; "If inflation is not increasing then the economy is not thriving." Are these propositions consistent? Can they both be true at the same time? How can we use the shorter truth table to find out? Try to answer these questions before you read on.

These two propositions can be abbreviated this way: $\sim(I \supset E)$, $\sim I \supset \sim E$. If they are consistent, then assuming that they are both true should result in no contradiction. So let's do that. As before, the propositions are symbolized and placed above a line. Then below each proposition place a T, implying that both propositions are true, like this:

KEY POINT

If you get a contradiction when assuming that two or more propositions are all true, then they are not consistent.

~(I ⊃ E)	~I ⊃ ~E
T	T

Now, will this assumption run us into a contradiction? To find out, we determine the forced truth values. Since the second proposition is a conditional which can be true for three out of four combinations of true and false, we can't really do anything with it. But if the first proposition is true, then the conditional $I \supset E$ must be false. This would imply that I is true and E is false. Carry these truth values over to the other proposition and continue this procedure, and you should end up with this:

~(I ⊃ E)	~I ⊃ ~E
TTF F	FTTTF

Assuming that the propositions were all true resulted in no contradiction. Thus they are consistent; they can all be true at the same time.

Now, suppose an attorney at first declared, "My client did not take those papers. The secretary took them." Then later he admitted, "It is false that the secretary took the papers if my client did not." Can his statements all be true? Let's find out. These propositions can be symbolized as follows:

~C	S	~(~C ⊃ S)
T	T	T

We assume the attorney's propositions are consistent. Does this lead us to a contradiction? Follow the shorter truth table procedure, and you should end up here:

~C	S	~(~C ⊃ S)	
T	T	TT TT	INCONSISTENT
		↑CONTRADICTION	

If ~C ⊃ S is true, then the third proposition must be false. Thus they cannot all be true; the propositions are **inconsistent**.

SUMMARY

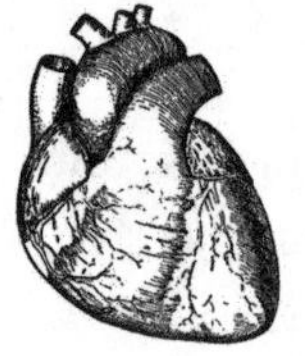

Propositions are consistent when assuming them all to be true involves no contradiction. Thus the shorter truth table can be used to determine consistency by making this assumption and checking for a contradiction.

EXERCISE 10 (25 points)

Problems 1–5: Use the shorter truth table method to determine the consistency of each proposition set. (3 each)

1. $p \quad {\sim}p \supset r$

   T FT T

   Consistent

2. ${\sim}{\sim}p \quad {\sim}p \bullet q$

   TFT FT T

   ↑

   Inconsistent

3. $p \supset q \quad p \quad {\sim}q$

   T T F T TF

   ↑

   Inconsistent

4. $p \vee q \quad {\sim}p$

   FTT TF

   Consistent

5. $p \equiv q \quad q \equiv r \quad p \quad {\sim}r$

   T T F FTF T TF

   ↑

   Inconsistent

Symbolize the propositions using the constants given, and then determine their consistency. (5 each)

6. Mr. Copia owns a Porsche and a mansion. If he owns a mansion then either he owns a Porsche or I am imagining things. I am not imagining things. (P, M, I)

   $P \bullet M \quad M \supset (P \vee I) \quad {\sim}I$

   TTT T T TTF TF

   Consistent

7. If I can use rhetoric then I learned grammar and logic. I did not learn logic but I can use rhetoric. (R, G, L)

   $R \supset (G \bullet L) \quad {\sim}L \bullet R$

   T T F F TFTT

   ↑

   Inconsistent

SHORTER TRUTH TABLES FOR EQUIVALENCE

Intermediate Logic, pp. 69–70

STUDENT OBJECTIVES

1. Use shorter truth tables to determine if a pair of propositions are equivalent.
2. Complete Exercise 11.

TEACHING INSTRUCTIONS

1. Remind students that yesterday they learned how to use a shorter truth table to determine whether propositions were consistent. Explain that today they will learn to use shorter truth tables to determine whether two propositions are equivalent. Have a student remind everyone what it means for two propositions to be equivalent (they imply each other, meaning that they always have identical truth values; if one is false the other is false, if one is true the other is true).
2. Ask students how they think you go about setting up a truth table to determine equivalence. Explain that, like the truth table for validity and unlike the truth table for consistency, **to determine equivalence we assume that the two propositions are *not* logically equivalent; that is, we assign them different truth values. Then we see whether this assumption leads to contradiction or not. If it does, then the two propositions are logically equivalent.**
3. Write on the board these two propositions: 1."If I leave my car home then if I ride my bike I will save money." 2."If I leave my car home and ride my bike, then I will save money." Have them symbolize these propositions using *C*, *B*, and *M*: $C \supset (B \supset M)$, $(C \bullet B) \supset M$. Then have them set up a shorter truth table to determine whether these two propositions are equivalent, assuming that the first proposition is true and the second false. The initial table should look like this:

C ⊃ (B ⊃ M)	(C • B) ⊃ M
T	F

4. Have students determine the rest of the truth values ($C \bullet B$ must be T and *M* must be F; therefore both *C* and *B* must be true, etc.) They should run into a contradiction in the first proposition. The completed table should look like this:

C ⊃ (B ⊃ M)	(C • B) ⊃ M
T T T F F	T T T F F

↑ CONTRADICTION

5. Explain that while it may look like we can just stop there and say that the two propositions are equivalent, all we really have shown is that the first proposition implies the second. We now have to check the other combination of true and false, assuming that the first proposition is false and the second true. The resulting table should look like this:

C ⊃ (B ⊃ M)	(C • B) ⊃ M
T F T F F	T T T T F

CONTRADICTION ↑

Make sure students see that since this assumption also leads to a contradiction, the two propositions are indeed equivalent. This second truth table shows that the second proposition implies the first. If students look again at the original propositions, they should see that they are obviously saying the same thing.

6. Write on the board these two propositions: 1."If I lock my keys in the car, I can't drive to work." 2."I did not lock my keys in the car and I can drive to work." Have students think for a moment about whether these two propositions seem to be equivalent or not. Then have them symbolize them, using *L* and *D*: *L*⊃~*D*, ~*L* • *D*. Then have them set up the truth table for equivalence, assuming first that the conditional (the first proposition) is false and the conjunction (the second proposition) is true. This truth table will result in a contradiction, but remind them that they cannot stop there. Have them switch the truth values and make the first proposition true and the second false. The resulting table could look like this:

L⊃~D	~L • D
F T TF	TF F F

Make sure students see that in this case, everything fits nicely without contradiction. The two propositions are therefore *not* equivalent, even though the first assumption made it look like they could be. If they look back at the original propositions, this should make sense; they are saying two subtly different things. This fact is seen most clearly when the propositions *L* and *D* are both false, as this truth table shows.

7. Write on the board the procedure for determining equivalence with the shorter truth table, and make sure students copy it down as well.

The Shorter Truth Table Method for Equivalence

1. **Write the two propositions in symbolic form on a line.**
2. **Assume the propositions are not equivalent by assigning one to be T and the other F.**
3. **If no contradiction occurs, the propositions are not equivalent.**
4. **If a contradiction is unavoidable, then switch the assigned truth values and try again.**
5. **If a contradiction is still unavoidable, then they are equivalent. However, if it is possible to avoid a contradiction, the propositions are not equivalent.**

ASSIGNMENT

Have students complete Exercise 11, and go over it with them.

LESSON 11

SHORTER TRUTH TABLES FOR EQUIVALENCE

The shorter truth table for equivalence works in a similar way as the shorter truth table for validity. In this method, we assume the two propositions are not logically equivalent, then check to see if that assumption runs us into a contradiction or not. If it does not, then our assumption is correct and they are not equivalent. However, if assuming they are not equivalent always results in a contradiction, then they must be equivalent.

Consider these two propositions: "If salt is dissolved in water then if an egg is placed in the salty water then it will float." "If salt is dissolved in water and an egg is placed in it, then the egg will float." Are they equivalent?

We symbolize the propositions and place them on a line. Then we assume they are not equivalent. How? By assuming one is true and the other false, as such:

S ⊃ (E ⊃ F)	(S • E) ⊃ F
T	F

Now determine the forced truth values and check for a contradiction. Doing so results in

S ⊃ (E ⊃ F)	(S • E) ⊃ F
TT TF F	TTT F F

↑CONTRADICTION

The contradiction seems to imply that our assumption of non-equivalence was wrong. However, we also need to check the other combination of true and false for non-equivalence. That is, we now should assume the first proposition is false and the second is true. Such an assumption leads us to this point:

KEY POINT

To test equivalence using shorter truth tables, assume the two propositions are not logically equivalent, then check to see if that leads to an unavoidable contradiction.

$S \supset (E \supset F)$	$(S \bullet E) \supset F$
T F T F F	T T T T F
	↑CONTRADICTION

We tried both possibilities for the propositions to not be equivalent: the first proposition true and the second false, and vice versa. Both attempts wound up in a contradiction, so the assumption was wrong and the propositions are equivalent.

For another example, consider these propositions: "If the lock is broken then the door won't open." "The lock is not broken and the door opens." To determine their equivalence we symbolize them and assume one to be true and the other false. Try to figure out which you should assume true and which false first.

If we first assume that the conditional is false and the conjunction is true, we end up with a contradiction (try it!). However, if we assume the conditional is true and the conjunction false, we can get to this point:

$L \supset {\sim}O$	${\sim}L \bullet O$
F T T F	T F F F

The truth values are all assigned and there are no contradictions. The conditional is true and the conjunction is false, thus they are not equivalent.

The following procedure summarizes our method for testing the equivalence of two propositions using shorter truth tables.

SUMMARY

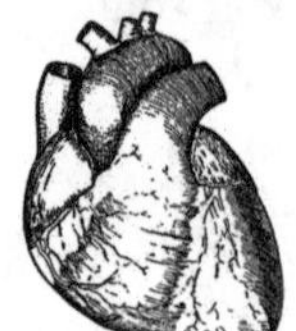

The Shorter Truth Table Method for Equivalence:

1. Write the two propositions in symbolic form on a line.
2. Assume the propositions are not equivalent by assigning one to be T and the other F.
3. If no contradiction occurs, the propositions are not equivalent.
4. If a contradiction is unavoidable, then switch the assigned truth values and try again.
5. If a contradiction is still unavoidable, then they are equivalent. However, if it is possible to avoid a contradiction, the propositions are not equivalent.

EXERCISE 11 (20 points)

Use the shorter truth table method to determine the equivalence of each pair of propositions.

1. ~ (p • q)   ~ p ∨ ~ q (4)

```
T TFT    FT F FT
  ↑
F TTT    FT T FT
           ↑
```

Equivalent

2. p ⊃ q   p ⊃ (p • q) (4)

```
T T F    T F  T F F
  ↑
T F F    T T  T F F
           ↑
```

Equivalent

3. p ∨ (p ⊃ q)   q ⊃ p (3)

```
F T  F T T    T F F
```

Not Equivalent

4. p   p ∨ (p • q) (4)

```
T    T F
       ↑
F    F T  F F
            ↑
```

Equivalent

5. If Christ's righteousness is not imputed to you, then you are condemned. Christ's righteousness is imputed to you or you are condemned. (5)

```
~ I ⊃ C    I ∨ C
TFT F      FFF
  ↑
TFF F      FTF
            ↑
```

Equivalent

TEACHER'S NOTES on LESSON 12

THE DILEMMA

Intermediate Logic, pp. 73–76

STUDENT OBJECTIVES

1. Write dilemmas.
2. Use the three methods of refuting dilemmas.
3. Complete Exercise 12.

TEACHING INSTRUCTIONS

1. Have students try to define "dilemma." They'll probably think of the usual ways we use the word: "problem", "predicament", "caught between a rock and a hard place", etc. Explain that any argument presenting two alternatives, either of which when chosen leads to certain conclusions, may be called a dilemma. For example, in the play *Agamemnon* by Aeschylus, Orestes is faced with a perfect dilemma: he must either kill his mother or be an accessory to the murder of his father. Both options have terrible consequences. On a lighter note, you might be faced with a dilemma every time you go out for ice cream: you can get either a sundae or a waffle cone; if you get the sundae, you can't get the waffle cone, and if you get the waffle cone you can't get the sundae. Have students come up with some examples of everyday dilemmas.
2. Explain that in logic the definition of "dilemma" is very close to how we use it in ordinary English, but is more specific. **A dilemma is a valid argument which presents a choice between two conditionals.**
3. Write this dilemma on the board: "If I wear my jacket, I will be too cold. If I wear my winter coat, I will look like a marshmallow. I will either wear my jacket or my winter coat. Therefore I will either be too cold or look like a marshmallow." Have students help you symbolize this argument using *p*'s, *q*'s, *r*'s, and *s*'s: $(p \supset q) \bullet (r \supset s)$, $p \vee r$, $\therefore q \vee s$. Explain that an argument that follows this form is called a **constructive dilemma.** Ask students if the argument reminds them of any other arguments they have studied so far. Explain that a **constructive dilemma works like an extended** *modus ponens*, or like two *modus ponens* arguments stuck together. Like *modus ponens*, a constructive dilemma presents conditionals in the first premise, affirms antecedents in the second premise, and concludes with consequents. Explain that it is called "constructive" because the second premise is affirming rather than negating something.
4. Now write this dilemma on the board: "If a superhero is Batman then he has a cape, and if he is Superman then he can fly. That guy has no cape, or at least he cannot fly. So either he is not Batman, or he is not Superman." Have students help you symbolize this (slightly trickier) dilemma: $(p \supset q) \bullet (r \supset s)$, $\sim q \vee \sim s$, $\therefore \sim p \vee \sim r$. Explain that this form is called a **destructive dilemma.** Ask students what argument this kind of dilemma resembles, and explain that **destructive dilemmas work like** *modus tollens* (negating the consequent).

5. Tell students that constructive and destructive are the two general categories of dilemma; you are now going to look at a few specific types of dilemmas. Write on the board this dilemma from Proverbs 26: "If you answer a fool according to his folly, then you will be like him. However, if you do not answer a fool according to his own folly, then he will be wise in his own eyes. Therefore no matter how you answer a fool, you will either be like him or he will be wise in his own eyes." Have students help you symbolize this argument, and explain that because the second premise is a tautology ("you will either answer him according to his folly or not answer him according to his folly") it is only implied in the original argument and has to be inserted when you symbolize it. The symbolized argument should look like this: $(p \supset q) \bullet (\sim p \supset r), p \vee \sim p, \therefore q \vee r$. Have students tell you whether it is a constructive or destructive dilemma (it's constructive). Ask students what is distinctive about it (the antecedent of one conditional is the negation of the antecedent of the other, so there are only three variables). Have students come up with a few example of dilemmas with this form. (i.e., "If I wear a coat then I'll be too hot, and if I don't wear a coat then I'll be too cold. I'll either wear a coat or not wear a coat. So I'll be either too hot or too cold.")

6. Tell students that another type of constructive dilemma is one in which the consequents of the conditionals are the same. See if they can come up with an argument of this kind (something like: "If I move to the right I will fall off the cliff. If I move to the left, I will also fall off the cliff. I have to move either to the right or to the left. I'm going to fall off the cliff.") Have them symbolize the argument; it should look like this: $(p \supset q) \bullet (r \supset q), p \vee r, \therefore q$.

7. Write this dilemma on the board: "To survive in the wilderness we need both food and water. But we either forgot the food or forgot the water. Therefore we cannot survive." Have students symbolize this dilemma: $p \supset (q \bullet r), \sim q \vee \sim r, \therefore \sim p$. Students will probably notice that this looks different from the other dilemmas. Have them figure out how to symbolize it so that it is equivalent to other destructive dilemmas (hint: p is the antecedent for both conditionals. It could look like this: $(p \supset q) \bullet (p \supset r), \sim q \vee \sim r, \therefore \sim p$.

8. Explain that being able to produce a dilemma is very useful in a debate, but that you have to be able to get out of dilemmas used against *you*. Explain that the problem is that all of these dilemmas you have just presented are *valid* arguments. How do you avoid the conclusion of a valid argument? Have students think back to the Orestes argument: "If Orestes kills his mother, he angers the gods. If he fails to avenge his father, he is an unfaithful son. He must either kill his mother or fail to avenge his father. Thus he must either anger the gods or be an unfaithful son." Explain that this is a valid argument. What should Orestes do when faced with this dilemma?

9. Tell students that because dilemmas have two "horns" (the two conditionals), facing a dilemma is often described as being "impaled on the horns of a dilemma" as if the dilemma were a charging bull. Explain that, when the dilemma is charging at you (or Orestes), there are three main ways to escape getting impaled.

10. Write on the board **1. Go between the horns**. Imagine that Orestes said, "Well, I'm not going to do either of these things. I'm going to call the police." He would be denying the disjunctive (second) premise and suggesting that in fact there is a third alternative. Explain that by going between the horns like this you are in fact claiming that the disjunction of the dilemma is an either/or fallacy, or a false dilemma.

11. Write on the board **2. Grasp it by the horns**. Explain that grasping a dilemma by the horns means rejecting one of the conditionals in the conjunctive premise. For example, Orestes could say: "If I fail to avenge my father that won't make me an unfaithful son," or "If I kill my mother the gods will understand." And if just one of the conditionals is false the whole first premise is false as well.
12. Write on the board **3. Rebut the horns**. Explain that rebutting the horns means coming up with a counter-dilemma that uses the same components as the original dilemma but shows the flip (and more positive) side of the dilemma. For example Orestes could instead say, "If I kill my mother, I will not be an unfaithful son. And if I fail to avenge my father I will not anger the gods. Therefore I will either not be an unfaithful son or not anger the gods." Make sure students see that this counter-dilemma does not claim that the original dilemma was false or invalid in any way; it is simply looking at the same facts from a different angle in order to arrive at a different conclusion.
13. Write this argument on the board: "If I study for the test, I can't go to the movies. But if I don't study, I'll fail the test. I'm either going to study or not study, so I either can't go to the movies or I'm going to fail this test." Have students use the three different methods they have just learned to deal with this dilemma. (If they need help, have them look at p. 75 of the student text).

ASSIGNMENTS

1. Have students complete Exercise 12, and go over it with them.
2. Remind students to study for next class's quiz over Lessons 10–12.

LESSON 12

THE DILEMMA

Any argument presenting two alternatives, either of which when chosen leads to certain conclusions, may be called a **dilemma**. The dilemma is often used to trap an opponent in debate. It is also a common way of thinking when we are trying to decide what course to take between two apparently opposing options.

For example, you might find yourself reasoning like this: "If I go to college then I delay making money, but if I go straight into business then I will get a low-paying job. I will either go to college or straight into business, so I will either delay making money or I will get a low-paying job." This argument follows the general form of a **constructive dilemma**:

$(p \supset q) \bullet (r \supset s) \quad p \vee r \quad \therefore q \vee s$

A similar type of argument is the **destructive dilemma**, which follow this form:

$(p \supset q) \bullet (r \supset s) \quad {\sim}q \vee {\sim}s \quad \therefore {\sim}p \vee {\sim}r$

Here is an example of such a destructive dilemma: "If something can be done, then it is possible, and if it can be done easily, then it is likely. Faster-than-light travel is either impossible or unlikely, so it either cannot be done, or it cannot be done easily."

You can see that constructive dilemmas are sort of an extended *modus ponens,* while destructive dilemmas are like *modus tollens.*

Let's look at a few specific dilemma types. In one constructive type, the antecedent of one conditional is the negation of the antecedent of the other:

$(p \supset q) \bullet ({\sim}p \supset r) \quad p \vee {\sim}p \quad \therefore q \vee r$

DEFINITIONS

A ***dilemma*** is a valid argument which presents a choice between two conditionals.

KEY POINT

Constructive dilemmas work like *modus ponens,* while destructive dilemmas work like *modus tollens.*

Because the second premise is a tautology, it is often left unstated. Here is such an argument, the premises of which come from Proverbs 26:4–5: "If you answer a fool according to his folly, then you will be like him. However, if you do not answer a fool according to his folly, then he will be wise in his own eyes. Therefore no matter how you answer a fool, you will either be like him or he will be wise in his own eyes."

In another type of constructive dilemma, the consequent of each conditional is the same, resulting in the following argument:

$$(p \supset q) \bullet (r \supset q) \qquad p \vee r \qquad \therefore q \vee q$$

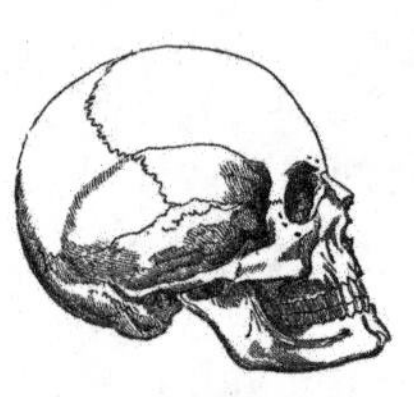

CAUTION

Dilemmas can appear in many special forms—make sure you understand the differences between them.

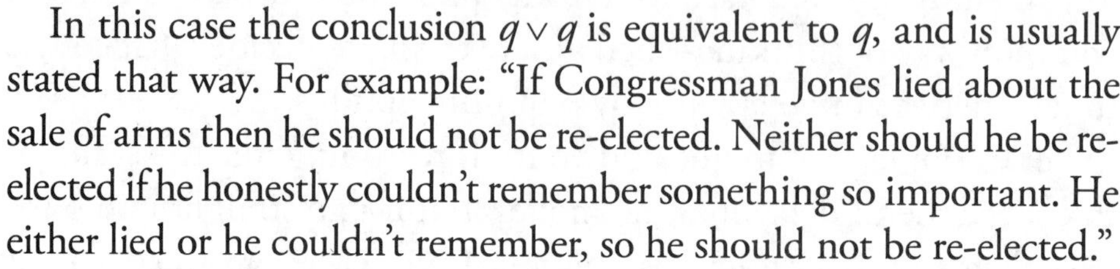

In this case the conclusion $q \vee q$ is equivalent to q, and is usually stated that way. For example: "If Congressman Jones lied about the sale of arms then he should not be re-elected. Neither should he be re-elected if he honestly couldn't remember something so important. He either lied or he couldn't remember, so he should not be re-elected."

Consider this dilemma: "If this bill is to become a law then it must pass the Congress and the President must sign it. But either it will not make it through Congress or the President will not sign it. Therefore this bill will not become a law." In symbolic form this follows the pattern

$$p \supset (q \bullet r) \qquad {\sim}q \vee {\sim}r \qquad \therefore {\sim}p$$

You should be able to show that this is equivalent to a destructive dilemma which has the same antecedent p for both conditionals.

The ability to produce a good dilemma is useful in debate, as is the ability to get out of a dilemma being used against you. Using the shorter truth table, we can easily prove these various dilemmas to be valid. How can we avoid the conclusion of a valid argument? One way is to claim that, though valid, the argument is not sound; that is, one or both of the premises is false. Another way is to produce a similar argument that may be used to prove something else.

Facing a dilemma has been picturesquely referred to as being "impaled on the horns of a dilemma," as if it were a charging bull. Three main options are usually presented for escaping the horns of a dilemma:

1. You could **go between the horns,** meaning you could deny the disjunctive premise and provide a third alternative, somewhere in

the middle. In the first example, someone could reply, "The choice isn't between college or a full-time business. You could go to college part time and work part time." The disjunction is charged with being an *either/or* fallacy (i.e., a false dilemma).

2. You could **grasp it by the horns.** This is done by rejecting one of the conditionals in the conjunctive premise. For example, with the dilemma about the bill above you could reply, "Even if the president refuses to sign it, the Congress could still override his veto with a two-thirds majority." And if one conjunct is false then the entire conjunction is false.

KEY POINT

There are three main ways to escape the horns of a dilemma: go between the horns, grasp the horns, or rebut the horns.

3. Finally, you could **rebut the horns** with a counter-dilemma. A counter-dilemma which is made up of the same components as the original dilemma is usually the most rhetorically effective. Consider the dilemma about answering a fool. One possible counter-dilemma is, "If you answer a fool according to his folly, then he will not be wise in his own eyes. And if you do not answer a fool according to his folly, then you will not be like him. Therefore he will either not be wise in his own eyes or you will not be like him." Notice that the counter-dilemma does not claim that the original dilemma is false or invalid. It simply is another way of looking at the facts in order to arrive at a different conclusion.

Let's consider one more example, and see how all three of these methods could be used against it. Suppose your friend complained, "If I study for the test then I'll miss my favorite show. But if I don't study then I'll fail the test. I will either study or not study, so I'll either miss my favorite show or I'll fail the test." How could you answer him?

First, you could go between the horns by saying, "You could study for the test a little while before your show comes on, then study a little before class tomorrow." Second, you could grasp his dilemma by the horns, saying "If you don't study you won't necessarily fail, not if you have been paying attention in class." Third, you could confront him with this counter-dilemma: "If you study for the test then you will surely pass, and if you don't study then you'll get to see your favorite show. Either you will study or not, so you will either pass the test or you will get to see your favorite show!"

SUMMARY

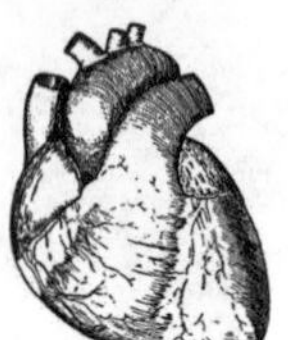

A dilemma is an argument presenting a choice between two conditionals joined by conjunction. The two main types of the dilemma are constructive and destructive. There are three means of avoiding being impaled on the horns of a dilemma: go between the horns by denying the disjunction, grasp it by the horns by denying a conditional, or rebut the horns by means of a counter-dilemma.

EXERCISE 12 (18 points)

Symbolize the dilemma from the end of this lesson about studying or watching your favorite show. Then symbolize the counter-dilemma below it. In the space below the lines, use shorter truth tables to demonstrate the validity of both arguments. (3 each)

1. The dilemma: (S ⊃ M)•(~ S ⊃ F)   S ∨ ~ S   ∴ M ∨ F

   F T F T T F T F   F T T F   F F F

   ↑

2. The counter-dilemma: (S ⊃ ~ F)•(~ S ⊃ ~ M)   S ∨ ~ S   ∴ ~ F ∨ ~ M

   T T F T T F T T F T   T T F T   F T F F T

   ↑

Refute each of the following dilemmas using the given methods. (2 each)

3. If angels are material, then they cannot all simultaneously fit on the head of a pin. If angels are immaterial, then they can neither dance nor be in contact with the head of a pin. Angels are either material or immaterial. Either way, all the angels that exist cannot simultaneously dance on the head of a pin. (Grasp the horns.)

   You can grasp a horn by denying the first conditional as follows: "Even if angels are material, they could fit on the head of a pin by being very small."

4. If Congressman Jones lied about the sale of arms then he should not be re-elected. Neither should he be re-elected if he honestly couldn't remember something so important. He either lied or he couldn't remember, so he should not be re-elected. (Go between the horns.)

   You could go between the horns, saying "He didn't lie, and he did remember, but he honestly had nothing to do with the sale of arms."

5. If you sin apart from the law then you will perish apart from the law, but if you sin under the law then you will be judged by the law. You either sin apart from the law or you sin under the law. Therefore you will either perish apart from the law or you will be judged by the law. (Grasp the horns.)

   You can grasp it by the horns by denying both conditionals as follows: "If I sin I will not necessarily perish, not if I have been justified by faith."

Continued on next page.

6. If God were perfectly good then He would always be willing to prevent evil, and if God were infinitely powerful then He would always be able to prevent evil. But God is either unwilling or unable to prevent evil. Therefore He is either not perfectly good or He is not infinitely powerful. (Grasp the horns.)

   You can grasp a horn by denying the first conditional: "God is perfectly good, but he allows evil to continue for a greater purpose of bringing good out of it, such as at the crucifixion."

7. If teachers cover more material, the students will be more confused. If teachers cover less material, the students will not learn as much. Teachers will cover more or less material, so either students will be confused or they will not learn as much. (Rebut the horns.)

   Example: "If teachers cover less material, then students will learn it well. If they cover more material, then students will get a good big-picture perspective. So students will either learn the material very well or they will get a good big-picture perspective."

8. If taxes increase then the public will complain, but if the deficit increases then the public will complain. Either taxes or the deficit will increase. Thus the public is bound to complain. (Use any or all three methods.)

   You could rebut it with this counter-dilemma: "If taxes increase, then the deficit will go down. If taxes decrease, then the public will be happy. Taxes will either increase or decrease, so either the deficit goes down or the public will be happy."

   You could also go between the horns by saying, "You could balance the budget by keeping taxes the same and decreasing spending, so that neither taxes nor the deficit increases. Then the public wouldn't complain."

   Or, you could grasp a horn: "The public likes their government services, and they want the deficit go down as well, so they will understand why taxes must increase and won't complain." Or, "The public doesn't take much notice of the deficit-it's too abstract and doesn't affect them. So if it increases they won't complain."

TEACHER'S NOTES

QUIZ 6 (LESSONS 10–12)

STUDENT OBJECTIVE

Complete Quiz 6.

TEACHING INSTRUCTIONS

1. Give Quiz 6. Allow 20 minutes. Grade quiz with students.
2. If you have extra time, begin reviewing for Test 3.

INTERMEDIATE LOGIC | Quiz 6

Lessons 10–12 (21 points)

Name ______________________________

Problems 1-2: Use a shorter truth table to determine if the propositions are consistent. (4 each)

1. $(p \supset q) \bullet (p \supset r)$ $\quad$ $p \bullet (\sim q \vee \sim r)$

T T T T T T T $\quad$ T T F [T/F] F

Consistent? YES **(No)**

2. $p \equiv \sim (q \vee r)$ $\quad$ $q \vee (p \bullet r)$

F T F T T T $\quad$ T T F F T

Consistent? **(YES)** No

Problems 3-4: Use a shorter truth table to determine if the propositions are equivalent. (4, 6)

3. $p \supset \sim q$ $\quad$ $\sim p \bullet \sim q$

F T F $\quad$ T F F

Equivalent? YES **(No)**

4. $\sim p \supset (\sim q \supset r)$ $\quad$ $\sim r \supset (p \vee q)$

T [T/F] T F F $\quad$ T F F F F

T F T F F $\quad$ T [T/F] F F F

Equivalent? **(YES)** No

5. Refute this dilemma by *going between the horns, grasping the horns,* or *rebutting the horns.* "If I cheer at the game, then I lose my voice for choir. But if I stay quiet, then I will look like I have no school spirit. I either cheer or I stay quiet, so I will either lose my voice for choir or appear to have no school spirit." (3)

"You don't need to cheer or stay quiet. You can clap and stomp!" (Going between)

"You can cheer at the game without losing your voice. Just don't yell loudly for too long." (Grasping)

Method used: ______________________

"If you cheer at the game, then you show spirit. And if you stay quiet, then you don't lose your voice for choir..." (Rebutting)

etc.

REVIEW FOR TEST 3 (LESSONS 8–12)

STUDENT OBJECTIVES

Complete the objectives from Lessons 8–12. Objectives are listed at the beginning of each lesson's teacher's notes.

TEACHING INSTRUCTIONS

1. To review for the test, choose problems from the Review Questions for Lessons 8–12 on pp. 80–81 of the student text and from the Review Exercises for Lessons 8–12 on pp. 91–98 of the student text for students to work through.
2. If you'd like, give students "Test 3: Form A" from the *Intermediate Logic Test and Quiz Packet* as a practice exam. Go over the answers together.

ASSIGNMENT

Have students study for Test 3.

TEACHER'S NOTES

TEST 3 (LESSONS 8–12)

STUDENT OBJECTIVE

Complete Test 3.

TEACHING INSTRUCTIONS

1. Give students Test 3: Form B from the *Intermediate Logic Test and Quiz Packet.* Allow one hour to complete it.
2. Grade tests. Have them ready to hand back to students within a week.

INTERMEDIATE LOGIC | Test 3, Form A

Lessons 8–12 (54 points)

Name ______________________

1. What does it mean that a set of propositions is *consistent*? (2) The propositions can all be true at the same time; there is no logical conflict between them.

2. Explain the process by which a shorter truth-table can show an argument to be *valid*. (3) The argument is symbolized, and assumed to be invalid by setting the premises to be true and the conclusion to be false. If the truth values of the remaining component parts cannot be determined without contradiction, the argument is valid.

Problems 3-4: Use the shorter truth-table method to determine the *consistency* of the given sets of propositions. Remember to write CONSISTENT or INCONSISTENT. (3, 4)

3. $p \vee q \quad \sim (p \bullet q)$

   T T F   T T F F

   CONSISTENT

4. $(p \bullet q) \supset r \quad (q \supset r) \supset s \quad p \bullet \sim s$

   T T T T/F F   T F F T F   T T T

   INCONSISTENT

Problems 5-6: Use the shorter truth-table method to determine the *equivalence* of the given pair of propositions. Remember to write EQUIVALENT or NOT EQUIVALENT. (4 each)

5. $p \supset \sim q \quad \sim (p \vee q)$

   F T F T   F F T T

   NOT EQUIVALENT

6. $p \equiv (p \supset q) \quad \sim q \supset \sim p$

   F F F T F   T T T

   NOT EQUIVALENT

Problems 7-8: Use the shorter truth-table method to determine the *validity* of the propositional argument. Remember to write VALID or INVALID. (4 each)

7. $\sim p \supset (q \supset r) \quad q \quad \therefore \sim r \supset p$

   T F T/F T F F   T   T F F F

   VALID

8. $(p \bullet q) \equiv r \quad \sim r \quad \therefore \sim p \bullet \sim q$

   T F F T F   T   F F T

   INVALID

Problems 9-11: Translate the argument into symbolic form using the constants provided. Then use the shorter truth-table method to determine the *validity* of the argument. Remember to write VALID or INVALID.

9. If you are a parent, then you have either daughters or sons. If you are not a parent, then you have neither daughters nor sons. Consequently, you are a parent if and only if not having a daughter implies that you have a son. (**P**, **D**, **S**) (8)

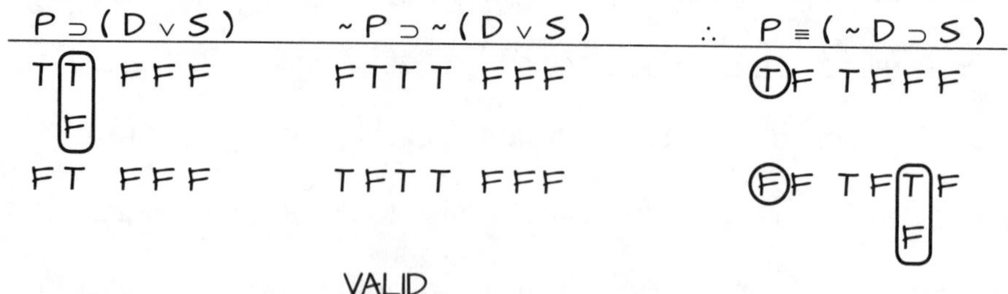

10. If this argument is valid, then the premises can be true or the conclusion can be false. If the premises can be true and the conclusion can be false, then the argument is invalid. So this argument is invalid. (**V**, **P**, **C**) (6)

V ⊃ (P ∨ C)	(P • C) ⊃ ~V	∴ ~V
TT TTF	TFF TFT	FT

INVALID

11. If I teach you what you know, then you learn nothing new. If I teach you what you do not know, then you cannot understand. I either teach you what you know or what you don't know. Therefore, you either learn nothing new or you cannot understand. (**K**, **N**, **U**) (6)

K ⊃ N	~K ⊃ U	K ∨ ~K	∴ N ∨ U
TTF	FTTF	T	FFF
F			

VALID

12. List the three methods of answering a dilemma, and use one of those methods to answer the dilemma presented in the last problem. Circle the method you use. (6)

1) Go between the horns 2) Grasp the horns 3) Rebut the horns

Grasp the horns: It's not true that if he teaches you what you do not know then you cannot understand. A good teacher will help you understand the unknown in terms of the known.

Go between the horns: He could teach you what you partly know.

INTERMEDIATE LOGIC | Test 3, Form B

Lessons 8–12 (51 points)

Name ______________________________

1. What does it mean that a set of propositions is *equivalent*? (2)

   The propositions imply each other.

2. Write a dilemma about rebuking a friend who is misbehaving in class. (3)

   If I rebuke my friend, then he will be angry at me. If I do not rebuke my friend, then I am not being a true friend. I either rebuke him or I do not. Therefore, he will either be mad at me or I am not being a true friend.

Problems 3-4: Use the shorter truth-table method to determine the *consistency* of the given sets of propositions. Remember to write CONSISTENT or INCONSISTENT. (3, 4)

3. $p \equiv q \quad p \supset \sim q$

   F T F   F T T

   CONSISTENT

4. $p \equiv \sim (q \vee r) \quad \sim (p \vee q) \bullet \sim r$

   F T T F F F   T F F F T T

   F

   INCONSISTENT

Problems 5-6: Use the shorter truth-table method to determine the *equivalence* of the given pair of propositions. Remember to write EQUIVALENT or NOT EQUIVALENT. (4, 5)

5. $(p \supset q) \bullet (\sim p \supset r) \quad q \vee r$

   F T T F T   F F   T T F

   NOT EQUIVALENT

6. $(p \bullet \sim q) \supset r \quad p \supset (q \vee r)$

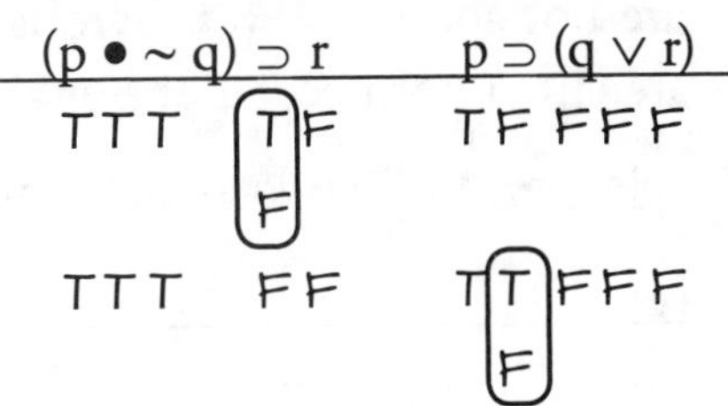

   EQUIVALENT

Problems 7-8: Use the shorter truth-table method to determine the *validity* of the propositional argument. Remember to write VALID or INVALID. (4, 6)

7. $p \supset (q \bullet r) \quad q \supset \sim r \quad \therefore \sim p$

   T T T T T   T T F   F

   F

   VALID

8. $p \supset q \quad p \vee r \quad q \supset \sim r \quad \therefore \sim (p \equiv r)$

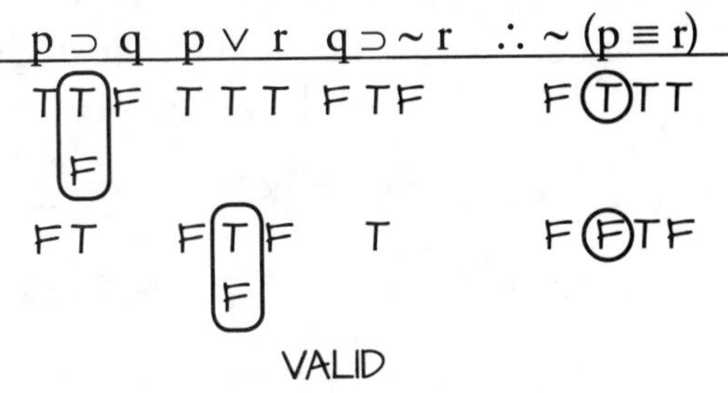

   VALID

Problems 9-10: Translate the argument into symbolic form using the given constants. Then use a shorter truth table to determine the *validity* of the argument. Remember to write VALID or INVALID.

9. Newton's theory and Einstein's theory are not both correct. Einstein's theory is correct if time dilation occurs. If our experiments are sound then time dilation does occur. Hence, either our experiments are not sound, or Newton's theory is not correct. (**N, E, T, S**) (6)

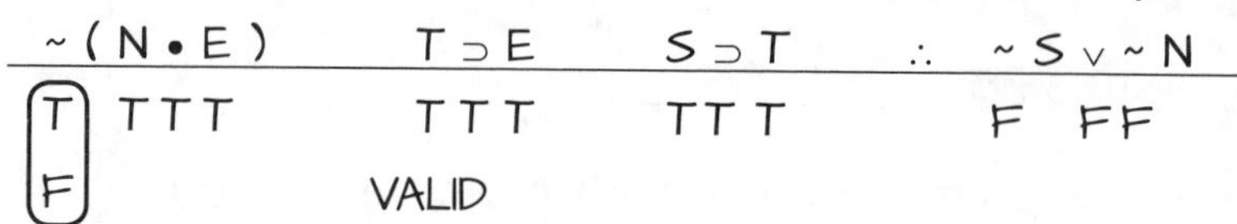

10. The white wizard was Saruman or Gandalf. Saruman was the white wizard only if he stayed true to the council. If Gandalf was the white wizard then Saruman did not stay true to the council. Therefore, Saruman was the white wizard if and only if he stayed true to the council. (**S, G, T**) (8)

$S \vee G$	$S \supset T$	$G \supset \sim T$	$\therefore$	$S \equiv T$
F T F	F T T	F T F		F F T
F				
T T	T T F	T T		T F F
	F			

VALID

Problems 11-12: Refute the dilemma. Do not use the same method for both problems. Identify the method used. (3 each)

11. If people are good then laws are not needed to prevent wrongdoing. If people are bad then laws are not able to prevent wrongdoing. People are either good or bad. Consequently, laws are either not needed or not able to prevent wrongdoing.

People are bad, but laws may still be able to prevent wrongdoing if the laws are enforced.

Method used: Grasping the horns.

12. If you study all the time then you will get out of shape, but if you play sports then you will get bad grades. You either study all the time or play sports, so you will either get out of shape or you will get bad grades.

If you study all the time then you will get good grades, and if you play sports then you will stay in shape. You either study all the time or play sports, so you will get good grades or stay in shape.

Method used: Rebut the horns.

REVIEW QUESTIONS

Answers can be found in the lesson under which the questions are listed.

Introduction

How is logic a science? How is it an art? How is it a symbolic language? What becomes more apparent about an argument when it is symbolized? How does propositional logic differ from categorical logic?

Lesson 1: Introduction to Propositional Logic

What is a proposition? What is a truth-functional proposition? Why is a self-report not truth-functional? What is a logical operator? How does a simple proposition differ from a compound proposition? What is a propositional constant? What is a propositional variable?

Lesson 2: Negation, Conjunction, and Disjunction

How is negation expressed in a sentence in regular English? What is the symbol for negation? How does negation affect the truth value of the negated proposition? What is a defining truth table? What English words express a conjunction? What is the symbol for conjunction? When is a conjunction true? How is a disjunction expressed in regular English? What is the difference between "inclusive or" and "exclusive or"? How is each of them symbolized? When is a disjunction true? When should parentheses be used in symbolizing compound propositions?

Lesson 3: Truth Tables for Determining Truth Values

How many rows are needed to express all combinations of true and false for two variables? for three variables? for *n* variables? What is the general method for determining the truth values of a compound proposition? How does this method differ for propositions using constants with known truth values?

Lesson 4: The Conditional

What type of sentence does the conditional represent? Which part of a conditional is the antecedent? Which part is the consequent? What is the symbol for conditional? When is a conditional considered false? Are conditionals in English with false antecedents actually truth functional? What other compound proposition is by definition equivalent to the conditional? What are several different ways of expressing conditionals in English? What is the rule of transposition?

Lesson 5: The Biconditional

What type of sentence does the biconditional represent? What is the symbol for biconditional? What other compound proposition is equivalent to the biconditional? When is a biconditional true, and when is it false?

Lesson 6: Logical Equivalence

When are two propositions logically equivalent? What is a tautology? What is a self-contradiction? How is the biconditional used to determine if two propositions are logically equivalent? How is it used to determine if two propositions are contradictory?

Lesson 7: Truth Tables for Determining Validity

What is a valid argument? How can a truth table be used to show that an argument is invalid? How can a truth table be used to show that an argument is valid? Can an invalid argument ever have true premises and a true conclusion?

Lesson 8: Shorter Truth Tables for Determining Validity

What should be initially assumed about an argument when using a shorter truth table to determine the argument's validity? Explain the procedure for determining validity using a shorter truth table.

Lesson 9: Using Assumed Truth Values in Shorter Truth Tables

Can all propositional arguments be analyzed for validity using a shorter truth table of only one line? What must be done when a truth table has no "forced" truth values? If a contradiction appears when a truth value is guessed while using a shorter truth table, what must then be done? Why?

Lesson 10: Shorter Truth Tables for Consistency

What does it mean that a set of propositions are consistent? How can a shorter truth table be used to determine the consistency of a set of propositions?

Lesson 11: Shorter Truth Tables for Equivalence

What does it mean that two propositions are equivalent? What is the method for using a shorter truth table to determine the equivalence of a pair of propositions? How is this similar to using truth tables to determine validity?

Lesson 12: The Dilemma

What is a dilemma? How is a standard constructive dilemma symbolized? How does a destructive dilemma differ from a constructive dilemma? What are the three methods for escaping the horns of a dilemma? Is it possible to use all three methods on every dilemma?

REVIEW EXERCISES

Students may do these exercises for further review of this unit.

ADDITIONAL EXERCISES FOR LESSON 1

1. Are simple propositions truth-functional? Why or why not?

   Yes. A simple proposition has one component part, so its truth value is entirely dependent on that one part. In other words, the truth value of "God loves the world" clearly depends entirely on the truth value of "God loves the world."

2. Is a tautology a truth-functional proposition? Is a self-contradiction truth-functional? Explain your answers.

   Neither tautologies nor self-contradictions are truth-functional, because they are true or false (respectively) by logical structure, which means that their truth values do not depend on the truth values of their component propositions. E.g. "$P \vee {\sim}P$", "$P \supset P$", and "$P \equiv {\sim}{\sim}P$" are true regardless of the truth value of P. Similarly, "$P \bullet {\sim}P$" is always false, regardless of the truth value of P.

3. Note which propositions are simple, and which are compound.

Proposition		
Something is rotten in the state of Denmark.	(SIMPLE)	COMPOUND
If it assume my noble father's person, I'll speak to it.	SIMPLE	(COMPOUND)
I did love you once.	(SIMPLE)	COMPOUND
I loved you not.	SIMPLE	(COMPOUND)
The lady doth protest too much.	(SIMPLE)	COMPOUND
It is not nor it cannot come to good.	SIMPLE	(COMPOUND)
Rosencrantz and Guildenstern are dead.	SIMPLE	(COMPOUND)

ADDITIONAL EXERCISES FOR LESSON 2

1. Assume M means "All men are mortal." Give three distinct translations for ~M. Explain why "No men are mortal" is *not* a good translation of ~M.

   Not all men are mortal

   It is false that all men are mortal

   Some men are not mortal.

   "No men are mortal" is a poor translation because it would mean that M and ~M could both be false (in the case that merely some men are mortal), but a proposition and its negation always have opposite truth values. (Answers will vary.)

2. Assume T means "John is a teacher" and S means "John is a soldier." Give four translations for $T \cdot S$. Give two translations for $T \vee S$.

   For T•S, "John is a teacher and John is a soldier," "John is a teacher and a soldier," "John is both a teacher and a soldier," and "John is a teacher, but he is also a soldier."

   For T∨S, "John is a teacher or John is a soldier," "John is a teacher or a soldier."

3. Give an example of a disjunction (a statement using *or*) that is best understood as an inclusive *or.* Give an example of a disjunction that is best understood as an exclusive *or.*

   Examples: "Dinner comes with your choice of coffee or tea" (exclusive); and "You may have cream or sugar with your coffee" (inclusive).

4. Let the + sign indicate the logical operator "exclusive *or*" so that $p + q$ means "*p* or *q*, but not both *p* and *q*." Complete a defining truth table for this logical operator. How then could the inclusive *or* be symbolized using this operator together with conjunction and negation?

p	q	p + q	p ∨ q	p + (~p • q)
T	T	F	T	T
T	F	T	T	T
F	T	T	T	T
F	F	F	F	F

5. Consider the defining truth table for conjunction. Notice that the conjunction of either truth value with a *true (T)* results in that same truth value (that is, $T \bullet T = T$, $F \bullet T = F$), and the conjunction of either truth value with a *false (F)* results in *F* (that is, $T \bullet F = F$, $F \bullet F = F$). This can be stated more briefly with these two rules: $P \bullet T = P$, $P \bullet F = F$. How would you complete these rules for disjunction: $P \vee T = ?$ $P \vee F = ?$

P∨T=T , P∨F=P

6. Express each compound proposition (from the book of Job, KJV) in symbolic form, using whatever propositional constants you think are reasonable:

That man was perfect and upright. (1:1) — P•U

In all this did not Job sin with his lips. (2:10) — ~S

It shut not up the doors of my mother's womb, nor hid sorrow from mine eyes. (3:10) — ~S•~H

I was not in safety, neither had I rest, neither was I quiet; yet trouble came. (3:26) — (~S•~R•~Q)•T

It stood still, but I could not discern the form thereof. (4:16) — S•~D

He shall lean upon his house, but it shall not stand: he shall hold it fast, but it shall not endure. (8:15) — (L•~S)•(H•~E)

With us are both the grayheaded and very aged men. (15:10) — G•A

Snares are round about thee, and sudden fear troubleth thee; or darkness . . . ; and abundance of waters cover thee. (22:10–11) — [(S•F)∨D]•W

For truly my words shall not be false. (36:4) — ~~W

(W = "My words shall be true")

ADDITIONAL EXERCISES FOR LESSON 3

Complete truth tables for the following compound proposition forms:

1.

p	∨	~	q
T	**T**	F	T
T	**T**	T	F
F	**F**	F	T
F	**T**	T	F

2.

~	(~	p	•	q)
T	F	T	F	T
T	F	T	F	F
F	T	F	T	T
T	T	F	F	F

3.

~	(p	∨	q)
F	T	T	T
F	T	T	F
F	F	T	T
T	F	F	F

4.

p	•	(q	∨	~	r)
T	**T**	T	T	F	T
T	**T**	T	T	T	F
T	**F**	F	F	F	T
T	**T**	F	T	T	F
F	**F**	T	T	F	T
F	**F**	T	T	T	F
F	**F**	F	F	F	T
F	**F**	F	T	T	F

5.

(p	∨	q)	•	(p	∨	r)
T	T	T	**T**	T	T	T
T	T	T	**T**	T	T	F
T	T	F	**T**	T	T	T
T	T	F	**T**	T	T	F
F	T	T	**T**	F	T	T
F	T	T	**F**	F	F	F
F	F	F	**F**	F	T	T
F	F	F	**F**	F	F	F

Assume that the propositions *A* and *B* are true, *X* and *Y* are false, and *P* and *Q* are unknown truth values. Determine the truth values (*true*, *false*, or *unknown*) of these compound propositions.

6.	~(A • X)	(T)	F	?
7.	(Y • A) ∨ (B ∨ P)	(T)	F	?
8.	~(A • ~X) ∨ (~B • Y)	T	(F)	?
9.	(P • ~P) ∨ Q	T	F	(?)
10.	~[(P ∨ ~P) • ~(~Q • Q)]	T	(F)	?

ADDITIONAL EXERCISES FOR LESSON 4

1. Write your own *if* FALSE *then* TRUE conditionals and *if* FALSE *then* FALSE conditionals that appear to be true. Then write similar *if* FALSE *then* TRUE conditionals and *if* FALSE *then* FALSE conditionals that appear to be false. With the second set of conditionals, try putting them in the form $\sim(p \bullet \sim q)$. Do they still appear to be false?

   If a triangle is a square [F] then a triangle is a polygon [T] – appears true

   If a triangle is a square [F] then a triangle has four sides [F] – appears true

   If a triangle is a square [F] then a triangle has three sides [T] – appears false

   If a triangle is a square [F] then a triangle is a circle [F] – appears false

   It is false that both a triangle is a square and a triangle does not have three sides.
   – appears true

   It is false that both a triangle is a square and a triangle is not a circle.
   – appears true

2. Express each compound proposition (from 1 Corinthians, KJV) in symbolic form, using whatever propositional constants you think are reasonable:

   If thou marry, thou hast not sinned; and if a virgin marry, she hath not sinned. (7:28) — $(M \supset \sim S) \bullet (V \supset \sim I)$

   Woe is unto me, if I preach not the gospel. (9:16) — $\sim P \supset W$

   When we are judged, we are chastened of the Lord. (11:32) — $J \supset C$

   No man can say that Jesus is Lord, but by the Holy Ghost. (12:3) — $S \supset H$

   Though I speak with the tongues of men and of angels, and have not charity, I am become as sounding brass, or a tinkling cymbal. (13:1) — $[(M \bullet A) \bullet \sim C] \supset (B \vee T)$

   By [the gospel] also ye are saved, if ye keep in memory what I preached unto you, unless ye have believed in vain. (15:2) — $\sim B \supset (K \supset S)$

3. What is a necessary condition for passing a class? What is a sufficient condition for passing a class? Give examples for each as standard *if/then* statements.

   A necessary condition for passing a class is something you must do in order to pass, though you may have to do other things in order to pass. "If you passed the class, then you must have attended class regularly." A sufficient condition is something that by itself is enough to pass. "If your final overall grade is greater than or equal to 70, then you will pass."

4. Write this as a standard *if/then* statement: "A person may be elected President of the United States only if that person has been a resident for fourteen years." Then use this conditional as the first premise of a *modus ponens* argument.

   "If a person is elected president of the United States, then that person has been a resident for fourteen years. Theodore Roosevelt was elected president of the United States. Thus he must have been a resident of the United States for fourteen years."

5. Rewrite this conditional using the rule of transposition: "If there be no resurrection of the dead, then is Christ not risen" (1 Cor. 15:13).

   If Christ is risen, then there is a resurrection of the dead.

6. Complete a truth table for the compound proposition $\sim p \supset p$ (this should require only two rows). What more basic proposition has the same truth table?

~p	⊃	p
FT	T	T
TF	F	F

   This has the same truth table as "p."

7. Consider the defining truth table for the conditional. Complete the following rules. (*T* and *F* here don't stand for propositions; they stand for *true* and *false*.)

   $P \supset T =$ T $P \supset F =$ ~P $T \supset Q =$ Q $F \supset Q =$ T

ADDITIONAL EXERCISES FOR LESSON 5

1. Complete the truth table for the compound proposition *(p • q) ∨ (~p • ~q)*. What more basic compound proposition has the same truth table?

p	q	(p • q) ∨ (~ p • ~q)	p ≡ q
T	T	T (T) F FF	T
T	F	F F F FT	F
F	T	F F T FF	F
F	F	F (T) T TT	T

2. Symbolize each proposition, letting B represent "The biconditional is true" and S represent "The truth values are the same."

The biconditional is true if the truth values are the same. S⊃B

The biconditional is true only if the truth values are the same. B⊃S

The biconditional is true if and only if the truth values are the same. B≡S

ADDITIONAL EXERCISES FOR LESSON 6

1. Logic is based on three laws of thought. The Law of Identity states, "If a statement is true, then it is true." The Law of Excluded Middle states, "A statement is either true or false." The Law of Non-contradiction states, "A statement cannot be both true and false." These laws can be represented by three tautologies: *p ⊃ p*, *p ∨ ~p*, and *~(p • ~p)*, respectively. Show these to be tautologies by completing a truth table for each.

p	p ⊃ p	p ∨ ~ p	~ (p • ~ p)
T	T T T	T T F T	T T F F T
F	F T F	F T T F	T F F T F

Determine whether each pair of propositions is *equivalent*, *contradictory*, or *neither*.

2. p ⊃ ~p, ~p ⊃ p — EQUIVALENT — (CONTRADICTORY) — NEITHER
3. p ∨ q, ~(~p ∨ ~q) — EQUIVALENT — CONTRADICTORY — (NEITHER)
4. p ≡ ~q, ~(p ≡ q) — (EQUIVALENT) — CONTRADICTORY — NEITHER
5. p ⊃ (~p • q), ~p ⊃ (p • ~q) — EQUIVALENT — (CONTRADICTORY) — NEITHER
6. p • (q ∨ r), (p • q) ∨ r — EQUIVALENT — CONTRADICTORY — (NEITHER)
7. ~[(p • q) ∨ (p • r)], ~p ∨ (~q • ~r) — (EQUIVALENT) — CONTRADICTORY — NEITHER

ADDITIONAL EXERCISES FOR LESSON 7

Use truth tables to determine the validity of the brief (but unusual) arguments.

1.

p	∴ q ⊃ q
T	T T T
T	F T F
F	T T T
F	F T F

Valid

2.

p	∴ q ⊃ p
T	T T T
T	F T T
F	T F F
F	F T F

Valid

3.

p	q	∴ p ≡ q
T	T	T
T	F	F
F	T	F
F	F	T

Valid

Translate the arguments in into symbolic form, and then use truth tables to determine their validity.

4. You cannot have your cake and eat it too. Therefore you cannot have your cake.

~(H • E)	∴ ~H	
F T T T	F	
T T F F	F	←Invalid
T F F T	T	
T F F F	T	

5. I can tell the future. Thus it will either snow tomorrow, or it will not snow tomorrow.

F	∴ S v ~S	
T	T	←Valid
T	T	
F	T	
F	T	

6. "But if there be no resurrection of the dead, then is Christ not risen. . . . But now Christ is risen from the dead. . . . So in Christ shall all be made alive" (1 Cor. 15:13–22).

~R ⊃ ~C	C	∴ R	
F T F	T	T	←Valid
F T T	F	T	
T F F	T	F	
T T T	F	F	

7. "Either your sister is telling lies, or she is mad, or she is telling the truth. You know she doesn't tell lies and it is obvious that she is not mad. . . . We must assume that she is telling the truth." (C.S. Lewis, *The Lion, the Witch, and the Wardrobe*)

(L ∨ M) ∨ T)	~L • ~M	∴ T	
T	F	T	
T	F	F	
T	F	T	
T	F	F	
T	F	T	
T	F	F	
T	T	T	←Valid
F	T	F	

8. "If the Son is not of the same substance with the Father, then He is a substance that was made, and if that substance was made, then all things were not made through Him. But, on the contrary, 'All things were made through him.' [Consequently], He is of the one and the same substance with the Father." (St. Augustine, *The Trinity*)

~F ⊃ M	M ⊃ ~A	A	∴ F	
T	F	T	T	
T	T	F	T	
T	T	T	T	←Valid
T	T	F	T	
T	F	T	F	
T	T	F	F	
F	T	T	F	
F	T	F	F	

ADDITIONAL EXERCISES FOR LESSON 8

Translate the following arguments into symbolic form, and then use shorter truth tables to determine their validity.

1. Pluto is a planet if and only if it is reasonably large and has an independent, circular orbit around the sun. Pluto is reasonably large. Pluto has an independent, circular orbit around the sun. But Pluto's orbit lies outside the ecliptic plane. Therefore, it is false that if Pluto is a planet then its orbit does not lie outside the ecliptic plane.

P ≡ (L • O)	L	O	E	∴ ~(P ⊃ ~ E)
F T T T T	T	T	T	FF T FT
↑				Valid

2. If the spirit of Samuel was raised by the witch at Endor, then spirits of dead men could be seen by the living. Ghosts at one time existed if spirits of dead men could be seen by the living. Ghosts exist now only if ghosts at one time existed. So either the spirit of Samuel was not raised by the witch at Endor, or ghosts exist now.

$R \supset S$	$S \supset E$	$N \supset E$	$\therefore \sim R \vee N$
T T T	T T T	F T T	F T F F

Invalid

3. A murder is committed if and only if an innocent person is killed and killed with either malice aforethought or the demonstration of an abandoned or malignant heart. If a fetus is aborted, then an innocent person is killed, without malice aforethought, but with a demonstration of an abandoned or malignant heart. Consequently, if a fetus is aborted, then a murder is committed.

$M \equiv [K \bullet (A \vee D)]$	$F \supset [K \bullet (\sim A \bullet D)]$	$\therefore F \supset M$
F T T T F T T	T T T T T F T T	T F F
↑ (under $\equiv$)		

Valid

4. If God exists, then He is both perfectly good and infinitely powerful. If God is perfectly good then He always desires to prevent evil. If God is infinitely powerful then He is always able to prevent evil. If evil exists, then either God does not always desire to prevent evil or He is not always able to prevent evil. Evil does exist. Therefore God does not exist.

$G \supset (P \bullet I)$	$P \supset D$	$I \supset A$	$E \supset (\sim D \vee \sim A)$	E	$\therefore \sim G$
T T T T T	T T T	T T T	T T F F F	T	F
			↑ (under $\supset$)		

Valid

5. If the last argument was valid, then if the conclusion was false, then one of the premises must be false. The conclusion was false. If you did the last problem correctly, then the argument was valid. Thus, either you did not do the last problem correctly or one of the premises must be false.

$V \supset (C \supset P)$	C	$D \supset V$	$\therefore \sim D \vee P$
T T T F F	T	T T T	F F F
↑ (under $\supset$)			

Valid

ADDITIONAL EXERCISES FOR LESSON 9

1. Write your own valid argument, different from any in the text, which requires you to guess a truth value to determine the validity by the shorter truth table.

$p \equiv (q \vee r)$	$q \supset r$	$\therefore p \equiv r$
T	T	F

(Example: The conclusion can be false in two ways.)

Translate each argument into symbolic form, and then determine its validity using the shorter truth table method.

2. If the switch is closed then the diode will light. The switch is closed or current is not flowing. Either the diode is not lit or current is flowing. Consequently, the switch is closed if and only if the diode is lit.

$C \supset L$	$C \vee {\sim}F$	${\sim}L \vee F$	$\therefore C \equiv L$
T T F	T T	T	<u>T</u> F F
↑			
F T T	F T F	F T T	<u>F</u> F T
	↑		

(guesses underlined)

Valid

3. If you can do judo and karate then you can defend yourself. You can do judo or karate. Therefore you can defend yourself.

$(J \bullet K) \supset D$	$J \vee K$	$\therefore D$
T F F T F	T T F	F

Invalid

4. If this argument is valid, then you can prove it to be valid if and only if you can use a truth table. Either this argument is valid and you can prove it to be valid, or this argument is valid and you can use a truth table. Therefore, you can prove this argument to be valid and you can use a truth table.

$V \supset (P \equiv T)$	$(V \bullet P) \vee (V \bullet T)$	$\therefore P \bullet T$
F T T F F	F F T T F F F	<u>T</u> F F
	↑	
T T F F T	T F F T T T T	<u>F</u> F T
↑		

Valid

ADDITIONAL EXERCISES FOR LESSON 10

Determine the consistency of the sets of propositions in problems 1–3 using shorter truth tables.

1.

p • (q ∨ r)	q • ~r	p ∨ r
T T T T F	T T T	T T F

Consistent

2.

~p ∨ (q • r)	p • ~r
F T F F	T T T
↑	

Inconsistent

3.

~(p ∨ q)	~p ⊃ (q ∨ r)	~r
T F F F	T T F F F	T
	↑	

Inconsistent

4. If you do not have your own business then if you want to make money then you must be an employee. You must be an employee. You have your own business and you want to make money.

~B ⊃ (M ⊃ E)	E	B • M
F T T T T	T	T T T

Consistent

5. Either Lefty or Capone is responsible for the fire. If Capone is responsible for the fire, then he knew about the dangerous conditions but did nothing about them. Capone knew about the dangerous conditions only if he did something about them. Lefty is not responsible for the fire.

L ∨ C	C ⊃ (K • ~D)	K ⊃ D	~L
F T T	T T T T T	T T F	T
		↑	

Inconsistent

ADDITIONAL EXERCISES FOR LESSON 11

1. Two propositions are logically equivalent if they imply each other. Explain how the shorter truth table method determines whether or not the propositions imply each other.

A shorter truth table for equivalence assumes that the first statement does not imply the second by assigning the first to be true and the second false, then assumes that the second statement does not imply the first by assigning the second to be true and the first to be false. It then looks for contradictions to these assumptions. In other words, the method is the same as shorter truth tables for validity in both directions.

Demonstrate the propositions to be equivalent using both the longer and the shorter truth table methods. In each case, which is the better method, and why?

2. $[p \bullet (p \vee q)] \equiv [p \vee (p \bullet q)]$ $p \bullet (p \vee q)$ $p \vee (p \bullet q)$

```
[p • (p ∨ q)] ≡ [p ∨ (p • q)]     p • (p ∨ q)     p ∨ (p • q)
 TT    T      T  TT    T          T T T T         T F T
 TT    T      T  TT    F                            ↑
 FF    T      T  FF    F          T F T T         T T T
 FF    F      T  FF    F            ↑
                                    F             F T F F
                                                    ↑
```

Equivalent

The longer truth table may be easier, though longer, because the shorter truth table requires you to guess a truth value, which is prone to errors.

3. $[\sim(p \equiv q)] \equiv [(p \vee q) \bullet \sim(p \bullet q)]$ $\sim(p \equiv q)$ $(p \vee q) \bullet \sim(p \bullet q)$

```
[~(p ≡ q)] ≡ [(p ∨ q) • ~(p • q)]     ~(p ≡ q)     (p ∨ q) • ~(p • q)
 F   T      T     T     F F   T        T T F F      T T F  F T T F F
 T   F      T     T     T T   F                            ↑
 T   F      T     T     T T   F        T F F T      F T T  F T F F T
 F   T      T     F     F T   F                            ↑
                                       F T T F      T T F  T T T F F
                                           ↑
                                       F F T F      F T F  T T F F F
                                                      ↑
```

Equivalent

The longer truth table is much easier, because you must guess both ways for the shorter truth table. The "shorter" truth table is not really shorter here.

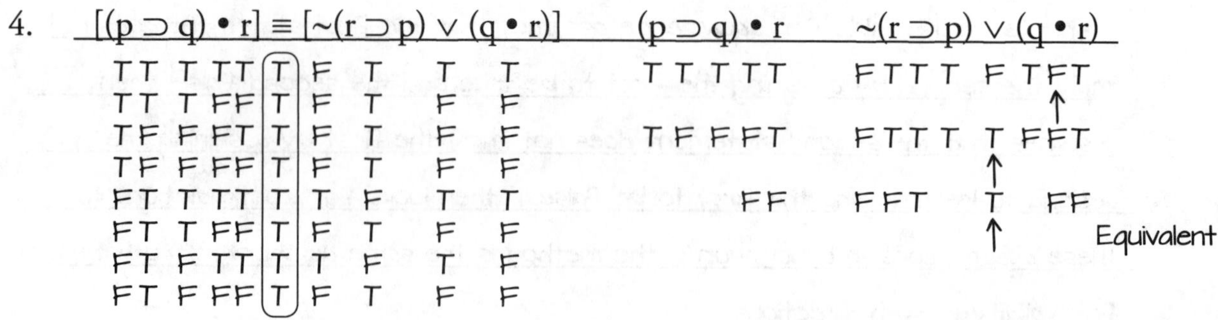

Translate each pairs of propositions into symbolic form, and then use the shorter truth table method to determine their equivalence.

5. If an animal can learn by trial and error and recognize words, then that animal can reason. If an animal can recognize words, then it is false that the animal can learn by trial and error but is not able to reason.

(L • W) ⊃ R	W ⊃ ~ (L • ~ R)
T T T T F	T F F T T T F
T T T F F	T T F T T T F

Equivalent

6. Pirates murder, and they either rape or pillage. Pirates rape and murder, or they pillage.

M • (R ∨ P)	(R • M) ∨ P
F F T T T	T F F T T

Not Equivalent

7. My grandfather was a soldier or a sailor, and he was not a soldier. My grandfather was a sailor.

(O ∨ A) • ~O	A
T T T F F T	T

Not Equivalent

ADDITIONAL EXERCISES FOR LESSON 12

1. In Matthew 22:15–22, Jesus was presented with a dilemma by the Pharisees and the Herodians. Write out the full dilemma. What method does Jesus use to refute it?

One possibility for the full dilemma: "If Jesus says it is lawful to pay taxes to Caesar, then he admits the legitimacy of Caesar's authority and the people will oppose him. If Jesus says it is not lawful to pay taxes to Caesar, then he denies the legitimacy of Caesar's authority and the civil rulers will oppose him. Jesus will either say it is lawful to pay taxes to Caesar or it is not lawful to pay taxes to Caesar. Therefore, he either admits the legitimacy of Caesar's authority and the people will oppose him, or he denies the legitimacy of Caesar's authority and the civil rulers will oppose him." Jesus appears to go between the horns, admitting the legitimacy of Caesar's authority to a point: Caesar may demand our money (which has his image on it), but he may not demand our worship (which belongs to God alone).

2. In Matthew 21:23–27, Jesus refutes a challenge brought to him by the chief priests and elders. Explain how this may be an example of rebutting the horns of a dilemma.

Given the response of Jesus, the Jews appeared to be assuming a dilemma such as this: "If Jesus says his authority of from heaven, then we can accuse him of blasphemy. If Jesus says nothing, then he admits our authority to silence him. Jesus will either say his authority is from heaven, or he will say nothing. Therefore we will either accuse him of blasphemy, or we will gain authority to silence him." Jesus rebuts the horns by producing a similar counter-dilemma: Is John's baptism from heaven or from men? Had they answered this question honestly, they would have answered their own question.

3. One year, a lazy farmer refused to work in his field, reasoning this way: "If God knows that I will have a crop, then it will not be necessary for me to work to produce one. If God knows that I will not have a crop, any work of mine will be ultimately wasted. God knows whether or not I will have a crop. So my work would be either unnecessary or wasted." Refute this dilemma.

Grasp the horns: God knows that you will have a crop by working to produce one.

4. One classic example of a dilemma is the legend of Caliph Omar's destruction of the Library of Alexandria. Omar is reported to have said, "If the books of this library merely repeat the Koran, then they are superfluous. If these books disagree with the Koran, then they are wicked. They either repeat the Koran or they disagree with it. In either case they are superfluous or wicked, and should be destroyed." Refute this dilemma using each of the three methods.

Grasp the horns: "Even if these books repeat what is in the Koran, they are not necessarily superfluous. Wouldn't you agree that more repeating of the Koran is better? Or if they disagree with the Koran, they are not necessarily wicked, not if the Koran is in error" (though this would likely not be persuasive).

Go between the horns: "The choices are not only repeating the Koran or disagreeing with it. These books may be consistent with the Koran without repeating it."

Rebut the horns: "When you speak, Mr. Omar, if you merely repeat the Koran, then your words are superfluous, or if you disagree with the Koran, then you are wicked. You either repeat the Koran or you disagree with it, even as these books. Therefore, you are either superfluous or wicked, and should be destroyed."

UNIT 2

FORMAL PROOFS OF VALIDITY

CONTENTS

THE RULES OF INFERENCE

Intermediate Logic, pp. 101–106

STUDENT OBJECTIVES

1. Identify and show the validity of the nine rules of inference.
2. Complete Exercise 13.

TEACHING INSTRUCTIONS

1. Tell students that they are about to leave truth tables behind and get into some wilder territory: formal proofs of validity. Explain that truth tables were useful because they allowed us to prove an argument either valid *or* invalid. Formal proofs of validity don't have that nice feature: they can only prove an argument *valid* (as their name implies). But what formal proofs are better at doing is showing the connection between the premises and conclusion of an argument. Tell students that you're going to throw a lot at them in this lesson and that they need to not get scared.
2. Explain that **a formal proof of validity is a step-by-step deduction of a conclusion from a set of premises, each step being justified by an appropriate basic rule**. In other words, if we are given an argument that we want to determine the validity of, we symbolize it and then see if we can deduce the conclusion from the premises using certain valid rules. If we can do so (without cheating), the argument is valid.
3. Write on the board this rather complicated argument (from Exercise 8):

   "If the book of Hebrews is Scripture then it was written by Paul or Apollos. If Paul wrote anonymously to the Hebrews then he wrote anonymously in some of his letters. If Hebrews was written by Paul then he wrote anonymously to the Hebrews. Paul did not write anonymously in any of his letters. The book of Hebrews is Scripture. Therefore Hebrews was written by Apollos."

   Have students symbolize the premises and conclusions of this argument using the constants *S*, *P*, *A*, *H*, and *L*. As they symbolize, number each symbolized premise on its own line and place the conclusion off to the side of the last line. The argument should look like this:

   1) S ⊃ (P ∨ A)
   2) H ⊃ L
   3) P ⊃ H
   4) ~L
   5) S   / ∴ A

4. Students should feel appropriately daunted at the thought of solving this. Explain that all they need to do is see if they can deduce A (the conclusion) from the premises. Tell them it is going to take several steps. Have them look at the premises and see if they can use any of the rules they already know to draw conclusions from them. If they need a hint, have them look at premises 1 and 5. Help them see that if constant S is represented by variable p and *P∨A* by q, these two premises

can be put into the form of $p \supset q$, p. Students should recognize that these are the premises of Modus Ponens, and that by Modus Ponens they can therefore conclude q, or $P \vee A$. Explain that we then write this intermediate conclusion on the next line of the proof with the justification next to it. The justification includes the numbers of the premises used and the rule used. In this case:

6) P ∨ A   1, 5 M.P.

In English we are taking "If Hebrews is Scripture then it was written by Paul or Apollos," and Hebrews is Scripture," and concluding that "Hebrews was written by Paul or Apollos."

5. Have students look at the proof again and see what other conclusions they can draw from the premises. If they need a hint, have them look at premises 2 and 3. They should see that from $P \supset H$ and $H \supset L$ they can conclude $P \supset L$ by the Hypothetical Syllogism ($p \supset q$, $q \supset r$, $\therefore p \supset r$). The next line of the proof should therefore look like this.

   7) P ⊃ L   3, 2 H.S.

   In English we are concluding "If Hebrews was written by Paul, then he wrote anonymously in some of his letters." Tell them the "3,2" gives the correct order of the premises.

6. Ask students if they see any further conclusion that can be drawn using line 7 and one of the other premises. Help them see that lines 7 and 4 taken together are the premises of Modus Tollens ($p \supset q$, $\sim q$, $\therefore \sim p$) and that we can use Modus Tollens to conclude $\sim P$. Line 8 should look like this:

   8) ~P   7, 4 M.T.

   We have thus deduced that "Hebrews was not written by Paul."

7. Tell students that just one more step will give them their conclusion. Explain that if they take line 6 ($P \vee A$) together with line 8 ($\sim P$), they can use the rule of the Disjunctive Syllogism (which they proved valid in Exercise 7a): $p \vee q$, $\sim p$, $\therefore q$. Line 9 should look like this:

   9) A   6,8 D.S.

   Explain that they have deduced the conclusion they were trying to deduce, and that they have therefore proved the argument valid. The entire proof should look like this:

   1) S ⊃ (P ∨ A)
   2) H ⊃ L
   3) P ⊃ H
   4) ~L
   5) S   / ∴ A
   6) P ∨ A   1, 5 M.P.
   7) P ⊃ L   3, 2 H.S.
   8) ~P   7, 4 M.T.
   9) A   6,8 D.S.
   Q.E.D.

   Explain that it is customary to end proofs with the letters "Q.E.D.," which stand for the Latin phrase "quod erat demonstrandum" or "what was to be demonstrated." Explain that that's just a refined way of saying, "Look, I did it!" They do want to be refined, don't they?

8. Explain that in the above proof students used the first four of the **nine rules of inference**. Tell students that **a rule of inference is a valid argument form which can be used to justify steps in a proof**. Write the nine rules of inference (see top of next page) on one side of the board and keep them up for the remainder of the lesson and/or have students turn to p. 103 of their textbooks (or Appendix B) for reference. Make sure students can see that each of these rules is a valid argument form; if they're having trouble grasping one, use English examples, i.e., for Simplification, "I am a genius and I am also beautiful. Therefore I am a genius."

9. Explain that you will now work through some proofs that use the last five rules. Write this argument on the board: "I like coffee and I like

Modus Ponens (M.P.)	*Modus Tollens (M.T.)*	*Hypothetical Syllogism (H.S.)*
$p \supset q$ p $\therefore q$	$p \supset q$ $\sim q$ $\therefore \sim p$	$p \supset q$ $q \supset r$ $\therefore p \supset r$
Disjunctive Syllogism (D.S.)	*Constructive Dilemma (C.D.)*	*Conjunction (Conj.)*
$p \vee q$ $\sim p$ $\therefore q$	$(p \supset q) \bullet (r \supset s)$ $p \vee r$ $\therefore q \vee s$	p q $\therefore p \bullet q$
Absorption (Abs.)	*Simplification (Simp.)*	*Addition (Add.)*
$p \supset q$ $\therefore p \supset (p \bullet q)$	$p \bullet q$ $\therefore p$	p $\therefore p \vee q$

tea. Therefore I like coffee or I like wine." Have students walk you through symbolizing it and setting up the proof. It should look like this:

1) C • T / ∴C ∨ W

Tell students that this proof should take two steps. Have them look at the rules and decide what should be done first. They should comes up with using the rule of Simplification on step 1 to get *C*:

2) C 1 Simp.

Explain that **Simplification always removes the *second* conjunct in the conjunction** ("T" in this case). Also warn students that **they can't simplify *within* a proposition; *~(p • q)* cannot be simplified to *~p*.** You can use a shorter truth table to show that this is not valid.

10. Ask students what to do next. They should see that they can now use the rule of Addition to get the desired conclusion:

    3) C ∨ W 2 Add.

    Point out that **Addition is the only rules that adds a new variable** (*W* in this case). The completed proof should look like this:

    1) C • T / ∴C ∨ W
    2) C 1 Simp.
    3) C ∨ W 2 Add.
    Q.E.D.

11. Explain that the last example is a bit complicated but that it will demonstrate some important concepts. Write this argument on the board: "If evil men are allowed freedom of speech then evil writings will be produced. If evil men are not allowed freedom of speech then their rights will be violated. Evil men will either be allowed freedom of speech or they won't. So either evil writings will be produced or evil men will not be allowed freedom of speech and their rights will be violated." Have students walk you through symbolizing this whopper and setting up a proof for it, using *F*, *W*, and *R*. It should look like this:

    1) F ⊃ W
    2) ~F ⊃ R
    3) F ∨ ~F / ∴ W ∨ (~F • R)

12. Ask students what argument this very closely resembles (a constructive dilemma). Explain that, although it is a dilemma, the conclusion complicates it a bit. Tell students that the first thing they should do is try to form the second disjunct of the conclusion *(~F • R)* which hasn't appeared yet in the proof. If they need a hint, tell them to use the premise that contains the same constants (premise 2). They should figure out that they can use the rule of Absorption on step 2 to get this:

    4) ~F ⊃ (~F • R) 2 Abs.

13. Tell students that they can now set up the first premise of the Constructive Dilemma, by combining lines 1 and 4 with Conjunctions. It should look like this:

    5) (F ⊃ W) • [~F ⊃ (~F • R)] 1, 4 Conj.

    Explain that students can now use the Constructive Dilemma to get the desired conclusion. Have them looks at steps 5 and 3, and makes sure they see that these steps fit the Constructive Dilemma pattern of *(p ⊃ q) • (r ⊃ s)*, *p ∨ r*, and that we can therefore conclude the equivalent of *q ∨ s*:

    6) W ∨ (~F • R) 5, 3 C.D.

14. The completed proof should look like this:

    1) F ⊃ W
    2) ~F ⊃ R
    3) F ∨ ~F / ∴ W ∨ (~F • R)
    4) ~F ⊃ (~F • R) 2 Abs.
    5) (F ⊃ W) • [~F ⊃ (~F • R)] 1, 4 Conj.
    6) W ∨ (~F • R) 5, 3 C.D.
    Q.E.D.

    Have students read through it slowly and carefully, making sure they follow the reasoning for each step. In closing, warn students that **when they solve proofs like this, they can never skip or combine steps, even if they seem obvious. They must explicitly perform each step and provide justification for it.**

ASSIGNMENT

Have students complete Exercise 13, and go over it with them.

LESSON 13

THE RULES OF INFERENCE

Truth tables are able to prove that an argument is invalid or valid. **Formal proofs of validity** are unable to prove that an argument is invalid. However, properly written they do show the connection between the premises and the conclusion of a valid argument more clearly than does a truth table. They do so by taking the premises of a valid argument and, following certain rules, deduce the conclusion from the premises in a step-by-step proof of validity.

DEFINITION

A ***formal proof of validity*** is a step-by-step deduction of a conclusion from a set of premises, each step being justified by an appropriate basic rule.

For example, consider this argument which we have seen before in Exercise 8:

> If the book of Hebrews is Scripture then it was written by Paul or Apollos. If Paul wrote anonymously to the Hebrews then he wrote anonymously in some of his letters. If Hebrews was written by Paul then he wrote anonymously to the Hebrews. Paul did not write anonymously in any of his letters. The book of Hebrews is Scripture. Therefore Hebrews was written by Apollos.

This argument may be symbolized as follows, each premise given a number and the conclusion placed off to the side on the last line:

1) $S \supset (P \vee A)$
2) $H \supset L$
3) $P \supset H$
4) $\sim L$
5) $S \quad / \therefore A$

KEY POINT

Formal proofs can only prove validity; they cannot prove invalidity.

How may we deduce the conclusion from the premises? First, consider premises one and five: $S \supset (P \vee A)$, S. If the constant S is represented by the variable p, and the compound proposition $P \vee A$ is represented by the variable q, these premises can be put into the form $p \supset q$, p. Now, you should recognize these as the premises to *modus ponens*, and thus from these premises we can conclude q, that is, $P \vee A$. In English, we have taken "If Hebrews is Scripture then it was written by Paul or Apollos; Hebrews is Scripture" and concluded "Hebrews was written by Paul or Apollos." In our proof this intermediate conclusion is written on the next line, with the justification written next to it. Included in the justification are the numbers of the premises used in order, and the rule which, using those premises, has this line as the conclusion, as follows:

6) P∨A   1, 5 M.P.

This says *modus ponens* (M.P.) was used on steps one and five to conclude $P \vee A$.

Now look at premises three and two. What can be concluded from $P \supset H$, $H \supset L$? It should be evident that the conditional $P \supset L$ can be concluded. This follows the rule of Hypothetical Syllogism: $p \supset q$, $q \supset r$, $\therefore p \supset r$. Thus we write the next line in our proof:

7) P⊃L   3, 2 H.S.

This conclusion says, "If Hebrews was written by Paul, then he wrote anonymously in some of his letters." We deduced it from steps three and two, using the Hypothetical Syllogism (H.S.).

We will now use this conclusion, $P \supset L$, along with the proposition in step four, "Paul did not write anonymously in any of his letters," $\sim L$. These two premises follow the pattern $p \supset q$, $\sim q$, from which we may conclude $\sim p$ using the rule of *modus tollens*. Thus we have deduced "Hebrews was not written by Paul," $\sim P$, and write this with the justification on the next line.

8) ~P   7, 4 M.T.

Now back in step 6 we concluded "Hebrews was written by Paul or Apollos," $P \vee A$, and here we conclude "Hebrews was not written by Paul," $\sim P$. From this we deduce "Hebrews was written by Apollos," A, using the rule of Disjunctive Syllogism (D.S.): $p \vee q$, $\sim p$, $\therefore q$ (which was proven valid in Exercise 7a). We write this as our final step:

9) A   6, 8 D.S.

The entire proof would thus look like this:

1)	$S \supset (P \vee A)$	
2)	$H \supset L$	
3)	$P \supset H$	
4)	$\sim L$	
5)	$S \ / \therefore A$	
6)	$P \vee A$	1, 5 M.P.
7)	$P \supset L$	3, 2 H.S.
8)	$\sim P$	7, 4 M.T.
9)	A	6, 8 D.S.

Q.E.D.

It is customary to end proofs with "Q.E.D." This stands for *quod erat demonstrandum,* which is Latin for "What was to be demonstrated."

From this proof we have seen the first four of the following **nine rules of inference** (these rules are also listed in Appendix B):

DEFINITION

A ***rule of inference*** is a valid argument form which can be used to justify steps in a proof.

Modus Ponens (M.P.)

$p \supset q$
p
$\therefore q$

Modus Tollens (M.T.)

$p \supset q$
$\sim q$
$\therefore \sim p$

Hypothetical Syllogism (H.S.)

$p \supset q$
$q \supset r$
$\therefore p \supset r$

Disjunctive Syllogism (D.S.)

$p \vee q$
$\sim p$
$\therefore q$

Constructive Dilemma (C.D.)

$(p \supset q) \bullet (r \supset s)$
$p \vee r$
$\therefore q \vee s$

Conjunction (Conj.)

p
q
$\therefore p \bullet q$

Absorption (Abs.)

$p \supset q$
$\therefore p \supset (p \bullet q)$

Simplification (Simp.)

$p \bullet q$
$\therefore p$

Addition (Add.)

p
$\therefore p \vee q$

KEY POINT

Memorize the nine basic rules of inference so that you can use them effortlessly when constructing formal proofs.

We will now look at examples of proofs which use the last five of these rules.

Consider this rather trivial argument: "I like coffee and I like tea. Therefore I like coffee or I like wine." This can be represented

1) C • T / ∴ C ∨ W

This proof will take two more steps. The first will be to use the rule of Simplification on step one, like this:

2) C   1 Simp.

Simplification always removes the second conjunct in the conjunction (in this case, T). Also, please note that you may not simplify within a proposition; for example, *~(p • q)* may not simplify to *~p*.

Now we can use the rule of Addition to obtain the desired conclusion:

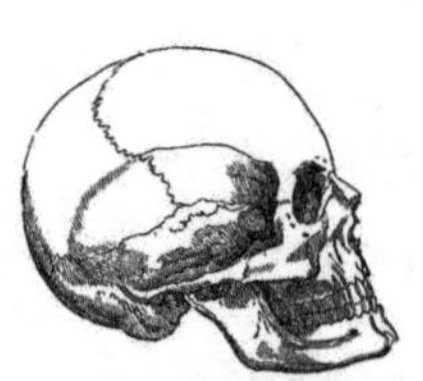

CAUTION

Compound propositions of the form ~(*p* • *q*) do not simplify to ~*p*.

3) C ∨ W   2 Add.

Note that the rule of Addition is the only rule which adds a new variable or constant—in this case, W.

The formal proof of validity written out in its entirety looks like this:

1) C • T / ∴ C ∨ W
2) C   1 Simp.
3) C ∨ W   2 Add.
Q.E.D.

The final example may be difficult to follow, but it will demonstrate many important concepts along with the last three rules of inference. Consider this dilemma: "If evil men are allowed freedom of speech then evil writings will be produced. If evil men are not allowed freedom of speech then their rights will be violated. Evil men will either be allowed freedom of speech or they will not be. So either evil writings will be produced or evil men will not be allowed freedom of speech and their rights will be violated." We can symbolize the argument like this:

KEY POINT

You may not skip or combine steps in a proof, even if it seems obvious. You must explicitly perform each step and provide justification for it.

1) F ⊃ W
2) ~F ⊃ R
3) F ∨ ~F / ∴ W ∨ (~F • R)

We may recognize it as a dilemma, but the second disjunct in the conclusion, $\sim F \bullet R$, leads us to believe we must first work with the premise in step two, because it uses the same constants. If we use the rule of Absorption on step two, we can obtain the following:

4) $\sim F \supset (\sim F \bullet R)$	2 Abs.

Now we can set up the first premise of the Constructive Dilemma, which must have the form $(p \supset q) \bullet (r \supset s)$. In our case if we combine step one with step four using Conjunction we will get this:

5) $(F \supset W) \bullet [\sim F \supset (\sim F \bullet R)]$	1, 4 Conj.

Notice that to do this, the p of the conjunction represented the conditional $F \supset W$, and q the compound proposition $\sim F \supset (\sim F \bullet R)$.

Now we have the propositions we need in order to use the Constructive Dilemma to arrive at our desired conclusion. Look at steps five, $(F \supset W) \bullet [\sim F \supset (\sim F \bullet R)]$, and three, $F \vee \sim F$. This fits the pattern $(p \supset q) \bullet (r \supset s)$, $p \vee r$, and thus we can conclude the equivalent of $q \vee s$:

6) $W \vee (\sim F \bullet R)$	5, 3 C.D.

Carefully follow through the variables and the propositions they represent, and you will see how this works. The entire proof can be written out as follows. Read it through slowly to make sure you can follow each step:

1)	$F \supset W$	
2)	$\sim F \supset R$	
3)	$F \vee \sim F \quad / \therefore W \vee (\sim F \bullet R)$	
4)	$\sim F \supset (\sim F \bullet R)$	2 Abs.
5)	$(F \supset W) \bullet [\sim F \supset (\sim F \bullet R)]$	1, 4 Conj.
6)	$W \vee (\sim F \bullet R)$	5, 3 C.D.
Q.E.D.		

SUMMARY

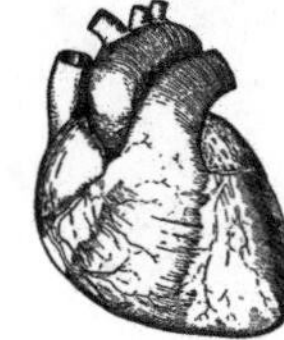

A formal proof of validity for a valid argument is a formal series of steps which deduce the argument's conclusion from its premise(s). First, the premise(s) are symbolized and numbered. Then, intermediate conclusions are deduced by applying the rules of inference to the premise(s). For each step a justification is given, in which the numbers of the steps used as premises for the rule are placed beside the abbreviation of the rule. This procedure is continued until the desired conclusion is reached. The nine rules of inference are listed in Appendix B.

EXERCISE 13 (18 points)

Demonstrate the validity of the rules of inference using the shorter truth-table method. (2 each)

1. Modus Ponens (M.P.)

$p \supset q$	p	$\therefore q$
T T F	T	F
↑		

2. Modus Tollens (M.T.)

$p \supset q$	$\sim q$	$\therefore \sim p$
T T F	T F	F T
↑		

3. Hypothetical Syllogism (H.S.)

$p \supset q$	$q \supset r$	$\therefore p \supset r$
T T F	F T F	T F F
↑		

4. Disjunctive Syllogism (D.S.)

$p \vee q$	$\sim p$	$\therefore q$
F T F	T F	F
↑		

5. Constructive Dilemma (C.D.)

$(p \supset q) \bullet (r \supset s)$	$p \vee r$	$\therefore q \vee s$
F T F T F T F	F T F	F F F
	↑	

6. Absorption (Abs.)

$p \supset q$	$\therefore p \supset (p \bullet q)$
T T F	T F T F F
↑	

7. Simplification (Simp.)

$p \bullet q$	$\therefore p$
F T	F
↑	

8. Addition (Add.)

p	$\therefore p \vee q$
T	T F
	↑

9. Conjunction (Conj.)

p	q	$\therefore p \bullet q$
T	T	T F T
		↑

RECOGNIZING THE RULES OF INFERENCE

Intermediate Logic, pp. 109–111

STUDENT OBJECTIVES

1. Identify the rules of inference when given in nonstandard form.
2. Provide justifications for short proofs.
3. Complete Exercises 14a and 14b.

SPECIAL NOTE

You have several classes to work through Lesson 14 and its exercises. Try to get through as much of the lesson as you can on the first day, and spend the following classes tying up loose ends and working through both parts of Exercise 14 with students.

TEACHING INSTRUCTIONS

1. Tell students that, as they have probably discovered through doing the exercises, recognizing the rules of inference in a proof is often tricky. The premises and conclusions in an actual proof are much more complex than the premises and conclusions simplified in a rule. Explain that there are a few reasons this is the case.
2. Write this argument on the board:

   $[(F \supset \sim C) \vee (Q \equiv X)] \supset (\sim E \vee J)$
   $[(F \supset \sim C) \vee (Q \equiv X)] \quad / \therefore \sim E \vee J$

   See if students can tell you—fast—what rule of inference this argument follows. It will probably take them a minute to figure out that it's Modus Ponens ($p \supset q, p, \therefore q$) because of the gaggle of symbols and parentheses they have to wade through first. Explain that **the variables in the rules of inference can represent very complicated compound propositions.** Warn students that these complicated propositions can be particularly hard to recognize as premises of the rules of inference when they are interspersed throughout a long and complicated proof. They need to be looking for them—hard.
3. Write on the board this dilemma:

   $(A \supset B) \bullet (\sim A \supset B)$
   $A \vee \sim A \quad / \therefore B \vee B$

   Students should recognize this argument as a Constructive Dilemma. But have them compare it with the Constructive Dilemma in variable form:

   $(p \supset q) \bullet (r \supset s)$
   $p \vee r \quad / \therefore q \vee s$

   Make sure students can see that in this instance *p* represents the constant *A*, but *r* represents *~A*, and even more strangely, *q* and *s* both represent the constant *B*. Explain that **in a proof, different variables in a rule of inference can represent the same or similar propositions.** Which is fine, just confusing. Students need to be on the lookout for it and not get flustered when they see it.
4. Write on the board the proof from the end of the last chapter:

1) $F \supset W$		
2) $\sim F \supset R$		
3) $F \vee \sim F$	/ ∴ $W \vee (\sim F \bullet R)$	
4) $\sim F \supset (\sim F \bullet R)$		2 Abs.
5) $(F \supset W) \bullet [\sim F \supset (\sim F \bullet R)]$		1, 4 Conj.
6) $W \vee (\sim F \bullet R)$		5, 3 C.D.
Q.E.D.		

Create this table to determine the values of the variables *p* and *q* in each successive step of the above proof:

Step	Rule	Value of p	Value of q
4	Abs.		
5	Conj.		
6	C.D.		

Have students tell you what the values of p and q are in steps 4, 5, and 6 where the rules of inference represent different propositions in the proof. For example, in step 4, which is an instance of Absorption, p in the rule of inferences represents *~F* in the actual proof. The completed table should look like this:

Step	Rule	Value of p	Value of q
4	Abs.	$\sim F$	R
5	Conj.	$F \supset W$	$\sim F \supset (\sim F \bullet R)$
6	C.D.	F	W

Make sure students can see from this table that **variables can change value from one step to the next within the same proof.**

5. Explain that really this same difficulty occurs in algebra: in one problem the variable x equals 20,000,000, in another −3. Tell students that they need to treat each new step of a proof as a new "problem" in which the variables of the rules of inference can represent something completely different from what they represented in the step before.
6. Reassure students that practice (and they'll get lots of it) is going to help them sort out these difficulties. It will also make them really excellent abstract thinkers. This might not thrill them now, but one day they'll be very grateful.

ASSIGNMENTS

1. Have students complete Exercise 14a and b, and go over it with them. The second part of Exercise 14b is review. You might note that, though a couple of the arguments in Exercise 14b are valid, they cannot yet be proven with only the rules of inference. More rules will be needed (coming soon, in Lesson 16!)
2. Remind students to study for next class's quiz over Lessons 13 and 14.

LESSON 14

RECOGNIZING THE RULES OF INFERENCE

From the examples in the last chapter, it should be evident that recognizing the rules of inference used in proofs is not always easy. The premises and conclusions of the rules can be more complex when used in a proof than when they appear simply as a rule. There are a few reasons for this.

First, the variables in the rules of inference can represent very complicated compound propositions. Here is an example of *modus ponens* with compound propositions:

[(F ⊃ ~C) ∨ (Q ≡ X)] ⊃ (~E ∨ J)
[(F ⊃ ~C) ∨ (Q ≡ X)] / ∴ ~E ∨ J

KEY POINT

The variables in the rules of inference can represent very complicated compound propositions.

You may at first have difficulty recognizing that this follows the pattern

p ⊃ q
p / ∴ q

Such complicated compound propositions are especially difficult to recognize as premises of rules of inference when they appear in the middle of a longer proof.

Second, variables in the rules of inference can represent propositions which are similar (or identical) to those represented by other variables. This occurs for all the rules of inference, but it is perhaps most common with the dilemma. Consider this dilemma:

(A ⊃ B) • (~A ⊃ B)
A ∨ ~A / ∴ B ∨ B

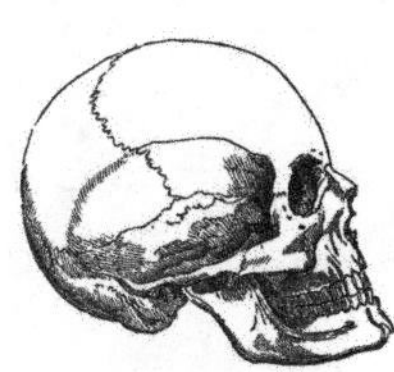

CAUTION

In a proof, different variables in a rule of inference can represent the same or similar propositions.

Compare this with the Constructive Dilemma as it is written in variable form:

(p ⊃ q) • (r ⊃ s)
p ∨ r ∴ q ∨ s

You see that *p* represents A, but *r* represents ~A. Even more oddly, both *q* and s represent the constant B. Such similar representations often occurs in proofs, requiring caution from the student.

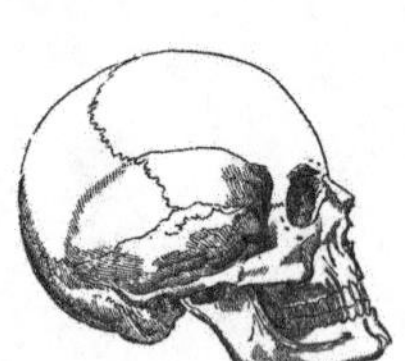

CAUTION

The variables in the rules of inference may represent different propositions in a proof from one step to the next—that's why they're called "variables." Propositions in a proof and variables in a rule of inference are only connected during the current step.

Finally, recognizing the rules of inference can be difficult when the temporary variables you use to simplify complex propositions change value from one step to the next. Consider again the proof from the end of the last chapter:

1) F ⊃ W
2) ~F ⊃ R
3) F ∨ ~F / ∴ W ∨ (~F • R)
4) ~F ⊃ (~F • R) 2 Abs.
5) (F ⊃ W) • [~F ⊃ (~F • R)] 1, 4 Conj.
6) W ∨ (~F • R) 5, 3 C.D.
Q.E.D.

In each successive step, the variables *p* and *q* had the values shown here:

Step	Rule	Value of p	Value of q
4	Abs.	~F	R
5	Conj.	F ⊃ W	~F ⊃ (~F • R)
6	C.D.	F	W

This same difficulty occurs in algebra. In one problem, the general purpose variable *x* may equal 25; in the next problem, *x* might equal -8.717. In the case of proofs you must take each new step as a new problem, in which the variables of the rules of inference can represent something completely different than before.

The best solution to these difficulties is simply practice. Consequently, you will be doing many proofs of validity in the next few chapters. It is the author's belief that such practice will exercise your mind toward abstract thought in a way that almost no other work can.

SUMMARY

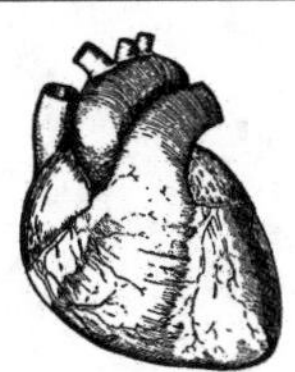

Recognizing the rules of inference in formal proofs can be hindered for the following reasons, among others:

1. Single variables can represent very complicated compound propositions;
2. Variables can represent propositions which are similar to those represented by other variables;
3. Variables can change value from one step to the next within the same proof.

EXERCISE 14a (28 points)

Identify the rule of inference used in each argument. You may abbreviate. (1 each)

1. $A \vee B$
   $\sim A$
   $\therefore B$
   D.S.

2. X
   $X \supset Y$
   $\therefore X \bullet (X \supset Y)$
   Conj

3. $(Q \supset R) \bullet (\sim Q \supset T)$
   $Q \vee \sim Q$
   $\therefore R \vee T$
   C. D.

4. $(C \supset D) \supset E$
   $C \supset D$
   $\therefore E$
   M.P.

5. $\sim U \supset (V \vee X)$
   $(V \vee X) \supset W$
   $\therefore \sim U \supset W$
   H.S.

6. $(F \bullet \sim G) \supset \sim H$
   $\sim\sim H$
   $\therefore \sim(F \bullet \sim G)$
   M.T.

7. $(A \supset B) \bullet (C \supset D)$
   $\therefore A \supset B$
   Simp.

8. $S \vee T$
   $\therefore (S \vee T) \vee R$
   Add.

9. $J \supset \sim K$
   $\therefore J \supset (J \bullet \sim K)$
   Abs.

Give the justification for each step in the following formal proofs of validity.

10. 1) $A \vee B$
    2) $A \supset C$
    3) $\sim C$ / $\therefore B$
    4) $\sim A$ 2, 3 MT.
    5) B 1, 4 DS. (2)

11. 1) $P \supset Q$
    2) R
    3) P / $\therefore R \bullet Q$
    4) Q 1, 3 MP.
    5) $R \bullet Q$ 2, 4 Conj (2)

12. 1) $\sim M \supset N$
    2) $L \supset \sim M$
    3) L / $\therefore L \bullet N$
    4) $L \supset N$ 2, 1 HS.
    5) $L \supset (L \bullet N)$ 4 Abs.
    6) $L \bullet N$ 5, 3 MP. (3)

13. 1) $X \supset Y$
    2) X
    3) $W \supset Z$ / $\therefore Y \vee Z$
    4) $(X \supset Y) \bullet (W \supset Z)$ 1, 3 Conj
    5) $X \vee W$ 2 Add.
    6) $Y \vee Z$ 4, 5 CD. (3)

14. 1) $\sim F \bullet G$
    2) $H \supset F$ / $\therefore \sim H \vee G$
    3) $\sim F$ 1 Simp.
    4) $\sim H$ 2, 3 MT.
    5) $\sim H \vee G$ 4 Add. (3)

15. 1) A
    2) $\sim A$ / $\therefore B$
    3) $A \vee B$ 1 Add.
    4) B 3, 2 DS. (2)

Continued on next page.

16. 1) $D \supset E$
2) $(D \bullet E) \supset (F \bullet G)$
3) D / ∴ F
4) $D \supset (D \bullet E)$ 1 Abs.
5) $D \supset (F \bullet G)$ 4, 2 HS.
6) $F \bullet G$ 5, 3 MP.
7) F 6 Simp. (4)

EXERCISE 14b (24 points)

Determine which rule of inference is used in each argument. (1 each)

1. If I trust God then I will obey Him. Therefore if I trust God then I will both trust and obey Him. Abs.
2. Jesus is Man. Jesus is God. So Jesus is both Man and God. Conj.
3. If Jesus is living then He is my Savior, but if Jesus did not rise from the dead then my faith is futile. Either Jesus is living or He did not rise from the dead. Thus either Jesus is my Savior or my faith is futile. C.D.
4. If God gave the law then it should be obeyed. God gave the law. We conclude that it should be obeyed. M.P.
5. Jesus was either a bad man or He was God. Jesus was not a bad man. Therefore He must have been God. D.S.
6. Ezekiel and Jeremiah were both prophets. Thus Ezekiel was a prophet. Simp.
7. If Ruth was a Gentile then Boaz married a Gentile. If Boaz married a Gentile then King David was part Gentile. So if Ruth was a Gentile then King David was part Gentile. H.S.
8. Judas betrayed Christ. So Judas betrayed Christ or he killed himself. Add.
9. If you love God then you love your neighbor. Judas did not love his neighbor. It is obvious that Judas did not love God. M.T.

Use the shorter truth table method to determine the validity of each argument. (5 each)

10. If God desires every man to be saved, then if God's desires are always fulfilled then every man will be saved. Every man will not be saved. Therefore it is false that both God desires every man to be saved and that God's desires are always fulfilled. (D, F, E)

D ⊃ (F ⊃ E)	~E	∴ ~ (D • F)
T T T F F	T F	F T T T

↑

Valid

Continued on next page.

11. If Mary Magdalene was with the women in the tomb then she would have seen a vision of angels. If she saw a vision of angels then she would have told the apostles about a vision of angels. She told the apostles about a vision of angels. Therefore Mary Magdalene saw a vision of angels and she was with the women in the tomb. (W, V, T)

$W \supset V$	$V \supset T$	T	$\therefore V \bullet W$
F T T	T T T	T	T F F

Invalid

12. If the first-century Christians were taught that Jesus was coming soon, and if the word "coming" means His final coming, and if "soon" means within a century, then the final coming occurred before the end of the second century. The final coming did not occur before the end of the second century. The first-century Christians were taught that Jesus was coming soon. Therefore, either the word "coming" does not mean His final coming, or the word "soon" does not mean within a century. (F, C, S, B)

$[(F \bullet C) \bullet S] \supset B$	$\sim B$	F	$\therefore \sim C \vee \sim S$
T T T T T T F	T F	T	F T F F T
↑			

Valid

TEACHER'S NOTES

QUIZ 7 (LESSONS 13–14)

STUDENT OBJECTIVE

Complete Quiz 7.

TEACHING INSTRUCTIONS

1. Give Quiz 7. Allow 20 minutes. Grade quiz with students.
2. If you have extra time, introduce Lesson 15 to get a head start on next class's material.

INTERMEDIATE LOGIC | Quiz 7

Lessons 13–14 (14 points)

Name ______________________________

1. What is a *rule of inference?* (3) A rule of inference is a valid argument form that can be used to justify steps in a proof.

Problems 2-7: Identify the rule of inference by writing its abbreviation on the line beneath the rule. (1 each)

2. $p \supset q$
   $q \supset r$
   $\therefore\ p \supset r$

   H.S.

3. $p \supset q$
   $\sim q$
   $\therefore\ \sim p$

   M.T.

4. $p \vee q$
   $\sim p$
   $\therefore\ q$

   D.S.

5. $p \bullet q$
   $\therefore\ p$

   Simp.

6. $p \supset q$
   $\therefore\ p \supset (p \bullet q)$

   Abs.

7. p
   $\therefore\ p \vee q$

   Add.

Problems 8-12: : Identify the rule of inference (given here in non-standard form) by writings its abbreviation on the line to the right. Note: They may be the same as those already above. (1 each)

8. $(A \supset R) \bullet (\sim A \supset S)$
   $A \vee \sim A\ \ \therefore R \vee S$ — C.D.

9. M N
   $\therefore M \bullet N$ — Conj.

10. $(F \vee G) \supset T$
    $F \vee G\ \ \therefore T$ — M.P.

11. $H \equiv E$
    $\therefore (H \equiv E) \vee D$ — Add.

12. $(J \supset L) \bullet (\sim J \supset P)$
    $\therefore J \supset L$ — Simp.

TEACHER'S NOTES on LESSON 15

DEVELOPING FORMAL PROOFS

Intermediate Logic, pp. 117–118

STUDENT OBJECTIVES

1. Write formal proofs of validity of up to four additional steps.
2. Complete Exercise 15.

SPECIAL NOTE

Depending on which schedule you're following, you have several days to work through Lesson 15 and its exercises. Try to get through as much of the lesson as you can on the first day, and spend the following classes tying up loose ends and working through both parts of Exercise 15 with students.

TEACHING INSTRUCTIONS

1. Before beginning the lesson do a bit of review: have students remind you what a formal proof of validity is and what the rules of inference are (students can look in their books if they need to). Tell them that they are about to start tackling proofs on their own now. Warn students that for most of them it will probably be pretty difficult at first, but that's okay: what they need is lots of practice and a few hints, both of which you are about to give them.
2. Explain that students may, when faced with a proof, have no idea where to begin. It's possible that they will just sit there and stare at the paper feeling clueless and helpless. Write on the board **Hint #1: Before trying to write your own proofs, make sure you completely understand what a proof is.** Explain to students that if they don't know what it is they are trying to do, they will naturally have no idea how to do it. Have students do their best to explain to you what a formal proof of validity is. Remind them that it is **a way of deducing the given conclusion from the given premises. It does this by working with the premises already given by using the rules of inference. Each step of the proof uses one or two of the previous steps as premises, which follow the pattern of the premises in one of the rules of inference, to come up with the desired conclusion, which follows the pattern of the conclusion of that rule.** Make sure everybody has a least a basic grasp of what a proof is.
3. Tell students that it is also very important to keep the goal in mind when working through a proof. Have them tell you what the goal of the proof is (to deduce the conclusion). Write on the board **Hint #2: Start a proof by comparing the conclusion with the premises**. Tell students that to do this it may be helpful for them to rewrite the premises and conclusions on a piece of scratch paper and ask themselves: "What is the difference between the premises and the conclusion? What do I need to do to these premises to get this conclusion?" Explain that if they are still stuck, students should also consider writing on a piece of scratch paper every possible deduction that can be made

from the premises to find something to use in the proof.

4. Write on the board **Hint #3: Try saying the premises out loud or in your head to help you recognize which rule of inference to use.** Explain that oftentimes all the symbols are a bit dizzying: students may see $\sim K \supset (P \bullet R)$ and $\sim (P \bullet R)$ in the same proof but not see the relationship between them at first; but if they say them out loud ("If not *K* then *P* and *R*" and "Not *P* and *R*") they might *hear* the relationship, stop, and realize that these two premises are the premises of a Modus Tollens argument.
5. Write on the board **Hint #4: Know all the rules of inference well, and especially learn how to use Absorption and Addition.** Explain that for some reason Absorption and Addition are the hardest rules of inference for new logic students to remember. Warn them that if they get stuck in the middle of a proof, they should see if they can use either of these rules. Tell students to make themselves very friendly with all the rules of inference: read them over and over, write them out, come up with schemes for remembering them, etc. Explain that just as an artists has to practice using the tools of his trade, getting familiar with his paints before he can start doing creative things with color and line, logicians have to practice using the tools of their trade—the rules—before they can build proofs quickly.
6. Write on the board **Hint #5: If you are stuck in the middle of a proof, check to see if there are any steps you have not yet used.** Explain that **each step in a proof is usually—though not always—used at some point later in the proof.**
7. Write on the board **Hint #6: If you're stuck, move on to another proof and come back later.** Reassure students that often all they need is a mental break and that when they come back to the problem they may be able to see a different approach.

ASSIGNMENTS

1. Have students complete Exercise 15a and b, and go over it with them.
2. Remind students to study for next class's quiz on Lesson 15.

LESSON 15

DEVELOPING FORMAL PROOFS

KEY POINTS

Before trying to write your own proofs, make sure you completely understand what a proof is.

Start a proof by comparing the conclusion with the premises.

Try saying the premises out loud or in your head to help you recognize which rule of inference to use.

Know all the rules of inference well, especially learn how to use Absorption and Addition.

You have now seen many examples of formal proofs of validity being developed. Hopefully you are getting a good grasp of the approach to writing such proofs. Before you tackle some on your own, here are a few helpful hints that you should consider.

1. When faced with a proof, the beginning student often does not know where to start. He may not have a good understanding of what formal proofs are, let alone know how to write one. If you find yourself in this situation, keep in mind that a formal proof of validity is a way of deducing the conclusion from the premises. It does this by working with the premises using the rules of inference. Each step in a proof uses one or two of the previous steps as premises, which follow the pattern of the premises in one of the rules of inference, to come up with a desired conclusion following the pattern of the conclusion of that rule.

2. Keep the goal in mind: you are trying to deduce the conclusion. Compare the conclusion with the steps you have written down. Rewrite the premises and the conclusion on scratch paper. Ask yourself, "What is different between the premises and the conclusion? What do I need to do to the premises to get the conclusion?" Consider writing down on scratch paper every possible deduction you can make from the premises, trying to find something which can be used in your proof.

3. Try pronouncing each step of the proof which you currently have, either in your head or out loud. This might help you recognize a rule. Read $\sim K \supset (P \cdot R)$ as *If not K then P and R.* Then when you read $\sim(P \cdot R)$ as *Not P and R,* you just might recognize the premises of a *modus tollens* and correctly conclude $\sim\sim K$.

4. For some reason, new logic students often do not see how to use the rules of Absorption or Addition when they are needed. If you

KEY POINT

Each step in a proof is usually used at some step later in the proof.

are stuck, consider whether or not you can use one of these rules. Become familiar with all the rules of inference. Read over them a few times. They are the tools of the art, and a good artist is familiar with all his paints and his brushes because he constantly uses them, trying new things with them, mixing them in different ways, and so on. A good artist practices. In order to write formal proofs of validity quickly, you must write many formal proofs of validity.

5. If you are in the middle of a proof and don't know what to try next, check to see if there are any steps you have not yet used. Usually, though by no means always, every step in a proof is used and used once.

6. Finally, remember that you are exercising your mind. If you get a mental block, go on to a different problem. When you come back to it, you may see a different approach. Your brain is maturing and growing like your muscles mature and grow. Give it time.

SUMMARY

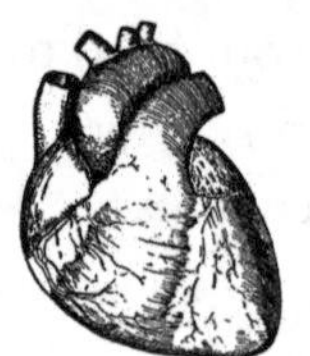

A formal proof of validity is a way of deducing a conclusion from a given set of premises in a series of steps. Each step uses some of the previous steps as premises, and then deduces an intermediate conclusion following a rule. These intermediate conclusions become premises for further conclusions until the final conclusion is reached. Doing this well requires practice and following the suggestions of this lesson.

EXERCISE 15a (67 points)

Provide the justification for each step in the formal proofs of validity.

1. 1) $P \vee Q$
   2) $\sim P$
   3) $Q \supset R \quad / \therefore R$
   4) Q — 1, 2 DS.
   5) R — 3, 4 MP (2)

2. 1) $X \supset Y$
   2) $W \supset Z$
   3) $X \vee W \quad / \therefore Y \vee Z$
   4) $(X \supset Y) \bullet (W \supset Z)$ — 1, 2 Conj.
   5) $Y \vee Z$ — 4, 3 C.D. (2)

3. 1) $\sim A \bullet B$
   2) $C \supset A$
   3) $C \vee D \quad / \therefore D$
   4) $\sim A$ — 1 Simp.
   5) $\sim C$ — 2, 4 MT.
   6) D — 3, 5 DS. (3)

4. 1) $F \supset G$
   2) $H \supset F$
   3) $\sim(H \bullet G) \quad / \therefore \sim H$
   4) $H \supset G$ — 2, 1 H.S.
   5) $H \supset (H \bullet G)$ — 4 Abs.
   6) $\sim H$ — 5, 3 MT. (3)

5. 1) $M \bullet L$
   2) $(M \vee N) \supset P \quad / \therefore P$
   3) M — 1 Simp.
   4) $M \vee N$ — 3 Add.
   5) P — 2, 4 MP. (3)

6. 1) $P \supset Q$
   2) S
   3) $Q \supset R \quad / \therefore (P \supset R) \bullet S$
   4) $P \supset R$ — 1, 3 H.S.
   5) $(P \supset R) \bullet S$ — 4, 2 Conj. (2)

Construct a formal proof for each argument in the number of steps given.

7. 1) $A \bullet B \quad / \therefore A \vee B$
   2) A — 1 Simp.
   3) $A \vee B$ — 2 Add. (4)

8. 1) $C \supset D$
   2) $(C \bullet D) \supset E \quad / \therefore C \supset E$
   3) $C \supset (C \bullet D)$ — 1 Abs.
   4) $C \supset E$ — 3, 2 H.S. (4)

9. 1) $F \vee G$
   2) $\sim F \quad / \therefore G \bullet \sim F$
   3) G — 1, 2 DS.
   4) $G \bullet \sim F$ — 3, 2 Conj. (4)

10. 1) $(H \supset I) \bullet (J \supset K)$
    2) $H \quad / \therefore I \vee K$
    3) $H \vee J$ — 2 Add.
    4) $I \vee K$ — 1, 3 C.D. (4)

Continued on next page.

11. 1) $M \bullet L$
2) $(M \vee N) \supset O$ / $\therefore O$
3) M 1 Simp.
4) $M \vee N$ 3 Add.
5) O 2, 4 MP. (6)

12. 1) $P \supset Q$
2) $Q \supset R$
3) $\sim R$ / $\therefore \sim P$
4) $P \supset R$ 1, 2 HS.
5) $\sim P$ 4, 3 MT. (4)

13. 1) $S \supset T$
2) $S \vee U$
3) $\sim T$ / $\therefore U \bullet \sim S$
4) $\sim S$ 1, 3 MT.
5) U 2, 4 DS.
6) $U \bullet \sim S$ 5, 4 Conj. (6)

14. 1) $X \supset V$
2) $V \supset W$
3) $\sim(X \bullet W)$ / $\therefore \sim X$
4) $X \supset W$ 1, 2 HS.
5) $X \supset (X \bullet W)$ 4 Abs.
6) $\sim X$ 5, 3 MT. (6)

15. 1) $Y \supset Z$
2) $(Y \bullet Z) \supset A$
3) $\sim(Y \bullet A)$ / $\therefore \sim Y$
4) $Y \supset (Y \bullet Z)$ 1 Abs.
5) $Y \supset A$ 4, 2 HS.
6) $Y \supset (Y \bullet A)$ 5 Abs.
7) $\sim Y$ 6, 3 MT. (8)

16. 1) $B \supset C$
2) $D \supset E$
3) $D \vee B$
4) $\sim E$ / $\therefore C$
5) $\sim D$ 2, 4 MT.
6) B 3, 5 DS.
7) C 1, 6 MP. (6)

EXERCISE 15b (15 points)

Examine this argument: "The sons of God were either righteous men or they were angels. If they were righteous then they would have pleased God. They did not please God. Thus they must have been angels." (See Genesis 6:1–5.) (*R*, *A*, *P*)

1. Prove the validity of the above argument using the shorter truth table method. (4)

$R \vee A$	$R \supset P$	$\sim P$	$\therefore A$
F T F	F T F	T F	F

↑ Valid

2. Write the formal proof of validity. (5)

1) $R \vee A$
2) $R \supset P$
3) $\sim P$ / $\therefore A$
4) $\sim R$ 2, 3 M.T.
5) A 1, 4 D.S.

Q.E.D.

3. Rewrite the argument and its proof in ordinary English as a dialogue between two people. Imagine that one is trying to convince the other of the truth of the conclusion by stepping him through the formal proof (without mentioning the justification for each step). (6)

"We can prove that the sons of God were angels."

"How?"

"Well, if the sons of God were righteous men, then they would have pleased God. But we know they didn't please God. So they were not righteous men."

"Yeah, so?"

"The only two options seem to be that they were either righteous men or angels. We have seen that they were not righteous men. We must conclude that they were angels."

"I see."

TEACHER'S NOTES

QUIZ 8 (LESSON 15)

STUDENT OBJECTIVE

Complete Quiz 8.

TEACHING INSTRUCTIONS

1. Give Quiz 8. Allow 20 minutes. Grade quiz with students.
2. If you have extra time, begin reviewing for Test 4.

INTERMEDIATE LOGIC | Quiz 8

Lesson 15 (23 points)

Name ____________________

Problems 1-4: Provide a justification from the rules of inference for each step in the formal proof. (1 point for each step)

1.
1. $A \vee B$
2. $\sim A$
3. $B \supset C \quad / \therefore C$
4. B 1, 2 D.S.
5. C 3, 4 M.P.

2.
1. $D \supset E$
2. $F \supset G$
3. $D \vee F \quad / \therefore E \vee G$
4. $(D \supset E) \bullet (F \supset G)$ 1, 2 Conj.
5. $E \vee G$ 4, 3 C.D.

3.
1. $H \supset J$
2. $K \supset H$
3. $\sim (K \bullet J) \quad / \therefore \sim K$
4. $K \supset J$ 2, 1 H.S.
5. $K \supset (K \bullet J)$ 4 Abs.
6. $\sim K$ 5, 3 M.T.

4.
1. $L \bullet M$
2. $(L \vee N) \supset P \quad / \therefore P \vee Q$
3. L 1 Simp
4. $L \vee N$ 3 Add
5. P 2, 4 M.P.
6. $P \vee Q$ 5 Add.

Problems 5-6: Write a formal proof of validity for the given argument. You may use more steps than indicated. (6 each)

5.
1. $R \supset S$
2. $S \supset (T \supset U)$
3. $U \supset V$
4. $R \quad / \therefore T \supset V$
5. S 1, 4 M.P.
6. $T \supset U$ 2, 5 M.P.
7. $T \supset V$ 6, 3 H.S.

6.
1. $W \supset X$
2. $W \vee Y$
3. $\sim X \quad / \therefore Y \bullet \sim W$
4. $\sim W$ 1, 3 M.T.
5. Y 2, 4 D.S.
6. $Y \cdot \sim W$ 5, 4 Conj.

TEACHER'S NOTES

REVIEW FOR TEST 4 (LESSONS 13–15)

STUDENT OBJECTIVES

Complete the objectives from Lessons 13–15. Objectives are listed at the beginning of each lesson's teacher's notes

TEACHING INSTRUCTIONS

1. To review for the test, choose problems from the Review Questions for Lessons 13–15 on p. 161 of the student text and from the Review Exercises for Lessons 13–15 on pp. 163–165 of the student text for students to work through.
2. If you'd like, give students "Test 4: Form A" from the *Intermediate Logic Test and Quiz Packet* as a practice exam. Go over the answers together.

ASSIGNMENT

Have students study for Test 4.

TEACHER'S NOTES

TEST 4 (LESSONS 13–15)

STUDENT OBJECTIVE

Complete Test 4.

TEACHING INSTRUCTIONS

1. Give students Test 4: Form B from the *Intermediate Logic Test and Quiz Packet.* Allow one hour to complete it.
2. Grade tests. Have them ready to hand back to students within a week.

INTERMEDIATE LOGIC | Test 4, Form A

Lessons 13–15 (50 points)

Name ____________________

1. What is a rule of inference? (3) a valid argument form that can be used to justify a step in a proof

Problems 2-4: Determine the validity of the following arguments using the shorter truth-table method. Remember to write VALID or INVALID. (3, 4, 5))

2. $\sim(p \bullet q)$ $\quad \therefore \sim p$

T TFF FT

INVALID

3. $p \vee q$ $\quad \sim q \bullet r$ $\quad \therefore \sim(p \supset \sim r)$

F(T/F)F TFTT F FTFT

VALID

4. $(p \bullet q) \supset r$ $\quad (q \supset r) \supset (s \supset t)$ $\quad s$ $\quad \therefore p \supset t$

TTT(T/F)F TFF T TFF T TFF

VALID

Problems 5-13: Identify the rule of inference by writing the abbreviation in the blank. (1 each)

5. $p \bullet q$
$\therefore p$
Simp.

6. $p \supset q$
$\therefore p \supset (p \bullet q)$
Abs.

7. p
$\therefore p \vee q$
Add.

8. $p \supset q$
$q \supset r$
$\therefore p \supset r$
H.S.

9. $p \supset q$
$\sim q$
$\therefore \sim p$
M.T.

10. $(p \supset q) \bullet (r \supset s)$
$p \vee r$
$\therefore q \vee s$
C.D.

11. $p \supset q$
p
$\therefore q$
M.P.

12. $p \vee q$
$\sim p$
$\therefore q$
D.S.

13. p
q
$\therefore p \bullet q$
Conj.

Problems 14-17: Provide the justification for each step of the proof. (1 point for each step)

14.
1. $A \supset B$
2. $B \supset C$
3. $D \supset E$
4. $A \vee D$ / $\therefore$ $C \vee E$
5. $A \supset C$ 1, 2 H.S.
6. $(A \supset C) \bullet (D \supset E)$ 5, 3 Conj.
7. $C \vee E$ 6, 4 C.D.

15.
1. $F \supset G$
2. $(F \supset H) \supset (I \vee G)$
3. $(F \bullet G) \supset H$
4. $\sim I$ / $\therefore$ G
5. $F \supset (F \bullet G)$ 1. Abs.
6. $F \supset H$ 5, 3 H.S.
7. $I \vee G$ 2, 6 M.P.
8. G 7, 4 D.S.

16.
1. $J \bullet K$
2. $(J \vee L) \supset M$ / $\therefore$ $J \bullet M$
3. J 1 Simp.
4. $J \vee L$ 3 Add.
5. M 2, 4 M.P.
6. $J \bullet M$ 3, 5 Conj.

17.
1. $N \supset P$
2. $Q \supset N$
3. $\sim (Q \bullet P)$ / $\therefore$ $\sim Q$
4. $Q \supset P$ 2, 1 H.S.
5. $Q \supset (Q \bullet P)$ 4 Abs.
6. $\sim Q$ 5, 3 M.T.

Problems 18-19: Write a formal proof of validity for the given argument. You may use more steps than indicated. (6 each)

18.
1. $(R \supset S) \bullet (T \supset U)$
2. $V \vee \sim S$
3. $\sim V$ / $\therefore$ $\sim R$
4. $R \supset S$ 1 Simp.
5. $\sim S$ 2, 3 D.S.
6. $\sim R$ 4, 5 M.T.

19.
1. $W \supset (X \vee Y)$
2. W
3. $\sim X$ / $\therefore$ $Y \vee Z$
4. $X \vee Y$ 1, 2 M.P.
5. Y 4, 3 D.S.
6. $Y \vee Z$ 5 Add.

INTERMEDIATE LOGIC | Test 4, Form B

Lessons 13–15 (45 points)

Name ______________________________

1. What is a formal proof of validity? (4) a step-by-step deduction of a conclusion from a set of premises, each step being justified by a rule

Problems 2-3: Translate the argument into symbolic form using the given constants, then determine the validity using the shorter truth-table method. Remember to write VALID or INVALID.

2. I am a member of a club only if the club is willing to have me and I join it. I do not join any club if the club is willing to have me. So I am not a member of a club. (**M**, **W**, **J**) (6)

$M \supset (W \bullet J)$	$W \supset \sim J$	$\therefore \sim M$
T T T T T	T T F F	F

VALID

3. The bank bill was constitutional if and only if it was both necessary and proper. The bank bill was proper. Therefore, the bank bill was constitutional. (**C**, **N**, **P**) (5)

$C \equiv (N \bullet P)$	P	$\therefore C$
F T F F T	T	F

INVALID

Problems 4-12: Identify the rule of inference by writing the abbreviation in the blank. (1 each)

4. $p \supset q$
$\therefore p \supset (p \bullet q)$
Abs.

5. p
$\therefore p \vee q$
Add.

6. $p \bullet q$
$\therefore p$
Simp.

7. $p \supset q$
p
$\therefore q$
M.P.

8. $p \supset q$
$q \supset r$
$\therefore p \supset r$
H.S.

9. p
q
$\therefore p \bullet q$
Conj.

10. $(p \supset q) \bullet (r \supset s)$
$p \vee r$
$\therefore q \vee s$
C.D.

11. $p \supset q$
p
$\therefore q$
M.P.

12. $p \vee q$
$\sim p$
$\therefore q$
D.S.

Problems 13-14: Provide the justification for each step of the proof. (1 point for each step)

13.
1. $A \supset B$
2. $(A \bullet B) \supset C$
3. $\sim C$ / $\therefore \sim A \vee D$
4. $A \supset (A \bullet B)$ — 1 Abs.
5. $A \supset C$ — 4, 2 H.S.
6. $\sim A$ — 5, 3 M.T.
7. $\sim A \vee D$ — 6 Add.

14.
1. $E \supset F$
2. $G \supset H$
3. $E \vee G$
4. $\sim F$ / $\therefore H$
5. $(E \supset F) \bullet (G \supset H)$ — 1, 2 Conj.
6. $F \vee H$ — 5, 3 C.D.
7. H — 6, 4 D.S.

Problems 15-17: Write a formal proof of validity for the given argument. You may use more steps than indicated. (4, 4, 6)

15.
1. $J \vee K$
2. $K \supset L$
3. $\sim J$ / $\therefore L$
4. K — 1, 3 D.S.
5. L — 2, 4 M.P.

16.
1. $M \supset N$
2. $\sim M \supset P$
3. $\sim N$ / $\therefore P$
4. $\sim M$ — 1, 3 M.T.
5. P — 2, 4 M.P.

17.
1. $(R \vee S) \supset T$
2. $R \bullet U$ / $\therefore T$
3. R — 2 Simp.
4. $R \vee S$ — 3 Add.
5. T — 1, 4 M.P.

TEACHER'S NOTES on LESSON 16

THE RULES OF REPLACEMENT

Intermediate Logic, pp. 123–126

STUDENT OBJECTIVES

1. Distinguish rules of replacement from rules of inference.
2. Identify the rules of replacement.
3. Identify the rules of replacement in justifications of proofs.
4. Write longer formal proofs of validity using the rules of inference and replacement.
5. Complete Exercise 16.

SPECIAL NOTE

Depending on which schedule you're following, you have a couple of days to work through Lesson 16 and its exercises. Try to get through as much of the lesson as you can in the first class, and spend the second class tying up loose ends and working through both parts of Exercise 16 with students.

TEACHING INSTRUCTIONS

1. Tell students that through doing all these proofs they may have realized that **not every valid argument can be proved using the only the nine rules of inference. We also need ten rules of replacement.** Explain that with the rules of inference and the rules of replacement one can (at least theoretically) prove any valid propositional argument.
2. Remind students that the rules of inference infer (naturally) one proposition from another proposition or other propositions. Have students guess how the rules of *replacement* work. Explain that **the rules of replacement are forms of equivalent statements**; they say that certain propositions are equivalent to other propositions and that therefore these equivalent propositions can replace each other whenever they occur. Point out that in proofs, where the rules of inference often require two steps to work, the rules of replacement only use one.
3. For example, have students turn to Exercise 11 problem #1 in their textbooks (p. 71) where they proved that $\sim(p \bullet q)$ is logically equivalent to $(\sim p \vee \sim q)$. Or in English: the proposition "It if false that both my eyesight is bad and I wear glasses" is equivalent to the proposition "Either my eyesight is not bad or I don't wear glasses." Explain that because these statements are logically equivalent they can replace each other. Tell students that this is the first rule of replacement. Write on the board **#1 De Morgan's Theorem (De M.):** $\sim(p \bullet q) \equiv (\sim p \vee \sim q)$. Explain that there is also a second part to De Morgan's Theorem: $\sim(p \vee q) \equiv (\sim p \bullet \sim q)$. Have students take a moment to do a truth table on their own proving that these two statements are logically equivalent. Remind them that these are two ways of symbolizing "neither *p* nor *q*."

4. Write on the board this argument:

   1) $\sim(P \bullet Q)$ / $\therefore \sim Q \vee \sim P$

   Ask students how they would go about proving this conclusion from this premise. With De Morgan's Theorem fresh in their minds they will probably think to do this:

   2) $\sim P \vee \sim Q$ 1, De M.

   But then they should see that they are stuck. They have no rule that will allow them to switch *P* and *Q* to *Q* and *P*. Explain that you have got that rule for them: write on the board **#2 Commutation (Com.):** $(p \vee q) \equiv (q \vee p)$ **and** $(p \bullet q) \equiv (q \bullet p)$. Explain that this rule is similar to the Commutative Property in algebra, which says that $a + b = b + a$, and $ab = ba$. Tell students that to help them remember the name "Commutation" they can think of two people living in different cities and "commuting" to each other's cities to work.

5. Explain that the third rule of replacement is similar to Commutation; it is called Association, and it basically allows us to move parentheses around in propositions whenever the logical operators are either both disjunction or both conjunction. Write on the board **#3 Association (Assoc.):** $[(p \vee q) \vee r] \equiv [p \vee (q \vee r)]$ **and** $[(p \bullet q) \bullet r] \equiv [p \bullet (q \bullet r)]$. Explain that this rule also has a counterpart in algebra; see if anyone can give you the Associative Property of Equality. It says that $a + (b + c) = (a + b) + c$, and $a(bc) = (ab)c$. Consider warning them not to abbreviate this rule further than "Assoc."

6. Tell students that the fourth rule of replacement also has a counterpart in algebra, the Distributive Property of Equality, which says that $a(b + c) = (ab + ac)$. See if students can figure out from this what the corresponding rule of replacement is (hint: it involves both conjunction and disjunction). Write on the board **#4 Distribution (Dist.)** $[p \bullet (q \vee r)] \equiv [(p \bullet q) \vee (p \bullet r)]$ **and** $[p \vee (q \bullet r)] \equiv [(p \vee q) \bullet (p \vee r)]$. Explain that because these sets of propositions are similar, it's easy to mix up all the conjunctions and disjunctions. The way to keep them straight is to remember that the first conjunction and disjunction (or vice versa) are in the same order on each side of the equivalence sign.

7. Tell students that the next one is an easy one. Write on the board **#5 Double Negation (D.N.):** $\sim\sim p \equiv p$. The negation of a negation of a proposition is equivalent to the proposition. Tell anyone who struggles with this that all they need to do is not not think about ordinary English.

8. Explain that the sixth rule of replacement is the first rule of replacement to start dealing with conditionals. Explain that this rule says that a conditional is equivalent to its contrapositive. Write on the board **#6 Transposition (Trans.):** $(p \supset q) \equiv (\sim q \supset \sim p)$. Students should see that this rule has all the ingredients of Modus Tollens and is saying something very similar: if it's true that if *p* then *q*, it must also be true that if not *q* then not *p*. Tell them to mind their *p*'s and *q*'s. Warn students that in a few minutes they are going to learn the rule of Exportation, and that they are probably going to be tempted to call these rules the rules of Transportation and Exposition instead. Then tell them not to.

9. Explain that you have already discussed the next two rules, just not by name. Write on the board **#7 Material Implication (Impl.):** $(p \supset q) \equiv (\sim p \vee q)$. Explain that this rule is extremely useful because it allows us to switch back and forth between the conditional and the disjunction. For example, it enables us to prove Modus Ponens without using Modus Ponens. Write this argument on the board:

   1) $p \supset q$
   2) p / $\therefore q$

Have students go about solving this, not using using Modus Ponens and (hint) using Implication. The completed proof should look like this:

1) p ⊃ q
2) p   / ∴ q
3) ~p ∨ q   1, Impl.
4) ~~p   2, D.N.
5) q   3, 4 D.S.
Q.E.D.

10. Write on the board **#8 Material Equivalence (Equiv.):** ***(p ≡ q) ≡ [(p ⊃ q) • (q ⊃ p)]*** **and** ***(p ≡ q) ≡ [(p • q) ∨ (~p • ~q)].*** Remind students that they saw the first equivalence when they defined the biconditional. Have them walk you through a truth table for the second equivalence. The completed table should look like this:

p ≡ q	(p • q) ∨ (~p • ~q)
T	T T F FF
F	F F F FT
F	F F T FF
T	F T T TT
↑	↑

Point out that the biconditional $p \equiv q$ is true either when p and q are both true or when p and q are both false. Help them see the connection between what you just said and the rule that says $(p \equiv q) \equiv [(p \bullet q) \vee (\sim p \bullet \sim q)]$.

11. Write on the board **#9 Exportation (Exp.):** ***[(p • q) ⊃ r] ≡ [p ⊃ (q ⊃ r)].*** Give an example for them (e.g., "If I walk and chew gum, then I fall down.") Have them come up with other examples. Have students use this rule to walk you through building a proof for this argument (from Problem 10 in Exercise 14b):

1) D ⊃ (F ⊃ E)
2) ~E   / ∴ ~(D • F)

The completed argument should look like this:

1) D ⊃ (F ⊃ E)
2) ~E   / ∴ ~(D • F)
3). (D • F) ⊃ E   1 Exp.
4) ~(D • F)   3, 2 M.T.
Q.E.D.

12. Explain that the tenth rule of replacement is the strangest one. Write on the board **#10 Tautology (Taut.):** ***p ≡ (p ∨ p)*** **and** ***p ≡ (p • p).*** In other words, a proposition is equivalent to the disjunction or conjunction of itself. Students may wonder when one would ever need to use a Tautology; whether or not they are wondering it, have them build a proof for this argument from Exercise 12, problem 4:

1) (L ⊃ ~R) • (C ⊃ ~R)
2) L ∨ C / ∴~R

The completed proof should look like this:

1) (L ⊃ ~R) • (C ⊃ ~R)
2) L ∨ C / ∴~R
3) ~R ∨ ~R   1, 2 C.D.
4) ~R   3, Taut.
Q.E.D.

13. Make sure students understand that the rules of replacement, unlike the rules of inference, allow equivalent propositions to replace each other *wherever they occur*, even in the middle of a larger propositions. Then tell them that the rules of replacement work from right to left as well as left to right.

14. Remind students that all the rules of replacement are listed on p. 126 of their textbooks as well as in Appendix B. Tell them that they need to start working on memorizing them—now.

ASSIGNMENTS

1. Have students complete Exercise 16, and go over it with them.
2. Remind students to study for next class's quiz over Lesson 16.

LESSON 16

THE RULES OF REPLACEMENT

Now that you have written a number of proofs, you may have recognized that not every valid argument can be proved using only the nine rules of inference. Some more tools, namely **the rules of replacement**, need to be added to your toolbox. With these and the rules of inference, any valid argument can (theoretically, at least) be proved.

KEY POINT

Not every argument can be proven using only the rules of inference; you also need the ten rules of replacement.

The rules of replacement say that certain propositions are equivalent to other propositions and may replace them wherever they occur. For example, in Exercise 11 you proved that $\sim(p \bullet q)$ is logically equivalent to $(\sim p \lor \sim q)$. This says, for instance, that the proposition "It is false that both amoebae and fungi are animals" is equivalent to the proposition "Either an amoeba is not an animal or a fungus is not an animal." This is **De Morgan's Theorem** (De M.), named after the English logician Augustus De Morgan (1806–1871). De Morgan's Theorem also says that $\sim(p \lor q)$ is equivalent to $(\sim p \bullet \sim q)$. You may prove this equivalence on your own.

DEFINITION

The *rules of replacement* are forms of equivalent statements.

The second rule of replacement is **Commutation** (Com.), which simply says that $(p \lor q)$ is equivalent to $(q \lor p)$, and that $(p \bullet q)$ is equivalent to $(q \bullet p)$. These are obvious, but very useful. You could not easily write this formal proof without the rule of Commutation:

1)	$\sim(P \bullet Q)$ /	$\therefore \sim Q \lor \sim P$
2)	$\sim(Q \bullet P)$	1 Com.
3)	$\sim Q \lor \sim P$	2 De M.

Q.E.D.

This rule is similar to the Commutative Property in algebra, which says that $a + b = b + a$, and $ab = ba$. To help remember the name, think of two people who live in two different cities, each "commuting" to the other person's city to work.

The third rule of replacement is the rule of **Association** (Assoc.), which basically allows us to move parentheses around whenever the logical operators are either both disjunction or conjunction. In symbolic form this rule says $[(p \vee q) \vee r] \equiv [p \vee (q \vee r)]$ and $[(p \bullet q) \bullet r] \equiv [p \bullet (q \bullet r)]$. Association also has a counterpart in algebra, the Associative Property of Equality, which says that $a + (b + c) = (a + b) + c$, and $a(bc) = (ab)c$.

The fourth rule of replacement also has a counterpart in algebra, the Distributive Property of Equality, which says $a(b + c) = (ab + ac)$. This is the rule of **Distribution** (Dist.), which grants the equivalence of these pairs of propositions:

$$[p \bullet (q \vee r)] \equiv [(p \bullet q) \vee (p \bullet r)]$$
$$[p \vee (q \bullet r)] \equiv [(p \vee q) \bullet (p \vee r)]$$
$$\uparrow \quad \uparrow \qquad\qquad \uparrow \quad \uparrow$$

Because these sets of propositions are so similar, students often confuse them. The way to keep the conjunctions and disjunctions straight is to note that the first conjunction and disjunction (or vice versa) are in the same order on each side of the equivalence sign, as the arrows show.

The fifth rule is the rule of **Double Negation** (D.N.), which says that the negation of a negation of a proposition is equivalent to that proposition, or $\sim\sim p \equiv p$. This was proved in the lesson on the Biconditional.

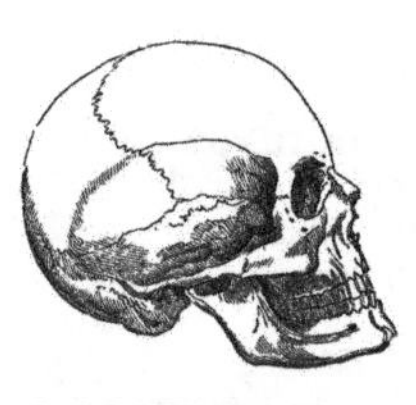

CAUTION

Two rules of replacement are named *Transposition* and *Exportation*. They are not named *Transportation* and *Exposition*.

The sixth rule of replacement is the rule of **Transposition** (Trans.). This rule says that a conditional is equivalent to its contrapositive, or symbolically, $(p \supset q) \equiv (\sim q \supset \sim p)$. This rule was introduced in Lesson 4. Notice that this rule is not the rule of transpo*rtation,* but the rule of transpo*sition.* Its similarity to *modus tollens* should be evident.

The next two rules have been mentioned before (though not by name) in the definition of their logical operators. They are the rules of **Material Implication** (Impl.) and **Material Equivalence** (Equiv.). The rule of Material Implication states that $(p \supset q) \equiv (\sim p \vee q)$. This is a very useful rule, allowing us to switch between the conditional and the disjunction when necessary. For example, it allows us to prove *modus ponens* without using *modus ponens*:

1) $p \supset q$
2) p / $\therefore q$
3) $\sim p \vee q$ 1 Impl.
4) $\sim\sim p$ 2 D.N.
5) q 3, 4 D.S.
Q.E.D.

Material Equivalence grants that the following pairs of propositions are logically equivalent:

$$(p \equiv q) \equiv [(p \supset q) \bullet (q \supset p)]$$
$$(p \equiv q) \equiv [(p \bullet q) \vee (\sim p \bullet \sim q)]$$

We saw the first of these when we defined the biconditional. The second equivalence is shown here in the longer truth table format (with the truth-value column for *p* and *q* left out for clarity):

$p \equiv q$	$(p \bullet q)$	$\vee$	$(\sim p$	$\bullet$	$\sim q)$
T	T	T	F	F	F
F	F	F	F	F	T
F	F	F	T	F	F
T	F	T	T	T	T
↑		↑			

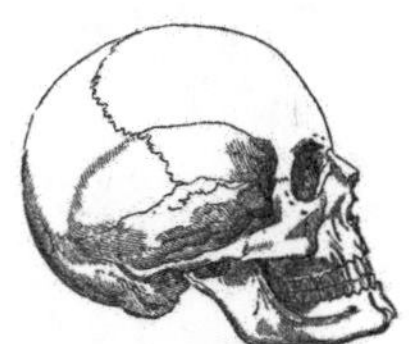

CAUTION

Notice that rules of replacement work in both directions across the equivalence sign, as in step 3 of the proof to the left. This is because if $p \equiv q$, then $q \equiv p$.

The ninth rule is **Exportation** (Exp.): $[(p \bullet q) \supset r] \equiv [p \supset (q \supset r)]$. This rule was proved when we introduced the shorter truth table for equivalence. Here is an example from Problem 10 in Exercise 14b:

1) $D \supset (F \supset E)$
2) $\sim E$ / $\therefore \sim(D \bullet F)$
3) $(D \bullet F) \supset E$ 1 Exp.
4) $\sim(D \bullet F)$ 3, 2 M.T.
Q.E.D.

The tenth and last rule of replacement is usually considered the oddest of the bunch. It is the rule of **Tautology** (Taut.). It says a

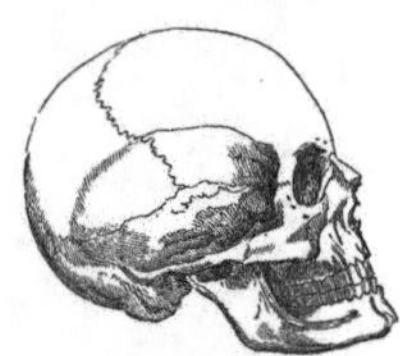

CAUTION

The rules of replacement allow one proposition to replace an equivalent proposition, even in the middle of a longer compound proposition. Rules of inference cannot be used this way.

proposition is equivalent to the disjunction or conjunction of itself. Written symbolically, the rule says $p \equiv (p \vee p)$ and $p \equiv (p \bullet p)$.

In anticipation of the question, "When will we ever need to use that?" consider the proof of Problem 4 in Exercise 12:

1)	$(L \supset \sim R) \bullet (C \supset \sim R)$	
2)	$L \vee C$ / $\therefore \sim R$	
3)	$\sim R \vee \sim R$	1, 2 C.D.
4)	$\sim R$	3 Taut.
Q.E.D.		

The rules of replacement, unlike the rules of inference, allow equivalent propositions to replace each other wherever they occur, even if it is in the middle of a larger proposition. This also means that the rules of replacement work from right to left as well as left to right.

SUMMARY

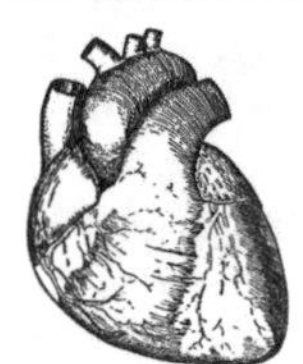

The following are the rules of replacement (listed with the rules of inference in Appendix B):

De Morgan's Theorems (De M.)	$\sim(p \bullet q) \equiv (\sim p \vee \sim q)$ $\sim(p \vee q) \equiv (\sim p \bullet \sim q)$
Commutation (Com.)	$(p \vee q) \equiv (q \vee p)$ $(p \bullet q) \equiv (q \bullet p)$
Association (Assoc.)	$[p \vee (q \vee r)] \equiv [(p \vee q) \vee r]$ $[p \bullet (q \bullet r)] \equiv [(p \bullet q) \bullet r]$
Distribution (Dist.)	$[p \bullet (q \vee r)] \equiv [(p \bullet q) \vee (p \bullet r)]$ $[p \vee (q \bullet r)] \equiv [(p \vee q) \bullet (p \vee r)]$
Double Negation (D.N.)	$p \equiv \sim\sim p$
Transposition (Trans.)	$(p \supset q) \equiv (\sim q \supset \sim p)$
Material Implication (Impl.)	$(p \supset q) \equiv (\sim p \vee q)$
Material Equivalence (Equiv.)	$(p \equiv q) \equiv [(p \supset q) \bullet (q \supset p)]$ $(p \equiv q) \equiv [(p \bullet q) \vee (\sim p \bullet \sim q)]$
Exportation (Exp.)	$[(p \bullet q) \supset r] \equiv [p \supset (q \supset r)]$
Tautology (Taut.)	$p \equiv (p \vee p)$ $p \equiv (p \bullet p)$

EXERCISE 16 (46 points)

Identify the rule of replacement used. Use the abbreviations. (1 each)

1. $A \equiv (A \vee A)$
   Taut.

2. $(M \bullet N) \equiv {\sim}{\sim}(M \bullet N)$
   D.N.

3. $[(R \supset S) \supset T] \equiv [{\sim}(R \supset S) \vee T]$
   Impl.

4. $(X \bullet Y) \equiv (Y \bullet X)$
   Com.

5. ${\sim}(P \bullet Q) \equiv ({\sim}P \vee {\sim}Q)$
   DeM.

6. $(F \supset G) \equiv ({\sim}G \supset {\sim}F)$
   Trans.

7. $[(B \vee C) \vee D] \equiv [B \vee (C \vee D)]$
   Assoc.

8. $[J \supset (K \supset L)] \equiv [(J \bullet K) \supset L]$
   Exp.

9. $[X \vee (Y \bullet Z)] \equiv [(X \vee Y) \bullet (X \vee Z)]$
   Dist.

10. $(W \equiv V) \equiv [(W \supset V) \bullet (V \supset W)]$
    Equiv.

Justify each step for the following proofs of validity.

11.
1) $P \supset Q$
2) $R \supset {\sim}Q$ / $\therefore P \supset {\sim}R$
3) ${\sim}{\sim}Q \supset {\sim}R$ — 2 Trans.
4) $Q \supset {\sim}R$ — 3 D.N.
5) $P \supset {\sim}R$ — 1, 4 H.S. (3)

12.
1) $(P \bullet Q) \supset R$
2) $(P \supset R) \supset S$ / $\therefore Q \supset S$
3) $(Q \bullet P) \supset R$ — 1 Com.
4) $Q \supset (P \supset R)$ — 3 Exp.
5) $Q \supset S$ — 4, 2 H.S. (3)

13.
1) $(P \bullet Q) \supset R$
2) ${\sim}R$ / $\therefore P \supset {\sim}Q$
3) ${\sim}(P \bullet Q)$ — 1, 2 M.T.
4) ${\sim}P \vee {\sim}Q$ — 3 DeM.
5) $P \supset {\sim}Q$ — 4 Impl. (3)

14.
1) $P \supset {\sim}Q$ / $\therefore {\sim}Q \vee (Q \bullet {\sim}P)$
2) ${\sim}{\sim}Q \supset {\sim}P$ — 1 Trans.
3) $Q \supset {\sim}P$ — 2 D.N.
4) $Q \supset (Q \bullet {\sim}P)$ — 3 Abs.
5) ${\sim}Q \vee (Q \bullet {\sim}P)$ — 4 Impl. (4)

15.
1) $(P \vee Q) \supset (R \bullet S)$
2) ${\sim}R$ / $\therefore {\sim}P$
3) ${\sim}R \vee {\sim}S$ — 2 Add.
4) ${\sim}(R \bullet S)$ — 3 DeM.
5) ${\sim}(P \vee Q)$ — 1, 4 M.T.
6) ${\sim}P \bullet {\sim}Q$ — 5 DeM.
7) ${\sim}P$ — 6 Simp. (5)

16.
1) $(P \vee Q) \supset [R \bullet (S \bullet T)]$
2) Q / $\therefore R \bullet S$
3) $Q \vee P$ — 2 Add.
4) $P \vee Q$ — 3 Com.
5) $R \bullet (S \bullet T)$ — 1, 4 M.P.
6) $(R \bullet S) \bullet T$ — 5 Assoc.
7) $R \bullet S$ — 6 Simp. (5)

Continued on next page.

17. 1) $(P \vee {\sim}Q) \vee R$
2) ${\sim}P \vee (Q \bullet {\sim}P)$ $\;/ \therefore Q \supset R$
3) $({\sim}P \vee Q) \bullet ({\sim}P \vee {\sim}P)$ — 2 Dist.
4) $({\sim}P \vee {\sim}P) \bullet ({\sim}P \vee Q)$ — 3 Com.
5) ${\sim}P \vee {\sim}P$ — 4 Simp.
6) ${\sim}P$ — 5 Taut.
7) $P \vee ({\sim}Q \vee R)$ — 1 Assoc.
8) ${\sim}Q \vee R$ — 7, 6 D.S.
9) $Q \supset R$ — 8 Impl. (7)

18. 1) $P \bullet (Q \vee R)$
2) $P \supset [Q \supset (S \bullet T)]$
3) $(P \bullet R) \supset {\sim}(S \vee T)$ $\;/ \therefore S \equiv T$
4) $(P \bullet Q) \supset (S \bullet T)$ — 2 Exp
5) $(P \bullet R) \supset ({\sim}S \bullet {\sim}T)$ — 3 DeM.
6) $[(P \bullet Q) \supset (S \bullet T)] \bullet [(P \bullet R) \supset ({\sim}S \bullet {\sim}T)]$ — 4, 5 Conj.
7) $(P \bullet Q) \vee (P \bullet R)$ — 1 Dist.
8) $(S \bullet T) \vee ({\sim}S \bullet {\sim}T)$ — 6, 7 C.D.
9) $S \equiv T$ — 8 Equiv. (6)

TEACHER'S NOTES

QUIZ 9 (LESSON 16)

STUDENT OBJECTIVE

Complete Quiz 9.

TEACHING INSTRUCTIONS

1. Give Quiz 9. Allow 20 minutes. Grade quiz with students.
2. If you have extra time, introduce Lesson 17 to get a head start on next class's material.

INTERMEDIATE LOGIC | Quiz 9

Lesson 16 (19 points)

Name__________________________________

Problems 1-10: Identify the rule of replacement. You may use the standard abbreviations. (1 each)

1. $p \equiv (p \vee p)$ Taut.
2. $[p \bullet (q \bullet r)] \equiv [(p \bullet q) \bullet r]$ Assoc.
3. $[\sim (p \bullet q)] \equiv (\sim p \vee \sim q)$ De M.
4. $p \equiv \sim\sim p$ D.N.
5. $[(p \bullet q) \supset r] \equiv [p \supset (q \supset r)]$ Exp.
6. $(p \supset q) \equiv (\sim q \supset \sim p)$ Trans.
7. $[p \vee (q \bullet r)] \equiv [(p \vee q) \bullet (p \vee r)]$ Dist.
8. $(p \supset q) \equiv (\sim p \vee q)$ Impl.
9. $(p \equiv q) \equiv [(p \supset q) \bullet (q \supset p)]$ Equiv.
10. $(p \vee q) \equiv (q \vee p)$ Com.

Problems 11-12: Justify each step in the proof using the rules of inference or replacement. (1 point for each step)

11.
1. $A \supset B$
2. $\sim A \supset B$ / $\therefore$ B
3. $\sim B \supset \sim A$ 1 Trans.
4. $\sim B \supset B$ 3, 2 H.S.
5. $\sim\sim B \vee B$ 4 Impl.
6. $B \vee B$ 5 D.N.
7. B 6 Taut.

12.
1. $\sim (C \vee D)$
2. E / $\therefore$ $(\sim D \bullet E) \bullet \sim C$
3. $\sim C \bullet \sim D$ 1 De M.
4. $(\sim C \bullet \sim D) \bullet E$ 3, 2 Conj.
5. $\sim C \bullet (\sim D \bullet E)$ 4 Assoc.
6. $(\sim D \bullet E) \bullet \sim C$ 5 Com.

TEACHER'S NOTES on LESSON 17

PRACTICE WITH PROOFS

Intermediate Logic, pp. 129–131

STUDENT OBJECTIVES

1. Write longer formal proofs of validity using the rules of inference and replacement.
2. Translate valid arguments into symbolic form and write proofs of them.
3. Complete Exercises 17a and 17b.

SPECIAL NOTE

Depending on which schedule you're following, you have several days to work through Lesson 17 and its exercises. Try to get through as much of the lesson as you can on the first day, and spend the other days working through both parts of Exercise 17 with students. A good way to divide the exercises up would be: Exercise 17a 1–6, Exercise 17a 7–9, Exercise 17a 10–14, and Exercise 17b.

TEACHING INSTRUCTIONS

1. Explain to students that adding ten more rules with which they can solve proofs has, naturally, complicated things a bit. They can solve many more proofs now, but the proofs are longer and harder. Tell students that the proofs have gotten more complicated the way that math gets more complicated when you learn the rules of calculus or art gets more complicated when you learn how to use paint as well as pencil. Logic is more challenging now, but also much more rewarding. Tell students that if they like solving puzzles, they're going to like solving formal proofs, because proofs are very much like puzzles and they are just as satisfying to solve.
2. Tell students that in order to feel the satisfaction of solving proofs they of course have to be able to *solve* the proofs and not simply spend hours staring at them, growling, and throwing their logic books against the walls (some of them may already have spent a lot of time doing this). Explain that they are going to spend the next few days practicing proofs and that in the lesson today they will learn some more hints for solving them.
3. Give students this argument: "I either read my Bible and pray or I do not grow in the Lord. If I read my Bible then I will be convicted of sin. Therefore if I am to grow in the Lord then I will be convicted of sin." Have students walk you through symbolizing this and putting it into proof form, using the constants, *R*, *P*, *G*, and *C*. The initial argument should look like this:

   1. $(R \bullet P) \lor {\sim}G$
   2. $R \supset C$ / $\therefore G \supset C$

4. Looks complicated, right? Ask students what the first thing is that they should do (besides hyperventilating for a few minutes). Tell them that they may be tempted to start haphazardly doing things to the premises to see if they happen upon the right conclusion, but that they should resist this temptation. Instead they should **first look at the conclusion and ask "How can I get that conclusion from those premises?"**

Explain that in fact **they might find it helpful to work a proof backwards, or simultaneously forward and backward from the conclusion, trying to get them to match somewhere in the middle.** Whatever they do, they need to make sure that they keep the conclusion they are seeking in the front of their minds.

5. Have students look at the conclusion $G \supset C$. First have them tell you where in the premises they are going to get each of the constants from (the G will be from the first premise and the C from the second). But how will they get the conditional? **Explain that when solving difficult proofs, students should look at the conclusion, compare it with the conclusion in the rules of inference and replacement, and figure out how to get the premises of those rules from the premises available in the proof.** Ask students what rules (of inference or replacement) have a simple conditional as the conclusion. They should come up with Hypothetical Syllogism and Material Implication. Have them assume that they will be using Hypothetical Syllogism; looking at the conclusion and the second premise, what do they need to get to be able to use H.S. with the second premise to get the conclusion? They should see that they need the premise $G \supset R$. Explain that that is what they need to try to get from the *first* premise.

6. Now have them look at the first premise. Ask how they can get a conditional like $G \supset R$ from a disjunction like $(R \bullet P) \vee {\sim}G$? Have them look through their rules for one that translates disjunctions into conditionals. They should see that Material Implication fits the bill, since it says that $({\sim}p \vee q) \equiv (p \supset q)$. Ask students if you should use Material Implication right away or if there is something else you need to do first. They should see that $(R \bullet P) \vee {\sim}G$ is in the wrong order and needs to be reversed by Commutation. Add step 3 to the proof on the board:

   3) ~G ∨ (R • P) 1 Com.

7. Ask students if it is now time to use Material Implication. Make sure students see that if they used it now they would get $G \supset (R \bullet P)$ which is not what they want. Since they want $G \supset R$, they need to somehow drop the constant P. What rule would allow them to do that? Explain that the only rule that drops constants is Simplification, and that's a problem, because we can't simplify within propositions. Have students looks for the form $p \vee (q \bullet r)$ in the premises of the rules. They should see that Distribution has this premise. Explain that Distribution is exactly what they need, since it will break apart R and P so that P can be simplified away. The next two steps should look like this:

   4) (~G ∨ R) • (~G ∨P) 3 Dist.
   5) ~G ∨ R 4 Simp.

8. Students should see that ${\sim}G \vee R$ is exactly what they need. They can use Material Implication on it to get the $G \supset R$ they were looking for. And they can use $G \supset R$ to get $G \supset C$. The last two steps of the proof should look like this:

   6) G ⊃ R 5 Impl.
   7) G ⊃ C 6,2 H.S.
   Q.E.D.

9. Make sure students see that the key to solving this proof was being able to see that they could translate between a disjunction and conditional using Material Implication. De Morgan's Theorem translates between conjunctions and disjunctions. Explain that **students need to familiarize themselves with Material Implication and De Morgan's Theorem, since so many rules of inference and replacement use conjunctions and disjunctions but not conditionals**. They should repeat Impl. and De M. before they go to bed every night. They should be saying them in their sleep.

10. Write on the board this argument:

   1) A ⊃ (B • C)
   2) (B ∨ C) ⊃ D / ∴ A ⊃ D

Form of Conclusion:	Consider Trying This:
1. $p \supset q$	Use H.S., trying to get the consequent of one conditional to match the antecedent of the other, or use Impl., translating between disjunction and conditional.
2. $p \bullet q$	Use Conj., deducing both conjuncts from the premises.
3. $p \vee q$	Either deduce one of the disjuncts from the premises and use Add. to get the other, or use DeM, C.D., or Impl., all of which have disjunctions as conclusions.
4. Constant in conclusion not in premises.	Use the rule of Addition somewhere in the proof to add that new constant.
5. Conditional in conclusion not in premises.	Use the rule of Material Implication somewhere in the proof to translate between and disjunction and a conditional.

Make sure students see that this proof, which they will solve in the exercises, is going to center around the use of the Hypothetical Syllogism. Explain that in most arguments built around H.S. where the consequent of one conditional is worded differently from the antecedent of the other, most of the proof is spent simply getting the consequent of the first to match the antecedent of the second. Explain that this particular proof will take seven steps to solve, and that six of those steps will be making the $B \bullet C$ match the $B \vee C$.

11. Have students turn to p. 131 of their textbooks and look at the table of hints for solving formal proofs. Explain that this is **a table of certain standard strategies that they can use to solve proofs with specific types of conclusions**. Walk them through it and make sure they understand each one. The table is reproduced above.

12. Reassure students that while this all may seem overwhelming right now, with practice it will become second nature and they'll start to do these things without even thinking about them. Also remind them that **although being as brief as possible in proofs is great, there are often many ways to solve a proof, and sometimes a longer method works just as well**.

13. Tell the students that Exercise 17a starts with the more basic proofs, and then the later proofs build on these. For example, the conclusion of problem 5, like problem 1, has a new constant in the antecedent of the conditional, and so the proof of problem 5 starts like the proof of problem 1. There are also similarities between the proof of problem 9 and the proofs of problems 3 and 4; problem 10 starts like problem 1and ends like problem 3. Feel free to give hints to struggling students.

ASSIGNMENTS

1. Have students complete Exercise 17a and b, and go over it with them.
2. Remind students to study for next class's quiz on Lesson 17.

LESSON 17

PRACTICE WITH PROOFS

Many proofs can be solved with nineteen rules that couldn't be solved with just nine. However, ten more rules do complicate things a bit. Once you learn the rules of calculus you can do more than you could without them, but the problems get more difficult. Having learned to draw with pencil, learning to paint takes more practice. But paints bring in a new beauty that was not possible with pencil alone. Once learned, painting, solving calculus, and solving formal proofs can be an enjoyable challenge. In fact, solving formal proofs is very much like solving puzzles, and can give the same kind of satisfaction.

A similar satisfaction comes in knowing that your reasoning skills are improving. Gaining those skills requires training through guided practice. To assist that training, we will consider some more helpful hints along with more examples of solving proofs. Imagine that you have to prove this argument: "I either read my Bible and pray or I do not grow in the Lord. If I read my Bible then I will be convicted of sin. Therefore if I am to grow in the Lord then I will be convicted of sin." This could be symbolized as such:

1) $(R \bullet P) \vee \sim G$
2) $R \supset C$ / $\therefore G \supset C$

KEY POINT

You might find it helpful to work a proof backwards, or simultaneously forward from the premises and backward from the conclusion, trying to get them to match somewhere in the middle.

What approach can I take to solving this proof? First, I look at the conclusion and ask, "How can I get that conclusion from those premises?" Well, the constants must come from somewhere. I must get the G from the first premise and the C from the second, since that is where they appear. The conditional must also come from somewhere. If a conditional is in the conclusion like it is here, I will most likely need to use either Hypothetical Syllogism or Material Implication, since these are the only two rules with a simple conditional as a conclusion. Comparing the conclusion with the second premise, I see that if I can get $G \supset R$, then I could use Hypothetical Syllogism with that second premise to get the conclusion. So I must get $G \supset R$ from the first premise.

The first premise is a disjunction. How do I get a conditional like $G \supset R$ from a disjunction like $(R \bullet P) \vee {\sim}G$? Well, looking through the rules I see that Material Implication translates disjunctions into conditionals, because $({\sim}p \vee q) \equiv (p \supset q)$. I first need to put the disjunction in the right order using Commutation, as follows:

3) $\sim G \vee (R \bullet P)$ 1 Com.

If I try Material Implication now, I will get $G \supset (R \bullet P)$. But I need $G \supset R$, so how can I drop the P? The only rule that drops constants is Simplification, and I cannot simplify within a proposition. But I note that I have a proposition of the form $p \vee (q \bullet r)$, so I can use Distribution. Doing so will then allow me to use Simplification, as follows:

4) $({\sim}G \vee R) \bullet ({\sim}G \vee P)$ 3 Dist.
5) $\sim G \vee R$ 4 Simp.

Again, notice that in order to realize that I could use Simplification, I had to think of the entire proposition $({\sim}G \vee R) \bullet ({\sim}G \vee P)$ as $p \bullet q$.

The disjunction ${\sim}G \vee R$ translates into the $G \supset R$ conditional I wanted, which will allow me to finish the proof.

KEY POINT

Because more rules of inference and replacement are written using conjunctions and disjunctions, you should make sure you are very familiar with the rules of Material Implication and De Morgan's Theorems.

6) $G \supset R$ 5 Impl.
7) $G \supset C$ 6, 2 H.S.
Q.E.D.

This proof, like many others, used Material Implication to translate between a conditional and a disjunction. De Morgan's Theorems likewise allow us to translate between conjunctions and disjunctions. Because more rules of inference and replacement are written using conjunctions and disjunctions, you should make sure you are very familiar with the rules of Material Implication and De Morgan's Theorems. You will need them.

With arguments built around a Hypothetical Syllogism where the consequent of the one conditional is worded differently from the antecedent of the other, much of the proof is simply getting the consequent of the first to match the antecedent of the second, as in this argument:

1) $A \supset (B \cdot C)$
2) $(B \vee C) \supset D$ / $\therefore A \supset D$

The solving of this proof requires seven more steps, all but the last step making the *(B • C)* match the *(B ∨ C)*. You will solve this in the exercise.

Before you go on to the exercise, however, here are some final hints for solving formal proofs:

Form of Conclusion	**Consider trying this:**
1) $p \supset q$	Use H.S., trying to get the consequent of one conditional to match the antecedent of the other, or use Impl., translating between disjunction and conditional.
2) $p \cdot q$	Use Conj., deducing both conjuncts from the premises.
3) $p \vee q$	Either deduce one of the disjuncts from the premises and use Add. to get the other, or use DeM, C.D. or Impl., all of which have disjunctions as conclusions.
4) Constant in conclusion, not in premises.	Use the rule of Addition somewhere in the proof to add that new constant.
5) Conditional in conclusion, not in premises.	Use the rule of Material Implication somewhere in the proof to translate between a disjunction and a conditional.

SUMMARY

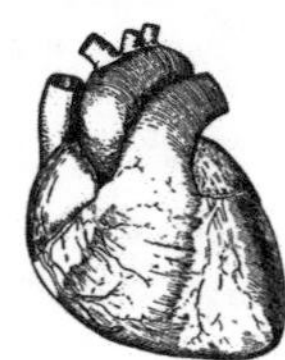

When solving difficult proofs, look at the conclusion, compare it with the conclusions in the rules of inference and replacement, and figure out how to get the premises of those rules from the premises available in the proof. Keep in mind that you have both the premises and the conclusion to work with. You might find it helpful to work forward from the premises and backward from the conclusion, trying to get them to match somewhere in the middle. Finally, remember that, though brevity is an admirable goal, there are usually many ways to solve a proof, and a longer method may be perfectly acceptable.

EXERCISE 17a (128 points)

Write a formal proof of validity for each argument.

1. 1) A / ∴ B⊃A
   2) A∨~B — 1 Add.
   3) ~B∨A — 2 Com.
   4) B⊃A — 3 Impl. (6)

2. 1) C⊃(D⊃E) / ∴ D⊃(C⊃E)
   2) (C•D)⊃E — 1 Exp.
   3) (D•C)⊃E — 2 Com.
   4) D⊃(C⊃E) — 3 Exp. (6)

3. 1) F⊃(G•H) / ∴ F⊃G
   2) ~F∨(G•H) — 1 Impl.
   3) (~F∨G)•(~F∨H) — 2 Dist.
   4) ~F∨G — 3 Simp.
   5) F⊃G — 4 Impl. (8)

4. 1) I⊃J / ∴ I⊃(J∨K)
   2) ~I∨J — 1 Impl.
   3) (~I∨J)∨K — 2 Add.
   4) ~I∨(J∨K) — 3 Assoc.
   5) I⊃(J∨K) — 4 Impl. (8)

5. 1) L⊃N / ∴ (L•M)⊃N
   2) (L⊃N)∨~M — 1 Add.
   3) ~M∨(L⊃N) — 2 Com.
   4) M⊃(L⊃N) — 3 Impl.
   5) (M•L)⊃N — 4 Exp.
   6) (L•M)⊃N — 5 Com. (10)

6. 1) P⊃Q
   2) ~Q / ∴ P≡Q
   3) ~Q∨P — 2 Add.
   4) Q⊃P — 3 Impl.
   5) (P⊃Q)•(Q⊃P) — 1, 4 Conj.
   6) P≡Q — 5 Equiv. (8)

7. 1) ~R⊃(S∨T)
   2) ~S
   3) ~T / ∴ R
   4) ~S•~T — 2, 3 Conj.
   5) ~(S∨T) — 4 DeM.
   6) ~~R — 1, 5 M.T.
   7) R — 6 D.N. (8)

8. 1) U⊃W
   2) ~(U⊃X) / ∴ W
   3) ~(~U∨X) — 2 Impl.
   4) ~~U•~X — 3 DeM.
   5) ~~U — 4 Simp.
   6) U — 5 D.N.
   7) W — 1, 6 M.P. (10)

9. 1) A⊃(B•C)
   2) (B∨C)⊃D / ∴ A⊃D
   3) ~A∨(B•C) — 1 Impl.
   4) (~A∨B)•(~A∨C) — 3 Dist.
   5) ~A∨B — 4 Simp.
   6) (~A∨B)∨C — 5 Add.
   7) ~A∨(B∨C) — 6 Assoc.
   8) A⊃(B∨C) — 7 Impl.
   9) A⊃D — 8, 2 H.S. (14)

10. 1) E / ∴ F⊃F (Hint: Use Impl. 3x)
   2) E∨~F — 1 Add.
   3) ~F∨E — 2 Com.
   4) F⊃E — 3 Impl.
   5) F⊃(F•E) — 4 Abs.
   6) ~F∨(F•E) — 5 Impl.
   7) (~F∨F)•(~F∨E) — 6 Dist.
   8) ~F∨F — 7 Simp.
   9) F⊃F — 8 Impl. (16)

Continued on next page.

11. 1) $(G \vee H) \supset I$
2) $(J \vee K) \supset \sim I$
3) K / ∴ $\sim H$
4) $K \vee J$ 3 Add.
5) $J \vee K$ 4 Com.
6) $\sim I$ 2, 5 M.P.
7) $\sim(G \vee H)$ 1, 6 M.T.
8) $\sim G \bullet \sim H$ 7 DeM.
9) $\sim H \bullet \sim G$ 8 Com.
10) $\sim H$ 9 Simp. (14)

12. 1) $(L \vee M) \supset N$
2) $P \supset M$
3) $\sim N$ / ∴ $\sim P \bullet \sim L$
4) $\sim(L \vee M)$ 1, 3 M.T.
5) $\sim L \bullet \sim M$ 4 DeM.
6) $\sim M \bullet \sim L$ 5 Com.
7) $\sim L$ 5 Simp.
8) $\sim M$ 6 Simp.
9) $\sim P$ 2, 8 M.T.
10) $\sim P \bullet \sim L$ 9, 7 Conj. (14)

Write out in English an argument (*not* the whole proof) that could be symbolized by problems 1 and 10 above. Do they sound valid? Why or why not? (3 each)

13. Problem #1

Example: "I study logic. Therefore if it's snowing outside then I study logic." This doesn't really sound valid; the conclusion doesn't seem implied by the premise.

14. Problem #10

Example: "I study logic. Therefore if it's snowing outside then it's snowing outside." This also doesn't seem valid. The premise and the conclusion are unrelated.

EXERCISE 17b (36 points)

Translate the following arguments into symbolic form and write a formal proof of validity for each. Each proof requires no more than four additional steps.

1. If evolutionary theory is correct then the biblical creation account is false. However, if the Bible is God's word then the biblical creation account is true. Therefore if evolutionary theory is correct then the Bible is not God's word. (E, C, G) (5)

   1) E ⊃ ~C
   2) G ⊃ C / ∴ E ⊃ ~G
   3) ~C ⊃ ~G 2 Trans.
   4) E ⊃ ~G 1, 3 H.S.

2. It is impossible both to spend eternity in heaven and be condemned to hell. So if you go to heaven you will not be condemned to hell. (H, C) (5)

   1) ~(H • C) / ∴ H ⊃ ~C
   2) ~H ∨ ~C 1 DeM.
   3) H ⊃ ~C 2 Impl.

3. If Jesus both helped others and argued rationally then he was not insane. If the gospel accounts are true then Jesus argued rationally and he helped others. Thus either the gospel accounts are false or Jesus was not insane. (H, A, I, G) (7)

   1) (H • A) ⊃ ~I
   2) G ⊃ (A • H) / ∴ ~G ∨ ~I
   3) G ⊃ (H • A) 2 Com.
   4) G ⊃ ~I 3, 1 H.S.
   5) ~G ∨ ~I 4 Impl.

4. If God and Satan are both omnipotent then our cosmology is essentially dualistic. God is omnipotent. We must conclude that if Satan is also omnipotent then our cosmology is dualistic. (G, S, D) (5)

   1) (G • S) ⊃ D
   2) G / ∴ S ⊃ D
   3) G ⊃ (S ⊃ D) 1 Exp.
   4) S ⊃ D 3, 2 M.P.

Continued on next page.

5. If the heavens are infinite then I cannot comprehend them, but neither can I comprehend them if they come to an end. If the heavens are not infinite then they come to an end. In any case, I cannot comprehend the heavens. (I, C, E) (9)

1) (I ⊃ C) • (E ⊃ C)
2) ~I ⊃ E / ∴ C
3) ~~I ∨ E 2 Impl.
4) I ∨ E 3 D.N.
5) C ∨ C 1, 4 C.D.
6) C 5 Taut.

6. Either Peter was a liar when he claimed that Jesus never lied, or Jesus never lied. If Peter was a liar when he made this claim then he was a hypocrite. Peter was no hypocrite. Therefore Jesus was no liar. (P, J, H) (5)

1) P ∨ J
2) P ⊃ H
3) ~H / ∴ J
4) ~P 2, 3 M.T.
5) J 1, 4 D.S.

TEACHER'S NOTES

QUIZ 10 (LESSON 17)

STUDENT OBJECTIVE

Complete Quiz 10.

TEACHING INSTRUCTIONS

1. Give Quiz 10. Allow 30 minutes. Grade quiz with students.
2. If you have extra time, begin reviewing for Test 5.

Lesson 17 (31 points)

Name ______________________

Problems 1-4: Justify each step in the proof using the rules of inference or replacement. (1 point for each step)

1.
1. $\sim A$ / $\therefore$ $\sim B \supset \sim (B \vee A)$
2. $\sim A \vee B$ — 1 Add.
3. $A \supset B$ — 2 Impl.
4. $\sim B \supset \sim A$ — 3 Trans.
5. $\sim B \supset (\sim B \bullet \sim A)$ — 4 Abs.
6. $\sim B \supset \sim (B \vee A)$ — 5 De M.

2.
1. $(C \supset D) \bullet (E \supset D)$
2. $\sim C \supset E$ / $\therefore$ D
3. $\sim\sim C \vee E$ — 2 Impl.
4. $C \vee E$ — 3 D.N.
5. $D \vee D$ — 1, 4 C.D.
6. D — 5 Taut.

3.
1. $(F \vee G) \supset [H \bullet (J \bullet K)]$
2. G / $\therefore$ $H \bullet J$
3. $G \vee F$ — 2 Add.
4. $F \vee G$ — 3 Com.
5. $H \bullet (J \bullet K)$ — 1, 4 M.P.
6. $(H \bullet J) \bullet K$ — 5 Assoc.
7. $H \bullet J$ — 6 Simp.

4.
1. $\sim L$
2. $(M \vee N) \supset L$ / $\therefore$ $M \equiv N$
3. $\sim (M \vee N)$ — 2, 1 M.T.
4. $\sim M \bullet \sim N$ — 3 De M.
5. $(\sim M \bullet \sim N) \vee (M \bullet N)$ — 4 Add.
6. $(M \bullet N) \vee (\sim M \bullet \sim N)$ — 5 Com.
7. $M \equiv N$ — 6 Equiv.

Problems 5-6: Write a formal proof of validity for the given argument. (6 each)

5.
1. $P \supset Q$
2. $P \supset (Q \supset R)$ / $\therefore$ $P \supset R$
3. $P \supset (P \bullet Q)$ — 1 Abs.
4. $(P \bullet Q) \supset R$ — 2 Exp.
5. $P \supset R$ — 3, 4 H.S.

6.
1. S
2. $T \vee U$
3. $\sim (S \bullet T)$ / $\therefore$ $S \bullet U$
4. $S \bullet (T \vee U)$ — 1, 2 Conj.
5. $(S \bullet T) \vee (S \bullet U)$ — 4 Dist.
6. $S \bullet U$ — 5, 3 D.S.

 |

REVIEW FOR TEST 5 (LESSONS 16–17)

STUDENT OBJECTIVES

Complete the objectives from Lessons 16 and 17. Objectives are listed at the beginning of each lesson's teacher's notes.

TEACHING INSTRUCTIONS

1. To review for the test, choose problems from the Review Questions for Lessons 16 and 17 on p. 161 of the student text and from the Review Exercises for Lessons 16 and 17 on pp. 165–168 of the student text for students to work through.
2. If you'd like, give students "Test 5: Form A" from the *Intermediate Logic Test and Quiz Packet* as a practice exam. Go over the answers together.

ASSIGNMENT

Have students study for Test 5.

TEST 5 (LESSONS 16–17)

STUDENT OBJECTIVE

Complete Test 5.

TEACHING INSTRUCTIONS

1. Give students Test 5: Form B from the *Intermediate Logic Test and Quiz Packet.* Allow one hour to complete it.
2. Grade tests. Have them ready to hand back to students within a week.

INTERMEDIATE LOGIC | Test 5, Form A

Lessons 16–17 (48 points)

Name ______________________________

1. Identify one major difference between the *rules of replacement* and the *rules of inference*. (3)

   Rules of replacement are forms of equivalent propositions, which may replace each other wherever they occur. Rules of inference are forms of valid arguments.

2. Prove that $\sim(\sim q \supset \sim p)$ is equivalent to $p \bullet \sim q$ by justifying the steps of the following proof using only rules of replacement. (You need not number the steps.) (4)

   1. $\sim(\sim q \supset \sim p)$ / $\therefore$ $p \bullet \sim q$
   2. $\sim(p \supset q)$ — Trans.
   3. $\sim(\sim p \vee q)$ — Impl.
   4. $\sim\sim p \bullet \sim q$ — De M.
   5. $p \bullet \sim q$ — D.N.

Problems 3-4: Justify each step in the proof using the rules of inference or replacement.

3.
   1. $A \bullet \sim B$ / $\therefore$ $B \supset C$
   2. $\sim B \bullet A$ — 1 Com.
   3. $\sim B$ — 2 Simp.
   4. $\sim B \vee C$ — 3 Add.
   5. $B \supset C$ — 4 Impl.

4.
   1. $D \supset E$
   2. $D \supset (E \supset F)$ / $\therefore$ $D \supset F$
   3. $D \supset (D \bullet E)$ — 1 Abs.
   4. $(D \bullet E) \supset F$ — 2 Exp.
   5. $D \supset F$ — 3, 4 H.S.

Problems 5-6: Write a formal proof of validity for the given argument. (6, 8)

5.
   1. $G \supset H$
   2. $I \supset H$
   3. $G \vee I$ / $\therefore$ H
   4. $(G \supset H) \bullet (I \supset H)$ — 1, 2 Conj.
   5. $H \vee H$ — 4, 3 C.D.
   6. H — 5 Taut.

6.
   1. $J \bullet (K \vee L)$
   2. $\sim J \vee \sim L$ / $\therefore$ $J \bullet K$
   3. $(J \bullet K) \vee (J \bullet L)$ — 1 Dist
   4. $(J \bullet L) \vee (J \bullet K)$ — 3 Com.
   5. $\sim(J \bullet L)$ — 2 De M.
   6. $J \bullet K$ — 4, 5 D.S.

Problems 7-8: Translate the argument into symbolic form using the given constants. Then construct a formal proof of validity for that symbolic argument. (10 each)

7. "If slave traders captured slaves then they were kidnapping. If they were kidnapping then if you bought a slave then you would be buying stolen goods. If you were buying stolen goods then you were breaking God's law. Slave traders captured slaves. Therefore, if you bought a slave then you were breaking God's law." **(C, K, B, S, G)**

1. $C \supset K$
2. $K \supset (B \supset S)$
3. $S \supset G$
4. C / $\therefore B \supset G$
5. K 1, 4 M.P.
6. $B \supset S$ 2, 5 M.P.
7. $B \supset G$ 6, 3 H.S.

8. "Bill is guilty of burglary if and only if he did not have permission to take the goods. Bill had permission to take the goods. Therefore Bill is not guilty of burglary." **(B, P)**

1. $B \equiv \sim P$
2. P / $\therefore \sim B$
3. $(B \supset \sim P) \bullet (\sim P \supset B)$ 1 Equiv.
4. $B \supset \sim P$ 3 Simp.
5. $\sim\sim P$ 2 D.N.
6. $\sim B$ 4, 5 M.T.

INTERMEDIATE LOGIC | Test 5, Form B

Lessons 16–17 (48 points)

Name ______________________

1. What is a *rule of replacement*? (2) A rule of replacement is a form of equivalence that can be used to justify a step in a proof.

2. Prove that $(p \bullet \sim q) \supset r$ is equivalent to $p \supset (q \vee r)$ by justifying the steps of the following proof using only rules of replacement. (You need not number the steps.) (5)

1. $(p \bullet \sim q) \supset r$ / $\therefore$ $p \supset (q \vee r)$
2. $\sim (p \bullet \sim q) \vee r$ Impl.
3. $(\sim p \vee \sim \sim q) \vee r$ De M.
4. $(\sim p \vee q) \vee r$ D.N.
5. $\sim p \vee (q \vee r)$ Assoc.
6. $p \supset (q \vee r)$ Impl.

Problems 3-4: Justify each step in the proof using the rules of inference or replacement. (2, 3)

3.
1. $A \vee B$
2. $A \supset C$
3. $\sim C$ / $\therefore$ B
4. $\sim A$ 2, 3 M.T.
5. B 1, 4 D.S.

4.
1. $(D \supset E) \bullet (F \supset E)$
2. $F \vee D$ / $\therefore$ E
3. $D \vee F$ 2 Com.
4. $E \vee E$ 1, 3 C.D.
5. E 4 Taut.

Problems 5-6: Write a formal proof of validity for the given argument. You may use more steps than indicated. (8, 6)

5.
1. $\sim G \supset \sim H$
2. $H \bullet J$ / $\therefore$ $H \bullet G$
3. $H \supset G$ 1 Trans.
4. H 2 Simp.
5. G 3, 4 M.P.
6. $H \bullet G$ 4, 5 Conj.

6.
1. $K \supset L$
2. $L \supset (K \supset M)$ / $\therefore$ $K \supset M$
3. $K \supset (K \supset M)$ 1, 2 H.S.
4. $(K \bullet K) \supset M$ 3 Exp.
5. $K \supset M$ 4 Taut.

Problems 7-8: Translate the argument into symbolic form using the given constants. Then construct a formal proof of validity for that symbolic argument.

7. "Jesus sinned if and only if He broke God's law. Jesus did not sin. Therefore, Jesus neither sinned nor broke God's law." (**S**, **B**) (12)

1.	$S \equiv B$	
2.	$\sim S \quad / \quad \therefore \quad \sim (S \vee B)$	
3.	$(S \bullet B) \vee (\sim S \bullet \sim B)$	1 Equiv.
4.	$\sim S \vee \sim B$	2 Add.
5.	$\sim (S \bullet B)$	4 De M.
6.	$\sim S \bullet \sim B$	3, 5 D.S.
7.	$\sim (S \vee B)$	6 De M.

8. "Either they saw the wizard and it was Gandalf, or they saw the wizard and it was Saruman. It was not Gandalf. It must have been Saruman." (**W**, **G**, **S**) (10)

1.	$(W \bullet G) \vee (W \bullet S)$	
2.	$\sim G \quad / \quad \therefore \quad S$	
3.	$W \bullet (G \vee S)$	1 Dist.
4.	$(G \vee S) \bullet W$	3 Com.
5.	$G \vee S$	4 Simp.
6.	S	5, 2 D.S.

TEACHER'S NOTES on LESSON 18

THE CONDITIONAL PROOF

Intermediate Logic, pp. 137–140

STUDENT OBJECTIVES

1. Use the Conditional Proof as an aid to writing proofs.
2. Complete Exercise 18.

SPECIAL NOTE

Depending on which schedule you're following, you have a couple of classes to work through Lesson 18 and its exercises. Try to get through as much of the lesson as you can in the first class, and spend the second class working through Exercise 18 with students.

TEACHING INSTRUCTIONS

1. Give students this argument: "If you love God, you may do as you please. Therefore if you love God and love others, you may do as you please." Ask students if this argument sounds valid to them. Tell them that it's not a trick question: it does most definitely sound valid. And it *is* valid. But explain that the proof required is the one they solved in Problem 5 of Exercise 17A (perhaps they remember?). Write it on the board to remind them:

1) L ⊃ N/ ∴ (L • M) ⊃ N	
2) (L ⊃ N) ∨ ~M	1 Add.
3) ~M ∨ (L ⊃ N)	2 Com.
4) M ⊃ (L ⊃ N)	3 Impl.
5) (M • L) ⊃ N	4 Exp.
6) (L • M) ⊃ N	5 Com.
Q.E.D.	

2. Tell students that it wasn't just them: this is a *hard* proof. It assumes that the person solving it will realize that he needs to build the proof around the rule of Exportation and that he needs to add *~M* at the beginning. Explain that most people just aren't that creative and would take many more steps to solve a proof like this. Tell students that there are many arguments like this: they are intuitively valid (you know they must be valid when you hear them) but they are a real challenge to actually prove. The argument is more intuitive than the proof.
3. Explain that part of the reason the argument itself is so obviously valid is that the conclusion is a conditional, and we tend to think of conditionals themselves as self-contained arguments. Change the initial argument only ever so slightly: "If you love God, you can do as you please. You love God and you love others. Therefore you can do as you please." Have students symbolize this new argument (again using *L*, *N*, and *M*) and walk you through proving it. The completed proof should look like this:

1) L ⊃ N	
2) L • M / ∴ N	
3) L	2 Simp.
4) N	1, 3 M.P.
Q.E.D.	

Students should see that obviously this argument is significantly easier to prove, but that in order to make it easier we had to change it slightly.

4. Explain that rather than changing the proof we can instead use the **Conditional Proof (C.P.)**. The Conditional Proof is **a special rule in a formal proof which says that whenever a conditional is used in a proof, we may assume the antecedent of the conditional; if from the antecedent we can deduce the consequent, we may conclude the entire conditional**. Have students once again set up the first "If you love God . . ." argument. This time have them use the C.P. to assume the antecedent of the conclusion, *L • M*, in the second step. The completed proof should look like this:

1) L ⊃ N / ∴ (L • M) ⊃ N		
2)L • M	C.P.A.	*(Assume antecedent)*
3) L	2 Simp.	
4) N	1, 3 M.P.	*(Deduce consequent)*
5) (L • M) ⊃ N	2–4 C.P	*(Conclude conditional)*
Q.E.D.		

Point out that the proof is still shorter than the original, and very easy to develop. Also point out that we use the abbreviation C.P.A. ("Conditional Proof Assumption") for assuming the antecedent, and that for the justification of C.P. at the end, we list all the steps (2–4) that we took based on the C.P.A. assumption.

5. Give students this argument "If I love others I will either serve them or boss them around. If I love others I will not boss them around. Therefore if I love others I will serve." Once again, have students walk you through symbolizing and setting up this argument (using constants *P*, *Q*, and *R*). The initial argument should look like this:

1) P ⊃ (Q ∨ R)
2) P ⊃ ~Q / ∴ P ⊃ R

6. Explain that once again we have an obviously valid argument with a very unobvious proof. Tell students that you are going to spare them the tiresome task of solving the ordinary proof, but write it out for them:

1) P ⊃ (Q ∨ R)	
2) P ⊃ ~Q	/ ∴ P ⊃ R
3) P ⊃ (~~Q ∨ R)	1 D.N.
4) P ⊃ (~Q ⊃ R)	3 Impl.
5) (P • ~Q) ⊃ R	4 Exp.
6) P ⊃ (P • ~Q)	2 Abs.
7) P ⊃ R	6, 5 H.S.
Q.E.D.	

Tell students that anyone who thinks they could have figured that out no problem can feel free to graduate right now and join some school of geniuses.

7. Now have students prove this same argument using the conditional proof. It should be pretty easy for them to figure out. The completed proof should look like this:

1) P ⊃ (Q ∨ R)	
2. P ⊃ ~Q / ∴ P ⊃ R	
3) P	C.P.A.
4) Q ∨ R	1, 3 M.P.
5) ~Q	2, 3 M.P.
6) R	4,5 D.S.
7) P ⊃ R	3–6 C.P.
Q. E.D.	

Point out that as students do more proofs they will probably notice that proofs that use C.P. tend to also use Modus Ponens.

8. Tell students that there are just a few more things they need to know before they do the exercises. Explain that, first of all, **the conclusion of an argument need not itself be a conditional in order for you to use the Conditional Proof to prove that argument. All that is necessary is that there is a conditional somewhere in the proof.** Give students this example:

1) P ⊃ Q	
2) Q ⊃ (P • R) / ∴ P ≡ Q	
3) Q	C.P.A.
4) P • R	2, 3 M.P.
5) P	4 Simp.
6) Q ⊃ P	3–5 C.P.
7. (P ⊃ Q) • (Q ⊃ P)	1, 6 Conj.
8) P ≡ Q	7, Equiv.
Q.E.D.	

Make sure students see that in this proof the C.P. was not used to get directly to the conclusion, but to make the in-between steps simpler. Tell students that in addition, **the proposition assumed in C.P.A. need not even have appeared previously in the proof. You can assume anything you want, as long as you then use it in a Conditional Proof.**

9. Explain that, secondly, **a Conditional Proof Assumption may only be made when using the Conditional Proof.** Write this proof of the board:

1) P ⊃ Q / ∴ P ∨ R	
2) P	C.P.A.
3) P ∨ R	2 Add.
Q.E.D.	ERROR

Ask students why this proof is in error. Explain that **you are not allowed to make an assumption and then use that to derive a conclusion which does not follow from the Conditional Proof.** Having used CPA, you must use CP.

10. Explain that, thirdly, **you may not select one step out of a Conditional Proof to use later on in the proof.** Write this proof on the board:

1) L ⊃ N / ∴ L • [(L • M) ⊃ N]	
2) L • M	C.P.A.
3) L	2, Simp.
4) N	1, 3 M.P.
5) (L • M) ⊃ N	2–4 C.P.
6) L • [(L • M) ⊃ N]	3, 5 Conj.
Q.E.D.	ERROR

Explain that up through step 5 the proof is just fine. But after coming out of the conditional proof we are not allowed to jump back inside it and steal things from it (like the *L* in step 6). Tell students that **when using any part of the Conditional Proof, you must use all of the Conditional Proof.**

ASSIGNMENT

Have students complete Exercise 18, and go over it with them.

LESSON 18

THE CONDITIONAL PROOF

Sometimes an argument is intuitively valid, but the proof is still fairly complicated. For example, Problem 5 of Exercise 17a required the following proof:

1) $L \supset N$ / $\therefore (L \bullet M) \supset N$
2) $(L \supset N) \vee {\sim}M$ 1 Add.
3) ${\sim}M \vee (L \supset N)$ 2 Com.
4) $M \supset (L \supset N)$ 3 Impl.
5) $(M \bullet L) \supset N$ 4 Exp.
6) $(L \bullet M) \supset N$ 5 Com.
Q.E.D.

This solution assumes that the person solving it was able to realize that he could build the proof around the rule of Exportation, not to mention realizing that he had to start by adding *~M.* Most people are less creative and would take many more steps to solve this proof. The argument is far more intuitive than the proof. Suppose someone said, "If you can run a four-minute mile then you are a world-class athlete." The conclusion "If you can run a four-minute mile and you are a teenager then you are a world-class athlete" follows rather obviously from that.

Part of the obviousness of this argument results from the fact that the conclusion is a conditional, and we tend to think of conditionals themselves as self-contained arguments. The above argument might be re-worded, "If you can run a four-minute mile then you are a world-class athlete. You can run a four-minute mile and you are a teenager. You must be a world-class athlete." This argument would be symbolized and proven as follows:

1) $L \supset N$
2) $L \bullet M$ / $\therefore N$
3) L 2 Simp.
4) N 1, 3 M.P.
Q.E.D.

DEFINITION

The ***conditional proof*** is a special rule in a formal proof which allows us to assume the antecedent of a conditional and, once we deduce the consequent, to conclude the entire conditional.

This argument is much easier to prove. But in order to make it easier we had to change the argument slightly. Rather than do that, we can introduce the **Conditional Proof** (C.P.). Whenever a conditional is used in a proof (such as in the conclusion of the argument), the Conditional Proof allows us to assume the antecedent of the conditional. If from the antecedent we can conclude the consequent, we can then conclude the entire conditional. Our example would work like this:

1) L⊃N / ∴ (L•M)⊃N		
2) L•M	C.P.A.	(Assume the antecedent)
3) L	2 Simp.	
4) N	1, 3 M.P.	(Deduce the consequent)
5) (L•M)⊃N	2-4 C.P.	(Conclude the conditional)
Q.E.D.		

This proof is still shorter than the original, and much easier to develop once you understand the conditional proof.

Notice how this worked. We saw that the conclusion was a conditional. We assumed the antecedent *L•M*, and justified it with the abbreviation C.P.A., or "Conditional Proof Assumption." We then derived the consequent N. This allowed us to conclude *(L•M)⊃N* in steps 2 through 4 by the Conditional Proof.

Let's try another argument as an example of using this method. Consider this argument:

1) P⊃(Q∨R)
2) P⊃~Q / ∴ P⊃R

If we do not use the Conditional Proof, it is not immediately obvious how to proceed. Some creative thinking is necessary. Try to prove it without using Conditional Proof on your own before reading on.

Here are two proofs of this argument. The first does not use the Conditional Proof; the second does.

1) P⊃(Q∨R)	
2) P⊃~Q / ∴ P⊃R	
3) P⊃(~~Q∨R)	1 D.N.
4) P⊃(~Q⊃R)	3 Impl.
5) (P•~Q)⊃R	4 Exp.
6. P⊃(P•~Q)	2 Abs.
7) P⊃R	6,5 H.S.
Q.E.D.	

1) P⊃(Q∨R)
2) P⊃~Q / ∴ P⊃R
3) P — C.P.A.
4) Q∨R — 1, 3 M.P.
5) ~Q — 2, 3 M.P.
6) R — 4, 5 D.S.
7) P⊃R — 3-6 C.P.
Q.E.D

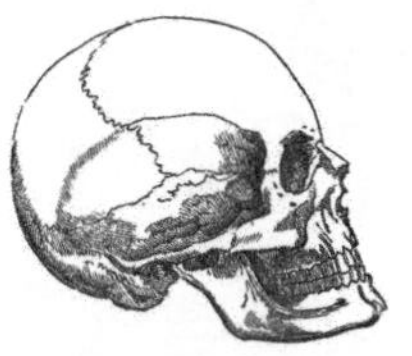

CAUTION

The proposition assumed in C.P.A. need not appear previously in the proof. You can assume anything you wish, as long as you then use it in a conditional proof.

The proof that uses the Conditional Proof is much easier to develop. As you practice this method, you may notice that, just as in the above examples, proofs that use the Conditional Proof also tend to use *modus ponens*.

We need to consider a few more factors before you can do the exercise. First, you should be aware that the conclusion itself need not be a conditional in order to use the Conditional Proof. All that is necessary is that a conditional is somewhere in the proof, as in this example:

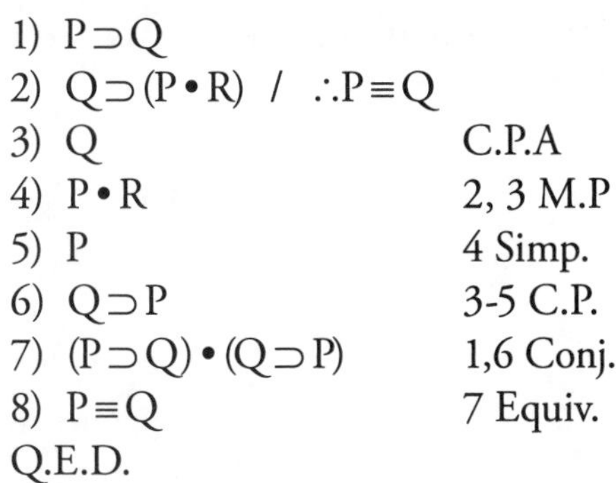

1) P⊃Q
2) Q⊃(P•R) / ∴P≡Q
3) Q — C.P.A
4) P•R — 2, 3 M.P
5) P — 4 Simp.
6) Q⊃P — 3-5 C.P.
7) (P⊃Q)•(Q⊃P) — 1,6 Conj.
8) P≡Q — 7 Equiv.
Q.E.D.

Second, a Conditional Proof Assumption may only be made when using the Conditional Proof. You are not allowed to make an assumption and then use that to derive a conclusion which does not follow from the Conditional Proof. For example, the following proof is not allowable:

1) P⊃Q / ∴ P∨R
2) P — C.P.A.
3) P∨R — 2 Add.
Q.E.D. — ERROR

Similarly, you may not select one step out of a Conditional Proof to use later on in the proof. We could not do the following:

1) L⊃N / ∴ L•[(L•M)⊃N]	
2) L•M	C.P.A.
3) L	2 Simp.
4) N	1, 3 M.P.
5) (L•M)⊃N	2-4 C.P.
6) L•[(L•M)⊃N]	3, 5 Conj.
Q.E.D.	ERROR

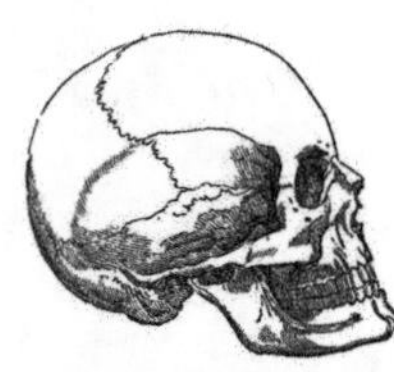

CAUTION

When using any part of the conditional proof, you must use all of the conditional proof.

When using any part of the Conditional Proof you must use all of the Conditional Proof.

SUMMARY

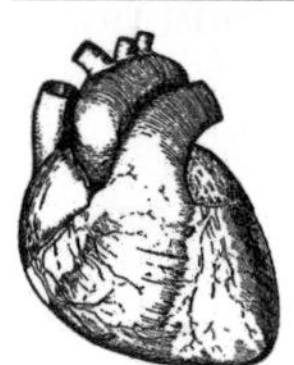

The Conditional Proof can be used when a conditional occurs somewhere in a proof. The antecedent of a conditional is assumed and the consequent is then derived. The steps involved in this are used to conclude the entire conditional.

EXERCISE 18 (90 points)

Write a formal proof of validity for the following arguments using the Conditional Proof.

1 1) A⊃(B•C) / ∴ A⊃B
2) A — C.P.A.
3) B•C — 1, 2 M.P.
4) B — 3 Simp.
5) A⊃B — 2-4 C.P. (8)

2. 1) D⊃E / ∴ D⊃(E∨F)
2) D — C.P.A.
3) E — 1, 2 M.P.
4) E∨F — 3 Add.
5) D⊃(E∨F) — 2-4 C.P. (8)

3. 1) G⊃H
2) G⊃I / ∴ G⊃(H•I)
3) G — C.P.A.
4) H — 1, 3 M.P.
5) I — 2, 3 M.P.
6) H•I — 4, 5 Conj.
7) G⊃(H•I) — 3-6 C.P. (10)

4. 1) J⊃K
2) L⊃K / ∴ (J∨L)⊃K
3) J∨L — C.P.A.
4) (J⊃K)•(L⊃K) — 1, 2 Conj.
5) K∨K — 4, 3 C.D.
6) K — 5 Taut.
7) (J∨L)⊃K — 3-6 C.P. (10)

5. 1) M⊃N
2) P⊃~N / ∴ ~M∨~P
3) M — C.P.A.
4) N — 1, 3 M.P.
5) ~~N — 4 D.N.
6) ~P — 2, 5 M.T.
7) M⊃~P — 3-6 C.P.
8) ~M∨~P — 7 Impl. (12)

6. 1) Q⊃(R•S)
2) (R∨S)⊃T / ∴ Q⊃T
3) Q — C.P.A.
4) R•S — 1, 3 M.P.
5) R — 4 Simp.
6) R∨S — 5 Add.
7) T — 2, 6 M.P.
8) Q⊃T — 3-7 C.P. (12)

7. 1) U / ∴ W⊃W
2) W — C.P.A.
3) W⊃W — 2-2 C.P. (4)

8. 1) X / ∴ Y⊃X
2) Y — C.P.A.
3) Y⊃X — 2-1 C.P. (4)

Continued on next page.

9. 1) $(A \supset B) \bullet (C \supset D)$ / ∴ $(A \bullet C) \supset (B \bullet D)$

2)	$A \bullet C$	C.P.A.
3)	A	2 Simp.
4)	$A \supset B$	1 Simp.
5)	B	4, 3 M.P.
6)	$C \bullet A$	2 Com.
7)	C	6 Simp.
8)	$(C \supset D) \bullet (A \supset B)$	1 Com.
9)	$C \supset D$	8 Simp.
10)	D	9, 7 M.P.
11)	$B \bullet D$	5, 10 Conj.
12)	$(A \bullet C) \supset (B \bullet D)$	2-11 C.P. (22)

TEACHER'S NOTES on LESSON 19

REDUCTIO AD ABSURDUM

Intermediate Logic, pp. 143–145

STUDENT OBJECTIVES

1. Use Reductio Ad Absurdum as an aid to writing proofs.
2. Complete Exercise 19.

TEACHING INSTRUCTIONS

1. Explain to students that in this lesson they will be learning another strategy, like the Conditional Proof, for writing proofs without severe mental anguish. Have any budding Latin scholars in the class take a stab at translating "reductio ad absurdum." Explain that it means "reducing to absurdity," and explain that this is exactly what the reductio ad absurdum rule allows us to do: reduce something to absurdity. Tell students that **Reductio ad Absurdum is a special rule which allows us to assume the negation of a proposition, deduce a self-contradiction, then conclude the proposition**.
2. That's a mouthful, so break it down. Tell students that in a reductio ad absurdum, as in the Conditional Proof, you assume something that you haven't been given and see where it leads. Say, for example, that you are trying to prove (to someone in the Bahamas) that snow is cold. Say you're not making very much headway. If you use reductio ad absurdum you can say, "All right, let's assume snow isn't cold. Where does that lead us?" Soon you will reach a contradiction (i.e., snow isn't cold, but people get frostbite in the snow.) Since the assumption led to a contradiction, it's obvious that it was a false assumption, and it's obvious that what you were initially trying to prove is true. Snow is indeed cold.
3. Explain that the reductio is a common method of proof in mathematics. For example, if you want to prove that you can't divide by zero, it's easiest to assume that you *can* and look for a contradiction to follow from that assumption. Write this reductio mathematical proof on the board:

$0 = 0$	Reflexive property of equality
$0 * 1 = 0 * 2$	Multiplication property of zero
$1 = 2$	Division by zero

   Obviously 1 does not equal 2, so division by zero doesn't work.
4. Explain that the reductio can be used in almost any argument or proof, and that it is a particularly common method in Christian apologetics. See if students can't think of arguments they have heard for the Christian faith that have used the reductio. Tell them to keep their ears open for anytime someone says, "All right, let's assume that what you're saying is true." For example, "All right, let's assume that there's no divine Lawgiver. But it that's the case, there's no Law that any of us have to obey. How come we call some things evil and some things good?"
5. Tell students that you are going to try to prove the rule of Addition *without* using the rule of Addition. Have them help you set up the argument using P and Q. It should look like this:

Ordinary Proof:		**Reductio:**	
1) P ⊃ Q		1) P ⊃ Q	
2) ~P ⊃ Q / ∴ Q		2) ~P ⊃ Q / ∴ Q	
3) ~Q ⊃ ~P	1 Trans	3) ~Q	R.A.A.
4) ~Q ⊃ Q	3, 2 H.S.	4) ~P	1, 3 M.T.
5) ~~Q ∨ Q	4 Impl.	5) ~~P	2, 3 M.T.
6) Q ∨ Q	5 D.N.	6) ~P • ~~P	4, 5 Conj.
7) Q	6 Taut.	7) Q	3-6 R.A.
Q.E.D		Q.E.D	

1. P   / ∴ P ∨ Q

Have students look at it for a moment. They should see that this argument is impossible to prove using only the standard rules of inference and replacement, because only the rule of Addition allows us to introduce new variables. We're stuck, unless we can use a reductio ad absurdum. Finish out the rest of the proof, using the reductio:

1) P   / ∴ P ∨ Q
2) ~(P ∨ Q)   R.A.A.
(Assume the negation of a proposition)
3) ~P • ~Q   2 De M.
4) ~P   3 Simp.
5) P • ~P   1, 4 Conj.
(Deduce a self-contradiction)
6) P ∨ Q   2–5 R.A.
(Conclude the original proposition)
Q.E.D.

Make sure students see how you assumed the negation of the conclusion, justified it with R.A.A. (Reductio ad Absurdum Assumption), and then followed the regular rules until you obtained a contradiction of the form p • ~p. Explain that the contradiction in step five shows that the original assumption in step two was wrong, and that you can therefore conclude its opposite (the conclusion) in step six. The justification in step six is labeled 2–5 for all the steps inside the reductio.

6. Explain that as in the last lesson you are now going to prove the same argument in two different ways, one using the normal rules of inference and replacement, the other using reductio ad absurdum. The initial argument should look like this:

   1) P ⊃ Q
   2) ~P ⊃ Q   / ∴ Q

   Do the two proofs one at a time side-by-side on the board, having students walk you through them, or, if you like, you can have half the class work through it one way and half the class work through it the other way and see who finishes faster. (If you have them work on their own, they may need lots of hints from you.) The completed proofs should look like the table at the top of the page.

7. Point out to students that although the two proofs have exactly the same number of steps, the reductio proof went (you assume) much faster and was much easier to develop. Also point out, if they haven't noticed yet, that the justification for step 3 in the reductio has no line number before R.A.A., because we are making the assumption out of thin air.

8. Explain that **the same considerations that applied to the Conditional Proof apply to Reductio Ad Absurdum.** First of all, the reductio need not be the entire proof, but can be part of a larger proof; it is perfectly fine to assume the negation of something (anything) other than the conclusion, as long as you go on to deduce a

contradiction and therefore prove true whatever proposition you negated. Secondly, the reductio *assumption* may only be made when you follow it up with the *whole* Reductio Ad Absurdum. Thirdly, the portion of the proof from the reductio assumption to the contradiction must be used collectively; you may not pluck one step out of the reductio to be used later in the proof.

ASSIGNMENTS

1. Have students complete Exercise 19, and go over it with them.
2. Remind students to study for next class's quiz over Lessons 18 and 19.

LESSON 19

REDUCTIO AD ABSURDUM

The shorter truth-table method for validity is a particular kind of *Reductio ad Absurdum*, which is Latin for "bringing to absurdity." In a *Reductio ad Absurdum*, the negation of what we are trying to prove is assumed. If this assumption leads to a contradiction, then it was wrong and we may conclude what we are trying to prove.

The reductio is a common method of proof in mathematics. For example, to prove that division by zero is not allowed, we could assume that division by zero *is* allowed and look for a contradiction. The proof might go like this:

$0 = 0$	Reflexive property of equality
$0 \times 1 = 0 \times 2$	Multiplication property of zero
$1 = 2$	Division by zero

Obviously $1 \neq 2$, so our assumption about the division by zero was false. The reductio can be used in almost any argument or proof. It is in fact a common method in Christian apologetics.

DEFINITION

Reductio ad Absurdum is a special rule which allows us to assume the negation of a proposition, deduce a self-contradiction, then conclude the proposition.

A similar procedure can be used in formal proofs of validity. Suppose that you were asked to prove the rule of Addition without using the rule of Addition. Such a proof is impossible using only the standard rules of inference and replacement, because no rule other than Addition allows us to introduce a new variable. However, we could use a *Reductio ad Absurdum*, as follows:

1) P / ∴ P ∨ Q		
2) ~(P ∨ Q)	R.A.A.	(Assume the negation of a proposition)
3) ~P • ~Q	2 De M.	
4) ~P	3 Simp.	
5) P • ~P	1, 4 Conj.	(Deduce a self-contradiction)
6) P ∨ Q	2-5 R.A.	(Conclude the original proposition)

Q.E.D.

We assumed the negation of our conclusion, and justified it with R.A.A. for "*Reductio ad Absurdum* Assumption." Then following our regular rules, we tried to obtain a contradiction of the form *p* • ~*p*, which we did in step five. The contradiction tells us that our original assumption in step two was wrong, and we thus conclude its opposite in step six. The justification is labelled "2-5 R.A." for *Reductio ad Absurdum* in steps two through five.

As in the previous lesson, let's consider two proofs for the same argument. The one on the left proves the argument using the techniques learned previously, and the one on the right uses *Reductio ad Absurdum*:

1) P⊃Q	
2) ~P⊃Q / ∴ Q	
3) ~Q⊃~P	1 Trans.
4) ~Q⊃Q	3, 2 H.S.
5) ~~Q∨Q	4 Impl.
6) Q∨Q	5 D.N.
7) Q	6 Taut.
Q.E.D.	

1) P⊃Q	
2) ~P⊃Q / ∴ Q	
3) ~Q	R.A.A.
4) ~P	1, 3 M.T.
5) ~~P	2, 3 M.T.
6) ~P • ~~P	4, 5 Conj.
7) Q	3-6 R.A.
Q.E.D.	

Notice that the proof which uses *Reductio ad Absurdum* employs no fewer steps than the proof which does not use it. However, the proof is somewhat easier to develop. Also, note that the step which makes the *Reductio ad Absurdum* assumption (step 3 on the right-hand proof above) has no line number in front of the justification R.A.A., because this assumption is made "out of thin air." In other words, you may assume whatever you like with this method, as long as you use the assumption correctly.

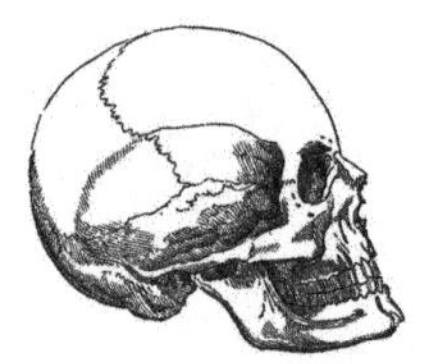

CAUTION

The same limitations that apply to the Conditional Proof (see *p.* 139-40) also apply to the *Reductio ad Absurdum.*

Similar considerations apply to *Reductio ad Absurdum* as to the Conditional Proof. First, *Reductio ad Absurdum* may be part of a larger proof. You may negate something other than just the conclusion and use the reductio on that to obtain a different conclusion. Second, the Reductio Assumption may only be made when using *Reductio ad Absurdum.* Finally, the portion of the proof from the Reductio Assumption to the contradiction must be used collectively; you may not select one step out of a *Reductio ad Absurdum* to be used later in the proof after the conclusion of the Reductio.

SUMMARY

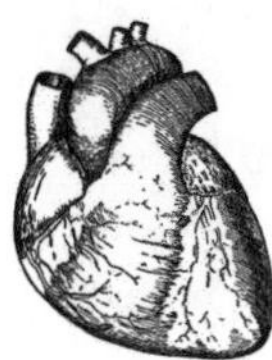

Reductio ad Absurdum allows us to assume the negation of a proposition. If that negation leads us to a contradiction of the form $p \cdot {\sim}p$, then we may conclude the original proposition.

EXERCISE 19 (42 points)

Write a formal proof of validity for the following arguments using Reductio ad Absurdum.

1. 1) ~P ⊃ (Q ∨ R)
   2) ~Q
   3) ~R / ∴ P
   4) ~P RAA
   5) Q ∨ R 1, 4 MP.
   6) R 5, 2 DS.
   7) R • ~R 6, 3 Conj.
   8) P 4-7 RA. (10)

2. 1) (~P ∨ Q) ⊃ (R • S)
   2) ~R / ∴ P
   3) ~P RAA.
   4) ~P ∨ Q 3 Add.
   5) R • S 1, 4 MP.
   6) R 5 Simp.
   7) R • ~R 6, 2 Conj.
   8) P 3-7 RA. (12)

3. 1) P ⊃ Q
   2) Q ∨ P / ∴ Q
   3) ~Q RAA.
   4) P 2, 3 DS.
   5) ~P 1, 3 MT.
   6) P • ~P 4, 5 Conj.
   7) Q 3-6 RA. (10)

4. 1) P / ∴ Q ⊃ Q
   2) ~(Q ⊃ Q) RAA.
   3) ~(~Q ∨ Q) 2 Impl.
   4) ~~Q • ~Q 3 DeM.
   5) Q • ~Q 4 DN.
   6) Q ⊃ Q 2-5 RA. (10)

QUIZ 11 (LESSONS 18 AND 19)

STUDENT OBJECTIVE

Complete Quiz 11.

TEACHING INSTRUCTIONS

1. Give Quiz 11. Allow 30 minutes. Grade quiz with students.
2. If you have extra time, introduce Lesson 20 to get a head start on next class's material.

INTERMEDIATE LOGIC | Quiz 11

Lessons 18–19 (36 points)

Name ________________________________

Problems 1-2: Prove the argument using the *conditional proof.* (9, 11)

1.
   1. $A \supset B$
   2. $A \supset C$ / ∴ $A \supset (B \bullet C)$
   3. A — C.P.A.
   4. B — 1, 3 M.P.
   5. C — 2, 3 M.P.
   6. $B \bullet C$ — 4, 5 Conj.
   7. $A \supset (B \bullet C)$ — 3-6 C.P.

2.
   1. $D \supset (E \bullet F)$
   2. $(E \vee G) \supset H$ / ∴ $D \supset H$
   3. D — C.P.A.
   4. $E \bullet F$ — 1, 3 M.P.
   5. E — 4 Simp.
   6. $E \vee G$ — 5 Add.
   7. H — 2, 6 M.P.
   8. $D \supset H$ — 3-7 C.P.

Problems 3-4: Prove the arguments using the *reductio ad absurdum.* (9, 7)

3.
   1. $J \supset K$
   2. $\sim J \supset K$ / ∴ K
   3. $\sim K$ — R.A.A.
   4. $\sim J$ — 1, 3 M.T.
   5. $\sim\sim J$ — 2, 3 M.T.
   6. $\sim J \bullet \sim\sim J$ — 4, 5 Conj.
   7. K — 3-6 R.A.

4.
   1. $\sim(L \bullet M)$
   2. L / ∴ $\sim M$
   3. M — R.A.A.
   4. $L \bullet M$ — 2, 3 Conj.
   5. $(L \bullet M) \bullet \sim(L \bullet M)$ — 4, 1 Conj.
   6. $\sim M$ — 3-5 R.A.

 |

TEACHER'S NOTES on LESSON 20

PROVING RULES UNNECESSARY

Intermediate Logic, pp. 149–150

STUDENT OBJECTIVES

1. Show that it is possible to reduce the number of rules of inference from nine to four.
2. Complete Exercise 20.

SPECIAL NOTE

Depending on which schedule you're following, you have a couple of days to work through Lesson 20 and its exercises. You should be able to get through all of the lesson and the first two of the exercise problems on the first day. Spend the second day working through problems 3–7.

TEACHING INSTRUCTIONS

1. Remind students of the proof in the previous chapter which proved the rule of Addition without using the rule of Addition. Ask students if this proof made them wonder anything about the rule of Addition. If everyone stares at your blankly, tell them that it *should* have made them wonder whether the rule of Addition is really a necessary rule. In every formal proof using the rule of Addition, we *could* replace that step with the steps of the *proof* for the rule of Addition. Tell students that this is true for other rules of inference as well. Explain that **we do not need all nine rules of inference to solve any proof of validity. Some of the rules can be removed.**
2. Ask students whether they think that, if this is the case, it would be wise to eliminate some of the rules of inference. It would be neater and tighter, not to mention there would be fewer rules to memorize. If they agree, ask them what the downside would be to having fewer rules of inference. They should recognize that the fewer rules we have to use, the longer the proofs get. Explain that a proof which uses the Constructive Dilemma would have to be about 9 steps longer if we couldn't use that rule. In that case, wouldn't it be better to have as many rules as possible? Should we add some?
3. Explain that what logicians have tried to do is strike a happy medium between the minimum number of rules and the minimum length of proofs. Explain that different logic textbooks come to different conclusions about what rules to include: some include the Destructive Dilemma as its own rule of inference; others leave out the Conditional Proof and Reductio ad Absurdum. Explain that it depends on the goals of the logician, and that this book includes the Reductio not because it is especially useful in solving proofs, but because it is a very useful technique in other fields, like mathematics, rhetoric, and apologetics.
4. Make sure students see that while the number of rules of inference is not completely random, it is also not absolute, and logicians have some freedom to choose what rules they wish to include. Explain that the exercises for this lesson will give students opportunities to explore the question a bit more and draw their own conclusions.

ASSIGNMENT

Have students complete Exercise 20, and go over it with them.

LESSON 20

PROVING RULES UNNECESSARY

The previous chapter included a proof of the rule of Addition which did not use that rule. This shows that, if other rules remain intact, the rule of Addition is to some degree unnecessary. Every formal proof that uses the rule of Addition could replace that step with the steps from the proof of the rule of Addition. Similar conclusions could be made about each of the other rules of inference. The very reasonable question could be asked, "If we eliminate some unnecessary rules, we would have fewer rules to memorize. How many rules can we prove unnecessary and yet still have the tools we need to prove any valid argument?"

KEY POINT

We do not need all nine rules of inference to solve any proof of validity. Some of the rules can be removed.

On the other hand, we should immediately recognize that the more rules we eliminate, the longer our proofs get. A proof which uses Constructive Dilemma, for example, would need to be about nine steps longer if that rule was eliminated. This raises the contrary question, "If doing so would result in shorter proofs, why not add more rules of inference?"

Logicians have tried to strike a happy medium somewhere between the theoretical minimum number of rules and the theoretical minimum average length of proofs. The various authors of logic books have come to different conclusions. Some, for example, include the rule of Destructive Dilemma (see p. 73) with the other rules of inference. Others not only leave out this rule, but also leave out the Conditional Proof and *Reductio ad Absurdum*. The decision concerning which rules to include and which to exclude depends largely upon the author's goals. For example, this textbook includes the *Reductio ad Absurdum*, not because it is a particularly useful tool (most proofs employing it are no shorter than otherwise), but because this author believes that a good understanding of the reductio technique is useful outside of the realm of formal proofs of validity, such as in mathematics, rhetoric, and apologetics.

The logic student should understand that the number of rules of inference, though not completely arbitrary, is also not absolute. Logicians have been granted some freedom to choose which rules to include based upon their desires and goals, according to the level of wisdom God has given them. The next exercise will give you some opportunities to consider these questions.

SUMMARY

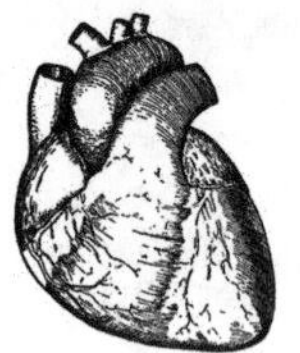

It is possible to prove some rules of inference without using them. This shows that some rules are not completely necessary though they may be helpful. Also, it is possible to have more rules of inference than those we have considered so far.

EXERCISE 20

Complete this assignment a separate sheet of paper.

1. Write a formal proof of validity for the Destructive Dilemma. This can be done in two additional steps. (4)

   Destructive Dilemma:

   1) $(P \supset Q) \bullet (R \supset S)$
   2) $\sim Q \vee \sim S \quad \therefore \sim P \vee \sim R$
   3) $(\sim Q \supset \sim P) \bullet (\sim S \supset \sim R)$ — 1 Trans. (2x)
   4) $\sim P \vee \sim R$ — 3, 2 C.D.

2. Invent and name your own rule of inference. Then use that rule to solve a proof from a previous exercise in fewer steps than it was previously solved. Include both proofs for comparison.

   EXAMPLE: "Consequent Replacement Rule" (C.R.)

   $p \supset (q \bullet r) \ / \ \therefore p \supset (q \vee r)$

   Ex. 17a, #9

1) $A \supset (B \bullet C)$		1) $A \supset (B \bullet C)$	
2) $(B \vee C) \supset D \ / \ \therefore A \supset D$		2) $(B \vee C) \supset D \ / \ \therefore A \supset D$	
3) $\sim A \vee (B \bullet C)$	1 Impl.	3) $A \supset (B \vee C)$	1 C.R.
4) $(\sim A \vee B) \bullet (\sim A \vee C)$	3 Dist.	4) $A \supset D$	3,2 H.S.
5) $\sim A \vee B$	4 Simp.		
6) $(\sim A \vee B) \vee C$	5 Add.		
7) $\sim A \vee (B \vee C)$	6 Assoc.		
8) $A \supset (B \vee C)$	7 Impl.		
9) $A \supset D$	8, 2 H.S.		

Show each rule to be unnecessary by writing formal proofs of validity for them without using those rules anywhere in your proofs. You may use any of the other rules of inference, the rules of Replacement, the Conditional Proof, and Reductio ad Absurdum.

3. Modus Tollens (5)

   1) $P \supset Q$
   2) $\sim Q \ / \ \therefore \sim P$
   3) $\sim Q \supset \sim P$ — 1 Trans.
   4) $\sim P$ — 3, 2 M.P.

4. Absorption (9)

   1) $P \supset Q \ / \ \therefore P \supset (P \bullet Q)$
   2) P — C.P.A.
   3) Q — 1, 2 M.P.
   4) $P \bullet Q$ — 2, 3 Conj.
   5) $P \supset (P \bullet Q)$ — 2-4 C.P.

Continued on next page.

5. Hypothetical Syllogism (9)

1) $P \supset Q$	
2) $Q \supset R$ / $\therefore P \supset R$	
3) P	C.P.A.
4) Q	1, 3 M.P.
5) R	2,4 M.P.
6) $P \supset R$	3-5 C.P.

6. Disjunctive Syllogism (7)

1) $P \vee Q$	
2) $\sim P$ / $\therefore Q$	
3) $\sim\sim P \vee Q$	1 D.N.
4) $\sim P \supset Q$	3 Impl.
5) Q	4,2 M.P.

7. Addition (11)

1) P / $\therefore P \vee Q$	
2) $\sim(P \vee Q)$	R.A.A.
3) $\sim P \bullet \sim Q$	2 DeM.
4) $\sim P$	3 Simp.
5) $P \bullet \sim P$	1, 4 Conj.
6) $P \vee Q$	2-5 R.A.

TRUTH-FUNCTIONAL COMPLETENESS

Intermediate Logic, pp. 153–157

STUDENT OBJECTIVES

1. Show that it is possible to reduce the number of logical operators from five to two.
2. Complete Exercise 21.

TEACHING INSTRUCTIONS

1. Remind students that in the last lesson they learned that we can reduce the number of rules of inference, though at the cost of lengthening proofs. Explain that we have a similar situation with logical operators. Have students give you the five logical operators they have learned (negation, conjunction, disjunction, conditional, and biconditional). Have them guess how many of those we actually *need* to symbolize all propositions. Tell them that by the end of the lesson you will have proved that two logical operators can do the work of all five.
2. Tell students that the first thing to do is write out all the possible combinations of true and false for two variables. Since they have to be in a certain order, simply copy out the table given below onto the board, but get students' verbal assent that they understand what you have just done. The completed table should look like this:

1	2	3	4	5	6	7	8
T	T	T	T	T	T	T	T
T	T	T	T	F	F	F	F
T	T	F	F	T	T	F	F
T	F	T	F	T	F	T	F

9	10	11	12	13	14	15	16
F	F	F	F	F	F	F	F
T	T	T	T	F	F	F	F
T	T	F	F	T	T	F	F
T	F	T	F	T	F	T	F

3. Have students think way, way back to truth tables and find the column that corresponds to the truth table for variable p (column 4). As soon as they find it, erase the number 4 and write p above the column instead. Now have them find the column for variable q (6). Replace the number 6 with q (continue to do this). Have students find the columns for $\sim p$ (13), $\sim q$ (11), $p \bullet q$ (8), $p \vee q$ (2), $p \supset q$ (5), and $p \equiv q$ (7).
4. Point out to students that columns one through eight are now almost complete, except for columns one and three. Have them look at column one. They should recognize it as a tautology. Label it $p \vee \sim p$. Then have them look at column three. Explain that this one is bit trickier and that there are a few possibilities for it. It could be identified as $q \supset p$, or an equivalent proposition like $\sim p \supset \sim q$ by transposition, $p \vee \sim q$ by implication and commutation, or $\sim(\sim p \bullet q)$ by implication, commutation, double negation, and De Morgan's Theorem. Explain that for reasons they will understand later, you are going to identify column three as $p \vee \sim q$. The table should now look like this:

p ∨ ~p	p ∨ q	p ∨ ~q	p	p ⊃ q	q	p ≡ q	p • q
T	T	T	T	T	T	T	T
T	T	T	T	F	F	F	F
T	T	F	F	T	T	F	F
T	F	T	F	T	F	T	F

9	10	~q	12	~p	14	15	16
F	F	F	F	F	F	F	F
T	T	T	T	F	F	F	F
T	T	F	F	T	T	F	F
T	F	T	F	T	F	T	F

5. Ask students if they recognize any of the columns from the second row. Point out that 16 is a self-contradiction, such as $p \bullet \sim p$, but tell students that for your own secret reasons your going to label it as disjunctive self-contradiction: $\sim(p \vee \sim p)$. Point out that column 16 is therefore the negation of column one. Have students look for other columns that are negations of each other. They should notice that columns four and six are the negations of columns 13 and 16 respectively. Help them see that for this table, the bottom row is the reverse of the negation of the top row. Let them be dizzy about that for a while.

6. Now that they know the pattern of negations, have students walk you through identifying the rest of the columns in the bottom row. The completed table should look like this:

p ∨ ~p	p ∨ q	p ∨ ~q	p	p ⊃ q	q	p ≡ q	p • q
T	T	T	T	T	T	T	T
T	T	T	T	F	F	F	F
T	T	F	F	T	T	F	F
T	F	T	F	T	F	T	F

~(p • q)	~(p ≡ q)	~q	~(p ⊃ q)	~p	~(p ∨ ~q)	~(p ∨ q)	~(p ∨ ~p)
F	F	F	F	F	F	F	F
T	T	T	T	F	F	F	F
T	T	F	F	T	T	F	F
T	F	T	F	T	F	T	F

7. Summarize for students what they have done: they have discovered the set of propositions by which every possible combination of true and false for two variables is identified, and they have done so using the five logical operators. Tell students that what this means is that the five logical operators are **truth-functionally complete**. Tell students that **a set of logical operators is truth-functionally complete if and only if all possible combinations of true and false for two variables are derivable using only those logical operators**. Have them go home and tell this to their father.

8. Remind students of what you told them at the beginning of class: that you were going to show that only two logical operators can do the work of five. Explain that, in other words, it should be possible to find two logical operators that are in themselves truth-functionally complete. Ask students if they have any ideas for determining which two operators these are.

9. Explain that one way to approach this question is to determine which logical operators are used most frequently in the table above. Have students tally it up. They should find that negation and disjunction are used most frequently. Explain that these two operators will therefore be the easiest to examine.

10. Have students find the rows that *don't* use only negation and disjunction (rows five, seven, eight, nine, ten and twelve). Ask if any of those rows are easily translatable into negation or disjunction. Students should see that row 5, $p \supset q$, can be translated into $\sim p \vee q$ by Material Implication. Point out that we can use Material Implication on row twelve as well, resulting in $\sim(\sim p \vee q)$. (Erase the old propositions and replace them with these new ones as you go.)

11. Have students look at row nine next: $\sim(p \bullet q)$. They should realize (eventually) that using De Morgan's they can turn this proposition into $\sim p \vee \sim q$. Remind them that row eight is a negation of row nine; row eight, $p \bullet q$, can therefore be translated into $\sim(\sim p \vee \sim q)$. Remind them what this means by using one example: "I am a teenager and I study logic" is equivalent to "It is false that I am not a teenager or I don't study logic."

12. Explain that this leaves only rows seven and ten, the biconditional rows. Ask students how we should go about converting a biconditional into negation and disjunction. If they look pale, explain that the best place to start is by looking at the rules of replacement that involve biconditionals (note: when students flip to the rules they might get freaked out, because it looks like every single rule involves the biconditional; remind them that the same symbol used for the biconditional is used to represent equivalence).

13. Students should see that the only rule involving the biconditional is Material Equivalence, which says that $p \equiv q$ is equivalent to $(p \bullet q) \vee (\sim p \bullet \sim q)$. Explain that this doesn't get us all the way there, but that it's a start; all we have to do now is translate the conjunctions into disjunctions. Remind students that they just translated the first conjunction for row eight. The second can be translated using De Morgan's Theorem. The final proposition for row seven should look like this: $\sim(\sim p \vee \sim q) \vee \sim(p \vee q)$.

14. Finally, how about $\sim(p \equiv q)$? Someone may point out that we could simply negate the translation we just came up with for $p \equiv q$. Explain that while that would work, it would give us a rather complicated proposition. Instead, have students look at the other half of the Material Equivalence rule. Have them use the rule on $p \equiv q$ to come up with $\sim[(p \supset q) \bullet (q \supset p)]$. Then have them use De Morgan's theorem, which will give us $\sim(p \supset q) \vee \sim(q \supset p)$. All we have left to do is convert the conditionals to disjunctions using Material Implication. The final result should be $\sim(\sim p \vee q) \vee \sim(p \vee \sim q)$.

15. Explain that we have done what we set out to do: we have found propositions for every possible combination of true and false using only negation and disjunction. Negation and disjunction are therefore truth-functionally complete. The table expressing this should look like this:

$p \vee \sim p$	$p \vee q$	$p \vee \sim q$	p	$\sim p \vee q$	q	$\sim(\sim p \vee \sim q) \vee \sim(p \vee q)$
T	T	T	T	T	T	T
T	T	T	T	F	F	F
T	T	F	F	T	T	F
T	F	T	F	T	F	T

$\sim(\sim p \vee \sim q)$	$\sim p \vee \sim q$	$\sim(\sim p \vee q) \vee \sim(p \vee \sim q)$	$\sim q$	$\sim(\sim p \vee q)$
T	F	F	F	F
F	T	T	T	T
F	T	T	F	F
F	T	F	T	F

$\sim p$	$\sim(p \vee \sim q)$	$\sim(p \vee q)$	$\sim(p \vee \sim p)$
F	F	F	F
F	F	F	F
T	T	F	F
T	F	T	F

16. If you have time, choose one or two of the above propositions and have students develop a truth table to test it.

17. Tell students that believe it or not it is possible to have only one logically operator that is truth-functionally complete. It just isn't one of the five logical operators they have already learned about. Explain that **one such truth-functionally complete logical operator is called NOR, symbolized by ∇, which is equivalent to $\sim(p \vee q)$**. Explain that NOR is capable of producing any possible combination of true or

false, but that demonstrating this would take pages and pages of propositions so complex it would make their brains explode. Tell students that you will just give them a little taste by showing how NOR can be used to produce truth table for conjunction and disjunction (and let them know they'll see more of NOR when you get to digital logic in Unit 5). Write this table on the board:

p	q	(p∇p) ∇ (q∇q)	(p∇q) ∇ (p∇q)
T	T	T	T
T	F	F	T
F	T	F	T
F	F	F	F

Help the students work though these using the defining truth table for NOR. For example, note that *(p ∇ p)* is equivalent to *~(p ∨ p)*, which is ~p by tautology. Similarly, *(q ∇ q)* is *~q*. So *(p ∇ p) ∇ (q ∇ q)* is *~p ∇ ~q*, which is *~(~p ∨ ~q)*. As this lesson showed, this is equivalent to *p • q*, or conjunction.

For the disjunction column, lead them through this:

1) (p ∇ q) ∇ (p ∇ q)	given
2) ~[(p ∇ q) ∨ (p ∇ q)]	definition of NOR
3) ~(p ∇ q)	tautology
4) ~~(p ∨ q)	definition of NOR
5) p ∨ q	double negation

18. If students are bewildered at the end of this lesson, reassure them that all these exercises are just to get their brains working and provide them with practice translating between logical operators. (This is an essential skill in the logic of digital electronics. Whet their appetites for digital logic if you're planning to teach it.)

ASSIGNMENTS

1. Have students complete Exercise 21, and go over it with them.
2. Remind students to study for next class's quiz over Lessons 20 and 21.

LESSON 21

TRUTH-FUNCTIONAL COMPLETENESS

In the last chapter we found that we could reduce the number of rules of inference to be used in proofs, at the cost of increasing the size of most proofs. A similar situation exists with the logical operators. Negation, conjunction, disjunction, conditional, and biconditional can be manipulated such that only two of them are used to do the work of all five, but at the cost of increasing the complexity of most propositions. Let's see how this can be done.

KEY POINT

Not all logical operators are strictly necessary—some operators can be used to do the work of others.

We first write out all the possible combinations of true and false for two variables. This requires sixteen columns of four truth values each, as follows:

1	2	3	4	5	6	7	8	9	10	11	12	13	14	15	16
T	T	T	T	T	T	T	T	F	F	F	F	F	F	F	F
T	T	T	T	F	F	F	F	T	T	T	T	F	F	F	F
T	T	F	F	T	T	F	F	T	T	F	F	T	T	F	F
T	F	T	F	T	F	T	F	T	F	T	F	T	F	T	F

Think back to the truth tables. You should recognize column four as the pattern for the variable p, and column six for the variable q. What other columns do you recognize? You should be able to quickly find the patterns for $\sim p$, $\sim q$, $p \bullet q$, $p \vee q$, $p \supset q$, and $p \equiv q$.

Having correctly identified those, columns one through eight should be completed except for columns one and three. However, column one should be recognized as a tautology, such as $p \vee \sim p$. What about column three? There are a few possibilities. Column three could be identified as $q \supset p$, or any equivalent proposition such as $\sim p \supset \sim q$ by transposition, $p \vee \sim q$ by implication and commutation, or $\sim(\sim p \bullet q)$ by implication, commutation, double negation and De Morgan's Theorem. Though any one of these will suffice, for reasons we shall later see we will identify it as $p \vee \sim q$. Thus we have the following columns identified:

p∨~p	p∨q	p∨~q	p	p⊃q	q	p≡q	p•q
T	T	T	T	T	T	T	T
T	T	T	T	F	F	F	F
T	T	F	F	T	T	F	F
T	F	T	F	T	F	T	F

9	10	~q	12	~p	14	15	16
F	F	F	F	F	F	F	F
T	T	T	T	F	F	F	F
T	T	F	F	T	T	F	F
T	F	T	F	T	F	T	F

Having completed those, we now recognize that, whereas column one is a tautology, column sixteen is a self-contradiction, such as *p* • *~p*, or even *~(p ∨ ~p)*. This should make us consider: column sixteen is the negation of column one, and columns four and six are the negations of columns thirteen and eleven, respectfully. You may notice that whenever the column numbers add up to seventeen, those two columns are negations of each other. Or considered another way, the bottom row is the reverse of the negation of the top row. This allows us to finish identifying the rest of the columns, as follows:

p∨~p	p∨q	p∨~q	p	p⊃q	q	p≡q	p•q
T	T	T	T	T	T	T	T
T	T	T	T	F	F	F	F
T	T	F	F	T	T	F	F
T	F	T	F	T	F	T	F

~(p•q)	~(p≡q)	~q	~(p⊃q)	~p	~(p∨~q)	~(p∨q)	~(p∨~p)
F	F	F	F	F	F	F	F
T	T	T	T	F	F	F	F
T	T	F	F	T	T	F	F
T	F	T	F	T	F	T	F

DEFINITION

A set of logical operators is ***truth-functionally complete*** if and only if all possible combinations of true and false for two variables are derivable using only those logical operators.

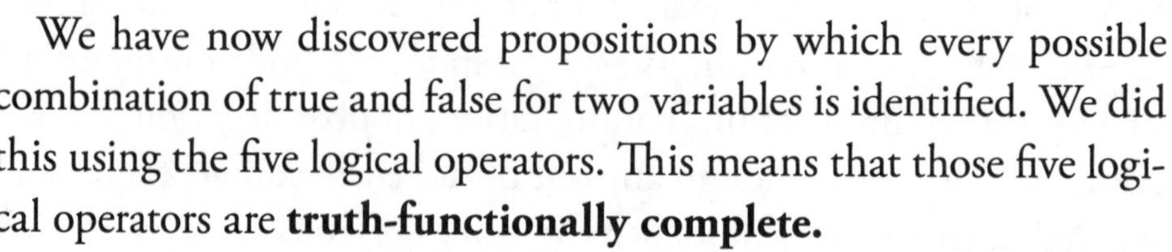

We have now discovered propositions by which every possible combination of true and false for two variables is identified. We did this using the five logical operators. This means that those five logical operators are **truth-functionally complete.**

However it was said in the first paragraph that only two logical operators could do the work of all five. In other words, we should be able to discover two logical operators which are in themselves truth-functionally complete. Which two?

One way to answer the question is to determine which logical operators are used most frequently in the system discovered above. If you tally them up, you will find that negation was used twelve times, disjunction was used six times, and conjunction, conditional, and biconditional each were used twice. This implies that negation and disjunction would be the easiest to examine in order to discover whether or not they are truth-functionally complete.

The only columns using logical operators other than negation and disjunction are columns five, seven, eight, nine, ten and twelve. Column five is the conditional $p \supset q$, which can be translated $\sim p \vee q$ by Material Implication. Similarly, column twelve could be changed to $\sim(\sim p \vee q)$.

Then look at column nine, $\sim(p \bullet q)$. Using De Morgan's Theorem on that proposition gives us one which uses negation and disjunction, $\sim p \vee \sim q$. Since column eight is the negation of column nine, we can assume that $p \bullet q$ can be converted into $\sim(\sim p \vee \sim q)$.

This leaves us only columns seven and ten, the propositions using the biconditional. How can we convert $p \equiv q$ into a proposition using negation and disjunction? One method would be to use the rule of Material Equivalence, which tells us that $p \equiv q$ is equivalent to $(p \bullet q) \vee (\sim p \bullet \sim q)$. All that remains is to translate the conjunctions. This first conjunction was translated in the previous paragraph, and the second can be translated using De Morgan's Theorem. Making these changes, $p \equiv q$ can be converted to $\sim(\sim p \vee \sim q) \vee \sim(p \vee q)$. Notice that we also could have found this as a disjunction of columns eight and fifteen.

How about $\sim(p \equiv q)$? We could simply negate the proposition just discovered, but that would not give us the simplest solution. Rather, consider the other half of the rule of Material Equivalence. That would lead us to write $\sim(p \equiv q)$ as $\sim[(p \supset q) \bullet (q \supset p)]$. Using De Morgan's Theorem would then give us $\sim(p \supset q) \vee \sim(q \supset p)$. All that remains is to convert the conditionals and re-arrange to finish with $\sim(\sim p \vee q) \vee \sim(p \vee \sim q)$, a disjunction of columns twelve and fourteen.

Thus we have found propositions using only negation and disjunction for every possible combination of true and false for two variables. This means that, together, negation and disjunction are truth-functionally complete. The final result is shown below. You may check the truth value patterns of any of those propositions by developing the truth table for it.

KEY POINT

Negation and disjunction form a truth-functionally complete set of logical operators. Other truth-functional sets are also possible.

The Truth-Functional Completeness of Negation and Disjunction

p ∨ ~p	p ∨ q	p ∨ ~q	p	~p ∨ q	q	~(~p ∨ ~q) ∨ ~(p ∨ q)
T	T	T	T	T	T	T
T	T	T	T	F	F	F
T	T	F	F	T	T	F
T	F	T	F	T	F	T

~(~p ∨ ~q)	~p ∨ ~q	~(~p ∨ q) ∨ ~(p ∨ ~q)	~q
T	F	F	F
F	T	T	T
F	T	T	F
F	T	F	T

~(~p ∨ q)	~p	~(p ∨ ~q)	~(p ∨ q)	~(p ∨ ~p)
F	F	F	F	F
T	F	F	F	F
F	T	T	F	F
F	T	F	T	F

We have found that we needed only two logical operators, negation and disjunction, to have a truth-functionally complete set. It is even possible to have only one logical operator that is truth-functionally complete, though it is not to be found among the five standard logical operators.

DEFINITION

The logical operator NOR (∇) is equivalent to ~(*p* ∨ *q*). It is truth-functionally complete.

One such truth-functionally complete logical operator is called NOR, which we will give the symbol ∇. Its defining truth table is

p	q	p ∇ q
T	T	F
T	F	F
F	T	F
F	F	T

The logical operator NOR is capable of producing any possible combination of true or false, though fully demonstrating this would require many pages and very complex propositions. Let it suffice to show how NOR may be used to produce the truth tables for conjunction and disjunction:

p	q	(p ∇ p) ∇ (q ∇ q)	(p ∇ q) ∇ (p ∇ q)
T	T	T	T
T	F	F	T
F	T	F	T
F	F	F	F

Working with truth-functional completeness is a fun challenge, as well as providing good practice with the logical operators, truth tables, and some of the rules of replacement. The ability to translate propositions into propositions using other logical operators is also an essential skill in the logic of digital electronics, as is shown in Unit 5.

SUMMARY

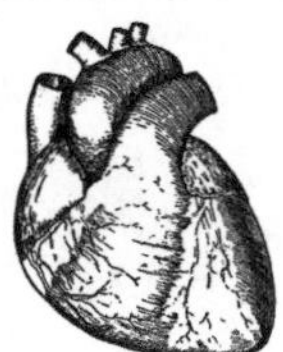

A given set of logical operators is truth-functionally complete when it is capable of forming propositions for every possible combination of true and false. The set of negation and disjunction is truth-functionally complete. Other truth-functionally complete sets are also possible.

EXERCISE 21 (30 points)

Demonstrate that negation and conjunction together form a truth-functionally complete set. For each problem, find the column of truth values under that number in the table below. Then form a compound proposition (using only ~, •, *p*, and *q*) that produces those truth values.

1	2	3	4	5	6	7	8	9	10	11	12	13	14	15	16
T	T	T	T	T	T	T	T	F	F	F	F	F	F	F	F
T	T	T	T	F	F	F	F	T	T	T	T	F	F	F	F
T	T	F	F	T	T	F	F	T	T	F	F	T	T	F	F
T	F	T	F	T	F	T	F	T	F	T	F	T	F	T	F

1. ~(p•~p) (2)
2. ~(~p•~q) (2)
3. ~(~p•q) (2)
4. p (1)
5. ~(p•~q) (2)
6. q (1)
7. ~(~p•q)•~(p•~q) (2)
8. p•q (2)
9. ~(p•q) (2)
10. ~(p•q)•~(~p•~q) (2)
11. ~q (2)
12. p•~q (2)
13. ~p (2)
14. ~p•q (2)
15. ~p•~q (2)
16. p•~p (2)

QUIZ 12 (LESSONS 20–21)

STUDENT OBJECTIVE

Complete Quiz 12.

TEACHING INSTRUCTIONS

1. Give Quiz 12. Allow 30 minutes. Grade quiz with students.
2. If you have extra time, begin reviewing for Test 6.

INTERMEDIATE LOGIC | Quiz 12

Lessons 20–21 (23 points)

Name ________________________________

1. What does it mean that a set of logical operators is *truth-functionally complete?* (3)

   All combinations of true and false for two variables are derivable using only those logical operators. In other words, any logical proposition can be symbolized using only those logical operators.

Problems 2-3: Prove <u>without</u> using *hypothetical syllogism* or *disjunctive syllogism.* (8, 6)

2.
1.	$P \supset Q$	
2.	$Q \supset R$ / ∴ $P \supset R$	
3.	P	C.P.A.
4.	Q	1, 3 M.P.
5.	R	2, 4 M.P.
6.	$P \supset R$	3-5 C.P.

3.
1.	$P \vee Q$	
2.	$\sim P$ / ∴ Q	
3.	$\sim\sim P \vee Q$	1 D.N
4.	$\sim P \supset Q$	3 Impl.
5.	Q	4, 2 M.P.

4. Translate the conditional $p \supset q$ into a proposition that uses only negation and conjunction. (3)

   $\sim(p \bullet \sim q)$

5. The logical operator NOR is truth-functionally complete. Translate the conjunction $p \bullet q$ into a proposition that uses only NOR. (3)

   $(p \triangledown p) \triangledown (q \triangledown q)$

REVIEW FOR TEST 6 (LESSONS 18–21)

STUDENT OBJECTIVE

Complete the objectives from Lessons 18–21. Objectives are listed at the beginning of each lesson's teacher's notes.

TEACHING INSTRUCTIONS

1. To review for the test, choose problems from the Review Questions for Lessons 18–21 on pp. 161–162 of the student text and from the Review Exercises for Lessons 18–21 on pp. 169–174 of the student text for students to work through.
2. If you'd like, give students "Test 6: Form A" from the *Intermediate Logic Test and Quiz Packet* as a practice exam. Go over the answers together.

ASSIGNMENT

Have students study for Test 6.

TEST 6 (LESSONS 18–21)

STUDENT OBJECTIVE

Complete Test 6.

TEACHING INSTRUCTIONS

1. Give students Test 6: Form B from the *Intermediate Logic Test and Quiz Packet.* Allow one hour to complete it.
2. Grade tests. Have them ready to hand back to students within a week.

INTERMEDIATE LOGIC | Test 6, Form A

Lessons 18–21 (65 points)

Name ______________________

1. Negation and conjunction are *truth-functionally complete*. Explain what this means. (3)

   All combinations of true and false for two variables are derivable using only negation and conjunction. In other words, any logical proposition can be symbolized using only negation and conjunction.

2. Translate the biconditional $p \equiv q$ into a proposition that uses only negation and disjunction. (4)

   $\sim(p \vee q) \vee \sim(\sim p \vee \sim q)$

Problems 3-4: Prove the argument using the *conditional proof.* (7, 9)

3.
   1. $A \supset (B \supset C)$
   2. $\sim C$ / ∴ $A \supset \sim B$

3.	A	C.P.A.
4.	$B \supset C$	1, 3 M.P.
5.	$\sim B$	4, 2 M.T.
6.	$A \supset \sim B$	3-5 C.P.

4.
   1. $D \supset F$
   2. $E \supset F$ / ∴ $(D \vee E) \supset F$

3.	$D \vee E$	C.P.A.
4.	$(D \supset F) \bullet (E \supset F)$	1, 2 Conj.
5.	$F \vee F$	4, 3 C.D.
6.	F	5 Taut.
7.	$(D \vee E) \supset F$	3-6 C.P.

Problems 5-6: Prove the argument using *reductio ad absurdum.* (9 each)

5.
   1. $G \supset H$
   2. $H \vee G$ / ∴ H

3.	$\sim H$	R.A.A.
4.	$\sim G$	1, 3 M.T.
5.	G	2, 3 D.S.
6.	$G \bullet \sim G$	5, 4 Conj.
7.	H	3-6 R.A.

6.
   1. $J \bullet (K \vee L)$
   2. $\sim(J \bullet L)$ / ∴ $J \bullet K$

3.	$\sim(J \bullet K)$	R.A.A.
4.	$(J \bullet K) \vee (J \bullet L)$	1 Dist.
5.	$J \bullet L$	4, 3 D.S.
6.	$(J \bullet L) \bullet \sim(J \bullet L)$	5, 2 Conj.
7.	$J \bullet K$	3-6 R.A.

 |

Problems 7-8: Translate the argument into symbolic form using the given constants. Then write a formal proof of validity for that symbolic argument using any of the rules from the text. (12 each)

7. "Judas could not serve both God and Mammon. If Judas was covetous then he served Mammon. Judas was covetous. Therefore, Judas did not serve God." (**G, M, C**)

1.	$\sim(G \bullet M)$	
2.	$C \supset M$	
3.	$C \quad / \quad \therefore \quad \sim G$	
4.	$\sim G \vee \sim M$	1 De M.
5.	M	2, 3 M.P.
6.	$\sim M \vee \sim G$	4 Com.
7.	$\sim\sim M$	5 D.N.
8.	$\sim G$	6, 7 D.S.

8. "You may be elected as president or vice president only if you were a native born citizen. If you were born in Africa then you are not a native born citizen. Therefore if you were born in Africa then you may not be elected as president." (**P, V, N, A**)

1.	$(P \vee V) \supset N$	
2.	$A \supset \sim N \quad / \quad \therefore \quad A \supset \sim P$	
3.	A	C.P.A.
4.	$\sim N$	2, 3 M.P.
5.	$\sim(P \vee V)$	1, 4 M.T.
6.	$\sim P \bullet \sim V$	5 De M.
7.	$\sim P$	6 Simp.
8.	$A \supset \sim P$	3-7 C.P.

INTERMEDIATE LOGIC | Test 6, Form B

Lessons 18–21 (65 points)

Name ______________________________

1. The logical operator NOR is *truth-functionally complete*. Explain what this means. (3)

   All combinations of true and false for two variables are derivable using only the logical operator NOR. In other words, any logical proposition can be symbolized using only NOR.

2. Translate the biconditional $p \equiv q$ into a proposition that uses only negation and conjunction. (4)

   $\sim(p \bullet \sim q) \bullet \sim(\sim p \bullet q)$

Problems 3-4: Prove the given arguments. Use *conditional proof* on #3, and *reductio ad absurdum* on #4. (9, 7)

3.

1.	$\sim A \supset (B \bullet C)$	
2.	$A \supset D$ / ∴ $\sim D \supset B$	
3.	$\sim D$	C.P.A.
4.	$\sim A$	2, 3 M.T.
5.	$B \bullet C$	1, 4 M.P.
6.	B	5 Simp.
7.	$\sim D \supset B$	3-6 C.P

4.

1.	$(E \vee \sim E) \supset F$ / ∴ F	
2.	$\sim F$	R.A.A.
3.	$\sim(E \vee \sim E)$	1, 2 M.T.
4.	$\sim E \bullet \sim\sim E$	3 De M.
5.	F	2-4 R.A.

Problems 5-6: Prove without using the rules of *Addition* or *Absorption*. (9, 7)

5.

1.	p / ∴ $p \vee q$	
2.	$\sim(p \vee q)$	R.A.A.
3.	$\sim p \bullet \sim q$	2 De M.
4.	$\sim p$	3 Simp.
5.	$p \bullet \sim p$	1, 4 Conj.
6.	$p \vee q$	2-5 R.A.

6.

1.	$p \supset q$ / ∴ $p \supset (p \bullet q)$	
2.	p	C.P.A.
3.	q	1, 2 M.P.
4.	$p \bullet q$	2, 3 Conj.
5.	$p \supset (p \bullet q)$	2-4 C.P.

Problems 7-8: Translate the argument into symbolic form using the given constants. Then write a formal proof of validity for that symbolic argument using any of the rules from the text.

7. If a number is even then it is a multiple of two. If a number is odd then it is not a multiple of two. Therefore, a number cannot be both even and odd." (**E, M, O**) (12)

1. $E \supset M$
2. $O \supset \sim M$ / ∴ $\sim (E \bullet O)$
3. $\sim \sim M \supset \sim O$ 2 Trans.
4. $M \supset \sim O$ 3 D.N.
5. $E \supset \sim O$ 1, 4 H.S.
6. $\sim E \vee \sim O$ 5 Impl.
7. $\sim (E \bullet O)$ 6 De M.

8. "If the Holy Spirit is eternal then He is God. If the Holy Spirit is God then He is both eternal and omnipresent. Therefore, the Holy Spirit is eternal if and only if He is God." (**E, G, O**) (14)

1. $E \supset G$
2. $G \supset (E \bullet O)$ / ∴ $E \equiv G$
3. $\sim G \vee (E \bullet O)$ 2 Impl.
4. $(\sim G \vee E) \bullet (\sim G \vee O)$ 3 Dist.
5. $\sim G \vee E$ 4 Simp.
6. $G \supset E$ 5 Impl.
7. $(E \supset G) \bullet (G \supset E)$ 1, 6 Conj.
8. $E \equiv G$ 7 Equiv.

UNIT 2

REVIEW QUESTIONS

Answers can be found in the lesson under which the questions are listed.

Lesson 13: The Rules of Inference

What is a formal proof of validity? How does a formal proof differ from a truth table? What is a rule of inference? List and state the nine rules of inference.

Lesson 14: Recognizing the Rules of Inference

Can a single variable in a rule of inference represent a more complicated proposition? Can different variables in the rules of inference represent the same proposition? Can the same variable represent different propositions from one step in a proof to the next step? How do the answers to these questions affect the writing of formal proofs?

Lesson 15: Developing Formal Proofs

Where do the premises for each step in a proof come from? What is the goal of a formal proof? Which two rules of inference are often less likely to be recognized when they are needed? How often is each step in a proof usually used later in the proof? Is this always the case?

Lesson 16: The Rules of Replacement

Can every argument be proven using only the rules of inference? What is a rule of replacement? How does a rule of replacement differ from a rule of inference? List and state the ten rules of replacement. Which rules of replacement give more than one form of equivalence?

Lesson 17: Practice with Proofs

What are some benefits of learning to write formal proofs? What rule must be used in a proof which has a constant that appears in the conclusion but not in the premises? What rule is likely to be used if a conditional appears in the conclusion but not in the premises?

Lesson 18: The Conditional Proof

What is the Conditional Proof? How does it differ from the rules taught in previous lessons? To use the Conditional Proof, must the conclusion of the argument being proven be a conditional? Where does the assumption in a Conditional Proof come from? May this assumption be made without using the Conditional Proof? May a step be taken from the middle of a Conditional Proof and used in the formal proof after the Conditional Proof is completed?

Lesson 19: The Reductio Ad Absurdum

What is a *Reductio ad Absurdum*? Where, other than in formal proofs of validity, is this technique used? What is the procedure for using the *Reductio ad Absurdum* rule in proofs? Where does the assumption in a *Reductio ad Absurdum* come from? What are several similarities between the *Reductio ad Absurdum* and the Conditional Proof?

Lesson 20: Proving Rules Unnecessary

Are all nine rules of inference necessary for writing any formal proof of validity? What would be the benefit of removing some of the given rules? What would be the benefit of adding new rules?

Lesson 21: Truth-Functional Completeness

What does it mean that the five logical operators are truth-functionally complete? What other sets of logical operators are truth-functionally complete? Is it possible for a single logical operator to form a truth-functionally complete set?

UNIT 2

REVIEW EXERCISES

Students may do these exercises for further review of this unit.

ADDITIONAL EXERCISES FOR LESSON 13

1. Three of the rules of inference contain one premise and one conclusion. In which rule of inference is the premise equivalent to the conclusion?

   The rule of absorption.

2. Consider this disjunctive syllogism: $p \vee q,\ p,\ \therefore \sim q$. Is this valid or invalid? Under what interpretation of the disjunction could it be considered valid? How could such a rule be written most concisely?

   This is invalid, as seen when p and q are both true. But if the "or" was taken to be an exclusive or, then this would be a valid argument, as in this example: "This argument is either valid or invalid. This argument is valid. Therefore it is not invalid." But rather than symbolizing the argument with the entire $(p \vee q) \bullet \sim(p \bullet q),\ p,\ \therefore \sim q$, you could use this more concise argument: $\sim(p \bullet q),\ p,\ \therefore \sim q$.

3. Consider this argument form: $\sim(p \bullet q),\ \therefore \sim p$. Students who are first learning formal proofs often try to simplify the compound proposition in this way. Show it is invalid.

   You may already have shown such an argument to be invalid, if you have done Problem 4 in the additional exercises for Lesson 7. The argument can be seen to be invalid by any method, when p is true and q is false.

4. In the rule of Addition, p, ∴ p ∨ q, where does the *q* "come from"?

The q comes "out of thin air." This means that, using the rule of Addition, you may add any proposition that you need.

ADDITIONAL EXERCISES FOR LESSON 14

1. Rewrite the proof for the argument in Exercise 14a, Problem 13, in one less step than the text shows.

1) X⊃Y
2) X
3) W⊃Z / ∴ Y∨Z
4) Y   1, 2 M.P.
5) Y∨Z   4 Add.

For the following formal proofs of validity, give the justification for each step.

2.
1) (A ∨ B) ⊃ C
2) A • D / ∴ C
3) A   2 Simp.
4) A ∨ B   3 Add.
5) C   1, 4 M.P.

3.
1) F ⊃ G
2) G ⊃ (H ∨ I)
3) ~H
4) F / ∴ I • F
5) F ⊃ (H ∨ I)   1, 2 H.S.
6) H ∨ I   5, 4 M.P.
7) I   6, 3 D.S.
8) I • F   7, 4 Conj.

4.
1) J ⊃ K
2) L ⊃ M
3) J ∨ L
4) K ⊃ N
5) ~N / ∴ M
6) (J ⊃ K) • (L ⊃ M)   1, 2 Conj.
7) K ∨ M   6, 3 C.D.
8) ~K   4, 5 M.T.
9) M   7, 8 D.S.

5.
1) P ⊃ Q
2) ~(P • Q) / ∴ ~P ∨ R
3) P ⊃ (P • Q)   1 Abs.
4) ~P   3, 2 M.T.
5) ~P ∨ R   4 Add.

ADDITIONAL EXERCISES FOR LESSON 15

1. Write three different proofs for this argument, each using exactly three additional steps:

1) A ⊃ B
2) B ⊃ C
3) A / ∴ A • C
4) A ⊃ C 1, 2 H.S.
5) C 4, 3 M.P.
6) A • C 3, 5 Conj.
Q.E.D.

1) A ⊃ B
2) B ⊃ C
3) A / ∴ A • C
4) B 1, 3 M.P.
5) C 2, 4 M.P.
6) A • C 3, 5 Conj.
Q.E.D.

1) A ⊃ B
2) B ⊃ C
3) A / ∴ A • C
4) A ⊃ C 1, 2 H.S.
5) A ⊃ (A • C) 4 Abs.
6) A • C 5, 3 M.P.
Q.E.D.

2. Write a different proof for Problem 4 in the Additional Exercises for Lesson 14.

1) J ⊃ K
2) L ⊃ M
3) J ∨ L
4) K ⊃ N.
5) ~N / ∴ M
6) ~K 4, 5 M.T.
7) ~J 1, 6 M.T.
8) L 3, 7 D.S.
9) M 2, 8 M.P
Q.E.D.

3. Prove this argument: "If this argument is valid, then if the premises are true then the conclusion is true. This argument is valid. The conclusion is false. Therefore, the premises are not true."

1) V ⊃ (P ⊃ C)
2) V
3) ~C / ∴ ~P
4) P ⊃ C 1, 2 M.P.
5) ~P 4, 3 M.T.
Q.E.D.

ADDITIONAL EXERCISES FOR LESSON 16

1. Material Implication says that *(p ⊃ q) ≡ (~p ∨ q)*. Some logic texts include an additional equivalence under this rule: *(p ⊃ q) ≡ ~(p • ~q)*. Prove this argument, using the rules of replacement, in order to demonstrate this equivalence: *P ⊃ Q, ∴ ~(P • ~Q)*.

1) P ⊃ Q / ∴ ~(P • ~Q)
2) ~P ∨ Q 1 Impl..
3) ~ P ∨ ~~Q 2 D.N.
4) ~(P • ~Q) 3 DeM.
Q.E.D.

2. We assume in the text that $p \equiv q$ implies $q \equiv p$. Prove this using the rules of Commutation and Material Equivalence.

1) $P \equiv Q$ / $\therefore Q \equiv P$	
2) $(P \supset Q) \bullet (Q \supset P)$	1 Equiv.
3) $(Q \supset P) \bullet (P \supset Q)$	2 Com.
4) $Q \equiv P$	3 Equiv.
Q.E.D.	

3. The rule of Exportation says that $[(p \bullet q) \supset r] \equiv [p \supset (q \supset r)]$. Show that this is true by proving the argument $(P \bullet Q) \supset R$, $\therefore P \supset (Q \supset R)$ *without* using Exportation.

1) $(P \bullet Q) \supset R$ / $\therefore P \supset (Q \supset R)$	
2) $\sim(P \bullet Q) \vee R$	1 Impl.
3) $(\sim P \vee \sim Q) \vee R$	2 DeM.
4) $\sim P \vee (\sim Q \vee R)$	3 Assoc.
5) $\sim P \vee (Q \supset R)$	4 Impl.
6) $P \supset (Q \supset R)$	5 Impl.
Q.E.D.	

4. Justify this one-step proof in two different ways:

1) $P \bullet P$ / $\therefore P$	
2) P	1 Simp.
Q.E.D.	

1) $P \bullet P$ / $\therefore P$	
2) P	1 Taut.
Q.E.D.	

ADDITIONAL EXERCISES FOR LESSON 17

1. Prove the argument from Problem 12 in Exercise 7a.

1) $S \supset G$	
2) $\sim S \supset P$ / $\therefore G \vee P$	
3) $\sim G \supset \sim S$	1 Trans.
4) $\sim G \supset P$	3, 2 H.S.
5) $\sim\sim G \vee P$	4 Impl.
6) $G \vee P$	5 D.N.
Q.E.D.	

2. Prove the argument from Problem 12 in Exercise 14b.

1) $[(F \bullet C) \bullet S] \supset B$	
2) $\sim B$	
3) F / $\therefore \sim C \vee \sim S$	
4) $[F \bullet (C \bullet S)] \supset B$	1 Assoc.
5) $F \supset [(C \bullet S) \supset B]$	4 Exp.
6) $(C \bullet S) \supset B$	5, 3 M.P.
7) $\sim(C \bullet S)$	6, 2 M.T.
8) $\sim C \vee \sim S$	7 DeM.
Q.E.D.	

3. Prove the argument from Problem 1 in Exercise 9.

1) $P \equiv Q$	
2) $Q \equiv R$ / $\therefore P \equiv R$	
3) $(P \supset Q) \bullet (Q \supset P)$	1 Equiv.
4) $(Q \supset R) \bullet (R \supset Q)$	2 Equiv.
5) $(Q \supset P) \bullet (P \supset Q)$	3 Com.
6) $(R \supset Q) \bullet (Q \supset R)$	4 Com.
7) $P \supset Q$	3 Simp.
8) $Q \supset R$	4 Simp.
9) $P \supset R$	7, 8 H.S.
10) $Q \supset P$	5 Simp.
11) $R \supset Q$	6 Simp.
12) $R \supset P$	11, 10 H.S.
13) $(P \supset R) \bullet (R \supset P)$	9, 12 Conj.
14) $P \equiv R$	13 Equiv.
Q.E.D.	

4. Prove the argument from Problem 4 in the Additional Exercises for Lesson 9.

1) $V \supset (P \equiv T)$	
2) $(V \bullet P) \vee (V \bullet T)$ / $\therefore P \bullet T$.	
3) $V \bullet (P \vee T)$	2 Dist.
4) V	3 Simp.
5) $P \equiv T$	1, 4 M.P.
6) $(P \bullet T) \vee (\sim P \bullet \sim T)$	5 Equiv.
7) $(\sim P \bullet \sim T) \vee (P \bullet T)$	6 Com.
8) $(P \vee T) \bullet V$	3 Com.
9) $P \vee T$	8 Simp.
10) $\sim\sim(P \vee T)$	9 D.N.
11) $\sim(\sim P \bullet \sim T)$	10 DeM.
12) $P \bullet T$	7, 11 D.S.
Q.E.D.	

5. Prove the argument from Problem 1 in the Additional Exercises for Lesson 8.

1) $P \equiv (L \bullet O)$	
2) L	
3) O	
4) E / $\therefore \sim(P \supset \sim E)$	
5) $[P \supset (L \bullet O)] \bullet [(L \bullet O) \supset P]$	1 Equiv.
6) $[(L \bullet O) \supset P] \bullet [P \supset (L \bullet O)]$	5 Com.
7) $(L \bullet O) \supset P$	6 Simp.
8) $L \bullet O$	2, 3 Conj.
9) P	7, 8 M.P.
10) $P \bullet E$	9, 4 Conj.
11) $\sim\sim(P \bullet E)$	10 D.N.
12) $\sim(\sim P \vee \sim E)$	11 DeM.
13) $\sim(P \supset \sim E)$	12 Impl.
Q.E.D.	

Symbolize and prove each argument.

6. It is not the case that the senator is a Republican or a Democrat. If the senator is not a Republican, then he is a Democrat or an Independent. Consequently, the Senator must be an Independent.

1) ~(R ∨ D)
2) ~R ⊃ (D ∨ I) / ∴ I
3) ~~R ∨ (D ∨ I) 2 Impl.
4) R ∨ (D ∨ I) 3 D.N.
5) (R ∨ D) ∨ I 4 Assoc.
6) I 5, 1 D.S.
Q.E.D.

7. If the Bible is true then the Holy Spirit is eternal. If the Bible is true and the Holy Spirit is eternal, then the Spirit has attributes of deity. If the Bible is true, then if the Spirit has attributes of deity, then the Spirit is God. Thus, if the Bible is true then the Spirit is God.

1) B ⊃ E
2) (B • E) ⊃ D
3) B ⊃ (D ⊃ G) / ∴ B ⊃ G
4) B ⊃ (B • E) 1 Abs.
5) B ⊃ D 4, 2 H.S.
6) B ⊃ (B • D) 5 Abs.
7) (B • D) ⊃ G 3 Exp.
8) B ⊃ G 6, 7 H.S.
Q.E.D.

8. If he does not move his pawn, then he will lose both his queen and his rook. If he moves his pawn or loses his queen, then he will lose his bishop. Therefore, he either moves his pawn and loses his bishop or he loses both his bishop and his queen.

1) ~P ⊃ (Q • R)
2) (P ∨ Q) ⊃ B / ∴ (P • B) ∨ (B • Q)
3) ~~P ∨ (Q • R) 1 Impl.
4) P ∨ (Q • R) 3 D.N.
5) (P ∨ Q) • (P ∨ R) 4 Dist
6) P ∨ Q 5 Simp.
7) B 2, 6 M.P.
8) B • (P ∨ Q) 7, 6 Conj.
9) (B • P) ∨ (B • Q) 8 Dist.
10) (P • B) ∨ (B • Q) 9 Com.
Q.E.D.

9. Either the prince will take the throne or the queen will, but they will not both take the throne. Therefore, either the prince will take the throne and the queen will not, or the queen will take the throne and the prince will not.

1) (P ∨ Q) • ~(P • Q) / ∴ (P • ~Q) ∨ (Q • ~P)
2) ~~(P ∨ Q) • ~(P • Q) 1 D.N.
3) ~(~P • ~Q) • ~(P • Q) 2 DeM.
4) ~(P • Q) • ~(~P • ~Q) 3 Com.
5) ~[(P • Q) ∨ (~P • ~Q)] 4 DeM.
6) ~(P ≡ Q) 5 Equiv.
7) ~[(P ⊃ Q) • (Q ⊃ P)] 6 Equiv.
8) ~(P ⊃ Q) ∨ ~(Q ⊃ P) 7 DeM.
9) ~(~P ∨ Q) ∨ ~(~Q ∨ P) 8 Impl. (2x)
10) (~~P • ~Q) ∨ (~~Q • ~P) 9 DeM. (2x)
11) (P • ~Q) ∨ (Q • ~P) 10 D.N. (2x)
Q.E.D.

ADDITIONAL EXERCISES FOR LESSON 18

1. One logic textbook attempted to show that using the Conditional Proof can make a proof simpler by using the example below. Use the Conditional Proof to rewrite this proof in six total steps, as that textbook did. Then rewrite the proof in six total steps *without* using the Conditional Proof.

1) A⊃(B⊃C)	
2) B / ∴ A⊃C	
3) ~A∨(B⊃C)	1 Impl.
4) ~A∨(~B∨C)	3 Impl.
5) (~A∨~B)∨C	4 Assoc.
6) (~B∨~A)∨C	5 Com.
7) ~B∨(~A∨C)	6 Assoc.
8) ~~B	2 D.N.
9) ~A∨C	7, 8 D.S.
10) A⊃C	9 Impl.

Shorter Proof, with C.P.A.

1) A⊃(B⊃C)	
2) B / ∴ A⊃C	
3) A	C.P.A.
4) B⊃C	1, 3 M.P.
5) C	4, 2 M.P.
6) A⊃C	3-5 C.P.

Q.E.D.

Shorter Proof, without C.P.A.

1) A⊃(B⊃C)	
2) B / ∴ A⊃C	
3) (A•B)⊃C	1 Exp.
4) (B•A)⊃C	3 Com.
5) B⊃(A⊃C)	4 Exp.
6) A⊃C	5, 2 M.P.

Q.E.D.

2. Solve Problem 9 in Exercise 18 without using the Conditional Proof.

1) (A⊃B)•(C⊃D) / ∴ (A•C)⊃(B•D)	
2) (~A∨B)•(~C∨D)	1 Impl. (2x)
3) ~A∨B	2 Simp.
4) (~C∨D)•(~A∨B)	2 Com.
5) ~C∨D	4 Simp.
6) (~A∨B)∨~C	3 Add.
7) (~C∨D)∨~A	5 Add.
8) [(~A∨B)∨~C]•[(~C∨D)∨~A]	6, 7 Conj.
9) [(B∨~A)∨~C]•[~A∨(~C∨D)]	8 Com. (2x)
10) [B∨(~A∨~C)]•[(~A∨~C)∨D]	9 Assoc. (2x)
11) [(~A∨~C)∨B]•[(~A∨~C)∨D]	10 Com.
12) (~A∨~C)∨(B•D)	11 Dist.
13) ~(A•C)∨(B•D)	12 DeM.
14) (A•C)⊃(B•D)	13 Impl.

Q.E.D.

Use Conditional Proof to do the following:

3. Prove the argument from Problem 3 in the Additional Exercises for Lesson 8.

1) M ≡ [K • (A ∨ D)]	
2) F ⊃ [K • (~A • D)] / ∴ F ⊃ M	
3) F	C.P.A.
4) K • (~A • D)	2, 3 M.P.
5) K • (D • ~A)	4 Com.
6) (K • D) • ~A	5 Assoc.
7) K • D	6 Simp.
8) (K • D) ∨ (K • A)	7 Add.
9) K • (D ∨ A)	8 Dist.
10) K • (A ∨ D)	9 Com.
11) {M ⊃ [K • (A ∨ D)]} • {[K • (A ∨ D)] ⊃ M}	1 Equiv.
12) {[K • (A ∨ D)] ⊃ M} • {M ⊃ [K • (A ∨ D)]}	11 Com.
13) [K • (A ∨ D)] ⊃ M	12 Simp.
14) M	13,10 M.P.
15) F ⊃ M	3-14 C.P.
Q.E.D.	

4. Prove the argument from Problem 5 in the Additional Exercises for Lesson 8.

1) V ⊃ (C ⊃ P)	
2) C	
3) D ⊃ V / ∴ ~D ∨ P	
4) D	C.P.A.
5) V	3, 4 M.P.
6) C ⊃ P	1, 5 M.P.
7) P	6, 2 M.P.
8) D ⊃ P	4-7 C.P.
9) ~D ∨ P	8 Impl.
Q.E.D.	

ADDITIONAL EXERCISES FOR LESSON 19

1. Solve Problem 3 in Exercise 19 without using Reductio ad Absurdum.

1) P ⊃ Q	
2) Q ∨ P / ∴ Q	
3) ~~Q ∨ P	2 D.N.
4) ~Q ⊃ P	3 Impl.
5) ~Q ⊃ Q	4, 1 H.S.
6) ~~Q ∨ Q	5 Impl.
7) Q ∨ Q	6 D.N.
8) Q	7 Taut.
Q.E.D.	

2. Use the Reductio ad Absurdum method to prove the argument from Problem 4 in the Additional Exercises for Lesson 8. Then prove the argument without using Reductio ad Absurdum. Which method is shorter? Which method is easier?

1) G⊃(P•I)	
2) P⊃D	
3) I⊃A	
4) E⊃(~D∨~A)	
5) E / ∴ ~G	
6) G	RAA.
7) P•I	1, 6 MP.
8) P	7 Simp.
9) I•P	7 Com.
10) I	9 Simp.
11) D	2, 8 MP.
12) A	3, 10 MP.
13) D•A	11, 12 Conj.
14) ~D∨~A	4, 5 MP.
15) ~(D•A)	14 DeM.
16) (D•A)•~(D•A)	13, 15 Conj.
17) ~G	6-16 RA.
Q.E.D.	

1) G⊃(P•I)	
2) P⊃D	
3) I⊃A	
4) E⊃(~D∨~A)	
5) E / ∴ ~G	
6) ~D∨~A	4, 5 MP.
7) (P⊃D)•(I⊃A)	2, 3 Conj.
8) (~D⊃~P)•(~A⊃~I)	7 Trans. (2x)
9) ~P∨~I	8, 6 C.D.
10) ~(P•I)	9 DeM.
11) ~G	1, 10 MT.
Q.E.D.	

The proof that does not use Reductio is six steps shorter, but the steps for the proof which uses Reductio might be easier to see.

Problems 3–5: Use the Reductio ad Absurdum method to prove each arguments.

3. (P ∨ ~P) ⊃ Q ∴ Q

1) (P∨~P)⊃Q / ∴ Q	
2) ~Q	RAA.
3) ~(P∨~P)	1, 2 MT.
4) ~P•~~P	3 DeM.
5) Q	2-4 RA.
Q.E.D.	

4. If God does not exist then there is neither rationality nor absolute morals. If there is no rationality then there is no foundation for logic. But there is a foundation for logic. Therefore God exists.

1) ~G⊃(~R•~A)	
2) ~R⊃~F	
3) F / ∴ G	
4) ~G	RAA
5) ~R•~A	1, 4 MP.
6) ~R	5 Simp.
7) ~F	2, 6 MP.
8) F•~F	3, 7 Conj.
9) G	4-8 RA.
Q.E.D.	

5. If the square root of two is not irrational then it can be written as a ratio of integers and those integers have no common factors. If it can be written as a ratio of integers then both integers are even. If both integers are even then they have common factors. Thus, the square root of two is irrational.

1) ~I ⊃ (R • ~C)	
2) R ⊃ B	
3) B ⊃ C / ∴ I	
4) ~I	R.A.A.
5) R • ~C	1, 4 M.P.
6) ~~R • ~C	5 D.N.
7) ~(~R ∨ C)	6 DeM.
8) ~(R ⊃ C)	7 Impl.
9) R ⊃ C	2, 3 H.S.
10) (R ⊃ C) • ~(R ⊃ C)	9, 8 Conj.
11) I	4-10 R.A.
Q.E.D.	

ADDITIONAL EXERCISES FOR LESSON 20

1. Prove the Constructive Dilemma rule without using Constructive Dilemma, Modus Tollens, Absorption, Hypothetical Syllogism, Disjunctive Syllogism, or Addition. If all of these are thus eliminated, which three rules of inference remain?

1) (P ⊃ Q) • (R ⊃ S)	
2) P ∨ R / ∴ Q ∨ S	
3) ~Q	C.P.A.
4) P ⊃ Q	1 Simp.
5) ~Q ⊃ ~P	4 Trans.
6) ~P	5, 3 M.P.
7) ~~P ∨ R	2 D.N.
8) ~P ⊃ R	7 Impl.
9) R	8, 6 M.P.
10) (R ⊃ S) • (P ⊃ Q)	1 Com.
11) R ⊃ S	10 Simp.
12) S	11, 9 M.P.
13) ~Q ⊃ S	3-12 C.P.
14) ~~Q ∨ S	13 Impl.
15) Q ∨ S	14 D.N.
Q.E.D.	

The three remaining rules of inference are Modus Ponens, Simplification, and Conjunction.

2. Limiting yourself to those three remaining rules of inference, the rules of replacement, the Conditional Proof, and Reductio ad Absurdum, write proofs for Problems 6 through 8 in the additional exercises for Lesson 17.

#6.

1) $\sim(R \vee D)$		
2) $\sim R \supset (D \vee I)$	/ $\therefore I$	
3) $\sim\sim R \vee (D \vee I)$	2 Impl.	
4) $R \vee (D \vee I)$	3 D.N.	
5) $(R \vee D) \vee I$	4 Assoc.	
6) $\sim\sim(R \vee D) \vee I$	5 D.N.	
7) $\sim(R \vee D) \supset I$	6 Impl.	
8) I	7, 1 M.P.	
Q.E.D.		

#7

1) $B \supset E$		
2) $(B \bullet E) \supset D$		
3) $B \supset (D \supset G)$	/ $\therefore B \supset G$	
4) $B \supset (E \supset D)$	2 Exp.	
5) B	C.P.A.	
6) $E \supset D$	4, 5 M.P.	
7) E	1, 5 M.P.	
8) D	6, 7 M.P.	
9) $D \supset G$	3, 5 M.P.	
10) G	9, 8 M.P.	
11) $B \supset G$	5-10 C.P.	
Q.E.D.		

#8

1) $\sim P \supset (Q \bullet R)$		
2) $(P \vee Q) \supset B$	/ $\therefore (P \bullet B) \vee (B \bullet Q)$	
3) $\sim\sim P \vee (Q \bullet R)$	1 Impl.	
4) $P \vee (Q \bullet R)$	3 D.N.	
5) $(P \vee Q) \bullet (P \vee R)$	4 Dist.	
6) $P \vee Q$	5 Simp.	
7) B	2, 6 M.P.	
8) $B \bullet (P \vee Q)$	7, 6 Conj.	
9) $(B \bullet P) \vee (B \bullet Q)$	8 Dist.	
10) $(P \bullet B) \vee (B \bullet Q)$	9 Com.	
Q.E.D.		

(Notice that #8 required no changes)

ADDITIONAL EXERCISES FOR LESSON 21

1. Do the logical operators negation and conditional form a truth-functionally complete set? Explain your answer.

Yes they do. It is sufficient to show that using only negation and conditional, both disjunction and conjunction can be formed, as follows:

$\sim p \supset q \equiv \sim\sim p \vee q \equiv p \vee q$

$\sim(p \supset \sim q) \equiv \sim(\sim p \vee \sim q) \equiv \sim\sim p \bullet \sim\sim q \equiv p \bullet q$

Given this, all truth tables can be formed. For example, the truth table for biconditional can be produced from this proposition: $\sim[(p \supset q) \supset \sim(q \supset p)]$.

2. Fully demonstrate the truth-functional completeness of the logical operator NOR.

What follows is one possibility (the numbers correspond to the column numbers in Exercise 21):

1) $[P \triangledown (P \triangledown P)] \triangledown [P \triangledown (P \triangledown P)]$
2) $(P \triangledown Q) \triangledown (P \triangledown Q)$
3) $[P \triangledown (Q \triangledown Q)] \triangledown [P \triangledown (Q \triangledown Q)]$
4) P
5) $[(P \triangledown P) \triangledown Q] \triangledown [(P \triangledown P) \triangledown Q]$
6) Q
7) $[P \triangledown (Q \triangledown Q)] \triangledown [(P \triangledown P) \triangledown Q]$
8) $(P \triangledown P) \triangledown (Q \triangledown Q)$
9) $[P \triangledown (P \triangledown P)] \triangledown [(P \triangledown P) \triangledown (Q \triangledown Q)]$
10) $(P \triangledown Q) \triangledown [(P \triangledown P) \triangledown (Q \triangledown Q)]$
11) $Q \triangledown Q$
12) $(P \triangledown Q) \triangledown Q$
13) $P \triangledown P$
14) $P \triangledown (Q \triangledown Q)$
15) $P \triangledown Q$
16) $P \triangledown (P \triangledown P)$

3. Another truth-functionally complete logical operator is NAND, which is a negated conjunction. Assume the symbol for NAND is #, so that $(p \# q) \equiv \sim(p \bullet q)$. Using only this logical operator, develop propositions equivalent to $\sim p$, $p \bullet q$, and $p \vee q$.

$\sim p \equiv \sim(p \bullet p) \equiv p \# p$
$p \bullet q \equiv \sim\sim(p \bullet q) \equiv \sim(p \# q) \equiv (p \# q) \# (p \# q)$
$p \vee q \equiv \sim\sim p \vee \sim\sim q \equiv \sim(\sim p \bullet \sim q) \equiv \sim p \# \sim q \equiv (p \# p) \# (q \# q)$

UNIT 3

TRUTH TREES

CONTENTS

TEACHER'S NOTES on LESSON 22

TRUTH TREES FOR CONSISTENCY

Intermediate Logic, pp. 177–181

STUDENT OBJECTIVES

1. Use a truth tree to determine the consistency of a set of propositions.
2. Complete Exercise 22.

TEACHING INSTRUCTIONS

1. Ask students what it means for a set of propositions to be *consistent.* Remind them that **a set of propositions is consistent if the propositions can all be true at the same time**. See if they remember using the shorter truth tables to determine the consistency of a set of propositions; remind them that we simply wrote the propositions in symbolic form and assumed they were consistent; if we found a contradiction, we knew they were inconsistent. Explain that **truth trees**, which we are about to start studying, also allow us to determine the consistency of a set of propositions, but they do so in a different way: by breaking those propositions down into simple components so we can look for contradictions. Explain that making a truth tree is a lot like taking apart a machine to see how it works. Just like we take a machine apart to see what exactly is broken, the truth trees will show exactly where the contradiction lies in an inconsistent set; just like taking apart a machine makes us familiar with what all the parts of the machine have to be doing in order for it to work correctly, making a truth tree allows us to determine the truth values of all the variables for which a set is consistent. Explain that truth trees are a useful tool in higher level logic.
2. But enough with the chit-chat. Tell students that **a truth tree is a diagram which shows a set of propositions being decomposed into their literals**. This sounds confusing, but tell students that **we say a compound proposition is "decomposed" when it is broken down into simple propositions (or the negation of simple propositions) which are called literals**.
3. For example, write on the board the set *{A, ~B • C}* which could represent the propositions "I like milk" and "I am not a gorilla but I am alive." Tell students that it should be obvious to everyone that these propositions are logically consistent, that they would have no problem all being true at the same time. But let's pretend we are not very bright and that we really aren't sure if it's possible to like milk and not be a gorilla but still be alive. In that case, we can set up a truth tree. Just like in the shorter truth tables, we start out by assuming that *A* and *~B • C* are consistent—that they can both be true at once. But what would the truth values of the individual constants (*A*, *~B*, and *C*) have to be for the propositions to both be true? Make sure students see that obviously *A* would have to be true. And because *~B • C* is a conjunction, in order for it to be true both the individual parts, *~B* and *C*, must also be true.

4. Explain that we can demonstrate this in a visual way by "decomposing" the compound propositions into their literals—variables or constant and their negations—like this (write it on the board):

   A
   ~B • C ✓
   ~B
   C

   Explain that this is a simple truth tree; we have "decomposed" a set of propositions down to their literals. Point out that once we have decomposed *~B • C* we check it off and from then on ignore it, because it had been replaced by its literals.

5. Explain that after we have decomposed the propositions in the truth tree, the next step is to recover the truth values, or to determine the truth values of the simple constants or variables that will make the propositions consistent. For this truth tree, we would come up with this table:

A	B	C
T	F	T

   In other words, the set {*A*, *~B • C*} is shown to be consistent when *A* is true, *B* is false (because *~B* was true), and *C* is true. If you like, have students walk you through completing a longer truth table for this set of propositions; show that the original set members are all true (and therefore consistent) on the row in which *A* and *C* are true and *B* is false.

6. Explain that just like in formal proofs of validity, it is customary (and we must at all times be customary) to number each step in a truth tree and provide justification for it. Write this more filled-out truth tree for the previous example on the board:

1)	A	SM	
2)	~B • C ✓	SM	CONSISTENT
3)	~B	2 •D	
4)	C	2 •D	
	○		

A	B	C
T	F	T

   Explain that we label the members of the original set "SM" for "Set Member." Steps 3 and 4 are justified by step 2 and the **conjunction decomposition rule** which says (write it on the board):

   p • q ✓
   p
   q

   Explain that we abbreviate this rule to *•D* for "conjunction decomposition." Finally, explain that we place a circle underneath the truth tree to identify it as an **open branch, or a path on a truth tree which includes no contradictions between the literals.**

7. Now write on the board the set {*D • ~E*, *~~E*}, which could signify, for example, "It is 7:00 in the morning and there cannot be a marching band outside," and "There is not an absence of a marching band outside." Once again, it should be obvious to everyone whether these propositions are consistent or not, but tell students to pretend it isn't. Ask them if either of the two propositions in this set is literal. Make sure they see that neither is, and so both must be decomposed. Remind them that since we are trying to determine consistency, we begin by assuming that both these propositions are true. If *~~E* is true, then its literal *E* must also be true. Thus, *~~E* decomposes down to *E* by the **double negation decomposition rule**, or:

   ~~p ✓
   p

   Just as in the previous example, for *D • ~E* to be true, both its literals, *D* and *~E*, must be true by the conjunction decomposition rule. Have students walk you through making the truth tree. It should look like this:

1)	D • ~E ✓	SM	
2)	~~E ✓	SM	
3)	E	2 ~~D	INCONSISTENT
4)	D	1 •D	
5)	~E	1 •D	
	3 × 5		

8. Make sure students follow that step 3 is justified by step 2 and the double negation decomposition rule (abbreviated ~~D), and that steps 4 and 5 are justified by a conjunction decomposition of step one. Make sure they also see the contradiction between steps 3 and 5, since E and ~E cannot both be true, and explain that we have therefore labeled the truth tree with 3 × 5, meaning "step three contradicts step 5," identifying it as a **closed branch, or a path on a truth tree which includes at least one contradiction**. These propositions are therefore inconsistent. Also point out that every decomposed compound proposition is checked off.

9. Tell students that now that we have seen how conjunctions and double negations are decomposed to their literals, it's time to look at something a little trickier: the decomposition of disjunctions. Write this set of propositions on the board: {*F* ∨ *G*, ~*F*}, which could symbolize something like "Either I'm crazy or you are crazy," and "I am not crazy." Remind students that we begin by assuming that the two propositions are consistent, so we assume that both ~*F* and *F* ∨ *G* are true. ~*F* is already a literal, but we have to decompose *F* ∨ *G* before we can do anything else with it.

10. Ask students what the truth values of *F* and *G* have to be for *F* ∨ *G* to be true. Remind them that a disjunction is true whenever either disjunct is true. So unlike with a conjunction, we have a couple options for how to decompose *F* ∨ *G*. Explain that we represent this in a truth tree by **branching** (branching . . . trees . . . get it?), where each branch represents a possible combination of literals that would need to be true for the proposition to be consisent. The **disjunction decomposition rule** looks like this:

```
    p ∨ q    ✓
     /\
    p  q
```

And this is how we set up the truth tree (write this on the board):

```
1)   F ∨ G    ✓
2)    ~F
      /\
3)   F  G
```

11. Have students look at the two branches. Make sure students see that for the set to be consistent, one branch or the other would have to be true: either the ~*F* and *F* branch, in which case both ~*F* and *F* would both have to be true, or the ~*F* and *G* branch, in which case ~*F* and *G* would both have to be true. The first is obviously impossible (I can't be crazy and not crazy), but the second is possible (I can be sane and you can be crazy). So we do have one consistent branch. Write the final truth tree on the board:

```
1)   F ∨ G  ✓   SM
2)    ~F        SM       CONSISTENT
      /\
3)   F  G       1 ∨D       F  G
    2×3  O                 ----
                           F  T
```

Make sure students understand that step 3 is justified by step one and disjunction decomposition (abbreviated ∨*D*), that the contradiction between steps 2 and 3 closes the left branch, but that the right branch is labeled as open, since there is no contradiction. Tell students that **as long as one or more branches in a truth tree is open, the set is consistent**. So the members of the set {*F* ∨ *G*, ~*F*} are true when *F* is false and *G* is true.

12. Tell students that you are going to do two more examples together before you set them loose on the exercises. Write on the board the set {*P* • ~*Q*, ~*P* ∨ *Q*}. Have students walk you through completing the truth tree, which should look like this:

```
1)  P • ~Q  ✓   SM
2)  ~P ∨ Q  ✓   SM
3)     P        1 •D    INCONSISTENT
4)     ~Q       1 •D
      / \
5)  ~P    Q     2 ∨D
   3×5  4×5
```

Make sure students understand that because both branches are closed, the two propositions are inconsistent.

13. Write on the board that set {*P* • *Q*, *Q* ∨ ~*R*}, and have students walk you through making the truth tree. It should look like this:

```
1)  P • Q   ✓   SM
2)  Q ∨ ~R  ✓   SM
3)    P         1 •D    CONSISTENT
4)    Q         1 •D
     / \                 P  Q  R
5)  Q  ~R       2 ∨D     T  T  F
    O   O                T  T  T
```

Now it's time to recover the truth values. Set up a truth table for all the truth values of *P*, *Q* and *R* for which these propositions are consistent. Begin with the right branch: for the right branch *P* and *Q* are true and *R* is false, so the truth table should look like this:

P	Q	R
T	T	F

On the left branch *P* and *Q* are once again true, but R does not appear at all. Tell students that when a proposition does not appear on an open branch like this, the recovered truth values should account for both possible truth values of that proposition. So the truth table for the left branch should look like this:

P	Q	R
T	T	F
T	T	T

Make sure students understand that in sum, the set of propositions is consistent when *P* and *Q* are true, regardless of the truth value of *R*.

14. Before students begin working on the exercises, have them review the procedure for determining consistency using truth trees on p. 181 of their textbooks.

ASSIGNMENT

Have students complete Exercise 22, and go over it with them.

LESSON 22

TRUTH TREES FOR CONSISTENCY

The consistency of a set of propositions is a foundational concept in symbolic logic. If you recall, a set of propositions is consistent if the propositions can all be true at the same time. The shorter truth table provided a relatively effortless method for determining the consistency of a set of propositions. We simply wrote the propositions in symbolic form, then assumed that they were consistent. If a contradiction was found, the propositions were inconsistent. Otherwise they were consistent.

DEFINITION

A ***truth tree*** is a diagram that shows a set of propositions being decomposed into their literals.

Truth trees allow us to determine the consistency of a set of propositions by breaking those propositions down into simple components and looking for contradictions. Like shorter truth tables, truth trees display exactly where the contradiction lies in an inconsistent set, as well as allowing us to easily determine the truth values of the variables or constants for which a set of consistent propositions is consistent. The truth tree is a useful tool in higher-level logic.

We will start with a very basic example. Consider the set *{A, ~B • C}*. This could represent the propositions *I like apples* and *I don't like bananas but I like carrots.* It should be obvious that these propositions are logically consistent; they could both be true at the same time. Now, what would be the truth values of each of the constants if these propositions were both true? Obviously A would have to be true. In order for the compound proposition ~B • C to be true, both ~B must be true and C must be true. This can be demonstrated by **decomposing** the compound proposition, meaning that we break it down into simple propositions or the negation of simple propositions, which together are called **literals**. Thus we would get something like this, which we call a **truth tree**:

DEFINITION

We say a compound proposition is ***decomposed*** when it is broken down into simple propositions (or the negation of simple propositions) which are called ***literals***.

DEFINITIONS

To ***recover the truth values*** for a set of propositions means to determine the truth values of the simple propositions for which the propositions in the set would all be true.

An ***open branch*** is a path on a truth tree which includes no contradictions.

KEY POINTS

The conjunction decomposes according to this rule:

$p \bullet q$ ✓
p
q

The double negation decomposes according to this rule:

$\sim\sim p$ ✓
p

A
~B • C ✓
~B
C

The literals can all be true without contradiction. The set is consistent.

We have just drawn a truth tree by decomposing the set of propositions down to their literals. Once the proposition *~B • C* has been decomposed, it is checked off, and from then on ignored. It has been replaced by its literals. With a consistent set like this, we can **recover the truth values** by assigning true to each literal. For the literals which are negations to be true, their simple propositions must be false. We write out the recovered truth values in a table:

A	B	C
T	F	T

The set *{A, ~B • C}* is seen to be consistent when *A* is true, *B* is false and *C* is true. Had we completed a longer truth table for this set of propositions, we would have found that the original set members would be true on the row with *A* and *C* as true and *B* as false (try it!).

As in the formal proofs of validity, it is customary to number each step in a truth tree and provide its justification. When this is done for the previous example, the final result looks like this:

1)	A	SM	
2)	~B • C ✓	SM	CONSISTENT
3)	~B	2 •D	
4)	C	2 •D	A B C
	O		T F T

The propositions which were members of the original set are labelled SM for "**S**et **M**ember." Steps three and four are justified with *2 •D* (meaning *step two, conjunction decomposition*). The circle underneath the truth tree identifies it as an **open branch**, meaning that all the propositions have been decomposed above the circle and no contradictions between literals exist.

Now consider the set *{D • ~E, ~~E}*. Neither proposition in this set is a literal, so both must be decomposed. First, for *~~E* to be true, *E* must be true. Thus *~~E* decomposes down to *E*. Then, for the proposition *(D • ~E)* to be true, D must be true and ~E must be true. The final truth tree looks like this:

1)	D • ~E	✓	SM	
2)	~~E	✓	SM	
3)	E		2 ~~D	INCONSISTENT
4)	D		1 •D	
5)	~E		1 •D	
	3 × 5			

Again, the decompositions are justified by the step number and the type of decomposition. The justifications show that step three is derived from a *double-negation decomposition* of step two and steps four and five from a conjunction decomposition of step one. There is a contradiction between the literals on steps three and five because E and ~E cannot both be true. Thus we have a **closed branch** which is labelled "3 × 5" (meaning *step three contradicts step five*), and the truth tree is identified as inconsistent. No truth values can be recovered for inconsistent sets. Also, notice that every line number with a justification has its proposition checked off.

We have seen how conjunctions and double negations are decomposed down to their literals. Now let's examine the decomposition of disjunctions.

Consider this set of propositions: {*F* ∨ *G*, *~F*}. Is this set consistent or inconsistent? The proposition *~F* is already a literal, so the decomposition of the disjunction F ∨ G is all that remains. When is F ∨ G true? A disjunction is true whenever either disjunct is true. To show this on a truth tree, the disjunction is decomposed by branching each disjunct and putting them on the same line, as shown:

```
1)   F∨G    ✓
2)    ~F
      / \
3)   F   G
```

Now that the propositions are all decomposed, consider each branch. For the set to be consistent, either *~F* and *F* would both have to be true, or *~F* and *G* would both have to be true. The first is impossible (it is a contradiction), but the second is possible. Thus we have a consistent set. The final product would look like this:

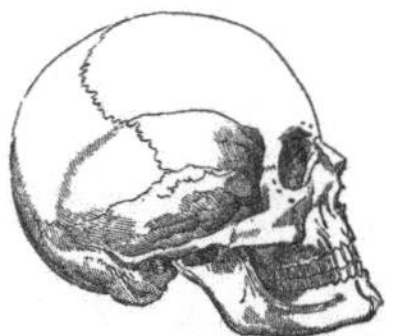

CAUTION

Remember to check off a compound proposition once it is decomposed.

DEFINITIONS

A ***closed branch*** is a path on a truth tree for which a contradiction has been found.

KEY POINT

The disjunction decomposes by branching into its disjuncts:

```
 p∨q ✓
  /\
 p  q
```

Truth trees may need to "branch" so you can consider several possible truth values for the literals. Each branch represents a possible combination of literals that would need to be true in order for the initial set of propositions to be consistent.

```
1)  F∨G   ✓    SM
2)   ~F        SM      CONSISTENT
     /\
3)  F   G      1∨D      F  G
  2×3   O               F  T
```

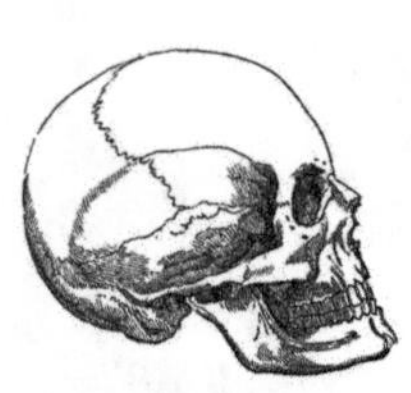

CAUTION

A set of propositions may have some closed branches on a truth tree and still be consistent, as long as at least one open branch exists.

Step three is justified as a *disjunction decomposition* of step one. The contradiction between steps two and three is identified on the left branch, but the right branch is labelled as open. If one or more branches is open, the set is consistent. The truth values were recovered from the open branch. They show that the members of the set *{F∨ G, ~F}* are true when *F* is false and *G* is true.

We will consider two more examples before going on to the exercise. First, let's determine the consistency of this set of proposition forms: *{P•~Q, ~P∨ Q}*. The truth tree is completed as follows:

```
1)  P•~Q   ✓   SM
2)  ~P∨Q   ✓   SM
3)    P        1•D    INCONSISTENT
4)   ~Q        1•D
     / \
5)  ~P   Q     2∨D
   3×5  4×5
```

Both branches are closed. Thus it is not possible for propositions of the forms *P•~Q* and *~P∨ Q* to both be true.

For our final example, we will examine the consistency of this set: *{P•Q, Q∨~R}*. The truth tree is shown:

```
1)   P•Q   ✓   SM
2)  Q∨~R   ✓   SM     CONSISTENT
3)    P        1•D
4)    Q        1•D
     /\                P  Q  R
5)  Q  ~R      2∨D     T  T  F
    O   O              T  T  T
```

Both branches are open. From the right branch we recovered the truth values as shown:

P	Q	R
T	T	F

On the left branch *P* and *Q* are true as well. But *R* does not appear on the left branch. When a proposition does not appear on an open branch like this, the recovered truth values should account for both possible truth values of that proposition. Thus from the left branch we would get *P* and *Q* as true, and *R* as true and false, as shown:

P	Q	R
T	T	F
T	T	T

Since we already recovered *P* and *Q* as true and *R* as false from the right branch, we do not repeat those values in the final answer. Thus the original set of propositions is consistent when the propositions *P* and *Q* are true, regardless of the truth value of *R*.

The overall procedure for determining the consistency of a set of propositions using the method of truth trees is summarized below.

SUMMARY

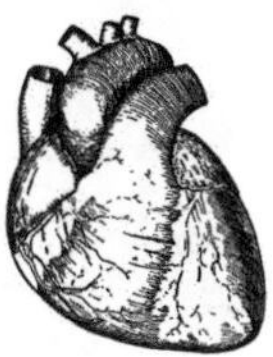

The Truth Tree Method for Consistency

1. Write down the set members on numbered lines, labeling them *SM*.
2. Continuing to number each step, decompose the compound propositions into literals.
3. Check off each proposition as it is decomposed. Justify each step by stating the line number of proposition along with the decomposition rule used.
4. When the set has been decomposed, examine each branch for contradictions. Branches which show no contradictions are open branches and are marked with a circle (O). Branches with a contradiction are closed branches, and are marked with an × between the step numbers which show the contradiction.
5. If there is at least one open branch, the set is consistent, and the truth values which show consistency may be recovered.

EXERCISE 22 (28 points)

Using the method of truth trees, determine the consistency of the following sets of propositions. Recover the truth values for all consistent sets.

1. { P, ~Q • R} (7)

1)	P	S.M.
2)	~Q • R ✓	S.M.
3)	~Q	2 • D
4)	R	2 • D
	O	

CONSISTENT

P	Q	R
T	F	T

2. { ~~P, ~P • Q} (6)

1)	~~P ✓	S.M.
2)	~P • Q ✓	S.M.
3)	P	1~~D
4)	~P	2•D
5)	Q	2•D
	3x4	

INCONSISTENT

3. { P, ~Q, ~P ∨ ~~Q} (7)

1)	P		S.M.
2)	~Q		S.M.
3)	~P ∨ ~~Q ✓		S.M.
	/	\	
4)	~P	~~Q ✓	3 ∨ D
	1x4	|	
5)		Q	4~~D
		2x5	

INCONSISTENT

4. { ~P • Q, Q ∨ R} (8)

1)	~P • Q ✓		S.M.
2)	Q ∨ R ✓		S.M.
3)	~P		1 • D
4)	Q		1 • D
	/	\	
5)	Q	R	2 ∨ D
	O	O	

CONSISTENT

P	Q	R
F	T	T
F	T	F

DECOMPOSITION RULES

Intermediate Logic, pp. 185–189

STUDENT OBJECTIVES

1. Recognize and use the decomposition rules for all five logical operators and their negations.
2. Complete Exercise 23.

TEACHING INSTRUCTIONS

1. Have students remind you of the three decomposition rules for truth trees that they learned yesterday (double negations, conjunctions, and disjunctions). Explain that they are now going to learn how to decompose all five logical operators and their negations, and when they have done so, they will have derived all the necessary decomposition rules for truth trees.
2. Tell students that the first new rule they will learn is the decomposition rule for a negated conjunction. Write *~(p • q)* on the board. Ask students what we initially assume about this this proposition (that it's true). Ask student what we know about *p • q* if *~(p • q)* is true (that it's false). Ask students what we know about *p* and *q* if *p • q* is false. They may get stuck here; explain that if *p • q* is false, then either p is false or q is false, or, put another way, either *~p* is true or *~q* is true. Make sure students see that we have two options here; so **the negated conjunction branches like disjunctions do**. Write on the board the **negated conjunction decomposition rule**:

```
 ~(p • q)   ✓
    / \
  ~p   ~q
```

In other words, if the literal on either branch (*~p* or *~q*) is true, then *~(p • q)* is true.

3. Tell students that the next rule to learn is the rule for decomposing a negated disjunction. Write *~(p ∨ q)* on the board. Again, ask students what we assume about this proposition (it is true), what we therefore know about *p ∨ q* (it's false), and what we therefore know about *p* and *q* (for the disjunction of them to be false, they both must be false, or, in other words, *~p* and *~q* must both be true). Have students walk you through writing the **negated disjunction decomposition** rule on the board:

```
 ~(p ∨ q)   ✓
   ~p
   ~q
```

Make sure students see that **the negated disjunction does *not* branch, just like the conjunction**. Ask students if these two rules remind them of anything. Explain that they are basically saying the same thing as De Morgan's Theorems and could have been derived using good old De Morg.

4. Tell students that they are going to work through a couple examples using these rules before moving on. Write on the board the set {*~(P • Q)*, *~(P ∨ Q)*}, and tell students that we are going to determine the consistency of this

set. Have them walk you through creating the truth tree if they can; it should look like this:

```
1) ~(P • Q)  ✓   SM
2) ~(P ∨ Q)  ✓   SM          CONSISTENT
3)    ~P         2 ~∨D
4)    ~Q         2 ~∨D
     /  \                      P  Q
5) ~P   ~Q       1 ~•D         F  F
    O    O
```

Explain that the justification for steps 3 and 4 is the abbreviation for "negated disjunction decomposition" and for step 5 "negated conjunction decomposition." Make sure students see that the truth tree is consistent along both branches. Quickly recover the truth values: ask students what the values of *P* and *Q* must be for the truth tree to be consistent (*P* must be false and *Q* must be false).

5. Now for a trickier one. Write {*~(~P • Q), ~(P ∨ ~R), Q ∨ R*} on the board. Are these three propositions consistent? Have students walk you through setting up the truth tree (have them decompose step 2 first, then step 1, and finally step 3); one possible truth tree looks like this:

```
1)   ~(~P • Q)✓     SM
2)   ~(P ∨ ~R)✓     SM
3)     Q ∨ R✓       SM
4)       ~P         2 ~∨D   CONSISTENT
5)      ~~R✓        2 ~∨D
6)        R         5 ~~D    P  Q  R
         / \                 F  F  T
7)  ~~P ✓  ~Q       1 ~•D
8)    P    / \      7 ~~D
   4 × 8  /   \
9)       Q     R    3 ∨D
       7 × 9   O
```

Make sure students see that once a branch is closed—that is, once a contradiction is found in a branch—as in steps 8 and 9, we do not continue to decompose propositions off of it. Also make sure they see that it is not okay to simply assume and skip any double negations—they must be done explicitly. Have students help you recover the truth values: in order for {*~(~ P • Q), ~(P ∨ ~R), Q ∨ R*} to be consistent, *P* must be false, *Q* must be false, and *R* must be true.

6. Tell students that it is time to learn the last four decomposition rules: the rules for the conditional, biconditional, negated conditional, and negated biconditional. First, have students walk you through making the defining truth table (not truth tree) for the conditional. It looks like this:

p	q	p ⊃ q
T	T	T
T	F	F
F	T	T
F	F	T

7. Ask students how many ways there are for the conditional to be true (three). Tell them that because there are three options, they may be thinking that a conditional decomposes into three branches (which would be a headache and a half). Explain that in fact, rather than saying that *p ⊃ q* is true whenever *p* is true and *q* is true, *p* is false and *q* is true, or *p* is false and *q* is false, we could shorten this significantly and say that ***p ⊃ q* is true whenever either *p* is false or *q* is true**. Make sure that students see that this summary covers all three of the options, but only requires two branches. Write the conditional decomposition rule on the board:

```
 p ⊃ q ✓
  / \
~p   q
```

Ask students if this rule reminds them of another rule they learned way back when. Explain that it is saying pretty much the same thing as Material Implication, which says that *(p ⊃ q) ≡ (~p ∨ q)*.

8. Now have students walk you through making the defining truth table for the biconditional, like so:

p	q	p ≡ q
T	T	T
T	F	F
F	T	F
F	F	T

Ask students what, given the table, the truth values of p and q must be in order for $p \equiv q$ to be true. Make sure they see that either p and q must both be true, or p and q must both be false. Have students symbolize this for you: $(p \equiv q) \equiv [(p \bullet q) \vee (\sim p \bullet \sim q)$; point out that this is exactly what the rule of Material Equivalence says. Explain that this might seem like it will be a bit harder to represent in a truth tree since we have to somehow represent a combination of disjunction and conjunction, but tell students that it's actually quite simple: we just put one conjunction into each branch. Write the **biconditional decomposition rule** on the board:

```
  p ≡ q  ✓
   / \
  p   ~p
  q   ~q
```

9. Explain that the negated conditional is much simpler than either of these. Write $\sim(p \supset q)$ on the board. Ask students what, if $\sim(p \supset q)$ is true, we can conclude about $p \supset q$ (that it's false). Ask students what the truth values of p and q must be in order for $p \supset q$ to be false. There's only one case: when p is true and q is false, or, in other words, when p and $\sim q$ are both true. So the **negated conditional decomposition rule** looks like this:

```
~(p ⊃ q)  ✓
    p
   ~q
```

10. Finally, have students walk you through creating the truth table for the negated biconditional, which should look like this:

p	q	~(p ≡ q)
T	T	F
T	F	T
F	T	T
F	F	F

Ask students what, given this table, the truth values of p and q must be in order for $\sim(p \equiv q)$ to be true. Make sure they see that $\sim(p \equiv q)$ is true when either p is true and q is false or vice versa. Again we have to combine disjunction and conjunction, but it only has to branch into two. Write the negated biconditional disjunction on the board:

```
~(p ≡ q)   ✓
   / \
  p   ~p
 ~q    q
```

Warn students that they are going to be tempted to mix up where the negations go in this rule.

11. Tell students that we are going to finish of the lesson by considering a couple truth tables for consistency that use these rules. Write this set on the board: $\{\sim(P \supset Q), Q \supset P, \sim P \supset R\}$, which could symbolize something like "It is not true that if I practice the tuba the neighbors will bang on the walls," "If the neighbors start banging on the walls then I am practicing the tuba," and "If I don't practice the tuba, then I have bad dreams." Remind students that because we are determining whether these three propositions are consistent, we start out by assuming that they are all true and see if we meet any contradictions. Have students walk you through creating a truth tree for this set. One truth tree would look like this:

```
1)        ~(P ⊃ Q) ✓          SM
2)           Q ⊃ P ✓          SM
3)          ~P ⊃ R ✓          SM
4)             P              1 ~⊃D
5)            ~Q              1 ~⊃D
              / \
6)      ~~P ✓       R         3 ⊃D
7)        P        / \        6 ~~D
         / \      /   \
8)     ~Q   P   ~Q     P      2 ⊃D
        O   O    O     O
```

Tell students that in general it is a good technique to decompose the propositions which do *not* branch *first*; it keeps the truth tree from becoming needlessly complicated. But no matter which proposition you start with, you will eventually obtain the same result. (Just try to make it sooner rather than later.)

12. Write this set of propositions on the board: {~(*P* ≡ *Q*), *Q* ≡ *R*, ~*P*}. It could symbolize something like "It is not true that if and only if I play the tuba will the girl next door be impressed with me," "The girl next door will be impressed with me if and only if I play some sort of instrument," and "I do not play the tuba." Have students walk you through making a truth tree to determine the consistency of these propositions. Tell them that in this case, even though both the propositions to be decomposed will branch, it's a good idea to start with ~(*P* ≡ *Q*), since it will allow us to close a branch sooner. It should look something like this:

```
1)       ~(P ≡ Q)  ✓        SM
2)         Q ≡ R   ✓        SM
3)          ~P              SM
           /  \
4)       P      ~P          1 ~≡D
5)      ~Q       Q          1 ~≡D
       3 × 4    / \
6)             Q   ~Q       2 ≡D
7)             R   ~R       2 ≡D
               O   5×6
```

Point out to the students that the *Q* on the left side of step 6 does *not* contradict the ~*Q* on the left side of step 5, because they are on different branches. Have students recover the truth values from the open branch to see that all the propositions in the original set are true when the constants have the recovered truth values.

13. Finally, tell the students that we need to see another example of a truth three with more than one branch on a given step. Write these two propositions on the board: {~(*P* ≡ *Q*), (*P* • *R*) ≡ *Q*}. Work through this truth tree carefully, looking for branches that can close.

```
1)              ~(P ≡ Q)    ✓          SM
2)             (P • R) ≡ Q  ✓          SM
               /           \
3)         P                   ~P      1 ~≡D
4)        ~Q                    Q      1 ~≡D
         /   \                 /  \
5) (P•R)   ~(P•R)✓   (P•R)✓   ~(P•R)   2 ≡D
6)   Q       ~Q        Q        ~Q     2 ≡D
7) 4 × 6     / \       P       4 × 6   5 • D
8)          /   \      R               5 • D
9)        ~P    ~R    3×7              5 ~ • D
         3 × 9   O
```

Recover the truth values by writing

P	Q	R
T	F	F

ASSIGNMENT

Have students complete Exercise 23, and go over it with them.

LESSON 23

DECOMPOSITION RULES

In using truth trees, we have learned how to decompose double negations, conjunctions, and disjunctions. We now must learn how to decompose all five logical operators and their negations. In doing so we will derive all the necessary decomposition rules.

First we will determine the decomposition rule for a negated conjunction *~(p • q)*. For this proposition to be true, the conjunction in parentheses must be false. This is the case when either *p* is false or *q* is false, that is, when *~p* is true or *~q* is true. Thus the negated conjunction decomposes like this:

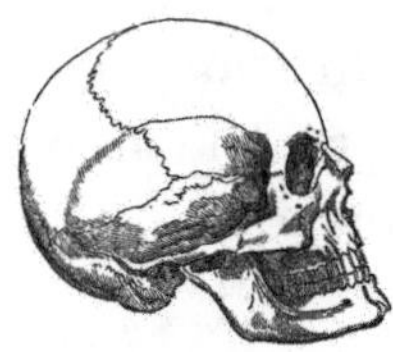

CAUTION

Conjunctions do not branch, but negated conjunctions do. Disjunctions branch, but negated disjunctions do not.

```
~(p • q) ✓
   /\
 ~p  ~q
```

If the literal on either branch is true, *~(p • q)* is true.

How about negated disjunction? For *~(p ∨ q)* to be true, *p ∨ q* must be false. In this case both *p* and *q* must be false, or *~p* and *~q* must both be true. Thus the negated disjunction decomposes like this:

```
~(p ∨ q) ✓
  ~p
  ~q
```

These two decomposition rules could also have been derived using De Morgan's Theorems.

Before we go on, we will look at two examples using these rules. First, we will determine the consistency of the set {*~(P • Q)*, *~(P ∨ Q)*}. The truth tree works out like this:

1)	~(P • Q) ✓	SM		
2)	~(P ∨ Q) ✓	SM	CONSISTENT	
3)	~P	2 ~∨D		
4)	~Q	2 ~∨D		
	/\		P	Q
5)	~P ~Q	1 ~•D	F	F
	O O			

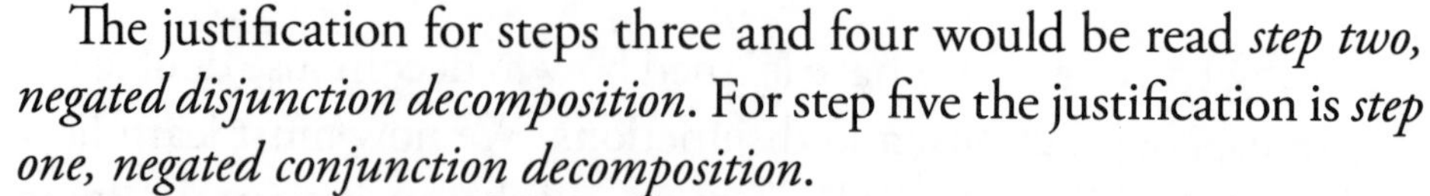

The justification for steps three and four would be read *step two, negated disjunction decomposition*. For step five the justification is *step one, negated conjunction decomposition*.

KEY POINT

Do not continue to decompose propositions off of a closed branch.

Now for a more complex truth tree. Is the set *{~(~P•Q), ~(P∨~R), Q∨R}* consistent? For what truth values? One possible truth tree looks like this:

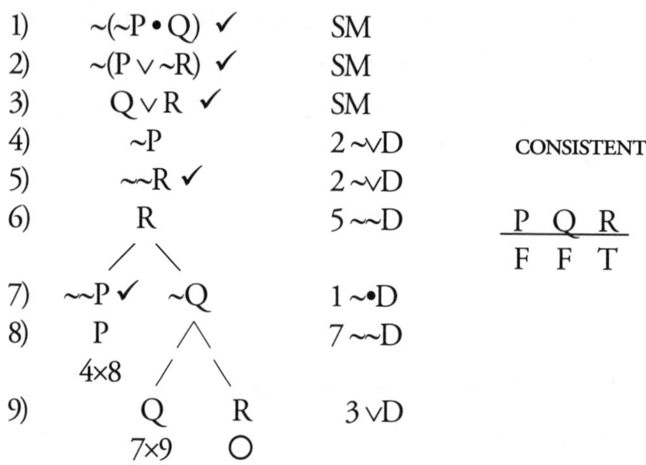

1)	~(~P • Q) ✓	SM				
2)	~(P ∨ ~R) ✓	SM				
3)	Q ∨ R ✓	SM				
4)	~P	2 ~∨D	CONSISTENT			
5)	~~R ✓	2 ~∨D				
6)	R	5 ~~D		P	Q	R
	/ \			F	F	T
7)	~~P ✓ ~Q	1 ~•D				
8)	P /\	7 ~~D				
	4×8 / \					
9)	Q R	3 ∨D				
	7×9 O					

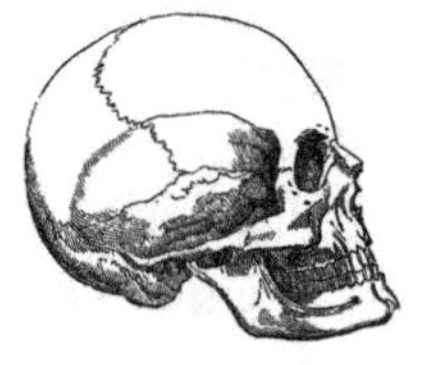

CAUTION

Do not skip the explicit decomposition of double negations.

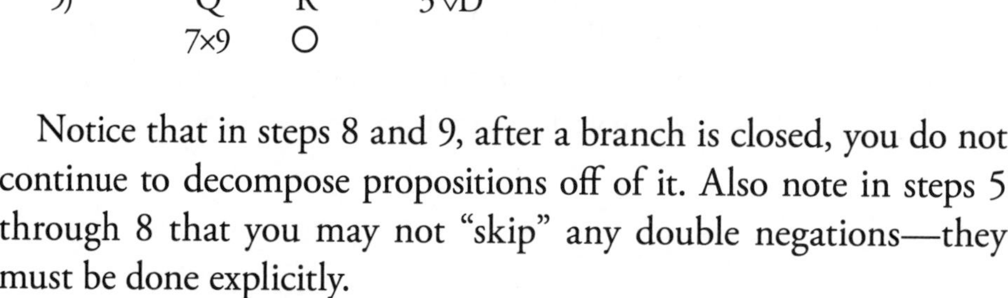

Notice that in steps 8 and 9, after a branch is closed, you do not continue to decompose propositions off of it. Also note in steps 5 through 8 that you may not "skip" any double negations—they must be done explicitly.

Now for the last four decomposition rules. First, look at the defining truth table for the conditional:

p	q	p⊃q
T	T	T
T	F	F
F	T	T
F	F	T

Because there are three ways for the conditional to be true, you may think that it decomposes into three branches. However, note that $p \supset q$ is true whenever either p is false or q is true. This means that the conditional decomposition needs only two branches, like this:

```
 p ⊃ q ✓
  /\
~p   q
```

This decomposition could also have been derived from the rule of Material Implication, which says that $(p \supset q) \equiv (\sim p \vee q)$.

Now look at the defining truth table for the biconditional:

p	q	p ≡ q
T	T	T
T	F	F
F	T	F
F	F	T

For $p \equiv q$ to be true, either p and q must both be true, or p and q must both be false. Or, using the rule of Material Equivalence, we know that $(p \equiv q) \equiv [(p \bullet q) \vee (\sim p \bullet \sim q)]$. Thus the biconditional decomposition is

```
 p ≡ q ✓
  /\
 p  ~p
 q  ~q
```

For the negated conditional $\sim(p \supset q)$ to be true, $p \supset q$ must be false. This is only the case when p is true and q is false. Thus the negated conditional decomposition is

```
~(p ⊃ q) ✓
    p
   ~q
```

The only situation in which $\sim(p \supset q)$ is true is when both p and $\sim q$ are true.

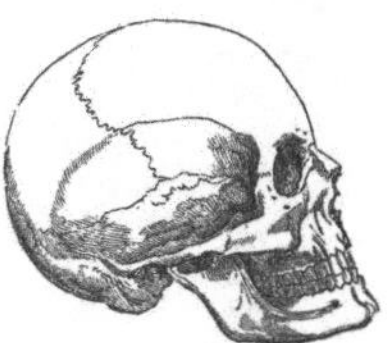

CAUTION

Conditional decomposition branches, but negated conditional decomposition does not.

Finally, consider the truth table for the negated biconditional:

p	q	~(p ≡ q)
T	T	F
T	F	T
F	T	T
F	F	F

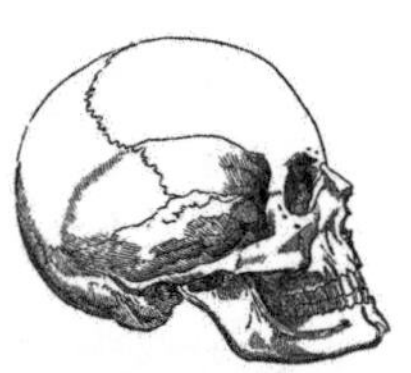

CAUTION

Note and memorize the different placement of the negation signs for biconditional and negated biconditional decomposition.

Since *~(p ≡ q)* is true when either *p* is true and *q* is false or vice versa, the negated biconditional decomposition rule is

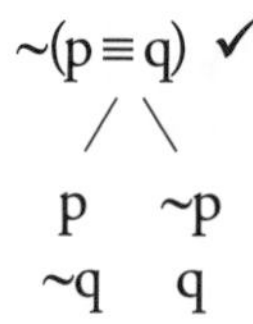

```
~(p≡q) ✓
  / \
 p   ~p
~q    q
```

Now we will consider some examples which use these rules. We will first determine the consistency of this set: *{~(P⊃Q), Q⊃P, ~P⊃R}*. One truth tree for this set is

```
1)        ~(P⊃Q) ✓          SM
2)          Q⊃P ✓           SM
3)         ~P⊃R ✓           SM
4)            P             1 ~⊃D        CONSISTENT
5)           ~Q             1 ~⊃D
            /   \                        P  Q  R
6)    ~~P ✓       R         3 ⊃D         T  F  T
7)      P        / \        6 ~~D        T  F  F
       / \      /   \
8)   ~Q   P   ~Q     P      2 ⊃D
      O   O    O     O
```

You may have noticed that, whenever possible, the propositions which do not branch are decomposed first, as in the example above. This helps prevent the truth tree from being needlessly complicated. However, had we decomposed the second proposition first, we would have obtained the same result.

Here is one final example before the exercise, this time giving us practice with the biconditionals. Let's determine the consistency of this set of propositions: *{~(P ≡ Q), Q ≡ R, ~P}*. The truth tree can be drawn as follows:

```
1)   ~(P≡Q) ✓          SM
2)     Q≡R ✓           SM
3)       ~P            SM        CONSISTENT
        / \
4)    P     ~P         1~≡D       P  Q  R
5)   ~Q      Q         1~≡D       ---------
     3×4    / \                   F  T  T
6)         Q  ~Q       2≡D
7)         R  ~R       2≡D
           O  5×6
```

We chose to decompose *~(P ≡ Q)* first because this allowed us to immediately close a branch after step five. You may again check to see that the original propositions are all true when the constants have the recovered truth values.

SUMMARY

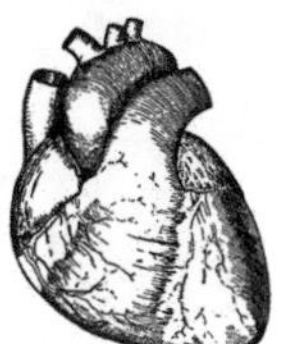

A truth tree decomposition rule can be developed for any compound proposition. To do so, the necessary truth values for the variables or constants must be determined such that the proposition is true. This has been done for conjunction, disjunction, conditional, biconditional, their negations, and double negation. The decomposition rules are listed in Appendix C.

EXERCISE 23 (47 points)

Using the method of truth trees, determine the consistency of the following sets of propositions. Recover the truth values for all consistent sets.

1. { A⊃ B, A, ~B } (6)

```
1)   A⊃B ✓      S.M.
2)     A        S.M.
3)    ~B        S.M.
      / \
4)  ~A   B      1⊃D
   2x4 3x4
```

INCONSISTENT

2. { ~C, ~(C⊃D) } (6)

```
1)     ~C           S.M.
2)  ~(C⊃D) ✓        S.M.
3)      C           2~⊃D
4)     ~D           2~⊃D
       1x3
```

INCONSISTENT

3. { E⊃~F, ~E • F } (8)

```
1)    E⊃~F ✓     S.M.
2)    ~E•F ✓     S.M.
3)      ~E       2•D
4)       F       2•D
        / \
5)    ~E   ~F    1⊃D
       O   4x5
```

CONSISTENT

E	F
F	T

4. { G≡H, ~H, G } (7)

```
1)    G≡H ✓      S.M.
2)     ~H        S.M.
3)      G        S.M.
       / \
4)    G   ~G     1≡D
5)    H   ~H     1≡D
    2x5   3x4
```

INCONSISTENT

5. { J⊃~(J≡K), ~(J⊃K) } (10)

```
1)  J⊃~(J≡K) ✓          S.M.
2)    ~(J⊃K) ✓          S.M.
3)        J             2~⊃D
4)       ~K             2~⊃D
       /     \
5)   ~J    ~(J≡K) ✓     1⊃D
    3x5      / \
6)          J   ~J      5~≡D
7)         ~K    K      5~≡D
            O   3x6
```

CONSISTENT:

J	K
T	F

6. { L⊃M, M⊃L, ~(L≡M) } (10)

```
1)            L⊃M ✓                S.M.
2)            M⊃L ✓                S.M.
3)          ~(L≡M) ✓               S.M.
           /         \
4)        L           ~L           3~≡D
5)       ~M            M           3~≡D
        /  \          /  \
6)    ~L    M       ~L    M        1⊃D
     4x6   5x6     / \   / \
7)               ~M   L ~M   L     2⊃D
                5x7 6x7 6x7 4x7
```

INCONSISTENT

TECHNIQUES FOR CONSTRUCTING TRUTH TREES

Intermediate Logic, pp. 193–196

STUDENT OBJECTIVES

1. Use the four basic techniques in constructing simpler truth trees.
2. Complete Exercise 24.

TEACHING INSTRUCTIONS

1. Tell students that they've probably already gotten a taste in the exercises of how complicated truth trees can become the larger the sets of propositions grow, especially since there are usually several ways to go about solving them. Explain that there are four basic techniques to keep in mind when constructing truth trees that will keep them from becoming monstrosities (the truth trees, that is, not the students).
2. Write this set of propositions on the board: {*P* ≡ *Q*, *Q* • *R*}. Choose two students (or if you don't have more than one, do this with your student) to each write a truth tree for this set of propositions, one decomposing the first proposition first, the other decomposing the second proposition first. The two truth trees should look like this:

```
1)   P ≡ Q  ✓       SM
2)   Q • R  ✓       SM
      /  \
3)   P    ~P        1 ≡D
4)   Q    ~Q        1 ≡D
5)   Q     Q        2 •D
6)   R     R        2 •D
     O    4 × 5
```

```
1)   P ≡ Q ✓        SM
2)   Q • R ✓        SM
3)     Q            2 •D
4)     R            2 •D
      /  \
5)   P    ~P        1 ≡D
6)   Q    ~Q        1 ≡D
     O   3 × 6
```

3. Make sure students see that even though there are the same number of steps and the truth trees communicate the same information (left branch is open, right branch contains a contradiction), the truth tree on the left required writing out a lot more constants because we had to decompose the conjunction in both branches, while in the right truth tree the branching didn't occur till after the decomposition of the conjunction had taken place. Explain that the more we have to write the more likely we are to mess up. Write the first technique on the board **1. Decompose nonbranching members first**. Tell students that when looking at their given propositions they should first determine which ones branch and which ones don't and decompose accordingly. There is no need to decompose them in numerical order.
4. Now write this set of propositions on the board: {*P* ⊃ *Q*, *Q* ⊃ *P*, ~*P*}. Have two more students (if you have them) take a turn constructing the truth tree for this set in two different ways, one decomposing the first proposition first, the other decomposing the second proposition

first. Explain that in this case both the propositions that need decomposition are going to branch, so we are looking for a new technique to simplify the truth tree. The two trees should look like this:

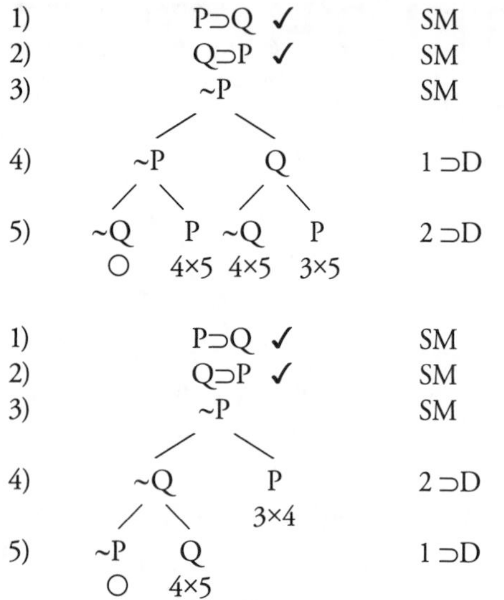

5. Make sure students see that decomposing the second proposition first saved the drawing of two branches, two literals, and one contradiction. Write on the board **2. Decompose members which result in the closing of one or more branches**. Explain that before constructing a truth tree students should look at the given propositions and figure out which one, when decomposed, will introduce a contradiction soonest, enabling them to close a branch earlier in the truth tree.

6. Write this set of propositions *{~[~P • (Q ∨ R)], ~(P ⊃ Q)}* and this truth tree on the board and ask students what is wrong with it:

1)	~[~P • (Q ∨ R)] ✓		SM
2)	~(P ⊃ Q) ✓		SM
3)	P		2 ~⊃D
4)	~Q		2 ~⊃D
5)	~~P ✓	~(Q∨R) ✓	1 ~•D
6)	P	|	5~~D
7)	O	~Q	5~∨D
8)		~R	5~∨D
		O	CONSISTENT

Students should notice that you could have stopped after step 6 instead of continuing to decompose everything: you already found the set to be consistent. Decomposing the right branch gives no more helpful information. Write on the board **3. Stop when the truth tree answers the question being asked**. Tell students that they may get so absorbed in making their truth tree that they fail to realize when they've accomplished what they set out to accomplish (draw any applications to the rest of life that you feel like drawing here).

7. Along the same lines, write on the board this set of propositions: *{~(P ≡ Q), (Q • R), ~R}*. Explain that if we fully decompose these propositions, the truth tree will be seven steps long. But if we stop when we find the consistency, it will only be five steps. See if students can figure out what proposition to start with (the second) and walk you through making the truth tree for it. The completed truth tree should look like this:

1)	~(P ≡ Q)	SM	
2)	Q • R ✓	SM	
3)	~R	SM	
4)	Q	2 •D	INCONSISTENT
5)	R	2 •D	
	3×5		

8. Tell students that the final technique they will learn today is only to be used as a last resort, when all other hopes have faded—in other words, when none of the first three rules apply. Write on the board **4. Decompose more complex propositions first**. Write this set of propositions on the board: *{~P, P ⊃ R, ~(~Q ≡ R)}*. Have students walk you through making a truth tree for these propositions, decomposing them in the order they were given. The completed truth tree should look like this:

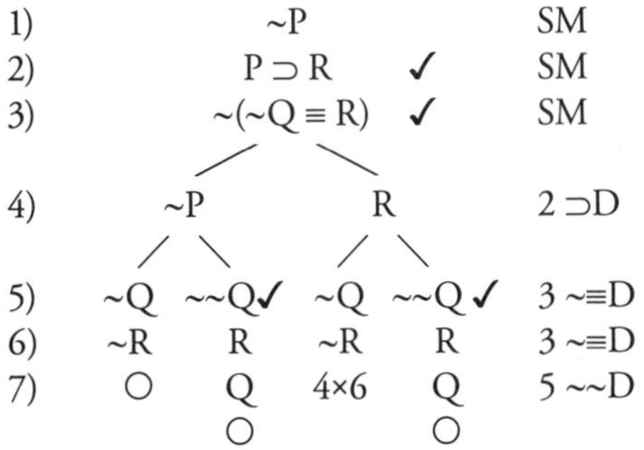

9. Students should feel that that is something they never want to do ever again. Make sure they see that this is because we were forced to decompose the negated biconditional under branches, which was a real headache. Have them walk you through another truth tree for the same propositions, this time beginning by decomposing the negated biconditional—the most complicated proposition—first. The completed truth tree should look like this:

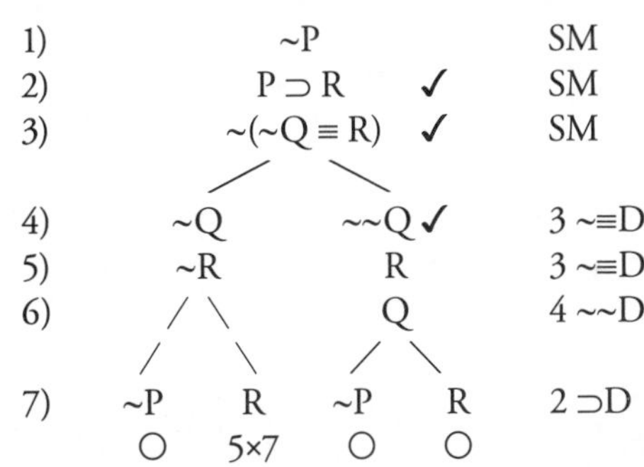

Make sure students see that while this truth tree was just as many steps as the previous one, it was not nearly as torturous, because we dealt with the most complicated proposition first. Remind them again that we only use this technique after considering the first three techniques.

10. Give students one last example; have them walk you through creating the truth tree for it, keeping all these principles in mind. Write on the board the set of propositions {*P≡(Q∨R), ~(Q • R), ~(Q⊃~P)*}. Remind students that the first thing to do is to look for a proposition that will not branch when decomposed (the third proposition) and decompose that one first. The next thing to do is look for a proposition that will immediately result in contradictions when decomposed (second proposition). After that, there's only one proposition left to decompose. The completed truth tree should look like this:

1)	P ≡ (Q ∨ R) ✓		SM
2)	~(Q • R) ✓		SM
3)	~(Q⊃~P) ✓		SM
4)	Q		3 ~⊃D
5)	~~P ✓		3 ~⊃D
6)	P		5 ~~D
7)	~Q 4×7	~R	2 ~•D
8)		P ~P	1 ≡D
9)		Q∨R✓ ~(Q∨R) 6×8	1 ≡D
10)		Q R O 7×10	9 ∨D

Explain that even though this truth tree was looooooooong and in its way complicated, each of the steps only required one branching. If we hadn't used the techniques from this lesson, the truth tree would have been a real mind-boggler.

ASSIGNMENTS

1. Have students complete Exercise 24, and go over it with them.
2. Remind students to study for next class's quiz over Lessons 22–24.

LESSON 24

TECHNIQUES FOR CONSTRUCTING TRUTH TREES

As sets of propositions grow larger, truth trees grow more complex. While constructing them, it helps to have a few basic techniques in mind to assure that they are as uncomplicated as possible.

1. Decompose non-branching members first. This technique will save you from unnecessarily rewriting propositions. For example, compare the two different truth trees below for this set of propositions: {*P* ≡ *Q*, *Q* • *R*}.

1)	P≡Q ✓		SM
2)	Q•R ✓		SM
	/	\	
3)	P	~P	1≡D
4)	Q	~Q	1≡D
5)	Q	Q	2•D
6)	R	R	2•D
	O	4×5	

1)	P≡Q ✓		SM
2)	Q•R ✓		SM
3)	Q		2•D
4)	R		2•D
	/	\	
5)	P	~P	1≡D
6)	Q	~Q	1≡D
	O	3×6	

KEY POINT

Decomposing non-branching members first will save you from rewriting propositions unnecessarily.

Though they are the same number of steps, the truth tree on the left requires the writing of more constants. This can lead to unnecessary complexity and errors, especially for larger truth trees.

KEY POINT

Simplify your truth trees by decomposing members which will allow you to close a branch by noting a contradiction.

2. Decompose members which result in the closing of one or more branches. As we have seen, once a branch in a truth tree is closed, no more branching should occur off of it. Thus, the sooner we can close a branch, the less complicated the truth tree. Compare these two truth trees for the propositions { *P* ⊃ *Q*, *Q* ⊃ *P*, ~*P* }.

```
1)       P⊃Q ✓       SM        1)      P⊃Q ✓      SM
2)       Q⊃P ✓       SM        2)      Q⊃P ✓      SM
3)        ~P         SM        3)       ~P        SM
         /  \                          /  \
4)  ~P          Q    1⊃D       4)  ~Q        P    2⊃D
    / \        / \                 / \      3x4
5) ~Q  P     ~Q   P  2⊃D       5) ~P  Q           1⊃D
   O  4x5   4x5  3x5              O  4x5
```

Decomposing the second proposition first saved us the drawing of two branches, two literals, and one contradiction. You can see how this technique can help you keep your truth trees simple.

3. Stop when the truth tree answers the question being asked. This may seem to be a rather obvious rule—why do more work than necessary? However, drawing a truth tree can be so absorbing that you might easily keep going after getting the information you need. Suppose, for example, that you were asked to determine the consistency of this set: { ~[*P* • (*Q* ∨ *R*)], ~(*P* ⊃ *Q*) }. You might draw the tree like this:

KEY POINT

Once your question is answered, you do not need to continue decomposing the members of the truth tree.

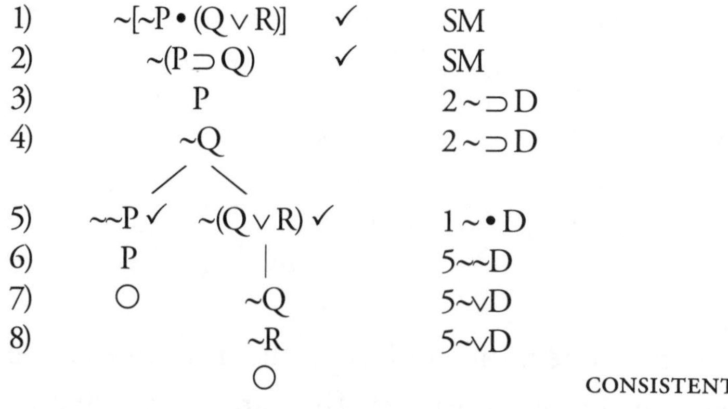

The answer is correct, but the truth tree could have been terminated after step six because the branch was decomposed and the set was found to be consistent. There was really no good reason for decomposing the negated disjunction.

Similarly, suppose you were asked to determine the consistency of this set of propositions: *{~(P≡ Q), Q • R, ~R}*. If the propositions were decomposed in the order given, the truth tree would be seven steps long. However, starting with the second proposition results in a tree with only five steps, since there is no need to continue after the contradiction has been reached:

1)	~(P ≡ Q)	SM	
2)	Q • R ✓	SM	
3)	~R	SM	
4)	Q	2 •D	INCONSISTENT
5)	R	2 •D	
	3×5		

4. Decompose more complex propositions first. This technique is included last because it should only be employed when the first three rules do not apply. Decomposing the more complex propositions (like the biconditionals) first may save you from unnecessarily re-drawing a complicated decomposition on unclosed branches. Such is the case with this set of propositions: { *~P, P⊃R, ~(~Q≡R)* }. When decomposed in the order given, the truth tree is:

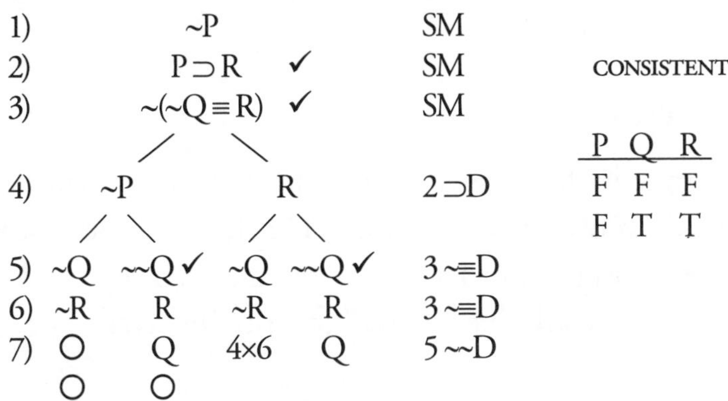

KEY POINT

If the first three suggestions for decomposition do not apply, then try decomposing the most complex propositions first. This will save you from rewriting them under multiple branches later.

However, if we decompose the negated biconditional first, we obtain this truth tree:

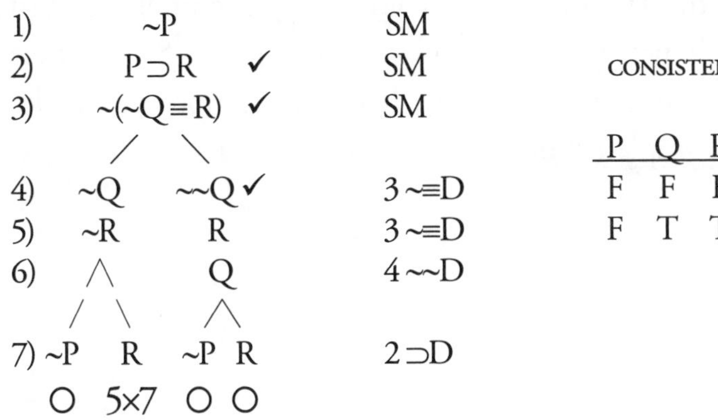

The results are the same, but this second truth tree is clearly less complex than the first. Also, note that more branches result in wider truth trees. Be sure to give yourself plenty of room at the start.

Let's do one more example, keeping these principles in mind. To determine the consistency of the set of propositions *{P ≡ (Q ∨ R), ~(Q • R), ~(Q ⊃ ~P)}*, the simplest truth tree is

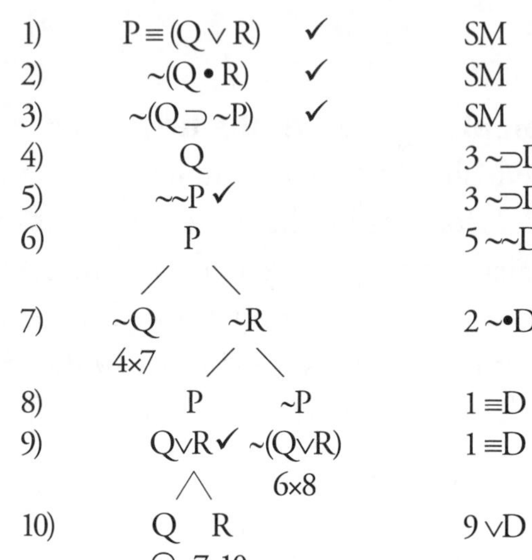

CAUTION

You do not need to decompose set members in the order in which they are given. Use the order which will yield the simplest truth tree.

Though this may look somewhat complicated, notice that each new step requires at most one branching. Had the propositions been decomposed in the original order (ignoring the techniques of this lesson), the truth tree would have been far more involved.

SUMMARY

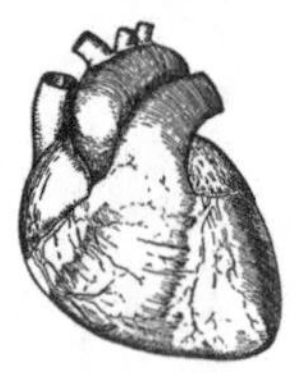

In order to keep truth trees as simple as possible, a few techniques may be employed: Decompose non-branching members, and members which result in the closing of branches, first; Stop when the truth tree yields the required result; If these are not applicable, decompose more complex propositions first.

EXERCISE 24 (54 points)

Using the method of truth trees, determine the consistency of the following sets of propositions. Recover the truth values for all consistent sets.

1. { A ⊃ B, (A • B) ⊃ C, ~(A • C), A } (12)
   (Hint: Each step need not have more than one branch)

```
1)          A⊃B ✓                 S.M.
2)        (A•B)⊃C ✓               S.M.
3)         ~(A•C) ✓               S.M.
4)            A                   S.M.
            /   \
5)        ~A     ~C               3~•D     INCONSISTENT
         4x5    /  \
6)         ~(A•B)✓  C             2⊃D
            /  \    5x6
7)        ~A    ~B                6~•D
          4x7  /  \
8)            ~A   B              1⊃D
             4x8  7x8
```

2. { D ≡ (E ⊃ F), ~D • E, D ≡ F } (14)

```
1)         D≡(E⊃F) ✓              S.M.
2)           ~D•E ✓               S.M.
3)           D≡F ✓                S.M.
4)            ~D                  2•D
5)             E                  2•D      CONSISTENT:  D E F
            /    \                                      -----
6)         D      ~D              1≡D                   F T F
7)       E⊃F   ~(E⊃F) ✓           1≡D
        4x6        |
8)                 E              7~⊃D
9)                ~F              7~⊃D
                 /  \
10)             D    ~D           3≡D
11)             F    ~F           3≡D
              4x10    O
```

Continued on next page.

3. $\{G \supset H, G \vee I, \sim H, \sim(I \bullet \sim G)\}$ (12)

```
1)          G⊃H ✓          S.M
2)          G∨I ✓          S.M
3)           ~H            S.M
4)        ~(I•~G) ✓        S.M
            /    \
5)        ~G      H        I⊃D        INCONSISTENT
         /  \    3x5
6)      G    I             2∨D
      5x6   / \
7)        ~I  ~~G ✓        4~•D
         6x7    |
8)              G          7~~D
               5x8
```

4. $\{\sim(J \equiv K), K \supset (\sim L \vee M), L \bullet \sim(K \bullet M)\}$ (16)
(Hint: Give yourself plenty of room)

```
1)                  ~(J≡K) ✓                         S.M
2)                 K⊃(~L∨M) ✓                        S.M
3)                 L•~(K•M) ✓                        S.M
4)                     L                             3•D
5)                  ~(K•M) ✓                         3•D
                 /            \
6)             J                ~J                   1~≡D
7)            ~K                 K                   1~≡D
            /    \             /    \
8)        ~K    ~L∨M ✓      ~K     ~L∨M ✓            2⊃D
          |      /  \       7x8     /  \
9)        I    ~L    M            ~L    M            8∨D
         / \   4x9  / \           4x9  / \
10)    ~K  ~M     ~K  ~M              ~K   ~M        5~•D
       O   O      O   9x10           7x10  9x10
```

CONSISTENT:

J K L M
T F T T
T F T F

QUIZ 13 (LESSONS 22–24)

STUDENT OBJECTIVE

Complete Quiz 13.

TEACHING INSTRUCTIONS

1. Give Quiz 13. Allow 30 minutes. Grade quiz with students.
2. If you have extra time, introduce Lesson 25 to get a head start on next class's material.

INTERMEDIATE LOGIC | Quiz 13

Lessons 22–24 (42 points)

Name ______________________________

1. What does it mean that a set of propositions is *consistent*? (2) The propositions can all be true without contradiction.

2. When considering truth trees, what is a *literal*? (2) A simple proposition represented by a variable or constant, or its negation.

Problems 3-6: Use truth trees to determine the consistency of the set of propositions. Include line numbers and justifications. Write CONSISTENT or INCONSISTENT, and recover at least one set of truth values for any consistent set. (7, 9, 10, 12)

3. { ~P, Q, ~(P • Q) }

```
1.        ~P              SM
2.        Q               SM
3.     ~(P•Q) ✓           SM
         /   \
4.    ~P      ~Q          3 ~•D
      O       2x4
CONSISTENT                P Q
                          F T
```

4. { P • Q, P ∨ ~Q }

```
1.        P • Q ✓         SM
2.        P ∨ ~Q ✓        SM
3.          P             1•D
4.          Q             1•D
          /   \
5.     P        ~Q        2 ∨ D
       O        4x5
CONSISTENT                P Q
                          T T
```

5. { ~(P ∨ ~Q), P ≡ Q }

```
1.     ~(P ∨ ~Q) ✓        SM
2.       P ≡ Q ✓          SM
3.        ~P              1 ~∨D
4.        ~~Q ✓           1 ~∨D
5.         Q              4 ~~D
         /   \
6.     P       ~P         2 ≡ D
7.     Q       ~Q         2 ≡ D
      3x6      5x7

   INCONSISTENT
```

6. { P ⊃ Q, ~(P ⊃ R), ~(Q ≡ R) }

```
1.        P ⊃ Q ✓         SM
2.       ~(P ⊃ R) ✓       SM
3.       ~(Q ≡ R) ✓       SM
4.          P             2 ~⊃D
5.         ~R             2 ~⊃D
         /   \
6.     ~P       Q         1 ⊃ D
      4x6      / \
7.            Q   ~Q      3 ~≡D
8.           ~R    R      3 ~≡D
              O   6x7

CONSISTENT                P Q R
                          T T F
```

TRUTH TREES FOR SELF-CONTRADICTION & TAUTOLOGY

Intermediate Logic, pp. 199–201

STUDENT OBJECTIVES

1. Use a truth tree to determine if a proposition is a self-contradiction.
2. Use a truth tree to determine if a proposition is a tautology.
3. Complete Exercise 25.

TEACHING INSTRUCTIONS

1. Ask students what, up to this point, we have been using truth trees to determine about a set of propositions (whether or not they are consistent). Explain that this is not all that truth trees can do—they are multitalented. They can also test *single* propositions for self-contradiction and tautology, as you will explore today.
2. Ask students how we know from a truth tree that a set of propositions is inconsistent (when every branch on the tree closes due to contradictions). Explain that the same concept carries over into self-contradictions within a single proposition. Write on the board the world's most obvious self-contradiction: $P \bullet \sim P$. Decompose it like so:

```
P • ~P   ✓
  P
 ~P
  ×
```

   Explain that if a self-contradiction is decomposed on a truth tree, every branch will close. Make sure students see that if every branch did not close, there be some way for the proposition to be true, which is impossible for a self-contradiction. **A proposition is a self-contradiction if and only if its decomposition results in a completely closed truth tree.**

3. Write on the board this rather complex proposition: $\sim\{[P \supset (P \bullet \sim Q)] \vee Q\}$. Explain that we can't really tell from looking at this freak of a proposition whether it is a self-contradiction or not, but that a truth tree will tell us immediately. Have students walk you through making a truth tree that decomposes this proposition. The completed proposition should look like this:

```
1)   ~{[P ⊃ (P • ~Q)] ∨ Q} ✓    SM
2)     ~[P ⊃ (P • ~Q)]    ✓    1 ~∨D
3)           ~Q                1 ~∨D
4)            P                2 ~⊃D
5)        ~(P • ~Q) ✓          2 ~⊃D
            /   \
6)        ~P     ~~Q ✓         5 ~•D
7)        4×6     Q            6 ~~D
                 3×7
```

   Make sure students see that $\sim\{[P \supset (P \bullet \sim Q)] \vee Q\}$ is therefore a self-contradiction.

4. Ask students what a tautology is. Remind them, if they need it, that a tautology is a statement that is necessarily true by logical structure, like $p \supset p$ or $p \vee \sim p$. Ask students what the relationship is between tautologies and self-contradictions. Remind students that we learned in the lesson on truth-functional

completeness that a self-contradiction is the negation of a tautology. If students are dubious, have them negate the tautology $p \vee {\sim}p$: ${\sim}(p \vee {\sim}p)$ is, by De Morgan's Theorem, ${\sim}p \bullet {\sim\sim}p$, which is obviously a self-contradiction.

5. Explain that, given this, if we negate a tautology and create a truth tree to decompose that negation, the truth tree should look just like the truth tree for a self-contradiction. In other words, the truth tree decomposing the negation of a tautology should also have all closed branches. Have students again consider the tautology $p \vee {\sim}p$. Have them negate it again: ${\sim}(p \vee {\sim}p)$. Have them walk you through decomposing the negation in a truth tree (without all the line numbering or justification). The truth tree should look like this:

```
~(p ∨ ~p)  ✓
   ~p
   ~~p     ✓
    p
    ×
```

Explain that because the negation of the proposition gave us a closed truth tree, the proposition itself is a tautology. **A proposition is a tautology if and only if the decomposition of its negation results in a completely closed truth tree.**

6. Students may be wondering at this point: why can't we just decompose the tautology itself? Why do we need to negate it first? Have them walk you through decomposing the tautology itself, like so:

```
 p ∨ ~p   ✓
   / \
  p   ~p
  O    O
```

Decomposing the tautology results in a completely open tree. Students may be tempted at this point to think that any tree which has all open branches like this must be the decomposition of a tautology, so why go through the extra work of negating the tautology before making the truth tree?

7. Give them this proposition, which is obviously not a tautology, to decompose: $p \vee {\sim}q$. It should look remarkably similar to the tautology truth tree:

```
 p ∨ ~q   ✓
   / \
  p   ~q
  O    O
```

Once again, the truth tree is completely open, even though this proposition is not a tautology. Have students negate this proposition and make a truth tree for it; they should discover that the negation of $p \vee {\sim}q$ also has a completely open truth tree. Explain that **propositions which are not tautologies may decompose into completely open truth trees. To identify a tautology, you must negate the proposition and look for a closed tree.**

ASSIGNMENT

Have students complete Exercise 25, and go over it with them.

LESSON 25

TRUTH TREES FOR SELF-CONTRADICTION AND TAUTOLOGY

Truth trees are not limited to determining the consistency of a set of propositions; they can also test single propositions for self-contradiction and tautology. Let's look at each technique in turn.

KEY POINT

A proposition is a self-contradiction if and only if its decomposition results in a completely closed truth tree.

Self-Contradiction

Truth trees show that propositions are inconsistent when every branch of the truth tree closes due to contradictions on each branch. This same concept carries over into self-contradictions within a single proposition. If a self-contradiction is decomposed on a truth tree, every branch will close. If they did not, then there would be a way for the proposition to be true, which of course is impossible with a self-contradiction.

This can clearly be seen in the simple self-contradiction *P • ~P*, which decomposes thus (line numbers and justifications are not shown):

```
P • ~P ✓
  P
 ~P
  ×
```

Now consider a more complex statement: *~{[P ⊃ (P • ~Q)] ∨ Q}*. It is also a self-contradiction, as its totally closed truth tree shows:

```
1)  ~{[P ⊃ (P •~Q)] ∨ Q} ✓        SM
2)      ~[P ⊃ (P • ~Q] ✓          1 ~∨D
3)            ~Q                  1 ~∨D
4)             P                  2 ~⊃D
5)        ~(P • ~Q) ✓             2 ~⊃D
            /   \
6)        ~P    ~~Q ✓             5 ~•D
7)       4×6     Q                6 ~~D
                3×7
```

KEY POINT

A proposition is a tautology if and only if the decomposition of its negation results in a completely closed truth tree.

Tautology

As we recognized in the lesson on truth-functional completeness, a self-contradiction is the negation of a tautology. Thus, if we negate a tautology, its decomposition should act like the decomposition of a self-contradiction. That is, the truth tree of the negation of a tautology will have no open branches.

Consider the tautology $P \vee \sim P$. The decomposition of its negation is as follows:

```
~(P ∨ ~P) ✓
  ~P
  ~~P ✓
   P
   ×
```

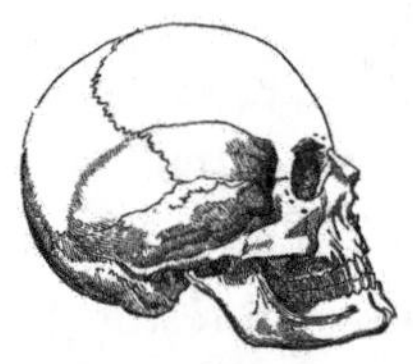

CAUTION

Propositions which are not tautologies may decompose into completely open truth trees. To identify a tautology, you must negate the proposition and look for a closed tree.

The negation of the proposition gave us a closed truth tree, so the proposition is a tautology.

Note that if we had decomposed the proposition itself, we would have obtained this tree:

```
P ∨ ~P ✓
  /\
 P  ~P
 O  O
```

This is an open tree. You may think that a tree which shows all open branches like this must be the decomposition of a tautology, and so we don't need to negate the proposition and look for closed branches, as we did in the example at the top of this page. But this is not true. Consider this very similar decomposition:

```
P ∨ ~Q ✓
  /\
 P  ~Q
 O  O
```

The proposition is certainly not a tautology, but the truth tree is completely open. The truth tree for the negation of this proposition is also open (try it!). Thus to test for a tautology we must negate the proposition and look for a closed truth tree.

SUMMARY

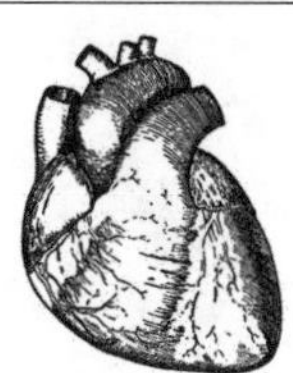

Truth trees may be used to determine if a compound proposition is a tautology or a self-contradiction. A proposition is a self-contradiction if and only if its decomposition results in a closed tree. It is a tautology if and only if the decomposition of its negation is a closed tree.

EXERCISE 25 (57 points)

For this exercise, you may omit line numbers and justifications.

For problems 1–4, decompose each compound proposition to determine if it is a *self-contradiction*. Write YES if it is and NO if it is not.

1. ~P • (P • Q) ✓ (4)

```
   ~P
  P•Q ✓
    P
    Q
    ×
YES
```

2. P • ~(P • Q) ✓ (4)

```
     P
  ~(P•Q) ✓
    / \
  ~P  ~Q
   ×   O
NO
```

3. (P ⊃ P) ⊃ (Q • ~Q) ✓ (6)

```
        /            \
  ~(P⊃P)✓         Q•~Q ✓
     P               Q
    ~P              ~Q
     ×               ×
YES
```

4. (P • Q) ≡ ~(P ∨ Q) ✓ (10)

```
        /             \
     P•Q ✓         ~(P•Q) ✓
  ~(P∨Q) ✓        ~~(P∨Q) ✓
      P              P∨Q ✓
      Q             /    \
     ~P           ~P      ~Q
     ~Q           / \     / \
      ×          P   Q   P   Q
                 ×   O   O   ×
NO
```

For problems 5–8, decompose the negation of each of compound propositions to determine if the proposition is a *tautology*. Write YES if it is and NO if it is not.

5. ~(P ∨ Q) ⊃ ~(P • Q) (7)

```
  ~[~(P∨Q)⊃~(P•Q)] ✓
       ~(P∨Q) ✓
      ~~(P•Q) ✓
        P•Q ✓
         P
         Q
        ~P
        ~Q
         ×
YES
```

6. ~(P • Q) ⊃ ~(P ∨ Q) (8)

```
  ~[~(P•Q)⊃~(P∨Q)] ✓
       ~(P•Q) ✓
      ~~(P∨Q) ✓
        P∨Q ✓
        /  \
       P    Q
      / \  / \
    ~P ~Q ~P ~Q
     ×  O  O  ×
NO
```

Continued on next page.

7. $(P \supset Q) \vee (Q \supset P)$ (6)

```
~[(P⊃Q)∨(Q⊃P)] ✓
    ~(P⊃Q) ✓
    ~(Q⊃P) ✓
       P
      ~Q
       Q
      ~P
       ×
```

YES

8. $\sim(P \bullet \sim Q) \equiv (Q \vee \sim P)$ (12)

```
      ~[~(P•~Q) ≡ (Q∨~P)] ✓
           /            \
   ~(P•~Q) ✓         ~~(P•~Q) ✓
   ~(Q∨~P) ✓           Q∨~P ✓
      ~Q                P•~Q ✓
     ~~P ✓               P
       P                ~Q
      / \               / \
    ~P   ~~Q ✓         Q   ~P
    ×     Q            ×    ×
          ×
```

YES

TEACHER'S NOTES on LESSON 26

TRUTH TREES FOR EQUIVALENCE

Intermediate Logic, pp. 205–206

STUDENT OBJECTIVES

1. Use a truth tree to determine whether two propositions are equivalent.
2. Complete Exercise 26.

TEACHING INSTRUCTIONS

1. Remind students that so far they have learned how to use truth trees to determine consistency, self-contradiction, and tautology. Now they are going to use them to determine equivalence.
2. Ask students what it means for two propositions to be equivalent (they are saying exactly the same thing). Ask students what the difference is between tautology and equivalence. Make sure they understand that a tautology is a *single* proposition that is necessarily true by logical structure, while equivalent propositions are, of course, *more than one* proposition. Explain that it is very easy to turn two equivalent statements into a tautology; see if students can guess how to do that. Explain that if two propositions are equivalent, their biconditional is a tautology. For example, p and p are equivalent statements; therefore $p \equiv p$ is a tautology.
3. Explain that we use this connection between equivalence and tautology to make the truth tree for equivalence. Have students think back to the last lesson: what did we do to determine whether a proposition was a tautology or not? Remind them that since the negation of a tautology is a self-contradiction, we negated the proposition; if it resulted in a truth tree with all closed branches, we knew we had a tautology on our hands.
4. Explain that we are going to do exactly the same thing here. We have two propositions that may or may not be equivalent. We turn them into what may or may not be a tautology by putting the biconditional between them. Then we negate the maybe tautology and build a truth tree for it. If all the branches close, we know that the negated proposition is a self-contradiction, which means the unnegated proposition is a tautology, which means the two statements we turned into the tautology are equivalent. In other words, **two propositions are equivalent if and only if the negation of their biconditional results in a completely closed truth tree**. Negate $p \equiv p$ and make the truth tree for it (without line numbers or justification), and show that it is indeed a closed truth tree:

```
  ~( p ≡ p) ✓
    /   \
   p    ~p
  ~p     p
   ×     ×
```

5. Students may be a bit dazed at this point. Write on the board the two propositions $P \supset Q$ and $\sim P \vee Q$. Explain that the first step to determining whether or not these are equivalent is to make these two propositions into a biconditional and then negate it, like

so: *~[(P ⊃ Q) ≡ (~P ∨ Q)]*. Now have students walk you through creating the truth tree for this new proposition. It should look like this:

	Left branch	Right branch	
1)	~[(P ⊃ Q) ≡ (~P ∨ Q)] ✓		SM
	/	\	
2)	P⊃Q✓	~(P⊃Q)✓	1~≡D
3)	~(~P∨Q)✓	~P∨Q✓	1~≡D
4)	|	P	2~⊃D
5)	|	~Q	2~⊃D
6)	~~P✓	|	3~∨D
7)	~Q	|	3~∨D
8)	P	/ \	6~~D
9)	/ \	~P Q	3∨D
10)	~P Q	4×9 5×9	2⊃D
	8×10 7×10		

Make sure students see that since every branch is closed, the negation of the biconditional is a self-contradiction, the biconditional is a tautology, and the two propositions that make up the biconditional are equivalent.

6. Now write on the board the propositions *~(P • Q)* and *~P • ~Q*. Have students walk you through making the truth true to determine the equivalency of these propositions. You only need to decompose the left-hand side of the truth tree to get the info you need. It should look like this:

	Left branch	Right branch	
1)	~[~(P • Q) ≡ (~P • ~Q)] ✓		SM
	/	\	
2)	~(P • Q) ✓	~~(P • Q)	1~≡D
3)	~(~P • ~Q) ✓	~P • ~Q	1~≡D
	/ \		
4)	~~P ✓ ~~Q ✓		3~•D
5)	P Q		4~~D
	/\ /\		
6)	~P ~Q ~P ~Q		2~•D
	5×6 O O 5×6		

Make sure students see that because there are open branches on the left-hand side, we do not even need to decompose the right side: we know that since the negated biconditional *can* be true, the biconditional is not a tautology, and *~(P • Q)* and *~P • ~Q* are therefore not equivalent propositions.

ASSIGNMENT

Have students complete Exercise 26, and go over it with them.

LESSON 26

TRUTH TREES FOR EQUIVALENCE

When two propositions are equivalent, their biconditional is a tautology. Symbolically, because p is equivalent to itself, $p \equiv p$ is a tautology. Thus, if we decompose the negation of this biconditional, we should get a closed truth tree, as we learned in the last lesson. The decomposition is shown here:

KEY POINT

Two propositions are equivalent if and only if the negation of their biconditional results in a completely closed truth tree.

~(p ≡ p) ✓
p   ~p
~p   p
×   ×

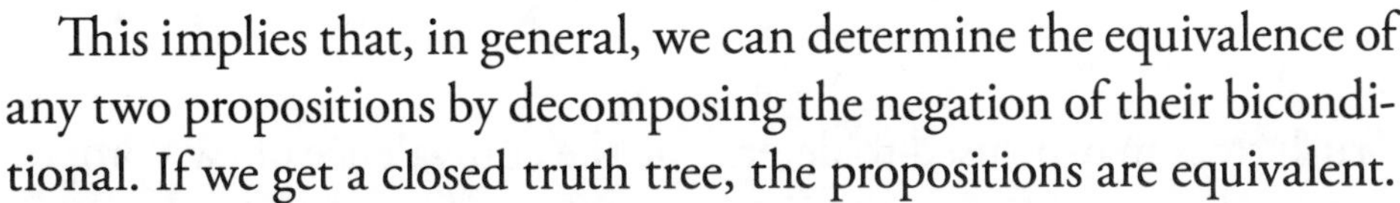

This implies that, in general, we can determine the equivalence of any two propositions by decomposing the negation of their biconditional. If we get a closed truth tree, the propositions are equivalent.

Let's use this to show the equivalence of $P \supset Q$ and $\sim P \vee Q$. The truth tree would be

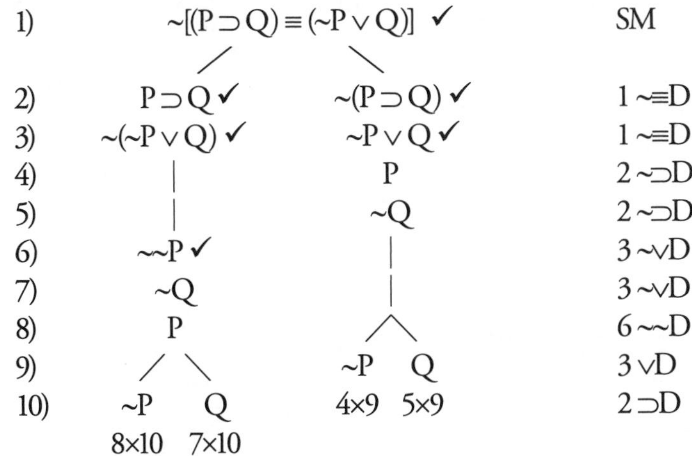

Every branch closed. Thus the biconditional is a tautology, which implies that the two propositions are equivalent.

For comparison, let's do a truth tree for two propositions which are *not* equivalent. We have seen a number of times that *~(P • Q)* is not equivalent to *~P • ~Q*. The truth tree which demonstrates this is shown:

Line	Left branch	Right branch	Justification
1)	~[~(P • Q) ≡ (~P • ~Q)] ✓		SM
2)	~(P • Q) ✓	~~(P • Q)	1 ~≡D
3)	~(~P • ~Q) ✓	~P • ~Q	1 ~≡D
4)	~~P ✓ | ~~Q ✓		3 ~•D
5)	P | Q		4 ~~D
6)	~P ~Q | ~P ~Q		2 ~•D
	5×6 O | O 5×6		

We need not decompose the right-hand side, since we have already found open branches on the left. The open branch shows that the negated biconditional can be true, implying that the biconditional is false. This means that the propositions are not equivalent.

SUMMARY

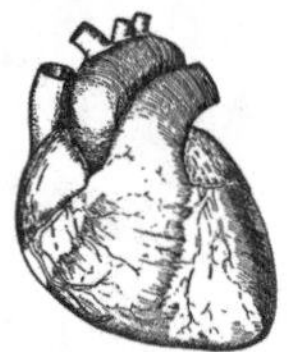

Truth trees may be used to determine the equivalence of two propositions. The propositions are put into a biconditional which is negated. This negated biconditional is then decomposed. The propositions are equivalent if and only if the result is a closed truth tree.

EXERCISE 26 (50 points)

Decompose the negation of the biconditional of the two propositions to determine if they are equivalent. Write YES if they are and NO if they are not. Include line numbers and justifications, and recover at least one set of truth values which show non-equivalence.

1. P, P ∨ (P • Q) (12)

Line	Left branch	Right branch	Justification
1)	~{P ≡ [P ∨ (P • Q)]} ✓		S.M.
2)	P	~P	~≡D
3)	~[P ∨ (P • Q)] ✓	P ∨ (P • Q) ✓	~≡D
4)	~P		3~∨D
5)	~(P • Q)		3~∨D
6)	2x4	P / P • Q ✓	3∨D
7)		2x6 / P	6•D
8)		Q	6•D
		2x7	

YES

2. P, P • (P ∨ Q) (12)

Line	Left branch	Right branch	Justification
1)	~{P ≡ [P • (P ∨ Q)]} ✓		S.M.
2)	P	~P	~≡D
3)	~[P • (P ∨ Q)] ✓	P • (P ∨ Q) ✓	~≡D
4)		P	3•D
5)		P ∨ Q	3•D
6)	~P / ~(P ∨ Q) ✓	2x4	3~•D
7)	2x6 / ~P		6~∨D
8)	~Q		6~∨D
	2x7		

YES

3. P ⊃ Q, Q ⊃ P (12)

Line	Left branch	Right branch	Justification
1)	~[(P ⊃ Q) ≡ (Q ⊃ P)] ✓		S.M.
2)	P ⊃ Q ✓	~(P ⊃ Q)	~≡D
3)	~(Q ⊃ P) ✓	Q ⊃ P	~≡D
4)	Q		3~⊃D
5)	~P		3~⊃D
6)	/ \		
7)	~P / Q		2⊃D
	O / O		

NO

P	Q
F	T

4. P ⊃ Q, ~Q ⊃ ~P (14)

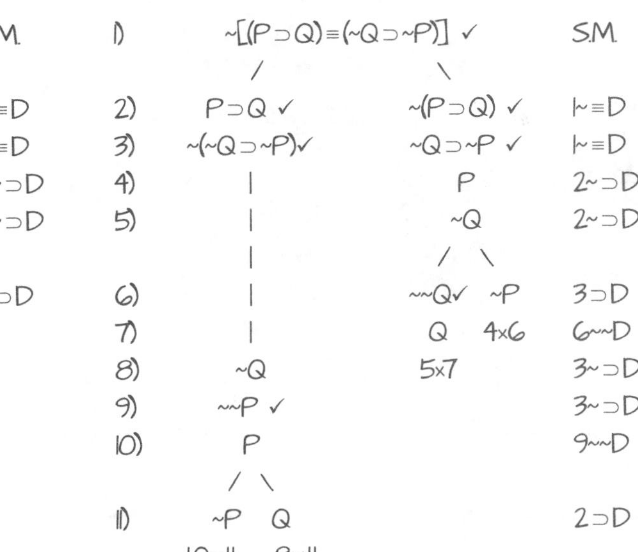

YES

TEACHER'S NOTES on LESSON 27

TRUTH TREES FOR VALIDITY

Intermediate Logic, pp. 209–212

STUDENT OBJECTIVES

1. Use a truth tree to determine whether an argument is valid or invalid.
2. Complete Exercise 27.

TEACHING INSTRUCTIONS

1. Remind students that we have used truth trees to determine consistency, equivalence, self-contradiction, and tautology. Tell students that there is one more thing we can use truth trees to determine. See if they can guess what it is (validity).
2. Have someone reach back into the dark corners of their brain and define validity. Make sure students remember that an argument is valid if and only if the premises necessarily imply the conclusion; that is, if the premises are assumed to be true, the conclusion must also be true. If, on the other hand, it is possible to have true premises and a false conclusion, the argument must be invalid.
3. This is tricky, but see if students can put into words what it is the common feature of all the uses of the truth trees we have seen in the past few lessons. What have all the truth trees demonstrated? Explain that truth trees demonstrate whether all the propositions in a set can be true at once. If it is possible for all to be true at once, at least one branch of the truth tree will be open. If all the branches are closed, the propositions cannot all be true.
4. See if students can guess how we will combine these two concepts—validity and truth trees—to develop a truth tree method for determining validity. Explain that we will do something very similar to the shorter truth tables for validity: we will assume the argument is invalid and then see if that results in a contradiction in the truth tree. Ask student what the name for this kind of argument—assuming the opposite of what we want to prove (it is *reductio ad absurdum*).
5. Ask students what we are assuming when we assume that an argument is invalid. Explain that we are assuming that the premises are true and that the conclusion is false—or rather, that the negation of the conclusion is true. So the propositions that we will bring into our truth tree are the premises and the negated conclusion. Then we will decompose these propositions as in any other truth tree. If this creates contradictions on every branch—that is, if the entire truth tree closes—then we know that the assumption was wrong and that the argument is in fact valid. If, however, we do have an open branch, we know that the argument is in fact invalid and that the truth values on that open branch will be the truth values by which the argument is invalid. Write on the board that **a propositional argument is valid if and only if the decomposition of the set containing its**

premises and the negation of its conclusion results in a completely closed truth tree.

6. Have someone give you the *modus ponens* argument and write it on the board: $p \supset q, p, \therefore q$. Tell students that you will use this argument as your first example. Ask them what we begin by assuming (that the argument is invalid; that the premises and the negation of the conclusion are true). Have students give you the three propositions to be decomposed in the truth tree ($p \supset q, p, \sim q$). The have them walk you through creating the truth tree for validity. Explain that instead of labeling the given propositions SM as we have in all the other truth trees, in the truth trees for validity we label the premises *P* and the negated conclusion NC. The completed truth tree should look like this:

1)	p ⊃ q ✓	P
2)	p	P
3)	~q	NC
	/ \	
4)	~p q	1 ⊃D
	2×4 3×4	

Make sure students see that since the truth tree is completely closed, our three given propositions cannot all be true at once and the *modus ponens* argument is not invalid but valid. Which makes sense, since we know for a fact that *modus ponens* is valid.

7. Have someone give you the *affirming the consequent* argument and write it on the board: $p \supset q, q, \therefore p$. Again have students walk you through creating the truth tree to determine the validity of this argument. The completed truth tree should look like this:

1)	p ⊃ q ✓	P
2)	q	P
3)	~p	NC
	/ \	
4)	~p q	1 ⊃ D
	O O	

Make sure students see that because this set of propositions is consistent, because it is possible for the premises and negated conclusion to be true at the same time, the argument is indeed invalid. Remind students that we can determine from the truth tree what truth values will make the set consistent: we recover the truth values from any open branches. The recovered truth values are therefore:

p	q
F	T

8. Quickly write out the longer truth table (given below) for this argument and show that these truth values are the same truth values by which the longer truth table shows this argument invalid.

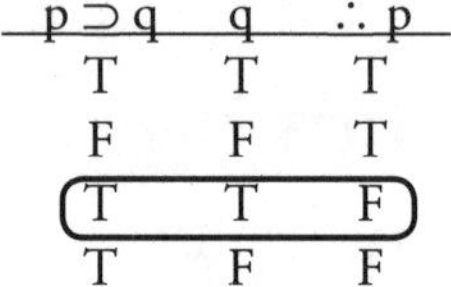

p ⊃ q	q	∴ p
T	T	T
F	F	T
T	T	F
T	F	F

9. Write on the board the argument $p \supset q, \sim q, \therefore p \equiv q$. Again have students put the premises and the negation of the conclusion in a set and decompose them in a truth tree, like so:

1)	p ⊃ q ✓	P
2)	~q	P
3)	~(p ≡ q) ✓	NC
	/ \	
4)	~p q	1 ⊃ D
	/ \ 2×4	
5)	p ~p	3~≡D
6)	~q q	3~≡D
	4×5 2×6 VALID	

Make sure students see that assuming the argument to be invalid resulted in nothing but contradictions. So the argument is valid.

10. Write on the board the argument $p \supset (q \supset r)$, $q \supset (p \supset r)$, $\therefore (p \vee q) \supset r$. Once again, have students make the premises and negated conclusion into a set and decompose them in a truth tree (they may need to be walked through it, as it is pretty complicated). It should look like this:

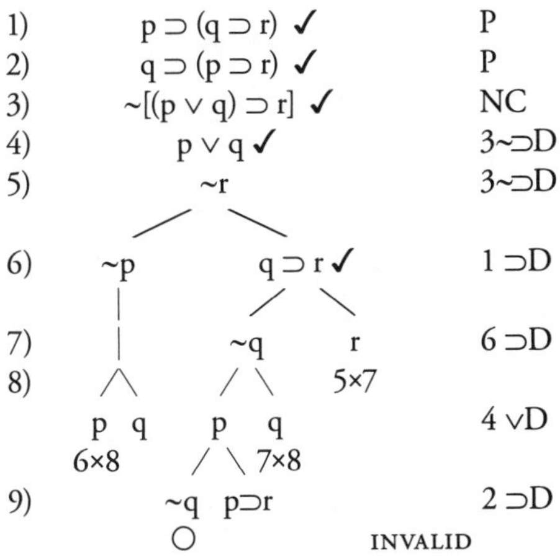

Make sure students see that we could stop the truth tree—even though not all the propositions were decomposed—because we found an open branch, with fully decomposed propositions and no contradictions above it. So without going further we know that there is at least one possible way for the premises to be true and the conclusion is false. Thus the argument is invalid.

11. Have students recover the truth values that demonstrate the argument invalidity (the truth values of the variables in the open branch):

p	q	r
T	F	F

Have students plug these truth values into the original argument to see that the premises do indeed come out true and the conclusion false.

ASSIGNMENTS

1. Have students complete Exercise 27, and go over it with them.
2. Remind students to study for next class's quiz over Lessons 25–27.

LESSON 27

TRUTH TREES FOR VALIDITY

So far we have found that truth trees are able to help us determine the consistency and equivalence of propositions, and to determine if a given proposition is a self-contradiction or a tautology. In this last lesson we shall see how truth trees may be used to determine the validity of arguments.

Recall once again the definition of validity. An argument is valid if and only if the premises necessarily imply the conclusion; if the premises are assumed to be true, then the conclusion must be true. If it is possible for the premises to be true and the conclusion to be false, the argument is necessarily invalid.

KEY POINT

A propositional argument is valid if and only if the decomposition of the set containing its premises and the negation of its conclusion results in a completely closed truth tree.

Recall also what truth trees do: truth trees demonstrate whether propositions in a set can all be true. If they can all be true, at least one branch of the truth tree is open. If the truth tree is completely closed, the propositions cannot all be true.

Now, how can we use these two concepts to develop a method to determine validity of arguments? We do so in a way very similar to the shorter truth tables; we assume the argument is invalid, then see if that results in contradictions. In other words, we do a *Reductio ad Absurdum* on the argument.

To assume that the argument is invalid, we simply assume that the premises are true and that the negation of the conclusion is true—that is, that the conclusion is false. Then we decompose these propositions (the premises and the negated conclusion) in a truth tree. If this leads us to contradictions in every way—that is, if the truth tree closes—then the assumption was wrong and the argument is valid. However, if we get an open truth tree, the truth values on the open branch will be those by which the propositions (the premises and the negated conclusion) can be true.

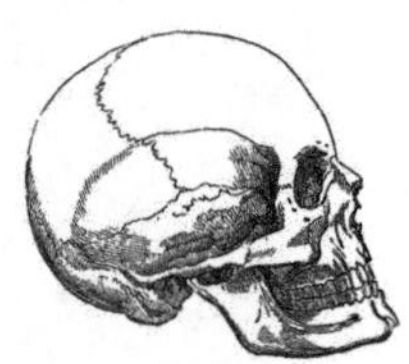

CAUTION

When using truth trees to determine validity, label the premises with P and the negated conclusion with NC rather than using the generic SM.

We will use the *modus ponens* argument $p \supset q$, p, $\therefore q$ as an example. We assume that the argument is invalid, that the premises are true and the negation of the conclusion is true. Then we complete a truth tree as follows to see if these assumptions are consistent (the premises are labeled P and the conclusion is labeled NC for "negated conclusion"):

```
1)    p⊃q ✓     P
2)      p       P
3)     ~q       NC
       / \
4)   ~p    q    1⊃D
    2×4   3×4
```

We see that, when we assume the premises are true and the conclusion is false, we end up with contradictions on every branch of the truth tree. This means that our assumption was wrong and the argument is therefore valid.

Now consider the argument of *affirming the consequent:* $p \supset q$, q, $\therefore p$. We write the premises and the negation of the conclusion as set members, then decompose them in the truth tree as shown:

```
1) p⊃q ✓    P
2)   q      P
3)  ~p      NC
    / \
4) ~p  q    1⊃D
    O  O
```

We see that the set is consistent; it is possible for the premises and the negated conclusion to be true. The recovered truth values are:

p	q
F	T

With these truth value assignments, the premises $p \supset q$ and q are true, and the conclusion p is false. Note that p as false and q as true are the same truth values by which the longer truth table shows this argument to be invalid:

$p \supset q$	q	$\therefore p$	
T	T	T	
F	F	T	
T	T	F	← INVALID
T	F	F	

Now for some slightly more complex examples. Consider this argument from Exercise 17a: $p \supset q$, $\sim q$, $\therefore p \equiv q$. We put the premises and the negation of the conclusion in a set and decompose them in a truth tree, as shown below:

```
1)        p⊃q✓             P
2)         ~q              P
3)       ~(p≡q) ✓          NC
           /  \
4)       ~p    q           1⊃D
        /  \  2×4
5)     p   ~p              3~≡D
6)    ~q    q              3~≡D
     4×5  2×6       VALID
```

Assuming the argument to be invalid resulted in nothing but contradictions. So the argument is valid.

For the final example we will look at the argument in the last problem from Exercise 9: $p \supset (q \supset r)$, $q \supset (p \supset r)$, $\therefore (p \vee q) \supset r$. We do the same procedure as before, resulting in the truth tree shown:

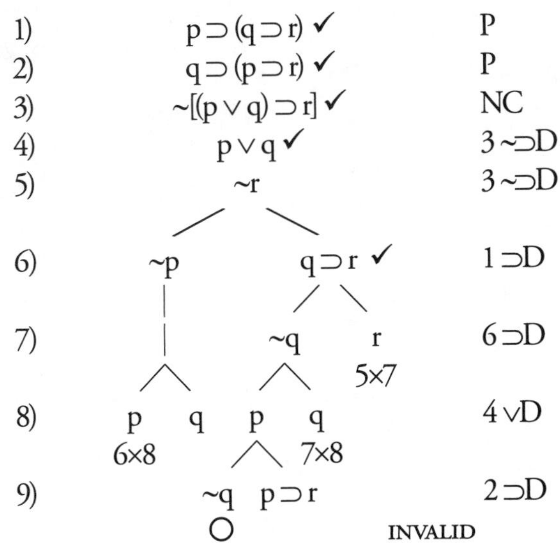

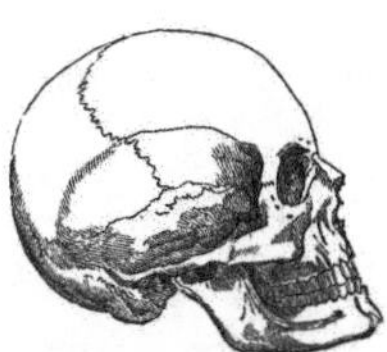

CAUTION

If there is even just *one* open branch, the argument is invalid, because it shows that the premises can be true and the conclusion false.

In step nine we find an open branch (with fully decomposed propositions and no contradictions above it). Without going any further we know that there exists at least one possible way to make the premises true and the conclusion false, and thus the argument is invalid. We can recover the truth values which demonstrate the invalidity:

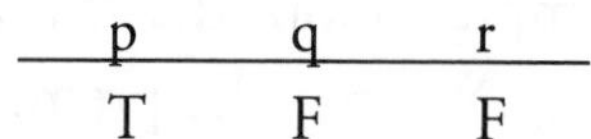

p	q	r
T	F	F

Had we continued the truth tree, we could have recovered more truth values which would demonstrate invalidity, but these are sufficient. You should check to see that, if you assign these truth values to the variables in the original argument, the premises come out to be true and the conclusion false.

SUMMARY

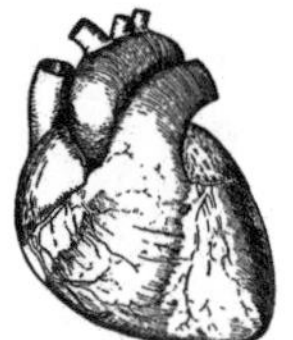

Truth trees can be used to determine the validity of arguments. The set members are the premises and the negation of the conclusion. These members are then decomposed in a truth tree. If the truth tree closes, the argument is valid. If the truth tree has at least one open branch, the argument is invalid and the truth values may be recovered which demonstrate the invalidity of the argument.

EXERCISE 27 (50 points)

Use truth trees to determine the validity of each argument. If an argument is found to be invalid, recover at least one set of truth values which demonstrate the invalidity.

1. A⊃B, B⊃C, ~C, ∴ ~A (8)

```
1)        A⊃B ✓          P
2)        B⊃C ✓          P
3)         ~C            P
4)        ~~A ✓          N.C.
5)          A            4~~D
           / \
6)       ~A    B         1⊃D
        5x6   / \
7)          ~B    C      2⊃D
           6x7   3x7
```

VALID

2. D⊃E, F⊃E, ∴ D∨F (10)

```
1)          D⊃E ✓            P
2)          F⊃E ✓            P
3)         ~(D∨F) ✓          N.C.
4)           ~D              3~∨D
5)           ~F              3~∨D
            /   \
6)        ~D     E           1⊃D
          / \   / \
7)      ~F   E ~F  E         2⊃D
        O    O  O  O
```

INVALID:

D	E	F
F	T	F
F	F	F

3. (G • H)⊃I, H, ∴ G⊃I (8)

```
1)          (G•H)⊃I ✓          P
2)              H              P
3)          ~(G⊃I) ✓           N.C.
4)              G              3~⊃D
5)             ~I              3~⊃D
             /     \
6)      ~(G•H) ✓     I         1⊃D
         /  \       5x6
7)     ~G    ~H                6~•D
       4x7   2x7
```

VALID

Continued on next page.

4. If an axe was found in the safe then the butler put it there. If the butler put it there then he was guilty of the crime. If he was guilty of the crime then he would be distressed. He was not distressed. Either an axe was found in the safe or the safe was empty. Therefore the safe was empty. (A, B, C, D, E) (12)

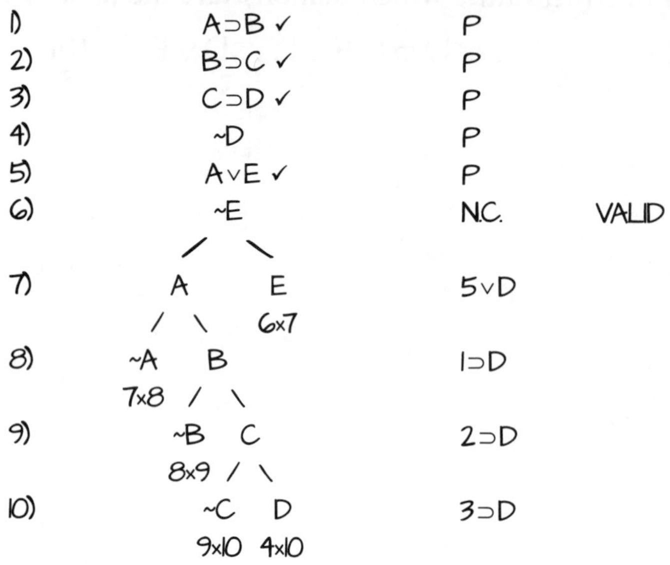

5. If you studied logic then if you did not learn logic then you will not know how to do this problem. If you did not learn logic but you are brilliant then you will know how to do this problem. You know how to do this problem. Thus you either studied logic or you are brilliant (S, L, K, B). (12)

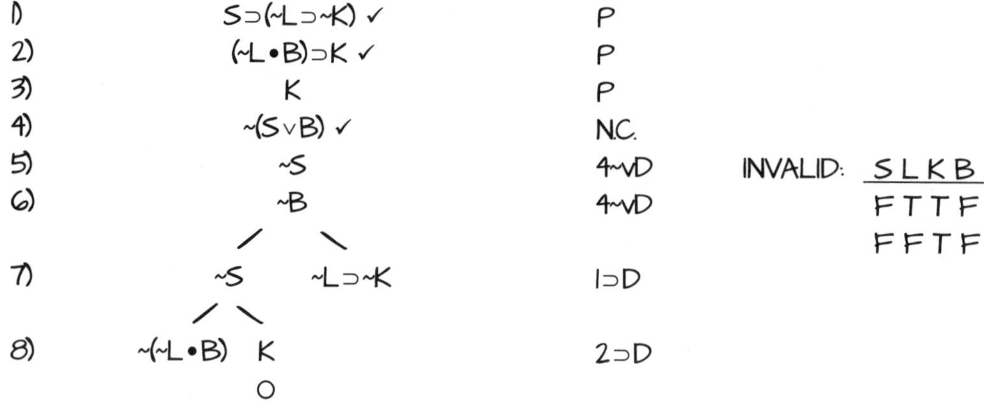

TEACHER'S NOTES

QUIZ 14 (LESSONS 25–27)

STUDENT OBJECTIVE

Complete Quiz 14.

TEACHING INSTRUCTIONS

1. Give Quiz 14. Allow 30 minutes. Grade quiz with students.
2. If you have extra time, begin reviewing for Test 7.

INTERMEDIATE LOGIC | Quiz 14

Lessons 25–27 (56 points)

Name ______________________________

1. Fill in the blank: If two propositions are Logically equivalent, then the negation of the biconditional of those propositions will decompose into a completely closed truth tree. (2)

Problems 2-3: Use the proper truth tree methods to determine if the proposition in problem 2 is a self-contradiction, and to determine if the proposition in problem 3 is a tautology. (9 each)

2. ~[A ∨ (B ⊃ ~A)]

1.	~[A ∨ (B ⊃ ~A)] ✓	SM
2.	~A	1 ~∨D
3.	~(B ⊃ ~A) ✓	1 ~∨D
4.	B	3 ~⊃D
5.	~~A ✓	3 ~⊃D
6.	A	5 ~~D
	2x6	

Is it a self-contradiction? (YES) NO

3. (C ⊃ D) ∨ ~C

1.	~[(C ⊃ D) ∨ ~C] ✓	SM
2.	~(C ⊃ D) ✓	1 ~∨D
3.	~~C ✓	1 ~∨D
4.	C	3 ~~D
5.	C	2 ~⊃D
6.	~D	2 ~⊃D
	O	

Is it a tautology? YES (NO)

4. Use the proper truth tree method to determine if the given propositions are logically equivalent. You may omit line numbers and justifications. (10)

p ⊃ ~q   ~(p • q)

~[(p ⊃ ~q) ≡ ~(p • q)] ✓

Left branch:
p ⊃ ~q ✓
~~(p • q) ✓
p • q ✓
p
q
~p (×) | ~q (×)

Right branch:
~(p ⊃ ~q) ✓
~(p • q) ✓
p
~~q ✓
q
~p (×) | ~q (×)

Are they equivalent? (YES) NO

Problems 5-6: Translate the arguments into symbolic form using the given constants. Then use the proper truth tree method to determine if the arguments are valid.

5. Algeria will send an envoy, or if Bosnia joins the union then so will Croatia. Bosnia joins the union. Therefore, Algeria will send an envoy or Croatia will join the union. (**A, B, C**) (12)

1.	$A \lor (B \supset C)$ ✓			P
2.	B			P
3.	$\sim(A \lor C)$ ✓			NC
4.	$\sim A$			$3 \sim \lor$ D
5.	$\sim C$			$3 \sim \lor$ D
	/	\		
6.	A	$B \supset C$ ✓		$1 \lor$ D
	4x6	/	\	
7.		$\sim B$	C	$6 \supset$ D
		2x7	5x7	

Is it valid? **(YES)** NO

6. If Denmark accepts the treaty then Estonia or France will reject it. If France rejects the treaty then Denmark will accept it. So if Denmark accepts the treaty then Estonia rejects it. (**D, E, F**) (14)

1.	$D \supset (E \lor F)$ ✓				P
2.	$F \supset D$ ✓				P
3.	$\sim(D \supset E)$ ✓				NC
4.	D				$3 \sim \supset$ D
5.	$\sim E$				$3 \sim \supset$ D
	/	\			
6.	$\sim D$	$E \lor F$ ✓			$1 \supset$ D
	4x6	/	\		
7.		E	F		$6 \lor$ D
		5x7	/	\	
8.			$\sim F$	D	$2 \supset$ D
			7x8	O	

Is it valid? YES **(NO)**

REVIEW FOR TEST 7 (LESSONS 22–27)

STUDENT OBJECTIVES

Complete the objectives from Lessons 22–27. Objectives are listed at the beginning of each lesson's teacher's notes.

TEACHING INSTRUCTIONS

1. To review for the test, choose problems from the Review Questions for Lessons 22–27 on pp. 215–216 of the student text and from the Review Exercises for Lessons 22–27 on pp. 217–225 of the student text for students to work through.
2. If you'd like, give students "Test 7: Form A" from the *Intermediate Logic Test and Quiz Packet* as a practice exam. Go over the answers together.

ASSIGNMENT

Have students study for Test 7.

TEST 7 (LESSONS 22–27)

STUDENT OBJECTIVE

Complete Test 7.

TEACHING INSTRUCTIONS

1. Give students Test 7: Form B from the *Intermediate Logic Test and Quiz Packet*. Allow one hour to complete it.
2. Grade tests. Have them ready to hand back to students within a week.

INTERMEDIATE LOGIC | Test 7, Form A

Lessons 22–27 (85 points)

Name ____

1. Explain what it means to decompose a compound proposition. (2)

   To decompose a compound proposition means to break it down into its literals, which when true make the entire proposition true.

Problems 2-5: Consider the following truth tree.

Step	Left branch	Right branch	Justification
1.	$(A \bullet B) \equiv (A \supset C)$ ✓		SM
2.	$\sim (B \vee C)$ ✓		SM
3.	$\sim B$		$2 \sim \vee D$
4.	$\sim C$		$2 \sim \vee D$
5.	$A \bullet B$ ✓	$\sim (A \bullet B)$ ✓	$1 \equiv D$
6.	$A \supset C$	$\sim (A \supset C)$ ✓	$1 \equiv D$
7.	A	|	$5 \bullet D$
8.	B	|	$5 \bullet D$
9.	×	A	$6 \sim \supset D$
10.		$\sim C$	$6 \sim \supset D$
11.		$\sim A$ (×) $\quad \sim B$ (O)	$5 \sim \bullet D$

2. Identify any open branches with O and any closed branches with ×. (3)
3. Write the decomposition justifications on the lines next to steps 3 through 11. (9)
4. Is the set of propositions consistent or inconsistent? (1) CONSISTENT
5. Why is it not necessary to decompose the conditional $A \supset C$ in line 6? (2)

   It is not necessary to continue to decompose a closed branch.

Problems 6-7: Using truth tree decomposition, determine the consistency of the set of propositions. Include line numbers and justifications, and recover the truth values if consistent. (7, 11)

6. $\{D \bullet \sim E,\ D \supset E\}$ 7. $\{F \vee \sim G,\ \sim(F \equiv \sim G)\}$

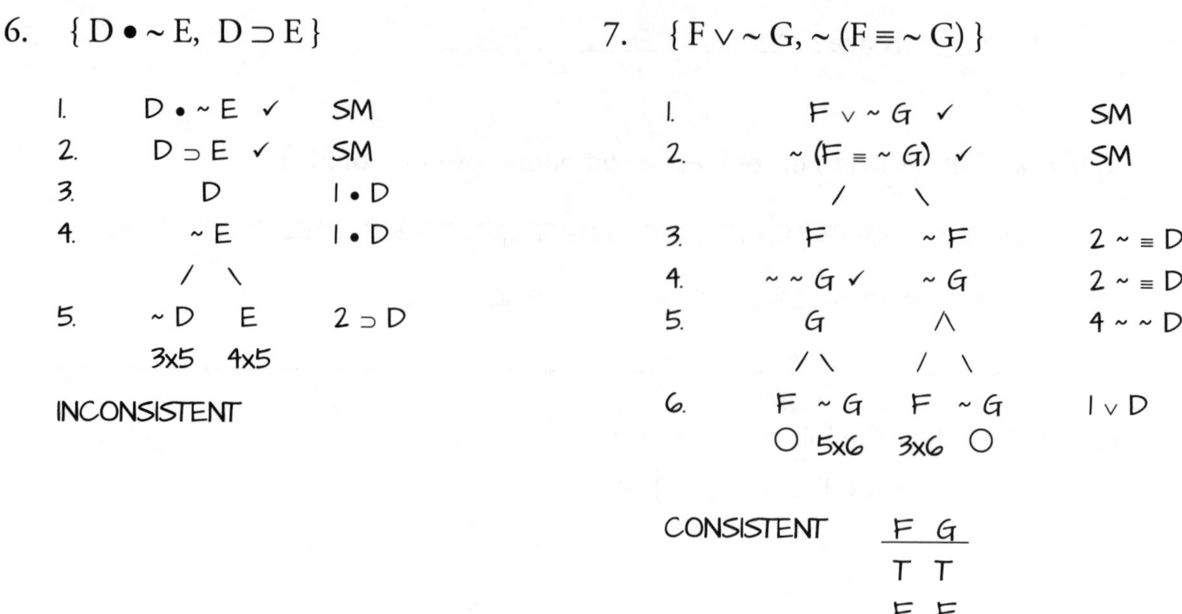

8. Determine if the given propositions are equivalent by constructing a truth tree of the negated biconditional. You may omit line numbers and justifications for this truth tree. (12)

$\sim(J \supset H)$ $(\sim H \bullet J)$

$\sim[\sim(J \supset H) \equiv (\sim H \bullet J)]$ ✓

Left branch	Right branch
$\sim(J \supset H)$ ✓	$\sim\sim(J \supset H)$ ✓
$\sim(\sim H \bullet J)$ ✓	$\sim H \bullet J$ ✓
J	$J \supset H$ ✓
$\sim H$	$\sim H$
	J
$\sim\sim H$ ✓ / $\sim J$	$\sim J$ / H
H / X	X / X
X	

Are the propositions equivalent? (YES) NO

9. Use the proper truth-tree method to see if this proposition is a self-contradiction.
~ p • (p ∨ q) (7)

1.	~ p • (p ∨ q) ✓	SM
2.	~ p	1 • D
3.	p ∨ q ✓	1 • D
	/ \	
4.	p q	3 ∨ D
	2x4 O	

Is it a self-contradiction? YES **(NO)**

10. Use the proper truth-tree method to see if this proposition is a tautology.
p ⊃ (p ∨ q) (7)

1.	~ [p ⊃ (p ∨ q)] ✓	SM
2.	p	1 ~ ⊃ D
3.	~ (p ∨ q) ✓	1 ~ ⊃ D
4.	~ p	3 ~ ∨ D
5.	~ q	3 ~ ∨ D
	2x4	

Is it a tautology? **(YES)** NO

Problems 11-12: Translate the argument into symbolic form using the given constants, then use the truth-tree method to determine the argument's validity. Number each line, justify each step (use P for the premises and NC for the negated conclusion), and write VALID or INVALID.

11. If Tumnus helped Lucy, then if the witch found out then she would turn Tumnus into stone. Tumnus helped Lucy and he was turned to stone. Therefore, the witch found out. (**H**, **W**, **S**) (11)

1.	H ⊃ (W ⊃ S) ✓	P
2.	H • S ✓	P
3.	~ W	NC
4.	H	2 • D
5.	S	2 • D
	/ \	
6.	~ H W ⊃ S ✓	1 ⊃ D
	4x6 / \	
7.	~ W S	6 ⊃ D
	O O	

INVALID

12. If Aslan saves Edmund then he will be killed at the stone table. He cannot be both killed at the table and begin the battle. Thus, if Aslan saves Edmund then he cannot begin the battle. **(S, K, B)** (13)

```
1.          S ⊃ K ✓                  P
2.        ~ ( K • B ) ✓              P
3.       ~ ( S ⊃ ~ B ) ✓             NC
4.             S                     3 ~ ⊃ D
5.           ~ ~ B ✓                 3 ~ ⊃ D
6.             B                     5 ~ ~ D
            /     \
7.        ~ S      K                 1 ⊃ D
          4x7     / \
8.            ~ K  ~ B               2 ~ • D
              7x8  6x8

        VALID
```

INTERMEDIATE LOGIC | Test 7, Form B

Lessons 22–27 (74 points)

Name ____________________

1. What is a *literal*? (2) A simple proposition (represented by a single variable or constant) or the negation of a simple proposition.

2. What is a *self-contradiction*? (2) A compound proposition that is false due to its logical structure.

Problems 3-5: Consider the following truth tree.

1.	$\sim p \supset (q \vee r)$ ✓					SM
2.	$\sim(r \bullet s)$ ✓					SM
3.	$\sim(p \vee s)$ ✓					SM
4.	$\sim p$					3 ~∨D
5.	$\sim s$					3 ~∨D
6.	$\sim\sim p$ ✓	$q \vee r$ ✓				1 ⊃D
7.	p					6 ~~D
8.	×	q		r		6 ∨D
9.		$\sim r$	$\sim s$	$\sim r$	$\sim s$	2 ~•D
		O	O	×	O	

3. Identify any open branches with O and any closed branches with ×. (5)
4. Write the decomposition justifications on the lines next to steps 4 through 9. (6)
5. Is the set of propositions consistent or inconsistent? (1) CONSISTENT

Problems 6-7: Using truth tree decomposition, determine the consistency of the set of propositions. Include line numbers and justifications, and recover the truth values if consistent. (8, 7)

6. $\{A \bullet B, \sim B \vee C\}$

1.	A • B ✓		SM
2.	~ B ∨ C ✓		SM
3.	A		1 • D
4.	B		1 • D
	/	\	
5.	~ B	C	2 ∨ D
	4x5	O	

CONSISTENT

A	B	C
T	T	T

7. $\{D \equiv E, \sim D, E\}$

1.	D ≡ E ✓		SM
2.	~ D		SM
3.	E		SM
	/	\	
4.	D	~ D	1 ≡ D
5.	E	~ E	1 ≡ D
	2x4	3x5	

INCONSISTENT

8. Determine if the given propositions are equivalent by constructing a truth tree of the negated biconditional. You may omit line numbers and justifications for this truth tree. (12)

$\sim(F \bullet G) \qquad (F \supset \sim G)$

~ [~ (F • G) ≡ (F ⊃ ~ G)] ✓

Left branch	Right branch
~ (F • G) ✓	~ ~ (F • G) ✓
~ (F ⊃ ~ G) ✓	F ⊃ ~ G ✓
F	F • G ✓
~ ~ G ✓	F
G	G
~ F / ~ G	~ F / ~ G
X X	X X

Are the propositions equivalent? (YES) NO

9. Decompose this compound proposition to determine if it is a self-contradiction. (6)

$(\sim P \bullet Q) \bullet \sim (P \supset Q)$

$(\sim P \bullet Q) \bullet \sim (P \supset Q)$ ✓

$\sim P \bullet Q$ ✓

$\sim (P \supset Q)$ ✓

$\sim P$

Q

P

$\sim Q$

X

Is it a self-contradiction? (YES) NO

10. Determine if the given proposition is a tautology by decomposing its negation. (5)

$P \supset (Q \supset P)$

$\sim [P \supset (Q \supset P)]$ ✓

P

$\sim (Q \supset P)$ ✓

Q

$\sim P$

X

Is it a tautology? (YES) NO

Problems 11-12: Use the truth-tree method to determine the validity of the following arguments. Remember to number each line, justify each line (using P for the premises and NC for the negated conclusion), and write VALID or INVALID. (10 each)

11. $A \supset B \quad B \supset \sim C \quad C \quad \therefore \sim A$

1.	$A \supset B$ ✓	P
2.	$B \supset \sim C$ ✓	P
3.	C	P
4.	$\sim\sim A$ ✓	NC
5.	A	$4 \sim\sim D$
	/ \	
6	$\sim B$ $\sim C$	$2 \supset D$
	/ \ 3x6	
7.	$\sim A$ B	$1 \supset D$
	5x7 6x7	

VALID

12. $D \vee (E \bullet F) \quad \sim (D \bullet E) \quad \therefore F$

1.	$D \vee (E \bullet F)$ ✓	P
2.	$\sim (D \bullet E)$ ✓	P
3.	$\sim F$	NC
	/ \	
4.	D $E \bullet F$ ✓	$1 \vee D$
5.	$\wedge$ E	$4 \bullet D$
6.	/ \ F	$4 \bullet D$
7.	$\sim D$ $\sim E$ 3x6	$2 \sim \bullet D$
	4x7 O	

INVALID

UNIT 3

REVIEW QUESTIONS

Answers can be found in the lesson under which the questions are listed.

Lesson 22: Truth Trees for Consistency

What does it mean to decompose a compound proposition? What is a literal? What is a truth tree? How can truth trees show a set of propositions to be consistent? What does it mean to recover the truth values for a consistent set of propositions? How is this done? What is an open branch on a truth tree? What is a closed branch? How are these shown on a truth tree? How are double negations decomposed? How are conjunctions decomposed? How are disjunctions decomposed?

Lesson 23: Decomposition Rules

How are negated conjunctions and negated disjunctions decomposed? How do their rules of decomposition differ from their non-negated counterparts? How are conditionals and negated conditionals decomposed? How are biconditionals and negated biconditionals decomposed? Why do they both branch?

Lesson 24: Techniques for Constructing Truth Trees

Must truth trees be decomposed in the order that the propositions are given? In constructing a truth tree, why should you decompose non-branching members first? Why should you decompose members which result in the closing of branches? Must truth trees be completely decomposed every time? If the other techniques do not apply, which should be decomposed first: more complex propositions, or less complex propositions?

Lesson 25: Truth Trees for Self-Contradiction and Tautology

What happens to every branch on a truth tree of a self-contradiction? What happens to every branch on a truth tree of a negated tautology? Why must the tautology be negated?

Lesson 26: Truth Trees for Equivalence

How can truth trees be used to show two propositions to be equivalent? Explain the reasoning behind this method.

Lesson 27: Truth Trees for Validity

How can truth trees be used to determine the validity of an argument? How do truth trees for validity differ from other truth trees?

UNIT 3

REVIEW EXERCISES

Students may do these exercises for further review of this unit.

ADDITIONAL EXERCISES FOR LESSON 22

Using the method of truth trees, determine the consistency of these sets of propositions. Recover the truth values for the consistent set.

1. Problem 1 in the Additional Exercises for Lesson 10.

Line	Tree	Justification
1)	$p \bullet (q \vee r)$ ✓	SM
2)	$q \bullet \sim r$ ✓	SM
3)	$p \vee r$ ✓	SM
4)	p	1•D
5)	$q \vee r$ ✓	1•D
6)	q	2•D
7)	$\sim r$	2•D
8)	p / r (7×8)	3∨D
9)	(under p:) q (O) / r (7×9)	5∨D

CONSISTENT

p	q	r
T	T	F

2. Problem 2 in the Additional Exercises for Lesson 10.

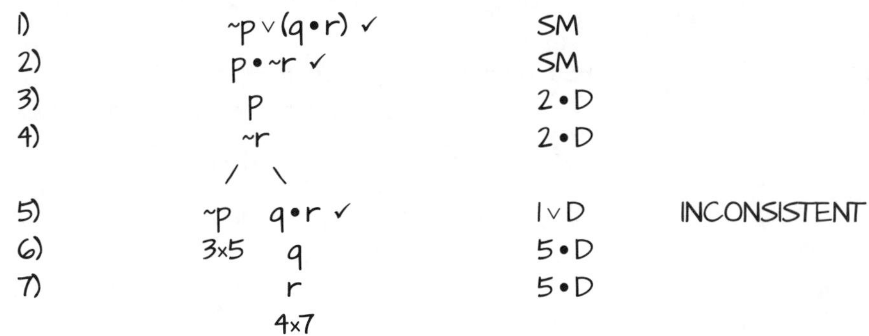

ADDITIONAL EXERCISES FOR LESSON 23

1. Compare the truth tables of the compound propositions with their decomposition rules. What do the truth tables have in common for those propositions whose truth trees decompose by branching?

   The truth table for those propositions which branch all have more than one way of being true (that is, the truth value T shows up more than once in the truth table).

2. How would a tautology such as $p \vee \sim p$ decompose? How would a self-contradiction such as $p \bullet \sim p$ decompose? Discuss the usefulness of these decompositions.

   The rules would look like this:

   p∨~p ✓
   / \
   p ~p

   p•~p ✓
   p
   ~p

   These decompositions are not very useful. The decomposition of the tautology would add no new information, and the decomposition of the self-contradiction would close immediately.

3. Below are truth tables for invented logical operators * and ×. Develop their decomposition rules. To which actual compound propositions do these logical operators correspond?

p	q	p*q	p×q
T	T	F	T
T	F	F	T
F	T	T	F
F	F	F	T

p*q ✓
~p
q

p×q ✓
/ \
p ~q

Thus, p*q corresponds to ~p•q, and p×q corresponds to p∨~q. So they also correspond to ~(q⊃p) and q⊃p, respectively.

Using the method of truth trees, determine the consistency of these sets of propositions. Recover the truth values for the consistent sets.

4. Problem 3 in the Additional Exercises for Lesson 10.

```
1)        ~(p∨q) ✓                SM
2)        ~p⊃(q∨r) ✓              SM
3)           ~r                   SM
4)           ~p                   I~∨D
5)           ~q                   I~∨D
           /    \
6)     ~~p✓    q∨r ✓              2⊃D        INCONSISTENT
7)      p      /   \              6~~D
8)     4x7    q     r             6∨D
             5x8   3x8
```

5. Problem 4 in the Additional Exercises for Lesson 10.

```
1)        ~B⊃(M⊃E) ✓              SM
2)            E                   SM
3)          B•M ✓                 SM
4)            B                   3•D
5)            M                   3•D
           /     \                           CONSISTENT     B M E
6)      ~~B ✓   M⊃E ✓             1⊃D                        T T T
7)       B      /   \             6~~D
8)       O    ~M     E            6⊃D
              5x8    O
```

B	M	E
T	T	T

6. Problem 5 in the Additional Exercises for Lesson 10.

```
1)          L∨C ✓                 SM
2)        C⊃(K•~D) ✓              SM
3)          K⊃D ✓                 SM
4)           ~L                   SM
           /    \
5)        L      C                ∨D
         4x5   /   \                          INCONSISTENT
6)           ~C    K•~D ✓         2⊃D
             5x6     K            6•D
8)                  ~D            6•D
                   /  \
9)               ~K    D          3⊃D
                 7x9  8x9
```

7. {~(P • Q), ~(P ⊃ Q), ~(P ≡ Q)}

```
1)         ~(P•Q) ✓            SM
2)         ~(P⊃Q) ✓            SM
3)         ~(P≡Q) ✓            SM
4)            P                2~⊃D
5)           ~Q                2~⊃D
            /  \                                  CONSISTENT    P Q
6)        ~P    ~Q             1~•D                             ---
          4x6   /  \                                            T F
7)            P    ~P          3~≡D
8)           ~Q     Q          3~≡D
              O    4x7
```

8. {P ⊃ [Q ∨ ~(R • S)], P • R, ~(Q ∨ ~S)}

```
1)      P⊃[Q∨~(R•S)] ✓         SM
2)         P•R ✓               SM
3)       ~(Q∨~S) ✓             SM
4)           P                 2•D
5)           R                 2•D
6)          ~Q                 3~∨D
7)          ~~S ✓              3~∨D
8)           S                 7~~D
           /   \
9)       ~P    Q∨~(R•S) ✓      1⊃D
         4x9     /   \                            INCONSISTENT
10)             Q    ~(R•S) ✓  9∨D
              6x10    /   \
11)                 ~R     ~S  10~•D
                   5x11   8x11
```

ADDITIONAL EXERCISES FOR LESSON 24

Determine the consistency of these sets of propositions using the simplest truth trees possible. You do *not* need to recover the truth values for consistent sets. For each step, explain why you chose that particular decomposition (i.e., tell which simplifying technique you are using).

1. $\{P \vee (R \bullet S), P \supset R, \sim(P \supset S)\}$

```
1)        P∨(R•S) ✓     SM
2)         P⊃R ✓        SM
3)        ~(P⊃S) ✓      SM
4)           P          3~⊃D  (#1)
5)          ~S          3~⊃D
          /    \
6)      ~P      R       2⊃D   (#2)
       4x6     / \
7)            P   R•S   1∨D   (#3)
              O

CONSISTENT
```

2. $\{\sim(P \equiv Q), (P \bullet Q) \vee \sim(P \vee Q)\}$

```
1)              ~(P≡Q) ✓              SM
2)         (P•Q)∨~(P∨Q) ✓             SM
              /        \
3)       (P•Q)✓      ~(P∨Q)✓          2∨D    (#4)
4)         P            |             3•D    (#1)
5)         Q            |             3•D
6)         |           ~P             3~∨D   (#1)
7)         |           ~Q             3~∨D
          / \          / \
8)       P   ~P       P   ~P          1~≡D   (#2)
9)      ~Q    Q      ~Q    Q          1~≡D
       5x9  4x8     6x8  7x9
INCONSISTENT
```

3. $\{(P \bullet Q) \equiv R, \sim(P \bullet R), \sim(\sim P \bullet \sim Q), Q \supset R\}$

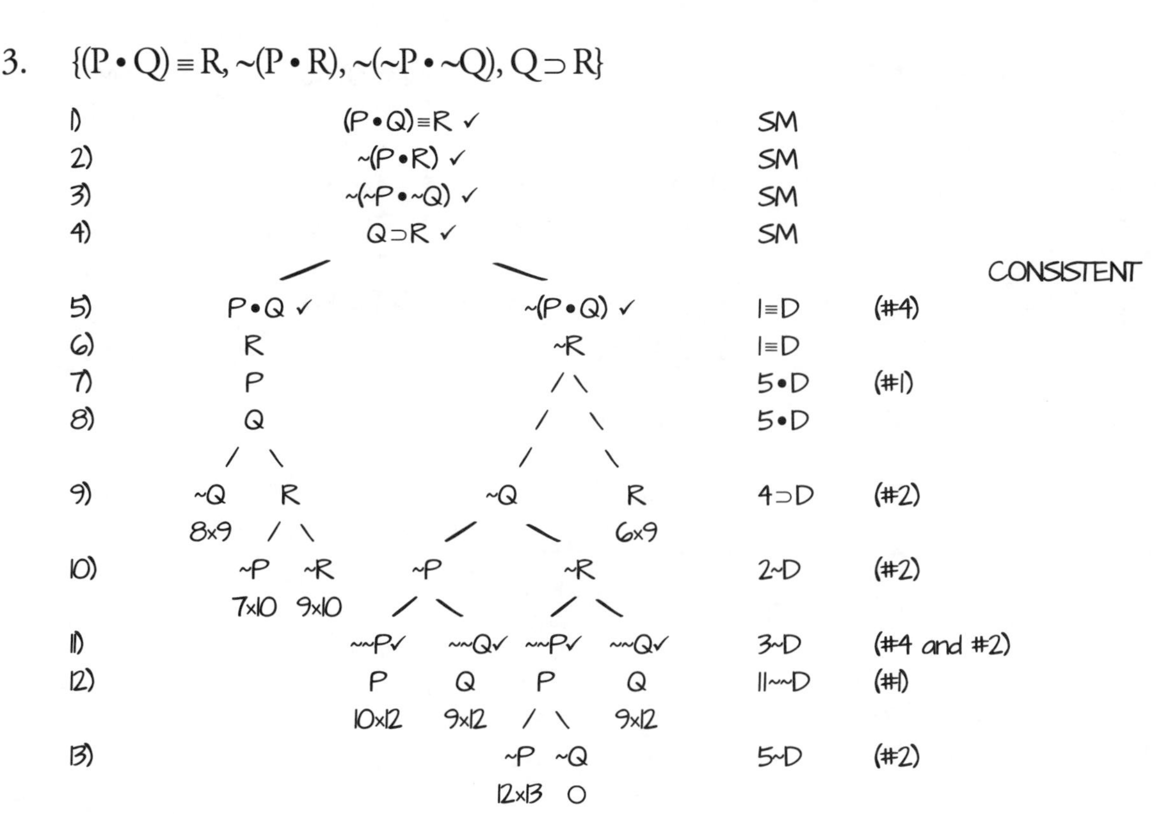

ADDITIONAL EXERCISES FOR LESSON 25

Decompose each of the following compound propositions to determine whether or not it is a self-contradiction.

1. ~[~(P • Q) ∨ (P ⊃ Q)]

```
1)   ~[~(P•Q)∨(P⊃Q)]✓   SM
2)   ~~(P•Q) ✓          1~∨D
3)   ~(P⊃Q) ✓           1~∨D
4)   P•Q ✓              2~~D
5)   P                  4•D
6)   Q                  4•D
7)   P                  3~⊃D
8)   ~Q                 3~⊃D
     6x8

SELF-CONTRADICTION
```

2. (P ≡ Q) • (P ≡ ~Q)

```
1)      (P≡Q)•(P≡~Q) ✓       SM
2)         P≡Q ✓             1•D
3)         P≡~Q ✓            1•D
          /      \
4)       P        ~P         3≡D
5)      ~Q        ~~Q ✓      3≡D
6)       |         Q         5~~D
        / \       / \
7)     P   ~P    P   ~P      2≡D
8)     Q   ~Q    Q   ~Q      2≡D
      5x8  4x7  4x7  6x8

SELF-CONTRADICTION
```

Decompose the negation of each of the following compound propositions to determine whether or not the proposition is a tautology.

3. P ⊃ (Q ⊃ Q)

```
1)   ~[P⊃(Q⊃Q)] ✓   SM
2)   P              1~⊃D
3)   ~(Q⊃Q) ✓       1~⊃D
4)   Q              3~⊃D
5)   ~Q             3~⊃D
     4x5
TAUTOLOGY
```

4. (P ⊃ Q) ⊃ Q

```
1)   ~[(P⊃Q)⊃Q] ✓   SM
2)      P⊃Q ✓       1~⊃D
3)       ~Q         1~⊃D
        /  \
4)     ~P   Q       2⊃D
       O   3x4
NOT A TAUTOLOGY
```

ADDITIONAL EXERCISES FOR LESSON 26

Decompose the negation of the biconditional of the two propositions to determine if they are equivalent. If they are not equivalent, recover at least one set of truth values which show the non-equivalence.

1. ~P ⊃ P, P ∨ (P • Q)

Line	Left	Right	Rule
1)	~{[~P ⊃ P] ≡ [P ∨ (P • Q)]} ✓		SM
	/	\	
2)	~P ⊃ P ✓	~(~P ⊃ P) ✓	~≡D
3)	~[P ∨ (P • Q)] ✓	P ∨ (P • Q) ✓	~≡D
4)	~P	|	3~∨D
5)	~(P • Q)	|	3~∨D
	/ \	|	
6)	~~P ✓ P	|	2⊃D
7)	P 4x6	|	6~~D
8)	4x7	~P	2~⊃D
9)		~P	2~⊃D
		/ \	
10)		P P • Q ✓	3∨D
11)		9x10 P	10•D
12)		Q	10•D
		9x11	

EQUIVALENT

2. P ∨ Q, P ⊃ ~Q

Line	Left	Right	Rule
1)	~[(P ∨ Q) ≡ (P ⊃ ~Q)] ✓		SM
	/	\	
2)	P ∨ Q ✓	~(P ∨ Q)	~≡D
3)	~(P ⊃ ~Q) ✓	P ⊃ ~Q	~≡D
4)	P		3~⊃D
5)	~~Q ✓		3~⊃D
6)	Q		5~~D
	/ \		
7)	P Q		2∨D
	O O		

NOT EQUIVALENT:

P	Q
T	T

ADDITIONAL EXERCISES FOR LESSON 27

Translate the following arguments into symbolic form. Then use the truth tree method to determine their validity. If an argument is invalid, recover at least one set of truth values to demonstrate the invalidity.

1. Problem 2 from the Additional Exercises for Lesson 9.

```
1)         C⊃L ✓                    P
2)         C∨~F ✓                   P
3)         ~L∨F ✓                   P
4)        ~(C≡L) ✓                  NC
          /        \
5)   C               ~C             4~≡D
6)   ~L               L             4~≡D
    /  \           /     \
7) ~C   L        ~C        L        1⊃D
   5x7  6x7     /  \      /  \
8)             C   ~F    C   ~F     2∨D
              7x8  / \  5x8  / \
9)                ~L  F     ~L  F   3∨D
                 6x9 8x9   7x9 8x9

   VALID
```

2. Problem 6 from the Additional Exercises for Lesson 17.

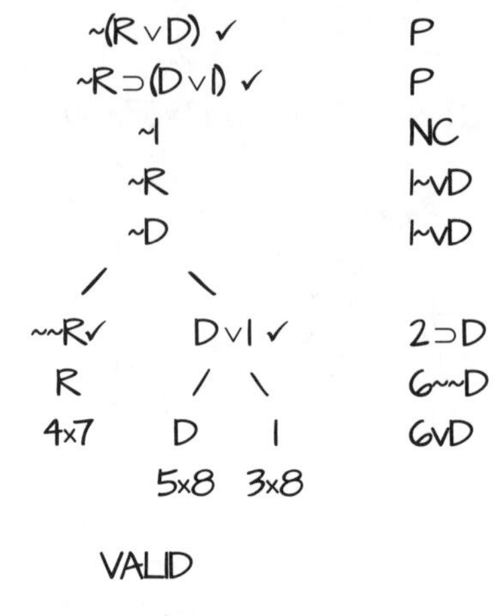

3. If Mr. Tumnus helped Lucy, then if the witch found out then he would be turned to stone. Mr. Tumnus helped Lucy and he was turned to stone. Therefore, the witch found out.

```
1)      H⊃(F⊃S) ✓      P
2)        H•S ✓        P
3)         ~F          NC
4)          H          2•D
5)          S          2•D
         /     \                 INVALID
6)     ~H     F⊃S ✓    1⊃D
       4x6    /   \              F H S
7)          ~F     S   6⊃D       F T T
             O     O
```

4. Newton's theory and Einstein's theory are not both correct. Time dilation exists only if Einstein's theory is correct. Time dilation exists. Thus, Newton's theory is not correct.

```
1)    ~(N•E) ✓      P
2)     T⊃E ✓        P
3)       T          P
4)     ~~N ✓        NC
5)       N          4~~D
        / \
6)    ~T    E       2⊃D
      3x6  / \
7)       ~N   ~E    ~•D
         5x7  6x7

      VALID
```

5. If Jesus has been given all authority in heaven and on earth, then Jesus is the ruler of this world. Either Jesus or Satan is the ruler of this world, but they are not both ruler of this world. If the Bible is true, then Jesus has been given all authority in heaven and on earth. The Bible is true. Therefore, Satan is not the ruler of this world.

```
1)              A⊃J ✓                    P
2)       (J∨S)•~(J•S) ✓                  P
3)              B⊃A ✓                    P
4)                B                      P
5)               ~~S ✓                   NC
6)                S                      5~~D
7)               J∨S                     2•D
8)              ~(J•S) ✓                 2•D
              /        \
9)          ~B          A                3⊃D
            4x9        / \
10)                  ~A   J              1⊃D
                   9x10  / \
11)                    ~J   ~S           8~•D
                     10x11  6x11

                        VALID
```

UNIT 4

APPLYING THE TOOLS TO ARGUMENTS

CONTENTS

APPLYING THE TOOLS TO ACTUAL ARGUMENTS

Intermediate Logic, pp. 229–232

STUDENT OBJECTIVES

1. Apply the tools of propositional logic to real-life arguments.
2. Complete Exercise 22 a, b, and c.

SPECIAL NOTE

Depending on which schedule you're following, you have several days to work through Lesson 28 and its exercises. Try to teach the lesson and work through Exercise 28a on the first day, and spend the following classes working through 28b and 28c.

TEACHING INSTRUCTIONS

1. Congratulate students on having made it through the first three units (as a reward Unit 4 is only one lesson long). Tell students that in propositional logic they have learned a whole bunch of tools that have significantly enlarged their brains but that they may feel like they will never use again. Explain that in this lesson they are going to learn about *applying* the tools they have learned to real life.
2. Flip to Exercise 28c in the student text and read aloud the passage from the *City of God.* Explain that Augustine, being brilliant, used very tight, dense arguments, but that students can use the tools they have learned to analyze and understand even very complicated arguments like this (which they will do in Exercise 28c). Explain that this is a very important skill to have when reading works of philosophy, theology or politics, which are usually trying to convince readers of a particular position through a chain of reasoning.
3. Explain that if students are flipping through theological tomes looking for these chains of reasoning, **what they should look for is a number of conditional propositions within a paragraph or two.** If they see several if/then statements close to each other, especially accompanied by premise and conclusion identifiers like "because" and "therefore," it is likely the author is leading his readers through an argument. And that argument can be analyzed using the tools of propositional logic. Have students skim Augustine's argument for these if/then statements and premise/conclusion identifiers.
4. Remind students that in real-life arguments of the kind they will find in books, conditional propositions are usually not written in standard form. See if anyone remembers some of the ordinary English forms of conditional propositions that they learned about in Lesson 4; if not have them flip back and refresh their memories. Tell students they need to keep a look out for these "disguised" conditionals.
5. Explain that there are a few more things to keep in mind when analyzing real-life arguments. **First of all, a conditional proposition can have a question for the consequent, rather than a statement.** For example, write on the

board this conditional from 1 Cor. 15:32: "If I fought with wild beasts in Ephesus for merely human reasons, what have I gained?" Ask students what Paul is doing here; what is his point in asking this question? Explain that he is asking a rhetorical question (a question with an answer so obvious no one has to say it); he is implying that if he fought for merely human reasons, he has gained *nothing*. Explain that to translate this proposition into something we can work with, we have to translate the rhetorical question into its expected answer: i.e., "If I fought with wild beasts for merely human reasons then I have gained nothing."

6. Secondly, **a conditional proposition sometimes has a command in the consequent rather than a statement**. For example, write on the board, "If the girl scouts come selling cookies, call the police." Ask students how this sentence can be translated into standard form. Explain that **we can insert "one should" before the command to make it into a normal conditional**: i.e., "If the girl scouts come selling cookies, then you should call the police."
7. Tell students that, thirdly, when interpreting any argument in normal English it is very important to understand the context. They should always **ask of the text "What is the author trying to prove?" The answer to that question is usually the main conclusion of the argument**.
8. Explain that authors will often leave some propositions in their arguments assumed, propositions that they consider obvious. Tell students that **they need to be able to "read between the lines" to determine what these assumed propositions are**. At the same time, they need to be careful not to get so enthusiastic about finding assumed propositions that they assume something the author was not intending to assume.
9. Finally, remind students that authors often use synonyms and repeat important points. **What looks like a new proposition is sometimes the same proposition reworded.**
10. Tell students that if they keep these strategies in mind they can analyze just about any argument for validity no matter where it turns up, determine the consistency or equivalence of real-life propositions, and follow complicated chains of reasoning by turning them into formal proofs. In the next three exercises students will get the chance to do this with several texts.

ASSIGNMENTS

1. Have students complete Exercise 28a, b and c, and go over it with them.
2. Remind students to study for next class's quiz over Lesson 28.

LESSON 28

APPLYING THE TOOLS TO ACTUAL ARGUMENTS

We have learned many different tools of propositional logic. This lesson will show how we can use these tools to help us analyze and understand arguments in real-life writings. The topics of such writings tend to be philosophy, theology, politics—works written to convince the readers of a particular position, through a chain of reasoning.

KEY POINT

Locate written arguments by finding multiple conditional propositions along with words indicating premises and conclusions.

These chains of reasoning can often be located in books by finding a number of conditional propositions within a paragraph. When you see several *if/then* statements standing close together, especially accompanied by premise or conclusion identifiers like "because" and "therefore," it may indicate that the author is leading his readers through an argument that can be analyzed using the tools of propositional logic. In such real-life arguments, conditional propositions are not always written in standard form. We have already learned about a number of ordinary-English forms of conditional propositions in Lesson 4, but we must consider a few more things.

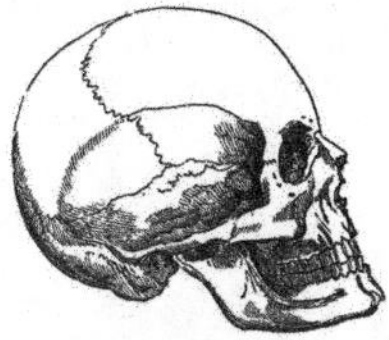

CAUTION

In real-life arguments, conditional propositions are not always written in standard form.

In arguments found in actual writings, a conditional proposition can have a question in place of the consequent, rather than a statement. This usually requires that we replace such a rhetorical question with its expected answer within the conditional. For example, consider this conditional, from 1 Cor. 15:32:

> If I fought wild beasts in Ephesus for merely human reasons, what have I gained?

The answer to the rhetorical question is that I have gained nothing, so this could be translated,

> If I fought with wild beasts in Ephesus for merely human reasons then I have gained nothing.

Similarly, a conditional statement that has a command for the consequent can be put into standard form by inserting "you should" before the command. For example, the conditional

> If someone breaks into your house, call the police

could be translated as

> If someone breaks into your house then you should call the police.

Authors will often leave propositions assumed, without explicitly stating them. You will need to "read between the lines" to determine these assumed propositions, while being careful not to infer a point that the author is not really making.

KEY POINT

To determine what is being assumed, find a proposition that, if added, would make a complete, valid argument.

One way to determine what is being assumed is to find a proposition that, if added, would make a complete, valid argument. For example, the author of Hebrews argues:

> Therefore we must give the more earnest heed to the things we have heard, lest we drift away. For if the word spoken through angels proved steadfast, and every transgression and disobedience received a just reward, how shall we escape if we neglect so great a salvation, which at the first began to be spoken by the Lord, and was confirmed to us by those who heard Him, God also bearing witness both with signs and wonders, with various miracles, and gifts of the Holy Spirit, according to His own will? (Hebrews 2:1-4)

This argument is fairly complex, but when unraveled it can be understood in this way:

> If the word spoken through angels was punished when disobeyed, then, if we neglect so great a salvation testified to by God, then we shall not escape such punishment. Therefore, we must not neglect so great a salvation testified to by God.

To find what is being assumed, we can symbolize this argument and consider what would make it valid. Symbolizing it would produce something like this:

$A \supset (N \supset \sim E) \quad \therefore \sim N$

What would give the conclusion ~N? First, we could assume A to complete the *modus ponens*, giving us $N \supset \sim E$. To conclude ~N requires a *modus tollens* with a premises of ~~E, which is E by double negation. This is perhaps clearer in a formal proof, as shown:

1. A⊃(N⊃~E) / ∴ ~N
2. A Assumed
3. N⊃~E 1,2 MP
4. E Assumed
5. ~~E 4 DN
6. ~N 3,5 MT

So this argument is complete when the unstated assumptions are A and E, that is

> The word spoken through angels was punished when disobeyed, and we would escape such punishment.

You can see from this argument from Hebrews that the same proposition can be written in different ways within a paragraph. Authors often use synonyms, and may repeat important points. This example also shows that, to properly interpret an argument in normal English, you need to understand the context. You should ask, "What is the author trying to prove?" to help you find the conclusion of his argument.

We might also be interested in determining if two compound propositions are consistent, and finding the truth values of the simple propositions that would allow them to be true. For example, Jesus teaches,

> "Do not be afraid of those who kill the body but cannot kill the soul. Rather, be afraid of the One who can destroy both soul and body in hell." (Matthew 10:28)

Are these two propositions consistent? A truth tree could be used to check this. The truth tree would be produced for the following set: {~(B • ~S), S • B}. Here is such a truth tree:

```
1.  ~(B • ~S) ✓      SM
2.      S • B ✓      SM
3.        S          2•D
4.        B          2•D
         / \
5.   ~B    ~~S ✓     1~•D
6.   4×5    S        5~~D
            O
```

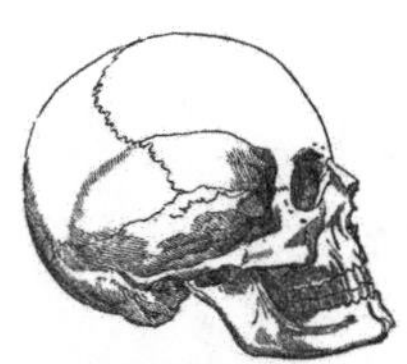

CAUTION

In real-life arguments, authors often use synonyms and repeat important points.

KEY POINT

To properly interpret an argument in normal English, you need to understand the context.

We can see that they are consistent, and to be so, both S and B are true: that is, we should fear one who can destroy the soul and the body.

By remembering these things and the tools we have learned, we can analyze the validity of arguments found in books, determine the consistency or equivalence of actual propositions, or follow a chain of reasoning in texts using a formal proof. The next few exercises will give you practice applying these tools to some real-life writings.

SUMMARY

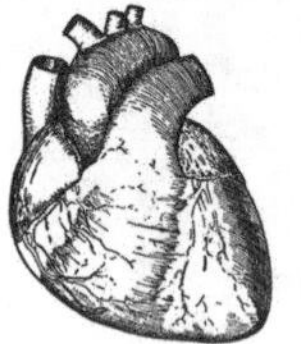

The tools of propositional logic can help us analyze arguments in ordinary discourse, especially written chains of reasoning. Such chains of reasoning are recognized most easily when writings contain several conditional propositions along with words indicating premises or conclusions. Conditional propositions are often not given in standard form, propositions may be left assumed, and different words may be used to communicate the same term or the same proposition. In such cases it is important to understand the context of the argument.

EXERCISE 28a (28 points)

Read this selection from *The Consolation of Philosophy*, written by the medieval philosopher Boethius, and complete problems 1 and 2. (Sentence numbers have been added for convenience.)

> [1]If you will consider carefully the following argument, you will have to admit that happiness cannot depend on things which are uncertain. [2]If happiness is the highest good of rational natures, and if nothing which can be lost can be a supreme good (because it is obviously less good than that which cannot be lost), then clearly unstable Fortune cannot pretend to bring happiness. [3]The man who enjoys fleeting happiness either knows that it is perishable, or he doesn't. [4]If he does not know it, his condition is unhappy because it rests on blind ignorance; [5]if he knows his happiness is perishable, he must live in fear of losing what he knows can be easily lost – and such constant fears will not let him be happy.

1. From sentences 1 and 2, what is the main point that Boethius is arguing in this selection? Write it as a single conditional, starting "If fortune is uncertain..." (2)

   If fortune is uncertain then fortune cannot bring happiness.

2. Apply the rule of transposition to the conditional you wrote in the last answer. (2)

   If fortune can bring happiness then fortune is certain.

Use the following constants for problems 3–6:

P = He knows fleeting happiness is perishable
U = His condition is unhappy
F = He lives in fear

3. Symbolize sentence 3. What is this special type of proposition called? (3)

   $P \vee {\sim}P$ This is a tautology.

4. Symbolize sentence 4 (ignore the explanatory "because..."). (2)

   ${\sim}P \supset U$

5. Symbolize sentence 5. Write your symbolized sentences 4 and 5 as premises, and make the conclusion "His condition is unhappy." Use a shorter truth table to demonstrate that that argument is valid. (8)

~P ⊃ U	(P ⊃ F) • (F ⊃ U)	∴ U
T T F F	F T F T F T F	F

VALID

Continued on next page.

6. Write a formal proof of validity for the symbolized argument of question 5. (11)

1)	$\sim P \supset U$	
2)	$(P \supset F) \bullet (F \supset U)$ / $\therefore U$	
3)	$P \supset F$	2 Simp.
4)	$(F \supset U) \bullet (P \supset F)$	2 Com.
5)	$F \supset U$	4 Simp.
6)	$P \supset U$	3,5 H.S.
7)	$\sim U \supset \sim P$	6 Trans.
8)	$\sim U \supset U$	7,1 H.S.
9)	$\sim\sim U \vee U$	8 Impl.
10)	$U \vee U$	9 D.N.
11)	U	10 Taut.

Q.E.D.

EXERCISE 28b (36 points)

Read the Apostle Paul's argument in 1 Corinthians 15:12-20.

> 12Now if Christ is preached that He has been raised from the dead, how do some among you
> say that there is no resurrection of the dead? 13But if there is no resurrection of the dead, then
> Christ is not risen. 14And if Christ is not risen, then our preaching is empty and your faith is
> also empty. 15Yes, and we are found false witnesses of God, because we have testified of God
> that He raised up Christ, whom He did not raise up — if in fact the dead do not rise. 16For if
> the dead do not rise, then Christ is not risen. 17And if Christ is not risen, your faith is futile;
> you are still in your sins! 18Then also those who have fallen asleep in Christ have perished.
> 19If in this life only we have hope in Christ, we are of all men the most pitiable. 20But now
> Christ is risen from the dead, and has become the firstfruits of those who have fallen asleep.

Use the following constants to complete the problems below:

R = There is a resurrection of the dead
C = Christ is risen
P = Our preaching is empty
F = Your faith is empty (futile)
T = We have testified that God raised up Christ
W = We are false witnesses
S = You are still in your sins
A = Those who have fallen asleep in Christ have perished
L = In this life only we have hope in Christ
M = We are of all men most pitiable

1. The main conclusion is, "There is a resurrection of the dead." Where does Paul indicate this? (2)

   In verse 12, Paul is challenging those who deny that there is a resurrection of the dead. The argument answers that challenge. Also, in verse 20 Paul concludes that Christ's resurrection is "the firstfruits of those who have fallen asleep," the firstfruits being a promise of the coming resurrection of the dead.

2. Symbolize the premise that is given in both verses 13 and 16, and the premise in the first part of verse 20. Use a shorter truth table to prove that the conclusion "There is a resurrection from the dead" is valid. (6)

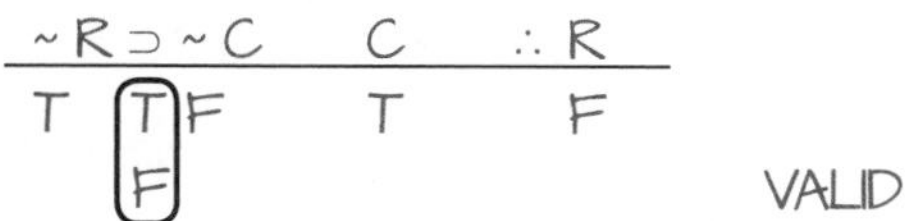

Continued on next page.

3. Verse 14 is a premise to support the intermediate conclusion that "Christ is risen." What proposition must be assumed to make it a complete, valid argument? Put the assumption in brackets, and demonstrate the argument's validity using a shorter truth table. (8)

The readers would assume that their faith is not empty (though they could also assume that Paul's preaching is not empty).

~C ⊃ (P • F)	[~F]	∴ C
T (T/F) F F	T	F

VALID

4. In the first half of verse 15 Paul argues, "If Christ is not risen, then we are found false witnesses of God, because we have testified of God that He raised up Christ." What proposition must be assumed to complete this argument? Put the assumption in brackets, and demonstrate the argument's validity using a shorter truth table. (8)

Paul apparently assumes this: If we have testified that God raised Christ, but Christ has not risen, then we are false witnesses. This is symbolized as (T • ~C) ⊃ W.

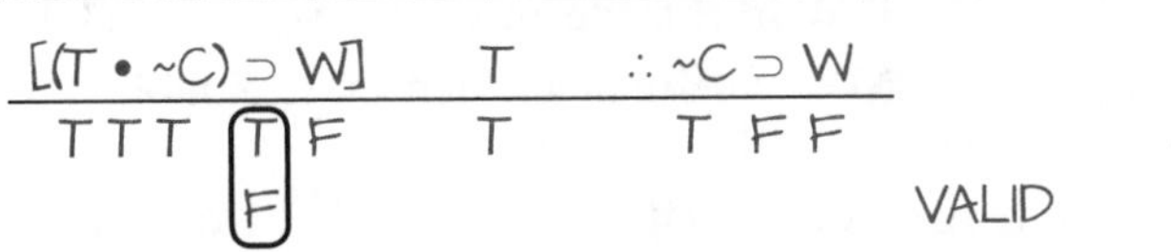

VALID

5. Symbolize the compound proposition in verse 17. (2) ~C ⊃ (F • S)

6. Verses 18 and 19 make up another supporting argument that Christ is risen. Paul argues that if Christ is not risen, "then also those who have fallen asleep in Christ have perished. If in this life only we have hope in Christ, we are of all men the most pitiable." Paul apparently assumes that, if those who have fallen asleep in Christ have perished, then in this life only we have hope in Christ. He also assumes that the apostles are not of all men the most pitiable. Using these assumptions, symbolize this entire supporting argument, and demonstrate its validity using a shorter truth table. (10)

~C ⊃ A	L ⊃ M	[A ⊃ L]	[~M]	∴ C
T (T/F) F	F T F	F T F	T	F

VALID

EXERCISE 28c (44 points)

Read this selection from *The City of God* by Augustine. (Sentence numbers have been added.)

> [1]Besides, this too has to be inquired into, whether, if the good angels made their own will good, they did so with or without will? [2]If without, then it was not their doing. [3]If with, was the will good or bad? [4]If bad, how could a bad will give birth to a good one? [5]If good, then already they had a good will. [6]And who made this will, which already they had, but He who created them with a good will, or with that chaste love by which they cleaved to Him, in one and the same act creating their nature, and endowing it with grace? [7]And thus we are driven to believe that the holy angels never existed without a good will or the love of God.

Use the following constants to complete the problems below:

O = Angels made their own will good
W = They did so with will
G = Their will was good
B = Their will was bad
C = Bad will can give birth to good will
A = They already had a good will
N = God created them with good will (creating their nature)
L = God created them with His love (endowing it with grace)

1. Translate the question in sentence 1 into a conditional proposition, and symbolize it. Then construct a truth tree of its negation to show that it is a tautology. (8)

If the angels made their own will good, they did so with or without will. $O \supset (W \vee \sim W)$

1)	$\sim[O \supset (W \vee \sim W)]$ ✓	S.M.
2)	O	1 $\sim\supset$D
3)	$\sim(W \vee \sim W)$ ✓	1 $\sim\supset$D
4)	$\sim W$	3 $\sim\vee$D
5)	$\sim\sim W$ ✓	3 $\sim\vee$D
6)	W	5 $\sim\sim$D
	4 x 6	

2. Symbolize sentence 2. (Note that "it was their doing" means "angels made their own will good.") Then apply the rule of transposition to the conditional to simplify it. (3)

$\sim W \supset \sim O$, simplified to $O \supset W$.

3. Translate the question in sentence 3 into a conditional proposition, and symbolize it. (3)

If they did so with will, then their will was good or bad. $W \supset (G \vee B)$

Continued on next page.

4. Sentence 4 is more complicated. It is a question, but it also assumes a negative answer. Translate this one sentence into two—a conditional proposition and its negative answer—then complete the *modus tollens*. Write it out first in words, then symbolize it. (4)

   If their will was bad, then bad will can give birth to good will. Bad will cannot give birth to good will. Therefore, their will was not bad.

   $B \supset C \quad {\sim}C \quad \therefore {\sim}B$

5. Symbolize sentence 5. (2) $G \supset A$

6. Sentence 6 is also complicated. Translate this into a conditional, with the antecedent being "they already had a good will." (Note that Augustine repeats the consequent for clarity, and shows that it should be a conjunction, not a disjunction.) Symbolize the translated proposition. (4)

   If they already had a good will then God created them with good will and with His love.

   $A \supset (N \bullet L)$

7. Sentence 7 is the conclusion. It could be understood as "It is not the case that God created them without good will or without His love." Symbolize this proposition, then translate it into an equivalent conjunction. Which rules of replacement must you employ to do this? (6)

   ${\sim}({\sim}N \vee {\sim}L) \equiv ({\sim}{\sim}N \bullet {\sim}{\sim}L)$ by De Morgan's Theorem

   $\equiv (N \bullet L)$ by Double Negation

8. Augustine appears to assume this proposition: "If it is not the case that God created angels with a good will and with His love, then the angels made their own will good." Symbolize this proposition. (2)

   ${\sim}(N \bullet L) \supset O$

9. With the propositions symbolized (and simplified) from your answers above, show that the entire argument is valid using a shorter truth table. (12)

$O \supset W$	$W \supset (G \vee B)$	${\sim}B$	$G \supset A$	$A \supset (N \bullet L)$	${\sim}(N \bullet L) \supset O$	$\therefore N \bullet L$
T T T	T T T T F	T F	T T T	T [T] F [F]	T F T T	F

VALID

Challenge: Write a formal proof of validity for the argument in problem 9.

Either of the following proofs is correct:

1)	O⊃W	
2)	W⊃(G v B)	
3)	~B	
4)	G⊃A	
5)	A⊃(N•L)	
6)	~(N•L)⊃O / ∴ N•L	
7)	O⊃(G v B)	1, 2 H.S.
8)	~O v (G v B)	7 Impl.
9)	(~O v G) v B	8 Assoc.
10)	B v (~O v G)	9 Com.
11)	~O v G	10, 3 D.S.
12)	O⊃G	11 Impl.
13)	O⊃A	12, 4 H.S.
14)	O⊃(N•L)	13, 5 H.S.
15)	~(N•L)⊃(N•L)	6, 14 H.S.
16)	~~(N•L) v (N•L)	15 Impl.
17)	(N•L) v (N•L)	16 D.N.
18)	N•L	17 Taut.
	Q.E.D.	

1)	O⊃W	
2)	W⊃(G v B)	
3)	~B	
4)	G⊃A	
5)	A⊃(N•L)	
6)	~(N•L)⊃O / ∴ N•L	
7)	~(N•L)	R.A.A.
8)	O	6, 7 M.P.
9)	W	1, 8 M.P.
10)	G v B	2, 9 M.P.
11)	~A	5, 7 M.T.
12)	~G	4, 11 M.T.
13)	B	10, 12 D.S.
14)	B•~B	13, 3 Conj.
15)	N•L	7-14 R.A.
	Q.E.D.	

TEACHER'S NOTES

QUIZ 15 (LESSON 28)

STUDENT OBJECTIVE

Complete Quiz 15.

TEACHING INSTRUCTION

Give Quiz 15. Allow 30 minutes. Grade quiz with students.

INTERMEDIATE LOGIC | Quiz 15

Lesson 28 (22 points)

Name ____________________________________

1. What are two different indications of a chain of reasoning in books or other writings? (3)

   When several conditional statements are located within a paragraph, along with premise and conclusion identifiers like "because" and "therefore."

Problems 2-3: Translate the conditional sentence into a standard conditional proposition. (2 each)

2. "If you love Me, keep my commandments" (John 14:15).

   If you love me, then you should keep my commandments.

3. "If we had found the truth ourselves, do you think that we should care much about the opinions of men?" (from Plato's *Phaedrus*).

   If we had found the truth ourselves, then we would not care much about the opinions of men.

Problems 4-5: In the book *The Trinity* St. Augustine wrote that

> if the Son is not of the same substance with the Father, then He is a substance that was made, and if that substance was made, then all things were not made through Him. But, on the contrary: "All things were made through Him." [Consequently], He is of the one and the same substance with the Father.

4. Symbolize the argument using the constants **F**, **M**, **A**, and prove that it is valid with a shorter truth table. (8)

~F ⊃ M	M ⊃ ~A	A	∴ F
T (T/F) F	F T F	T	F

VALID

5. Demonstrate that the conclusion is valid by writing a formal proof of the argument. (7)

1.	$\sim F \supset M$	
2.	$M \supset \sim A$	
3.	A / $\therefore$ F	
4.	$\sim F \supset \sim A$	1, 2 H.S.
5.	$A \supset F$	4 Trans.
6.	F	5, 3 M.P.

UNIT 4

REVIEW QUESTIONS

Answers can be found in the lesson under which the questions are listed.

Lesson 28: Applying the Tools to Actual Arguments

In what types of written material are you likely to find arguments or propositions that can be analyzed using the tools learned in this text? What are some indications of real-life arguments (chains of reasoning) in such written material? How may a conditional that uses a question or a command for the consequent be translated into a conditional proposition? When authors leave propositions assumed, what should you do to "read between the lines" in order to determine the assumed propositions?

UNIT 4

REVIEW EXERCISES

Students may do these exercises for further review of this unit.

ADDITIONAL EXERCISES FOR LESSON 28

1. The movie *Get Smart* (Warner Bros. 2008) included the following exchange between two characters:

SIEGFRIED:	How do I know you're not Control?
MAX:	If I were Control, you'd already be dead.
SIEGFRIED:	If you were Control, you'd already be dead.
MAX:	Neither of us is dead, so I am obviously not from Control.
SHTARKER:	That actually makes sense.

Show that Shtarker is correct in his assessment of the argument by symbolizing it from the middle three sentences, and using a formal proof of validity to deduce the conclusion. Use the following constants:

C = Max is from Control
S = Siegfried would already be dead
M = Max would already be dead

1)	$C \supset S$	
2)	$C \supset M$	
3)	$\sim(S \vee M)$ / $\therefore \sim C$	
4)	$\sim S \bullet \sim M$	3 De M.
5)	$\sim S$	4 Simp.
6)	$\sim C$	1, 5 M.T.

2. Read Deuteronomy 22:6-7. Translate the commands into propositions, symbolize them, and demonstrate their consistency by truth tree. Use the following constants:

B = You find a bird's nest with the mother bird sitting with her young or on her eggs
M = You take the mother
Y = You take the young

If you find a bird's nest with the mother bird sitting with her young or on her eggs, then you should not take both the mother and the young. You should not take the mother but you may take the young.

```
1)      B⊃~(M•Y) ✓            S.M.
2)        ~M•Y ✓              S.M.
3)         ~M✓                2•D
4)          Y                 2•D
          /   \                              Consistent
5)     ~B    ~(M•Y) ✓         1⊃D
        O     /    \                          B M Y
6)          ~M      ~Y        5~•D            T F T
             O     4x6                        F F T
```

3. Read this translated and edited portion of a sermon on John 1:1-14 by Martin Luther: "If the Word preceded all creatures, and all creatures came by the Word and were created through it, then the Word must be a different being than a creature. For when all things began it was already there; yea, all creatures were created through it. That which is not a creature must be God. Hence, the Word of God must be God eternal and not a creature."

Symbolize this argument, and demonstrate its validity by writing a formal proof. Use the following constants:

P = The Word preceded all creatures (when all things began it was already there)
A = All creatures were created through (or by) the Word
C = The Word is a creature
G = The Word is God

```
1)  (P•A)⊃~C
2)  P
3)  A
4)  ~C⊃G  /  ∴ G•~C
5)  P•A            2, 3  Conj.
6)  ~C             1, 5  M.P.
7)  G              4, 6  M.P.
8)  G•~C           7, 6  Conj.
```

4. Find an argument in some written material other than those given in this text, and demonstrate its validity by shorter truth table, truth tree, or by writing a formal proof.

(Answers will vary.)
Here is an excerpt from "On the Teacher," Article I, by Thomas Aquinas:

"Moreover, if signs of certain things be proposed one man to another, either the one to whom they are proposed knows the things of which they are the signs or he doesn't. If he knows them, he is not taught concerning the things. If he does not know them but is ignorant of the things, the meanings of the signs cannot be known by him... Not knowing the meaning of the signs, he cannot learn anything through the signs. Therefore if all a man does in teaching is to propose signs, it seems that one man cannot be taught by another man."

This can be symbolized as follows, with a shorter truth table showing its validity:

S ⊃ (K v ~K)	K ⊃ ~T	~K ⊃ ~M	~M ⊃ ~T	∴ S ⊃ ~T
T T TTF	T [T] F	F TF	F TF	TFF
	[F] VALID			

Here is a formal proof for the argument:

1) S⊃(K v ~K)
2) K⊃~T
3) ~K⊃~M
4) ~M⊃~T / ∴ S⊃~T
5) S — C.P.A.
6) ~~T⊃~K — 2 Trans.
7) T⊃~K — 6 D.N.
8) ~K⊃~T — 3, 4 H.S.
9) T⊃~T — 7, 8 H.S.
10) ~T v ~T — 9 Impl.
11) ~T — 10 Taut.
12) S⊃~T — 5-11 C.P.

Q.E.D.

CHOOSE YOUR OWN ADVENTURE!

CONTINUE TO UNIT 5: UNLOCKING THE LOGIC OF DIGITAL DEVICES

Turn to page T-clxi.

PROCEED TO THE COMPREHENSIVE TEST ON UNITS 1–4

Turn to page T-clvii.

REVIEW FOR COMPREHENSIVE TEST

STUDENT OBJECTIVES

Complete the objectives from Lessons 1–28. Objectives are listed at the beginning of each lesson's teacher's notes.

SPECIAL NOTES

1. Remember, if you are continuing to Unit 5, skip to p. T-clxi.
2. Depending on which schedule you're following, you have two days to review for the Comprehensive Test.

TEACHING INSTRUCTIONS

1. To review for the test, choose problems from the Review Questions and Review Exercises at the end of each unit for students to work through.
2. If you'd like, give students "Comprehensive Test: Form A" from the Intermediate Logic Test and Quiz Packetas a practice exam. Let them know that they can skip problems 18-19 (those questions come from Unit 5). Go over the answers together. Your answer key is in this book following p. T-ccxix.

ASSIGNMENT

Have students study for Comprehensive Test.

TEACHER'S NOTES

COMPREHENSIVE TEST

STUDENT OBJECTIVE

Complete Comprehensive Test.

TEACHING INSTRUCTIONS

1. Give students Comprehensive Test: Form B from the Intermediate Logic Test and Quiz Packet. Allow one hour to complete it. Let them know that they can skip problems 19-20 (those questions come from Unit 5).
2. Grade tests. Your answer key is in this book following p. T-ccxix. Have graded tests ready to hand back to students within a week.

UNIT 5

DIGITAL LOGIC

CONTENTS

DIGITAL DISPLAYS

Intermediate Logic, pp. 249–250

STUDENT OBJECTIVES

1. Give a numeric output corresponding to the segments of a digital display.
2. Complete Exercise 29.

TEACHING INSTRUCTIONS

1. Tell students that in Unit 5 they are going to be studying an entirely new branch of logic: **digital logic. Digital logic is formal logic applied to electronics.** It was (obviously) developed relatively recently, during the last century, and we are now surrounded by all sorts of electronic devices—clocks, cameras, telephones, and computers to name a few—that use digital logic.
2. Tell students that, believe it or not, computers process information following the patterns of formal logic, and that **digital logic is therefore the internal language of computers**. Ask students if anyone knows what it is that makes computers so useful. If there aren't any computer geeks in the class, explain that computers are useful because of their ability to store and process enormous amounts of information at lightning speed. The smallest amount of information a computer stores is called a **bit**, which has a binary value of 1 or 0 (tell students you'll be explaining that in a minute), and eight bits make up a single **byte**, which is required to encode one character. Explain that computers can store *trillions* of bytes of information.
3. Explain that digital logic is actually very similar to ordinary propositional logic, but that there are some key differences. Ask students what they think the word "binary" means. Explain that its ordinary meaning is simply "having two parts" or "twofold." Explain that **both propositional and digital logic are "binary" in that they both operate in terms of two possible values—true and false—but that in digital logic these binary values are usually thought of not in terms of true and false but in terms of "on" and "off," or 1 and 0**. Explain that both branches of logic also use the same logical operators (and, or, not, etc.), but that in digital logic these operators are often represented by special diagrams, which will be considered later.
4. Ask students what the first thing is that comes to mind when they hear the words "digital." Many students may say digital clocks. Explain that what most people think of when they hear "digital" is **digital displays**: what we see on the screens of our wristwatches, calculators, stereos, bathroom scales, microwaves, etc. Explain that these digital displays are a good example of a number of the principles involved in digital logic.
5. Ask for a volunteer to come up and draw what a number 8 looks like when it shows up on the screen of their watch or calculator. (If no one can remember have them all get their calculators out.) What someone ends up drawing should look something like this.

6. Show students that this number 8 has seven "segments." Explain that each of those segments is represented by a letter, from "a" to "g," and label it like the image:

7. Tell students that all the numbers from 0 to 9 use this same "grid" of seven segments. They have probably all noticed on their calculators or clocks that even when a screen is showing up a "1" or a "7" or a "0" you can see the shadow of the 8 behind it. Explain that this is because the display shows all ten numerals by turning off and on different segments. Write out all the numerals 0–9 using the seven segments and drawing dotted lines for the segments that are "off" in each number. The list should look like this:

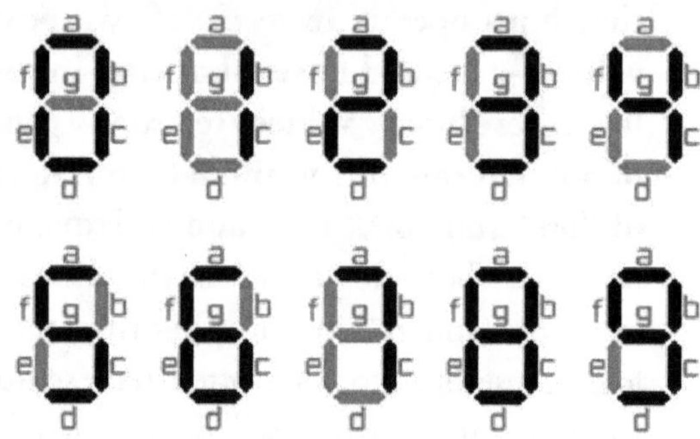

Make sure students see that the segments that form the numeral are "on" while the remaining segments not needed to form the numeral are "off."

8. Explain that, as you mentioned earlier, in digital logic 1 represents "on" and 0 represents "off." So each of the lettered segments above can be represented with either a 1 if it is on or a 0 if it is off. Do this with the numeral 4: list all the letters from a to g in a row representing the different segments, and then write 0s beneath the segments that are off and 1s beneath the segments that are on. This is the binary representation for the digital display of the numeral four:

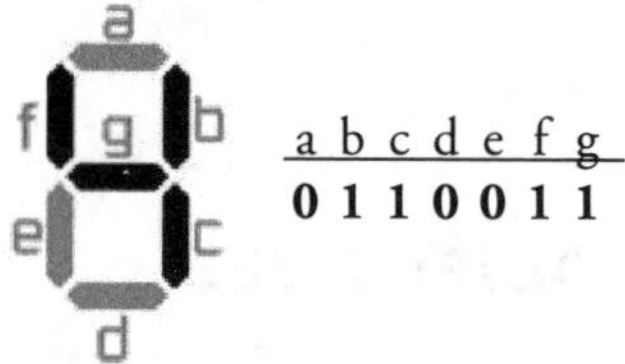

Make sure students see that there is a 1 beneath letters b, c, f, and g because those are the segments that must be on to produce 4.

9. Have students walk you through doing the same thing for the digital representations of 9 and 7 (see below).

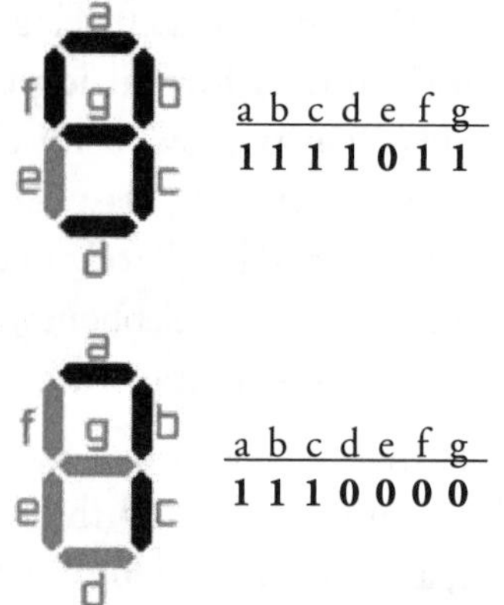

ASSIGNMENT

Have students complete Exercise 29, and go over it with them.

LESSON 29

DIGITAL DISPLAYS

A major branch of logic developed in the last century is **digital logic**. Digital logic is a particular branch of formal logic that is applied to electronics. In our modern world, we are surrounded by electronic devices that use digital logic: clocks and cameras, toys and telephones, calculators and computers, and gadgets that combine all of these and more.

DEFINITIONS

Digital logic is the branch of formal logic that is applied to electronics.

A ***bit*** is the smallest amount of information that a computer stores.

A ***byte*** is eight bits.

Digital logic is also the internal language of computers. Computers process information following the patterns of formal logic. What makes computers so useful is their ability to store and process large amounts of information very quickly. The smallest amount of information that the computer stores in its memory is called a **bit**, which has a binary value of 1 or 0. Usually, eight bits make up a single **byte**, which is required to encode one character. Computers can store trillions of bytes of information.

Digital logic is similar to ordinary propositional logic, though there are some differences. Both branches of logic operate in terms of true and false, but in digital logic these binary states are often thought of as "on" and "off," or as 1 and 0. Both branches of logic use the same logical operators—AND, OR, NOT, etc.—but in digital logic these are often represented by means of special diagrams, which we will consider later.

When many people see the word "digital," the first things that come to mind are **digital displays**. We see digital displays on our wristwatches, calculators, stereo systems, and electronic measuring devices. These digital displays are a good example of several of the principles involved in digital logic. The basic digital display consists of seven segments, each segment represented by a letter, from a to g.

By turning off and on different segments, this display can show all ten numerals in the decimal system, from 0 to 9, as shown here:

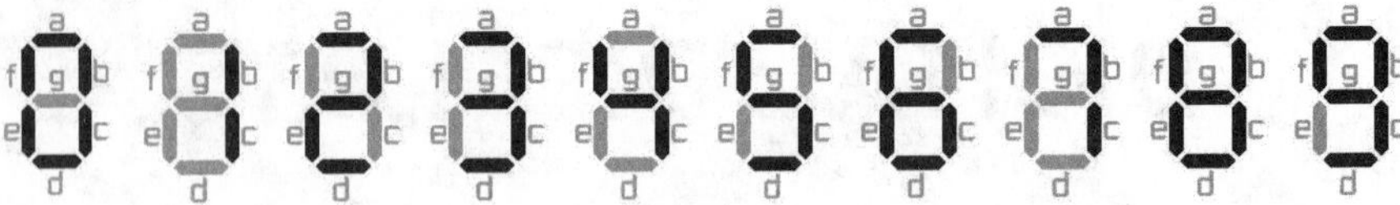

KEY POINT

In binary representation, a "1" means "on," and a "0" means "off."

We can represent each lettered segment as being on or off by the numbers one or zero, with "1" for *on* and "0" for *off*. For example, to represent the numeral "four," first make a list of all the letters from *a* to *g* representing the different segments, and then write 0s for the segments that are off, and 1s for the segments that are on. Here is the binary representation for the digital display of the numeral four:

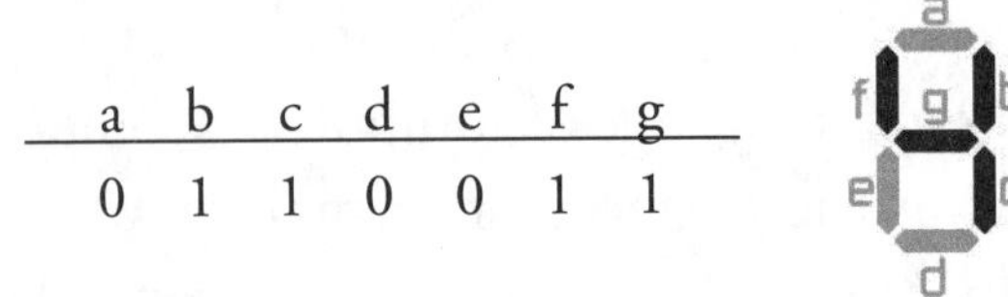

a	b	c	d	e	f	g
0	1	1	0	0	1	1

There is a 1 beneath the letters *b, c, f* and *g* because those are the segments that must be on to produce the numeral 4. In the representation for 9, every segment is on except *e*, so all the letters have 1s underneath them except *e*, which has a 0:

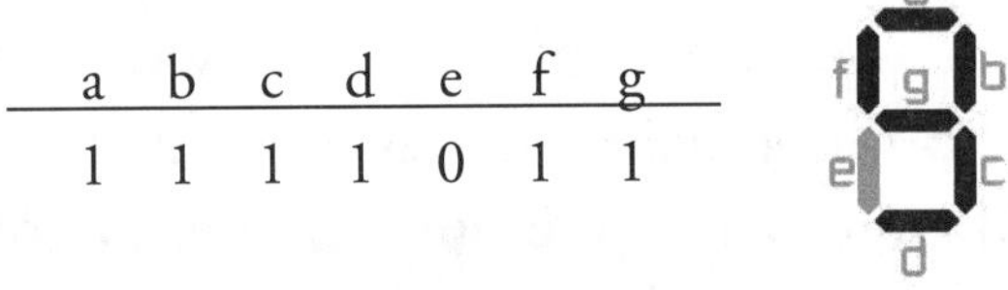

a	b	c	d	e	f	g
1	1	1	1	0	1	1

SUMMARY

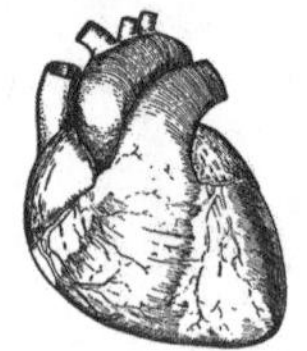

Digital logic is the branch of formal logic that is applied to electronics, and is also the internal language of computers. Following the patterns of formal logic, computers process information by using bits, which have a binary value of 1 or 0. Similarly, digital displays work by representing "on" segments with 1s and "off" segments with 0s.

EXERCISE 29 (12 points)

In the digital display, fill in the segments that would be "on" for the given numerals. Then complete the binary representation by writing 1s and 0s beneath the segment letters. (3 each)

1. The numeral 1

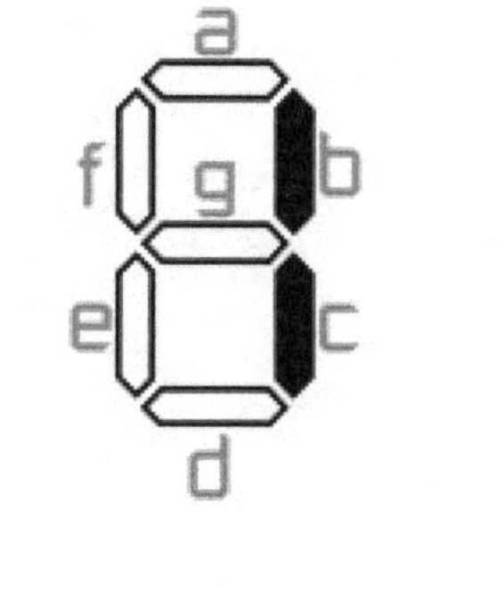

a	b	c	d	e	f	g
0	1	1	0	0	0	0

2. The numeral 3

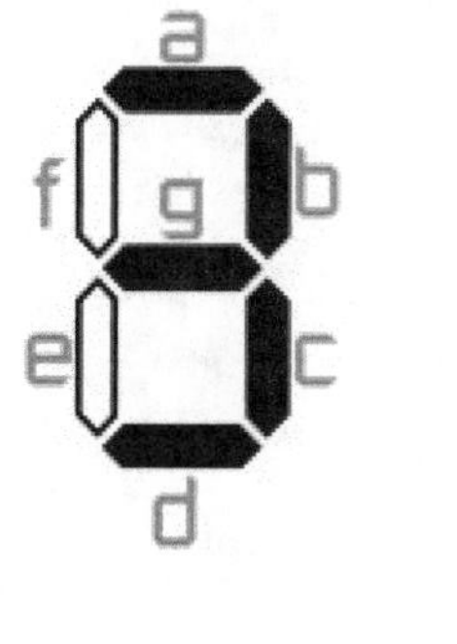

a	b	c	d	e	f	g
1	1	1	1	0	0	1

3. The numeral 5

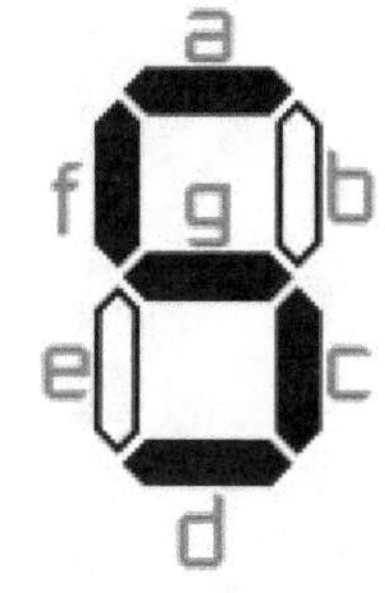

a	b	c	d	e	f	g
1	0	1	1	0	1	1

4. The numeral 6

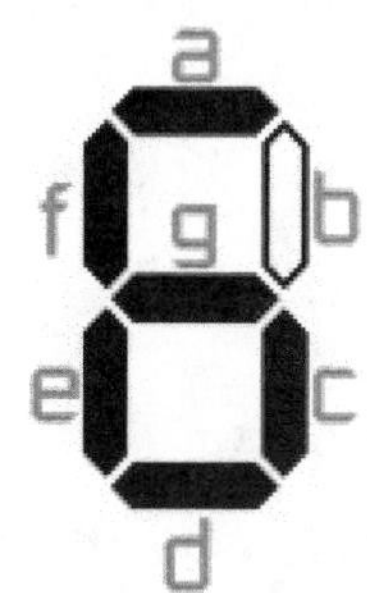

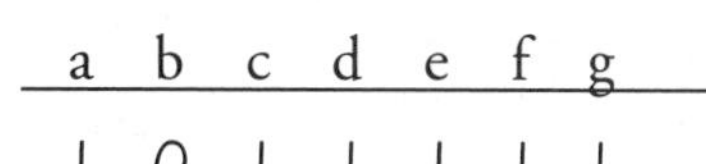

a	b	c	d	e	f	g
1	0	1	1	1	1	1

NUMBERS IN DIFFERENT BASES

Intermediate Logic, pp. 253–256

STUDENT OBJECTIVES

1. Count in binary.
2. Convert between decimal and binary numbers.
3. Complete Exercise 30.

TEACHING INSTRUCTIONS

1. Explain to students that class today will probably seem a lot more like a math class than a logic class, because they are going to be learning how to convert decimal numbers into binary numbers. Tell them that you're going to start out simple: with some review from elementary school.
2. Ask if anyone remembers what the system of numbers that we usually use is called (the decimal system). Ask how many numerals the decimal system uses to represent all numbers (ten: 0 through 9). Tell students that another name for the decimal system is "base ten."
3. Ask students if anyone remembers learning about **place values** in second grade or so. Explain that all number systems work with place values. Write the number 208 on the board and ask students which place the numeral 8 is in. Remind them that although it may seem counterintuitive, the 8—and not the 2—is in the first place because we start from the right and move to the left. Ask students how many possible values a place can hold (ten: 0, 1, 2, 3, 4, 5, 6, 7, 8, 9). Explain that when we are counting in the first place we can only count as far as 9; to go any higher we have to put a 1 in the *next* place and a 0 in the first place for the number 10.
4. Remind students that we call the first place the "ones" place because it holds the number of ones, the second place the "tens" place because it holds the number of tens, the third places the "hundreds" place because it holds the number of hundreds, the fourth place the "thousands" place because it holds the number of thousands, and so on.
5. Have students remember back to when they learned about powers or exponents in math. Ask students how many tens the first place or ones place can hold. It can't hold any tens, so its power is "ten to the zero" or 10^0. The second place, or tens place does hold tens, so the power "ten to the one" or 10^1. The third place or hundreds place holds hundreds, or tens times tens, so the power is "ten to the two" or 10^2. And so on. Explain that this pattern continues on indefinitely and that it can be put into a helpful table, which you will draw on the board.

Place	**Fifth**	**Fourth**	**Third**	**Second**	**First**
Can hold	10,000s	1000s	100s	10s	1s
Power	10^4	10^3	10^2	10^1	10^0
Example					

6. Use the number 527 as an example. Ask students how many hundreds, tens, and ones it has in it (five, two, and seven). Explain that we can write this more briefly as $5*10^2 + 2*10^1 + 7*10^0 = 527$. Insert this into the example row of the table; it should now look like this:

Place:	Fifth	Fourth	Third	Second	First
Can hold	10,000s	1000s	100s	10s	1s
Power	10^4	10^3	10^2	10^1	10^0
Example			**5**	**2**	7

7. Erase the above example and have students walk you through doing the same thing with the number 1728.
8. Tell students that when, in the last lesson, they wrote out the code of 1s and 0s for the digital displays, they were *not* using the decimal number system. Instead, they were using a number system called **binary** which means "two parts." Ask students why they think that this system is called "binary." Explain that where the "decimal" system is a "base ten" system that uses ten numerals (0 through 9) to represent any number (budding Latin scholars will remember that the Latin for "ten" is "decem"), the "binary" system is a "base two" system that uses only two numerals, 0 and 1, to represent any number. Explain that all of the basic math operations that we use in the decimal system—counting, adding, subtracting, multiplying, and dividing—can also be performed using binary numbers.
9. Tell students that you will begin by teaching them how to do binary counting. Remind them that in binary counting, all numbers have to be represented by only the numerals 0 and 1. Copy out the table on the right while students watch, and after you get about halfway through, see if students have recognized the pattern and can tell you how to complete the table.

Decimal Number	Binary Number
0	0
1	1
2	10
3	11
4	100
5	101
6	110
7	111
8	1000
9	1001
10	1010
11	1011
12	1100
13	1101
14	1110
15	1111

The first thing to note about the pattern is that in order for binary to add the binary equivalent of a decimal place (i.e., change from a 1 to a 10 or 111 to 1000), every combination of 1s and 0s possible for that number of "binary places" has to have happened. So at 1000 a space has been added because every combination of 1s and 0s possible for three spaces (100, 101, 110, and 111) has been used. The only way to get a new number at this point (since there are only two numerals) is to add another space. The bigger the number gets, the more combination of 1s and 0s we have to go through before we have to add a space.

10. Once students have grasped this, the second thing to note is the pattern of the ones and zeroes. Every time a place is added, the pattern is to start out with as few 1s as possible (i.e., 0, 10, 100, 1000, etc.) and then to add 1s beginning as far from the original 1 as possible (1, 11, 101, 1001, etc.). Then we move the 1 in closer to the original 1 (110, 1010), until it is pressed up against the original 1 (11, 110, 1100). Then, if possible, we add more 1s, again beginning as far from the original 1s as possible (111, 1101). When all we have is 1s (1, 11, 111, 1111), it's time to add another place.
11. When students seem to have a handle on this, enlarge the table to include 16–20 and have then count from 16–20 in binary. The completed table should look like this.

Decimal Number	Binary Number
16	10000
17	10001
18	10010
19	10011
20	10100

12. Tell students that next you are going to show them how to go about converting between binary and decimal. Explain that it helps to understand the relationship between binary (base two) and decimal (base ten) numbers in terms of place values. Have students remind you what the place values for the decimal system are (ones, tens, hundreds, thousands,

ten thousands, etc.) Explain that there are also place values in the binary system, but that, because the binary system is base two, the names of the place values are different. Instead of ones, tens, hundreds, etc., the place values for binary are ones, twos, fours, eights, sixteens, etc. Draw this table on the board to demonstrate:

Place:	Fifth	Fourth	Third	Second	First
Decimal	10,000s	1000s	100s	10s	1s
Binary	16s	8s	4s	2s	1s

Point out that the binary place values double as they move from right to left.

13. Explain that just like decimal numbers, binary numbers can be expressed in terms of powers. Draw this table on the board:

Place:	Fifth	Fourth	Third	Second	First
Can hold	16s	8s	4s	2s	1s
Powers	2^4	2^3	2^2	2^1	2^0

14. Tell students that, with these tables in hand, converting a binary number to a decimal is easy. Say that the binary number we want to convert is 11011. The first step is to write out the base 2 place values beginning with the largest (16, 8, 4, 2, 1). Next, write out the binary number 11011 underneath it, setting each 1 and 0 below its proper place value. The final step is to add up the place values that have a 1 underneath them; since 16, 8, 2, and 1 have 1s underneath them, we add those up. The sum, 27, is the decimal equivalent of 11011. Draw the chart below on the board to show students the conversion again:

Place value	16	8	4	2	1
Binary numeral	**1**	**1**	**0**	**1**	**1**
Decimal value	16 + 8 + 0 + 2 + 1				
Sum = 16 + 8 + 0 + 2 + 1 = 27					

Explain that we get the same answer when instead of adding up the base 2 place values, we add up the equivalent base 2 powers. In other words:

11011 (in binary) = $(1 * 2^4) + (1 * 2^3) + (0 * 2^2) + (1 * 2^2) + (1 * 2^0)$ = 27 (in decimal).

16. Have students walk you through a second example: converting the binary number 10010 into a decimal number. The completed table should look like this:

Place value	16	8	4	2	1
Binary numeral	**1**	**0**	**0**	**1**	**0**
Decimal value	16 + 0 + 0 + 2 + 0				
Sum = 16 + 0 + 0 + 2 + 0 = 18					

17. Have students work through a final example on their own: converting binary number 10101 into a decimal. The completed table should look like this:

Place value	16	8	4	2	1
Binary numeral	1	0	1	0	1
Decimal value	16 + 0 + 4 + 0 + 1				
Sum = 16 + 0 + 4 + 0 + 1 = 21					

18. Tell students that now that they know how to convert from binary to decimal, you're going to teach them how to go the other way and convert a number from decimal into binary. First set up another table like the ones above with place value, binary numeral, and decimal value, but leave the other spaces blank. Explain that **the first question students need to ask when converting from decimal to binary, is "How many 1s, 2s, 4s, 8s, 16s, or further powers of two add up to this decimal number?"**

19. Explain that there are several steps to this. Say that the number you are trying to convert is 53. **First, figure out what is the largest multiple of two that, when subtracted from the decimal, will leave a positive remainder.** Remind students of the multiples of two that we have to work with: 1, 2, 4, 8, 16, 32, 64, etc.) Makes sure students see that in the case of 53, 16 is too small and 64 is too big (because it is greater than 53 it would leave a negative, not a positive remainder), so the largest multiple of two that can be subtracted from 53 is 32. So put 32 in the furthest left box on the chart beside "place value" and fill in the rest of the

multiples of 2 smaller than it (16, 8, 4, 2, 1). The chart should look like this:

Place value	32	16	8	4	2	1
Binary numeral						
Decimal value						

20. Have students do the subtraction of 32 from 53; the answer is 21. Explain that because 32 goes into 53 once, we put a 1 in the chart underneath 32 beside binary numeral. Tell students that the next step is to do exactly what they just did, but with the remainder 21 that we just got. Ask students what is the largest multiple of two that goes into 21 (16). Have them subtract 16 from 21 (5) and put a 1 underneath 16 on the chart.

21. The next step is to do exactly the same thing with the remainder we just got, 5. But point out to students that the next multiple of two on the chart, 8, cannot be subtracted from 5 with a positive remainder. Explain that we therefore put a 0 underneath the 8 and move to the next multiple on the chart, 4. We put a 1 underneath the 4 and then subtract it from 5, getting a remainder of 1. Once again, the next multiple on the chart, 2, cannot be subtracted from this remainder 1, so again we put a 0 underneath the two and move on to the next multiple on the chart, 1. We put a 1 underneath the 1 and do the subtraction, which leaves us with 0. The table so far should look like this:

Place value	32	16	8	4	2	1
Binary numeral	1	1	0	1	0	1
Decimal value						

22. Tell students that our binary number is staring us right in the face on our chart: the decimal 53 is the binary 110101. Explain that there is an easy way to double check ourselves: we can simply convert this binary back into decimal and make sure it's 53. To do this we simply add up all the place values on the chart that have ones underneath them. Have students walk you through doing this. The completed table should look like this:

Place value	32	16	8	4	2	1
Binary numeral	1	1	0	1	0	1
Decimal value	32 + 16 + 0 + 4 + 0 + 1					
Sum = 32 + 16 + 0 + 4 + 0 + 1 = 53						

23. Have students walk you through converting he decimal number 42 into binary. The binary equivalent is and the completed table should look like this:

Place value	32	16	8	4	2	1
Binary numeral	1	0	1	0	1	0
Decimal value	32 + 0 + 8 + 0 + 2 + 0					
Sum = 32 + 0 + 8 + 0 + 2 + 0 = 42						

ASSIGNMENT

Have students complete Exercise 30, and go over it with them.

LESSON 30

NUMBERS IN DIFFERENT BASES

The most commonly used system of numbers is the decimal system. The decimal number system uses ten numerals, zero through nine (the Hindu-Arabic numerals), to represent all other numbers. Another name for this system is base ten.

Number systems work with **place values**. In a decimal number, the right-most digit is the first place. In the number 208, the numeral 8 is in the first place. A place has ten possible values: 0, 1, 2, 3, 4, 5, 6, 7, 8, 9. When we are counting in the first place and we reach nine, we cannot count any higher in that place because we have already used up all ten numerals. So we put a one in the next place to the left and a zero in the first place (the number 10). This first place is called the ones place, because it holds the number of ones. The second place holds the number of tens, so it is called the tens place. After writing a one in the tens place, we can continue counting in the ones place. To the left of the tens place come the hundreds place, then the thousands place, the ten thousands place, and so on.

Numbers operate in terms of what mathematicians call powers. The first place cannot hold any tens in it; thus the power is "ten to the zero" or 10^0. The second place holds tens, thus the power is "ten to the one" or 10^1. The third place holds hundreds, or tens of tens; this place is 10^2. The place after that holds thousands and is 10^3. This pattern continues on indefinitely and applies to all decimal numbers.

Take the number 527 for example. This number has five "hundreds," two "tens," and seven "ones." This can be written more briefly as $5\times10^2 + 2\times10^1 + 7\times10^0 = 527$.

Place	**Fifth**	**Fourth**	**Third**	**Second**	**First**
Can hold	10,000s	1000s	100s	10s	1s
Power	10^4	10^3	10^2	10^1	10^0
Example			5	2	7

DEFINITIONS

The ***decimal system*** uses the numerals 0 to 9 to represent any number. This is called ***base ten***.

The ***binary system*** uses the numerals 0 and 1 to represent any number. This is called ***base two***.

When we write out the code or set of numbers using 0's and 1's, as we did for the digital displays, we are no longer using a decimal number system. Instead, we are writing in a system of **binary numbers**. Binary literally means "two parts." Whereas the decimal system (base ten) uses the numerals 0 through 9 to represent any number, the binary system (base two) uses only the numerals 0 and 1. All of the basic math operations—counting, adding, subtracting, multiplying, and dividing—can be performed using binary numbers.

In **binary counting**, all numbers are represented using the two numerals 0 and 1. The table on the right counts from zero to fifteen, listing both the decimal numbers and their binary equivalents. We will see how this works in the next section. For now, just consider the pattern.

Decimal Number	Binary Number
0	0
1	1
2	10
3	11
4	100
5	101
6	110
7	111
8	1000
9	1001
10	1010
11	1011
12	1100
13	1101
14	1110
15	1111

So the number 7 in decimal is 111 in binary. The decimal 12 is the binary 1100.

For easy and quick **conversion from binary to decimal**, it helps to understand the relationship between binary (base two) and decimal (base ten) numbers in terms of place values. We went over the place values for the decimal system: ones, tens, hundreds, thousands, ten thousands, etc. There are comparable place values in the binary system: ones, twos, fours, eights, sixteens, and so on.

Place	**Fifth**	**Fourth**	**Third**	**Second**	**First**
Can hold	16s	8s	4s	2s	1s

Like decimal, binary numbers can also be expressed in terms of powers:

Place	**Fifth**	**Fourth**	**Third**	**Second**	**First**
Can hold	16s	8s	4s	2s	1s
Power	2^4	2^3	2^2	2^1	2^0

Converting a binary number to decimal is easy. First write out the base two place values: 1, 2, 4, 8, 16 (doubling each time) from right to left (note: NOT left to right). Second, write out the binary number, setting each 1 or 0 below its proper place value. Third, add up the place values that have a 1 under them. The sum is the decimal number.

For example, to convert the binary number 11011 to decimal, look at the rightmost digit (the digit in the first place), which is "1." This means that you have one 2^0, or 1. The digit in the second place is also a 1, meaning that you have one 2^1, or 2. The digit in the third place is 0, thus you have zero 2^2 (that is, no 4s). The digit in the fourth place is a 1, meaning that you have one 2^3, or 8. The digit in the fifth place is 1, so you have one 2^4, or 16. The sum of these (16+8+0+2+1) is twenty-seven. The chart below shows the conversion of binary 11011 to decimal 27.

Place Value	16	8	4	2	1
Binary Numeral	**1**	**1**	**0**	**1**	**1**
Decimal Value	16 +	8 +	0 +	2 +	1
Sum = 16 + 8 + 0 + 2 + 1 = 27					

So the binary 11011 is equivalent to the decimal 27. More briefly, using powers:

$$11011\ \textit{(in binary)} = (1\times 2^4) + (1\times 2^3) + (0\times 2^2) + (1\times 2^1) + (1\times 2^0) = 27\ \textit{(in decimal)}.$$

Let's do another example. Consider the binary number 10010. This has a 1 in the second place, one 2^1, which is 2. It also has a 1 in the fifth place, one 2^4, which is 16. The sum is 16+2, or 18, as shown:

Place Value	16	8	4	2	1
Binary Numeral	**1**	**0**	**0**	**1**	**0**
Decimal Value	16 +	0 +	0 +	1 +	0
Sum = 16 + 0 + 0 + 2 + 0 = 18					

The reverse idea is used for **conversion from decimal to binary**. Given a decimal number you wish to convert, you need to ask, "How many 1s, 2s, 4s, 8s, 16s, or further powers of two add up to this number?"

To answer this, follow this procedure. Subtract from the given decimal number the largest multiple of two that will leave a positive

KEY POINT

To convert binary to decimal, 1) write out the base two place values from right to left, 2) write out the binary number below its proper place value, and 3) add the place values that have a 1 under them.

THINKING DEEPER

If you understand how to convert between binary and decimal *whole* numbers, you should be able to figure out how to convert between binary and decimal *fractional* values. The place values to the right of the decimal point (or *binary* point as we must now consider it) are the one-half's place, one-fourth's place, one-eighth's place, and so on. Try converting the binary 0.11 into decimal. Can you see that it equals three-fourths, or 0.75, in decimal?

KEY POINT

To convert decimal to binary, 1) subtract from the given decimal number the largest multiple of two that will leave a positive remainder, 2) put a 1 in the place representing the multiple of two subtracted or a 0 where the remainder is not positive, and 3) repeat until there is no remainder.

remainder. Put a 1 in the place representing the multiple of two subtracted, and a 0 in each place where it is not subtracted (that is, where the remainder is not positive). Repeat the process with the remainder. Continue until there is no remainder.

For example, to convert the decimal number 53 to binary, subtract the largest multiple of two that leaves a positive remainder, in this case, 32 (since 64 is greater than 53 and will not leave a positive remainder). Subtract the 32 from the 53, and put a 1 in the thirty-twos place. The remainder is 21. From 21, the largest multiple of two that can be subtracted is 16, with a remainder of 5. Put a 1 in the sixteens place. Subtracting 8 from 5 will not leave a positive remainder, so put a 0 in the eights place. Subtracting 4 from 5 will leave a remainder of 1. Put a 1 in the fours place. Subtracting 2 from 1 will not leave a positive remainder, so put a 0 in the twos place. Put the remaining 1 in the ones place. The table below shows this process:

53	21	5	1
−32	−16	−4	−1
21 *remainder*	5 *remainder*	1 *remainder*	0 *remainder*

Place Value	32	16	8	4	2	1
Binary Numeral	**1**	**1**	**0**	**1**	**0**	**1**
Decimal Value	32 +	16 +	0 +	4 +	1 +	0
Check: Sum = 32 + 16 + 4 + 1 = 53						

So the decimal 53 is the binary 110101. To double-check ourselves, we can simply convert our binary number back into decimal. We have one "thirty-two" plus one "sixteen" plus one "four" plus one "one." The sum of this is fifty-three.

SUMMARY

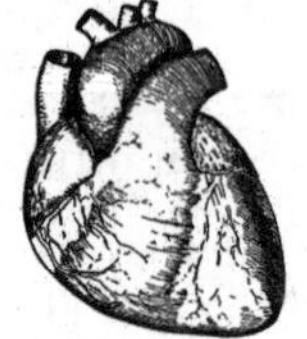

Number systems work with place values. In a decimal system, a place value has ten possible values (0-9, which is base ten). In a binary system, a place value has two possible values (0-1, which is base two). We convert decimal to binary or vice versa by taking advantage of comparable place values between decimal and binary.

EXERCISE 30 (26 points)

1. Fill in the missing binary numbers: (7)

Decimal Number	Binary Number
6	110
7	111
8	1000
9	1001
10	1010
11	1011
12	1100
13	1101
14	1110
15	1111
16	10000
17	10001

2. Convert the following binary numbers to decimal: (1, 1, 2, 2, 3)
   a.) 1100 ___12___
   b.) 1111 ___15___
   c.) 1010101 ___85___
   d.) 1001001 ___73___
   e.) 10111010 ___186___

3. Convert the following numbers from decimal to binary: (1, 2, 2, 2, 3)
   a.) 7 ___111___
   b.) 22 ___10110___
   c.) 32 ___100000___
   d.) 63 ___111111___
   e.) 165 ___10100101___

TEACHER'S NOTES on LESSON 31

BINARY ARITHMETIC

Intermediate Logic, pp. 259–261

STUDENT OBJECTIVES

1. Add, subtract, and multiply numbers in binary.
2. Complete Exercise 31.

TEACHING INSTRUCTIONS

1. Have students remind you of what they learned how to do yesterday (count in binary and convert between decimal and binary). Explain that today you're going to show them how to take binary a step further and do simple arithmetic in it.
2. Have students name some of the operations of arithmetic (addition, subtraction, multiplication, etc.). Explain that we can perform all these operations with binary numbers in basically the same way as we do with decimal numbers, as long we remember some basic concepts.
3. Tell students that you'll start with addition, and that the first thing to do is give them the basic concepts they'll have to work with. Write this table of basic concepts of binary addition on the board:

    Basic Concepts
    0 + 0 = 0
    0 + 1 = 1
    1 + 0 = 1
    1 + 1 =10

    These equations probably look reassuringly familiar until number 4. Remind students that 10 in binary equals 2 in decimal.
4. On the board write 2 + 2 = 4, which everyone should be okay with. Explain that in binary addition as well as in decimal addition two plus two equals four, but that in binary we use binary numbers rather than decimal numbers. See if students can tell you what the equation 2 + 2 = 4 would look like in binary (10 + 10 = 100). Write this equality vertically

$$\begin{array}{r} 10 \\ +\ 10 \\ \hline 100 \end{array}$$

    and walk through the addition with students. In the ones place both the numbers being added have zeroes, and we know from our basic concepts above that 0 + 0 = 0, so we write 0 below the first column; moving on to the twos place, there are ones in both numbers being added, and we know from the basic concepts that 1 + 1 = 10. (Do *not* let the students read this as "one plus one equals *ten*.") So we write a 0 below the twos place of the second column and carry the 1 to the fours place. Thus the sum of 10 and 10 is 100 (read as "one-zero plus one-zero equals one-zero-zero), which, students might (or might not) remember from the counting in binary they did last lesson, is the binary of 4.
5. Tell students you're going to give them an example that's a bit more complex: adding 28 and 25 in binary. Tell them that the first step is converting 28 and 25 to binary. See if they can remember how to go about doing this, and

if they can't, draw this table on the board and see if it jogs their memory:

Place value					
Binary numeral					
Decimal value					

Remind them that the first thing to do, converting 28 first, is to find the largest multiple of two that can be subtracted from 28 with a positive remainder. It's 16, so put 16 in the furthest left box of the place value row in the table, and fill in the rest of the place values (8, 4, 2, 1). Put a 1 underneath the 16 in the binary numeral row. Subtract 16 from 28 (12) and repeat the process with 12 (8 is the largest multiple that goes into it), and so on. The final result should be this:

Place value	16	8	4	2	1
Binary numeral	1	1	1	0	0
Decimal value					

The binary equivalent of 28 is therefore 11100. (If you like, have students check their work by converting 11100 back into decimal). Have students walk you through the same process to convert 25 into binary. The binary equivalent of 25 is 11001.

6. Write the addition problem vertically on the board:

   11100
   \+ 11001

   Tell students that they already know how to add the first three columns. In the ones place, 0 + 1 = 1, so we put a 1 underneath the first column. In the twos place 0 + 0 + 0, so we put a 0 underneath the second column. In the fours place 1 + 0 = 1, so we put a 1 underneath the third column. In the eights place both numbers we are adding have 1, and 1 + 1 = 10, so we put a 0 below the eights place and carry the 1 to the sixteens place, where we add it to the two ones that are already being added there: 1 + 1 + 1, which equals 10 + 1 or 11. So we place one 1 below the sixteens column and carry the other to the thirty-twos place. The completed equation should look like this:

   11100
   \+ 11001
   110101

   Students should see how similar adding binary numbers is to adding decimal numbers. If you want, have them check their work by converting 110101 back into decimal; it's 53.

7. Give students these three binary addition problems to work through; if they have a good handle on this, walk them through the first and then have them do the second two on their own.

   101100 / + 111010   11111 / + 1   110100 / + 11101

   Have them check their work by converting all the numbers in the addition problems to decimals. The answers should be: 1100110, 100000, 1010001.

8. Tell students that the next skill to learn is binary subtraction. Explain that, just like in decimal subtraction, the key to binary subtraction is "borrowing." Make sure students remember what borrowing is; if anyone is rusty, do the subtraction problem 32 – 14 vertically on the board and show that it's necessary for the 2 in the ones place to "borrow" a ten from the 3 in the tens place to become 12 so that 4 can be subtracted from it.

9. Write this table of basic concepts of binary subtraction on the board:

   Basic Concepts
   0 – 0 = 0
   1 – 0 = 1
   1 – 1 = 0
   10 – 1 =1

Once again, the first three are pretty straightforward, while the last may cause some head scratching. Remind students that 10 is the equivalent of 2 in binary, and that we already learned under the basic addition concepts that 1 + 1 = 10.

10. Write on the board (vertically) 25 - 12. Ask students what the first step is if we want to do this problem in binary. Have them first walk you through converting the two decimals to binary using the system learned earlier (finding the largest multiple of two that goes in . . . yup, you remember). 25 in binary is 11001, and 12 is 1100. Write these new numbers in a vertical subtraction problem like so:

```
 11001
- 1100
------
```

Tell students that the next step is to go at it like any old subtraction problem. The first two columns should be easy: 1 – 0 = 1 and 0 – 0 = 0. But in the third column the value above (0) is less than the value below (1), and so we need to borrow from the fourth column. We borrow a "10," just like in decimal subtraction, so now the subtraction in the third column is 10 – 1, which we know from the table of concepts = 1. Now we can move on to the fourth column, which looks all right, but remind students that since we borrowed the 1 from this column it became a 0. Once again we have 0 – 1 and we have to borrow from the fifth column, which again gives us 10 – 1 = 1. And since we borrowed the one, there is no more fifth column. The completed subtraction problem should look like this:

```
 11001
- 1100
------
  1101
```

11. Give students the binary subtraction problems below to work through. The students may need help with the borrowing on the fifth problem. Tell them that after they borrow a 10 for the second column from the right, the rest of the zeroes become 1's until a 1 is reached, which becomes a zero. If you like, work through the first couple with them and give them the rest to do on their own. Have them check their answers either by converting to decimal or by adding.

```
  1001       1111       101
- 1000      - 110      - 10
------     ------     -----

  1101      10001      10101
- 1011     - 1011    - 11010
------     ------     ------
```

The answers are 1, 1001, 11, 10, 110, and INVALID (the number being subtracted below is greater than the number it is being subtracted from. Kudos to anyone who realized this before they started solving it).

12. The final thing to learn is binary multiplication. Tell students that (hooray!) binary multiplication is also very similar to decimal multiplication; in fact the multiplication part of it is identical to decimal multiplication, and the addition component they have already learned. So if they can add it binary, multiplying in binary will be very easy for them. Write this table of basic concepts of binary multiplication on the board:

Basic Concepts

0 * 0 = 0
0 * 1 = 0
1 * 0 = 0
1 * 1 = 1

13. Start small: write 5 * 2 on the board and have students walk you through converting it into binary and setting up the multiplication problem. It should look like this:

```
 101
* 10
----
```

Tell students that we multiply these binary numbers just as we do decimal numbers, first multiplying all the number above by the 0 and then by the 1. The problem should now look like this:

```
   101
  * 10
------
   000
  101
```

The next step is adding these two rows together, which should be pretty straightforward. The completed problem should look like this:

```
   101
  * 10
------
   000
 + 101
------
  1010
```

14. That was a pretty simple multiplication problem; now write 25 * 14 on the board and have students walk you through the conversion, setup, multiplication, and addition. The completed problem should look like this beast:

```
       11001
      * 1110
------------
       00000
      11001
     11001
 +  11001
------------
   101011110
```

15. Give students the three multiplication problems below to work through. Have them check their answers by converting the binary numbers to decimal and multiplying.

```
  100       101      1001
 * 10      * 11     * 101
-----     -----     -----
```

The answers are 1000, 1111, and 101101.

ASSIGNMENTS

1. Have students complete Exercise 31, and go over it with them.
2. Remind students to study for next class's quiz over lessons 29–31.

LESSON 31

BINARY ARITHMETIC

The operations of arithmetic (addition, subtraction, multiplication, and so on) can be performed with binary numbers in basically the same way they are done with decimal numbers, as long as you remember the basic concepts. Let's see how.

Addition is a fundamental operation. The basic concepts of **binary addition** are simple:

Basic Concepts of Binary Addition	
0 + 0 = 0	
0 + 1 = 1	
1 + 0 = 1	
1 + 1 = 10	*Remember: 10 in binary equals 2 in decimal.*

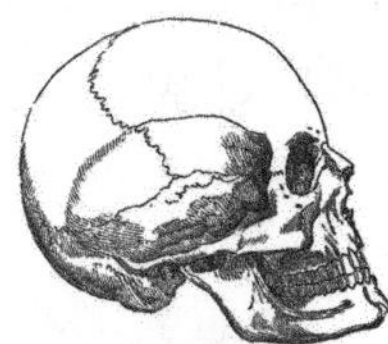

CAUTION

Don't forget that "10" in binary equals "2" in decimal.

Everyone is familiar with decimal addition; everyone knows that two plus two equals four. In binary addition, two plus two also equals four. The main difference is that two and four are written out in binary instead of decimal, as shown here.

Decimal	Binary
2	10
+ 2	+10
4	100

To add the two binary numbers above, look at the first column; the ones place has zeroes for both numbers, and 0 + 0 = 0, so a 0 is written below the first column. Next look at the twos place. There are ones in the twos place in both numbers. In binary, 1 plus 1 equals 10 (that is, two). Write the 0 below the twos place—the second column—and carry the 1 to the fours place. Thus the sum of 10 and 10 is 100.

KEY POINT

If your total is more than 1 while adding in binary, put a zero in the current place value and carry a 1 into the next place value up.

For another example, let's add twenty-eight and twenty-five. First, convert the numbers to binary: 28 is 11100, and 25 is 11001. You already know how to add the first three columns. In the ones

Decimal	Binary
28	11100
+ 25	11001
53	110101

place (the far right column), 0+1=1. In the twos place, 0+0=0, and in the fours place, 1+0=1. Now, in the eights place both numbers have a 1. Remember that in binary 1+1=10, so when these numbers are added, the 0 is placed below the eights place, and the 1 is carried to the sixteens place. Since there is already a 1 in the sixteens place for both numbers, add 1+1+1 to get 11. Place the 1 in the sixteens place and the 1 in the thirty-twos place. To check our work, we have 1 in the ones place, 0 in the twos place, 1 in the fours place, 0 in the eights place, 1 in the sixteens place, and 1 in the thirty-twos place. This is 110101, or 53 in decimal.

Binary subtraction basically uses the same principles as addition, and is performed in a very similar way to decimal subtraction. The key is to remember to "borrow" from the next highest place when the value above is less than the value below.

KEY POINT

If the value above is less than the value below while subtracting in binary, borrow from the next highest place.

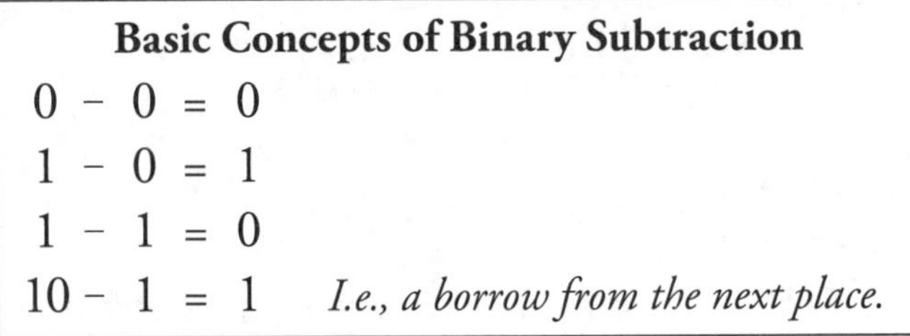

Basic Concepts of Binary Subtraction

0 - 0 = 0
1 - 0 = 1
1 - 1 = 0
10 - 1 = 1 *I.e., a borrow from the next place.*

To subtract twelve from twenty-five, convert the decimal numbers to binary. Twenty-five is 11001, and twelve is 1100. The first two columns are easy: 1-0=1, and 0-0=0. In the fours place, the third column, the value above (0) is less than the value below (1), and so requires borrowing from the eights place. This makes the subtraction in the third column 10-1=1. The eights place (the fourth column) is then 0-1 again, since the 1 on the top was borrowed and so became a zero. This requires borrowing the 1 from the sixteens place, again giving 10-1=1. The final difference is 1101.

Decimal	Binary
25	11001
- 12	- 1100
13	1101

Note: In the subtraction problem shown at right, the number being subtracted below is greater than the number it is being subtracted from above. In *positive* binary subtraction, this problem is invalid and should be answered by writing INVALID.

```
  10101
- 11010
-------
INVALID
```

Binary multiplication is very similar to decimal multiplication. Multiplying row by row is in fact identical to decimal multiplication. The adding of the numbers in columns follows the pattern of binary addition already learned. So if you can add in binary, multiplying in binary is fairly easy.

Basic Concepts of Binary Multiplication
0 × 0 = 0
0 × 1 = 0
1 × 0 = 0
1 × 1 = 1

To multiply five by two in binary, first write out the numbers five and two in binary, then multiply them as you would if they were decimal numbers. The procedure is exactly the same, except for the final adding, which must be done in binary.

```
Decimal   Binary
   5        101
 × 2       × 10
 ----     ------
  10        000
           101
          ------
           1010
```

For an example of multiplying large numbers in binary, consider the multiplication of 25 and 14, shown here. When multiplying the value above by 0, you simply write a row of zeros. When multiplying by 1, you simply rewrite the value above. Remember to shift left with each new row. When done with all the rows, add them up to get a final value.

```
      11001
    × 1110
  ----------
      00000
     11001
    11001
 + 11001
  ----------
  101011110
```

THINKING DEEPER

It is relatively easy to extend the concepts of this chapter to solving long division problems in binary. If you think about it, long division is basically a process that applies three concepts to numbers: comparing the size of two values, multiplying, and subtracting. Since the largest binary digit is one, binary division uses no multiplication and is thus simpler than decimal division. Try dividing 100111 by 11 with binary subtraction. If you do it correctly, you should get 1101.

SUMMARY

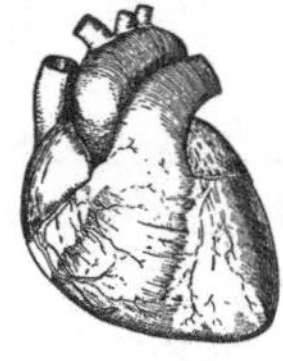

Using the basic concepts of binary addition, subtraction, and multiplication, it's easy to combine binary numbers. If necessary, remember to carry a 1 into the next place up while adding. Borrow from the next place up while subtracting. Multiply binary as in the decimal system except for the final addition, which must be done in binary.

EXERCISE 31 (43 points)

Problems 1–6: Solve the binary addition problems. (2, 2, 3, 3, 3, 4)

1. 1001 + 110 = 1111

2. 101 + 100 = 1001

3. 1111 + 111 = 10110

4. 1011 + 1011 = 10110

5. 11010 + 1101 = 100111

6. 101111 + 110101 = 1100100

Problems 7-12: Solve the binary subtraction problems. (2, 3, 3, 2, 3, 1)

7. 1111 − 110 = 1001

8. 10101 − 1011 = 1010

9. 10110 − 1011 = 1011

10. 100 − 11 = 1

11. 11010 − 101 = 10101

12. 10111 − 11010 = INVALID

Problems 13-15: Solve the binary multiplication problems. (3, 4, 5)

13. 1101 × 111

```
   1101
  1101
 1101
1011011
```

14. 10110 × 1011

```
    10110
   10110
  00000
 10110
11110010
```

15. 100100 × 11001

```
      100100
     000000
    000000
   100100
  100100
1110000100
```

QUIZ 16 (LESSONS 29–31)

STUDENT OBJECTIVE

Complete Quiz 16.

TEACHING INSTRUCTIONS

1. Give Quiz 16. Allow 20 minutes. Grade quiz with students.
2. If you have extra time, introduce Lesson 32 to get a head start on next class's material.

INTERMEDIATE LOGIC | Quiz 16

Lessons 29–31 (40 points)

Name ________________________________

1. The smallest amount of information a computer stores in memory is called a what? (1) bit

2. In the digital display, fill in the segments that would be on for the numeral 2. Then complete the binary representation by writing 1s and 0s beneath the segment letters. (3)

a	b	c	d	e	f	g
1	1	0	1	1	0	1

3. Complete the binary counting table. (5)

Decimal	Binary
6	110
7	111
8	1000
9	1001
10	1010
11	1011
12	1100

Problems 4-5: Convert the binary number into a regular decimal number. (3 each)

4. 11001 25

5. 101100 44

Problems 6-7: Convert the regular decimal number into binary. (3, 4)

6. 39 100111

7. 144 10010000

Problems 8-11: Complete the binary arithmetic. (4, 4, 5, 5)

8. 101100 + 11001 = 1000101

9. 10011 − 1110 = 101

10. 1011 × 110 = 1000010

11. 11011 + 101 = 100000

TEACHER'S NOTES on LESSON 32

BASIC LOGIC GATES

Intermediate Logic, pp. 265–268

STUDENT OBJECTIVES

1. Draw the basic logic gates NOT, AND, and OR, and give their truth tables.
2. Draw logic circuits for basic logical propositions.
3. Complete Exercise 32.

TEACHING INSTRUCTIONS

1. Remind students that they learned that computers use basic mathematical operations (addition, subtraction, multiplication—the kind of math they learned in third grade) through binary. Explain that computers also use basic *logic* operations that students have already studied this year: OR, AND, and NOT. Explain that in digital logic these logical operators are represented by the same symbols and defined by almost the same truth tables as in propositional logic; but in digital logic these operators are called **gates** that you put certain things into and get certain things out of. It may be helpful for students to think of a logical operator or gate as a machine—like an electric mixer, or Calvin's transmogrifying cardboard box. You put ingredients into the machine, the machine does its stuff, and *voilà*! something new comes out. Explain that each of the logic gates you are about to teach them about has one or two inputs (ingredients) but just a single output (result). Tell students that you are also going to show them how gates can be combined in digital logic circuits to perform more complex operations.
2. Tell students that you will begin with the simplest gate: the NOT gate. Explain that it is simplest because it only has one input and one output. Ask students what the logical operator negation does to a variable. It negates it; that is, it turns it into its opposite. Explain that that's exactly what the NOT gate does: it turns an ingredient into its opposite. The input is therefore the opposite of the output. So if the input is true the output must be (have them say it) false, and vice versa. Have students think about it in binary, as they learned to do in the first lesson of this unit: if the input is 1, the output must be 0, and vice versa, since in binary 1 and 0 are considered opposites.
3. Tell students that this gate is also called an **inverter** and see if they can explain why it would be called that (because to invert something is to flip something on it's head). Draw this diagram of a NOT gate on the board:

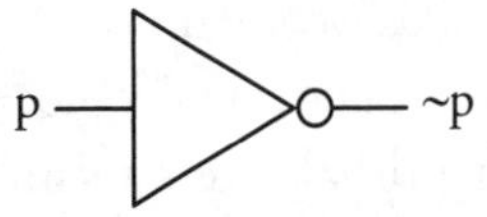

   p —▷o— ~p

   Explain that the *p* on the far left represents the input, the large triangle with the tiny circle at its point represent the "NOT machine" and the *~p* on the right represents the output.

4. Tell students that the NOT gate has a defining truth table that we express in binary. Write it on the board:

p	~p
0	1
1	0

Make sure students see that in the truth tables for digital logic we use 0 for "false" and 1 for "true." Also make sure they see another funny thing: that in this truth table we started the truth table with false (0) rather than true (1) like we do in propositional logic. Explain that starting with false is standard for digital logic and they will see why in a moment.

5. Tell students that the next gate they are going to learn is the AND gate. Remind them that the NOT gate did the job of the logical operator "negation"; ask them what logical operator they think the AND gate does the job of (conjunction). Explain that the AND gate has *two* inputs (ingredients) and again just one output. Draw this diagram of an AND gate on the board:

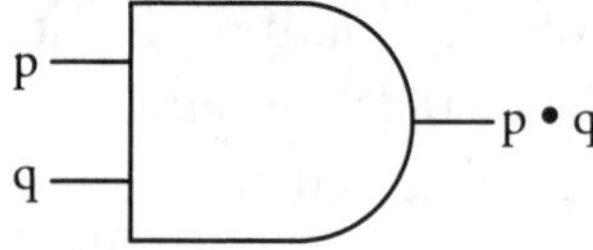

Make sure students see that the p and q on the far left represent the two inputs, the pocket-shaped box represents the conjunction machine, and *p* • *q* is the output.

6. Tell students that we set up the truth table for the AND gate exactly like we set up the truth table for conjunction in propositional logic, and that the relationship of truth values is the same. If both *p* and *q* are true, *p* • *q* is also (have them say it) true, but if either of them or both of them are false *p* • *q* is also (have them say it) false. Remind students that in digital logic we replace Ts and Fs with 0s and 1s, and that we start the truth tables with a 0 rather than a 1. See if they can walk you through completing this truth table, or at least make sure they follow you as you do it (reading the 0's as "false" and the 1's as "true"):

p	q	p • q
0	0	0
0	1	0
1	0	0
1	1	1

Point out the pattern of 0s and 1s under the *p* and *q* in the left column of the truth table. Ask students if it looks familiar (have them think of the two columns pressed together). If they are clueless, explain that this is the pattern of binary counting, from zero (00) up to three (11). Explain that the reason we usually start digital logic truth tables with false (0) is to get this pattern.

7. Tell students that the final gate they need to learn is the OR gate. Ask students what logical operator the OR gate does the job of (disjunction). Ask how many inputs they think the OR gate has (2). How many outputs (1)? Draw the OR diagram on the board:

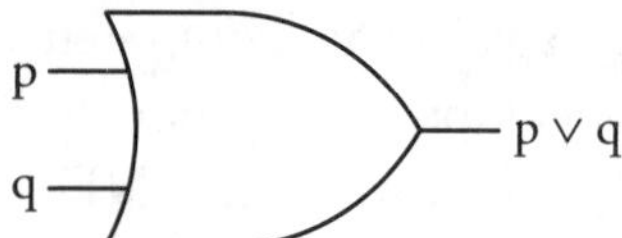

Make sure students see the difference between the AND gate and the OR gate: the OR gate is more shield-shaped than pocket-shaped. Have them practice drawing these gates to look like the examples in the book.

8. Given what they know about disjunction, ask students what the truth value of the output ($p \vee q$) will be if the inputs are both true (True). If they're both false (False). If one of them is true and the other false (True). Explain that, just like in the truth table for disjunction in propositional logic, the output will be false if and only if both inputs are false.

9. Have students walk you through setting up a defining truth table for the OR gate using binary

instead of Ts and Fs. Remind them to start with 0. The completed table should look like this:

p	q	p ∨ q
0	0	0
0	1	1
1	0	1
1	1	1

10. Take a minute to point out to students that there are a few different ways in digital logic of representing the symbols for negation, conjunction, and disjunction than the ones they learned in propositional logic. For the symbol for NOT digital logic uses the tilde (~), which we are used to, or a bar above the variable: $\bar{p}$. For the AND symbol, digital logic either places the dot between the two variables (*p* • *q*), which we are pros at, or simply pushes the two variables up against each other like this: pq. And for the OR symbol digital logic sometimes puts a ∨ in between the variables like normal people do (*p* ∨ *q*), but sometimes it puts a plus sign in between them (*p* + *q*). Explain that in this course, for the sake of ease, you will continue using the symbols students are familiar with from propositional logic: ~, •, and ∨.
11. Tell students that we don't just draw weird looking gates for the sake of drawing weird-looking gates. In applications of digital logic, gates are joined together to form **logic circuits.** Explain that in order to join gates into circuits we have to take the outputs of some gates and make them inputs for other gates to make a "chain" of gates. Explain that logic circuits represent logical propositions the same way that logic gates represent logical operators.
12. So say that we have the proposition "Not both A and B" or *~(A • B)*, and we want to create a circuit that represents that. Explain (and draw as you explain) that our **initial inputs must always be the given variables in their simplest form**, in this case *A* and *B*. So we draw the AND gate, with *A* and *B* as the two inputs. Then we make the output of the AND gate into the input of the NOT gate. The output of the whole circuit is therefore *A* • *B* negated, or *~(A • B)*. The circuit should look like this:

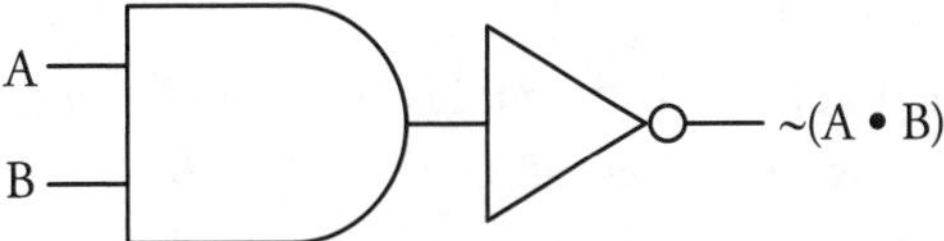

13. Make sure students have a handle on that, and then tell them that you're going to get a bit more complicated. Say we want to make a circuit for the propositions "*A* or *B*, and not *C*." First, have students symbolize this for you: *(A ∨ B) • ~C.* Ask students what kind of proposition this is overall (negation, conjunction, or disjunction?) Make sure they see that overall it is a conjunction, even though it involves the other operators as well. Explain that in this case, our first step will be to form the component parts of the propositions, or the conjuncts, *(A ∨ B)* and *~C*, first, and then use a conjunction gate to conjunct those two conjuncts.
14. Remind students that when making circuits we always begin with the variables in their simplest forms as our inputs. In this case, we have three variables, and they won't all be going into the same gates. The *A* and *B* will be going into the OR gate so we can disjunct them, and the *C* will be going into the NOT gate so that we can negate it. Explain (and draw as you explain) that we can do this at the same time, one gate above the other. Then, just as we did in the previous example, we make the outputs from both of these gates into the inputs of the AND gate. The output of the AND will be our proposition: *(A ∨ B) • ~C.* The completed circuit should look like this:

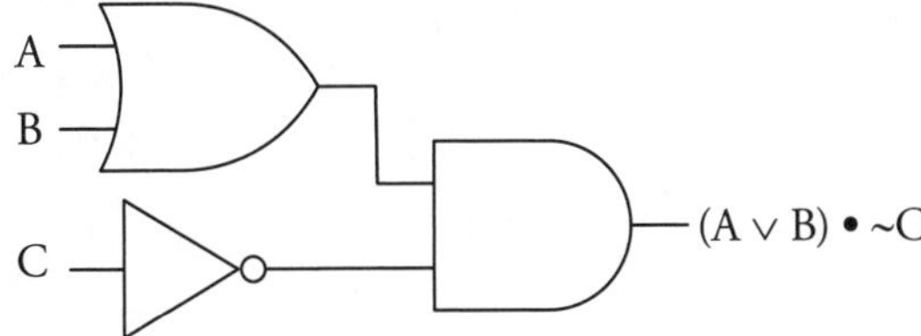

15. Say that we want to make a circuit for a proposition like the one above, except that the variables for the component parts are the same. So instead of *(A ∨ B) • ~C*, we have *(A ∨ B) • ~(A • B)*. Explain that in this case, we don't use the variables as input twice; rather we make the variables the input for one gate and then branch off that input to use it as input for the second gate, like this:

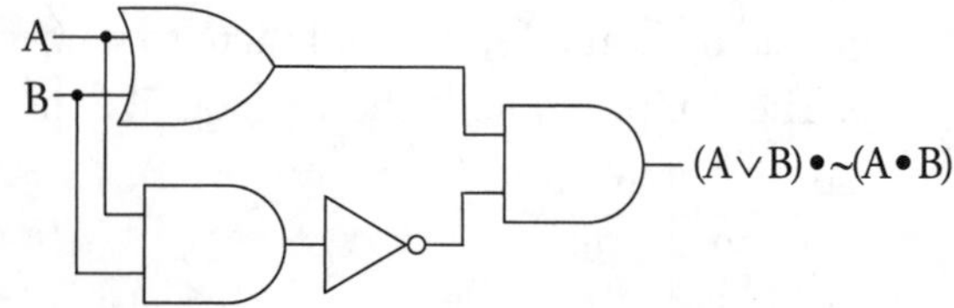

Point out that where one line connects to another, we place a dot at the point of connection.

ASSIGNMENT

Have students complete Exercise 32, and go over it with them.

LESSON 32

BASIC LOGIC GATES

In addition to performing basic mathematical operations, computers also use the logical operations OR, AND, NOT. Computers can perform many logical operations like these very quickly, giving them the versatility that they have. In digital logic, these logical operators are called **gates**. Logic gates are represented by symbols and defined by truth tables. Each logic gate has one or more inputs, and a single output. Gates are combined in digital logic **circuits** to perform complex operations.

The first gate we will consider is **the NOT gate**. The NOT gate is the simplest of the gates; it has one input and one output. This gate does the job of the logical operator *negation*; the output is simply the opposite of the input. If the input to the NOT gate is true, the output will be false, or in binary, if the input is 1, the output will be 0, and vice versa. This gate is also known as an **inverter**. The representation for the NOT gate is

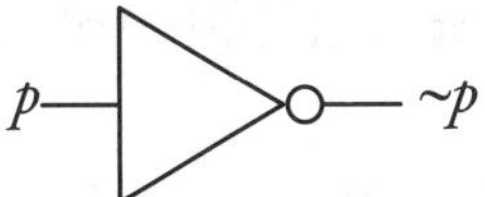

The defining truth table for the NOT gate is:

p	$\sim p$
0	1
1	0

You see that NOT switches the truth value of the proposition from 0 to 1, and vice versa. The symbol for the NOT is the tilde (~). Digital logic also uses a bar above the variable for negation ($\overline{p}$). Note that truth tables in digital logic use 0 for false and 1 for true. You should also note that, unlike propositional logic, it is standard to start the truth table with false. We will see why this is so below.

DEFINITIONS

Logic gates are logical operators that are represented by symbols and defined by truth tables. They have one or more inputs and a single output. Logic gates joined together are ***logic circuits***.

KEY POINT

The output of the NOT gate is the negation (~) of the input.

KEY POINT

The output of the AND gate is the conjunction (•) of the inputs, and is true if and only if both inputs are true.

The AND gate is only slightly more complex than the NOT gate. The standard AND gate has two inputs and one output. This gate does the job of the logical operator *conjunction*. In order for the output to be true, both inputs need to be true. In other words, if either or both of the inputs are false, the output is false. The AND gate is represented by the following symbol:

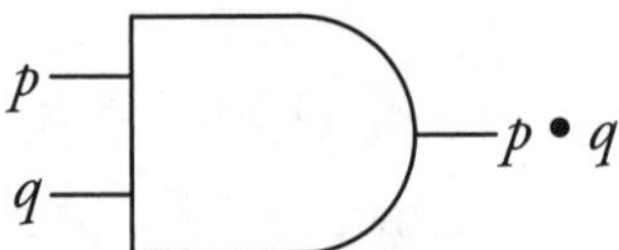

The defining truth table for the AND gate is:

p	q	p • q
0	0	0
0	1	0
1	0	0
1	1	1

Consider the pattern of 0s and 1s under the *p* and *q* in the left column of the truth table. You should recognize this pattern as binary counting, from zero (00) up to three (11). This helps to explain why we start digital logic truth tables with false (0).

In digital logic there are a couple ways of representing AND. The proposition *p and q* is represented either by placing a dot between the two variables ($p \cdot q$) or simply by placing the variables next to one another (pq).

KEY POINT

The output of the OR gate is the disjunction (∨) of the inputs, and is false if and only if both inputs are false.

The next basic gate is **the OR gate**. The standard OR gate has two inputs and one output. This gate does the job of the logical operator *disjunction*. If either or both of the inputs is true, the output is true. Put another way, the output is false if and only if both inputs are false. The OR gate is represented by the following symbol:

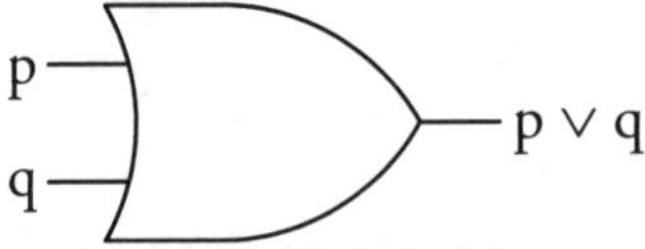

Note the differences between the OR gate and the AND gate. The OR gate is curved at the input, and comes to a point at the output. You should practice drawing the gates to look like these in the text.

The defining truth table for the OR gate is:

p	q	$p \vee q$
0	0	0
0	1	1
1	0	1
1	1	1

There are a couple of ways of representing the OR as well. The proposition *p or q* is represented either by placing a ∨ in between the variables ($p \vee q$), or it is represented by placing a plus between them ($p + q$). In this book, we will use the tilde ~ for NOT, the dot • for AND, and the ∨ for OR.

In applications of digital logic, gates are joined together to form **logic circuits**. To join the different gates, we take the outputs of some gates and make them inputs for other gates. Logical propositions convert easily into digital logic circuits. To represent the proposition "Not both A and B" we would write ~(A • B). The circuit would look like this:

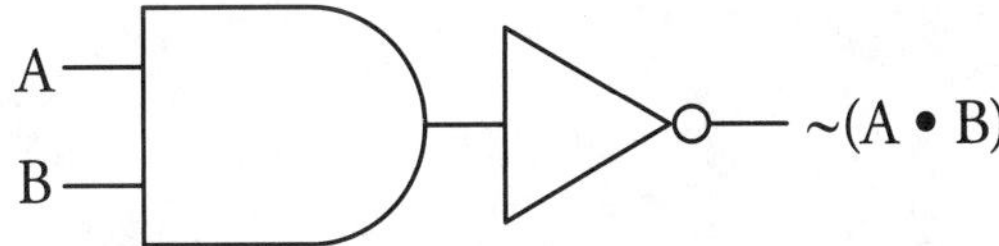

Now let's get a bit more complicated. To represent the proposition "A or B, and not C" we would write (A ∨ B) • ~C. The circuit for (A ∨ B) • ~C looks like this:

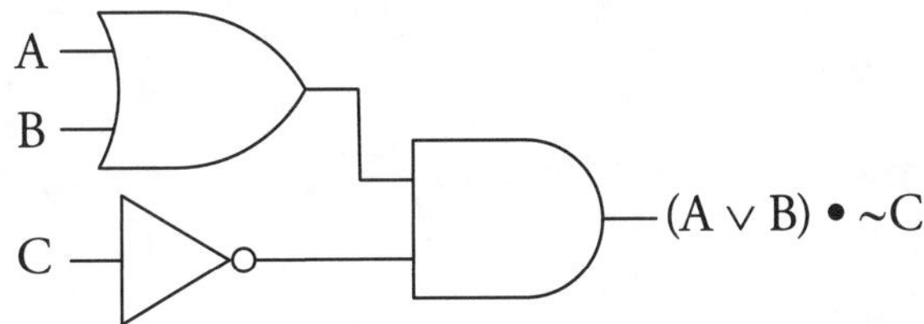

You can also branch off an existing input when using the same input for two different gates. For example, the circuit for (A ∨ B) • ~(A • B) would look like this:

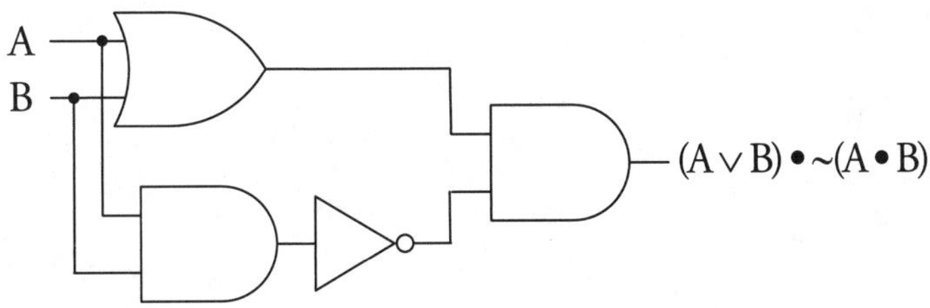

HISTORY

The rules of propositional logic were first developed by George Boole, an English mathematician and logician, in his book *An Investigation of the Laws of Thought* (1854). Over eighty years later, Boole's work was applied to electronic circuits by Claude Shannon in his master's thesis at MIT. This was the birth of modern digital logic.

Note that where one line connects to another, a dot is placed at the point of connection.

SUMMARY

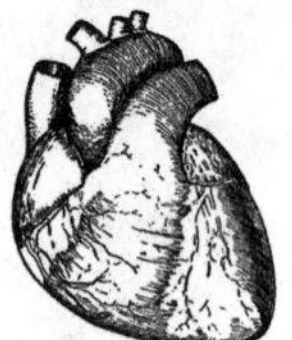

The NOT gate is the negation of the input, the AND gate is the conjunction of the inputs, and the OR gate is the disjunction of the inputs. You can join logic gates together by making the outputs of some gates inputs for other gates. This creates logic circuits, which can represent compound propositions.

EXERCISE 32 (21 points)

Problems 1-4: Draw the digital logic circuits for the given propositions. (3, 3, 4, 4)

1. A • ~B

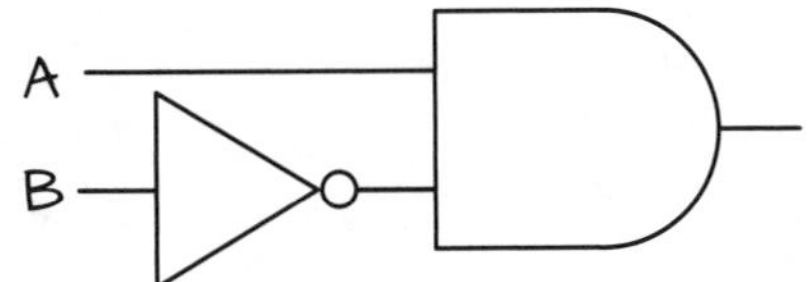

2. ~A ∨ B

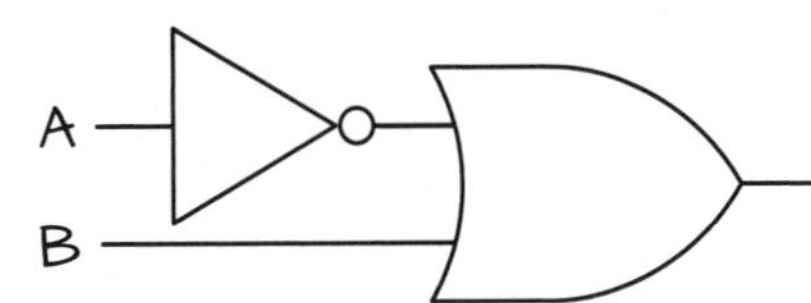

3. (A • B) ∨ (B • C)

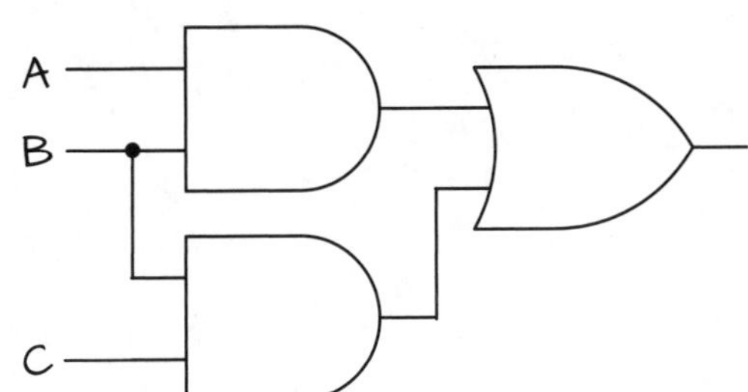

4. ~(A ∨ B) • C

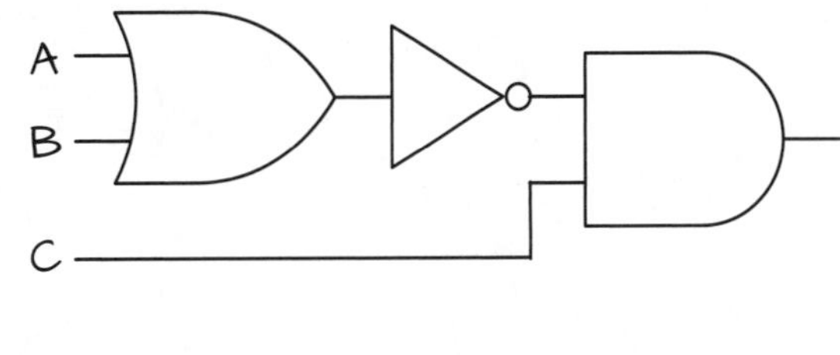

Problems 5-6: Write the proposition for the given digital logic circuit. (3, 4)

5.

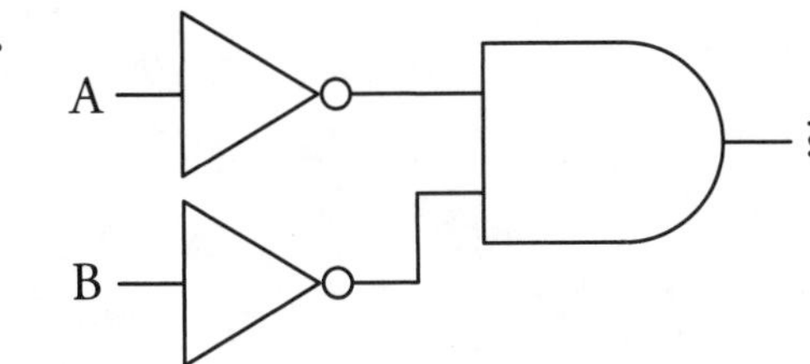

~A • ~B

6.

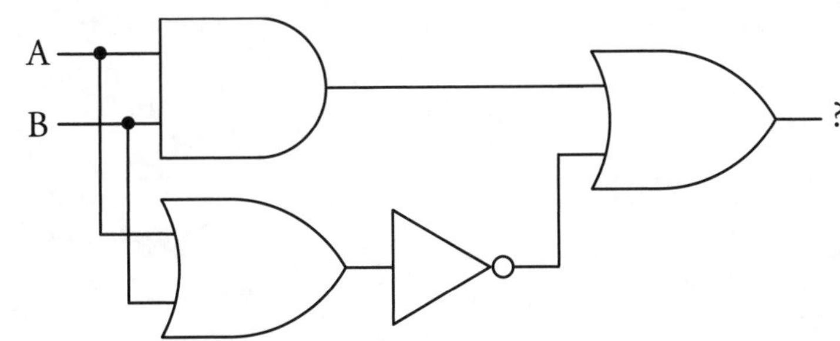

(A • B) ∨ ~(A ∨ B)

TEACHER'S NOTES on LESSON 33

FINDING TRUTH TABLES FROM DIGITAL LOGIC CIRCUITS

Intermediate Logic, pp. 271–273

STUDENT OBJECTIVES

1. Determine a binary truth table for a given logic circuit.
2. Complete Exercise 33.

TEACHING INSTRUCTIONS

1. Remind students that they learned yesterday how to turn a proposition into a circuit and vice versa. Have them tell you what the three kinds of logic gates are (NOT, AND, OR). Remind students that for each of the three gates, we came up with defining truth tables that looked suspiciously like the defining truth tables for negation, conjunction, and disjunction, just in binary and upsidedown. Explain that in today's lesson students will learn how to use these defining truth tables for the different gates to find the truth table for *any* logic circuit.
2. Have students walk you through drawing a logic circuit for $\sim A \vee B$. If they need help, remind them that the initial inputs must be the simplest form of the variables (A and B), but that something needs to happen to the A while it's on its way into the OR gate. The completed circuit should look like this, with X symbolizing the output:

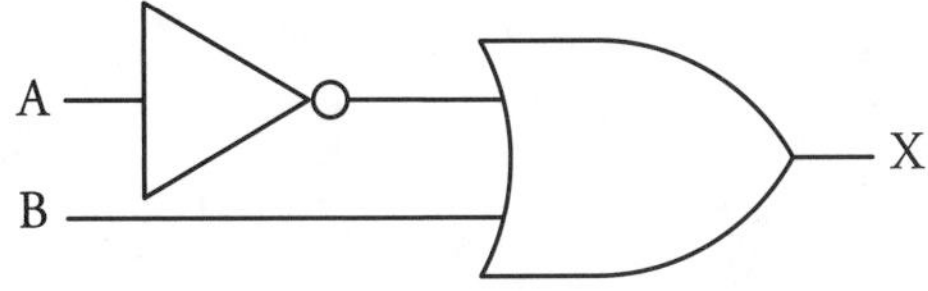

3. Explain that to put together a truth table for this circuit we need to determine what the truth value of X would be for every possible truth value of the inputs. Tell students that you'll begin with both A and B being false ($A = 0, B = 0$). Erase the A and B in the circuit and replace them both with 0. Show students that if A is false, or 0, then the output from the NOT gate ($\sim A$), must be 1. Write a 1 over the output line of the NOT gate. This 1, along with the false or 0 from the B input, are the inputs of the OR gate. Remind students that we know from the defining truth table for the OR gate that "true or false" is "true," or rather, $1 \vee 0 = 1$. So the output of this circuit will be 1. It should look like this:

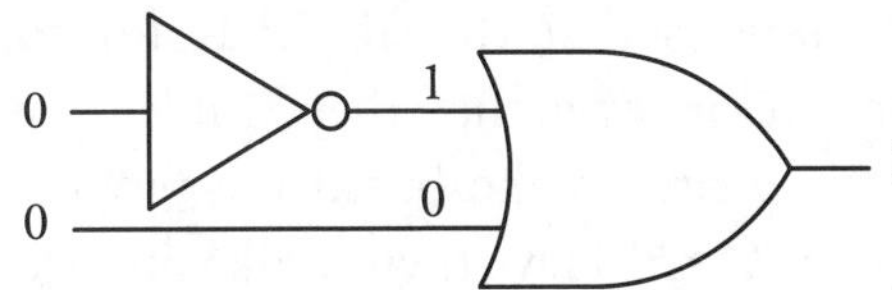

4. Have students walk you through the same procedure for each of the other possible input combinations: 01, 10, and 11 (and point out again that these input combinations are the first four numbers in binary). The results should look like this:

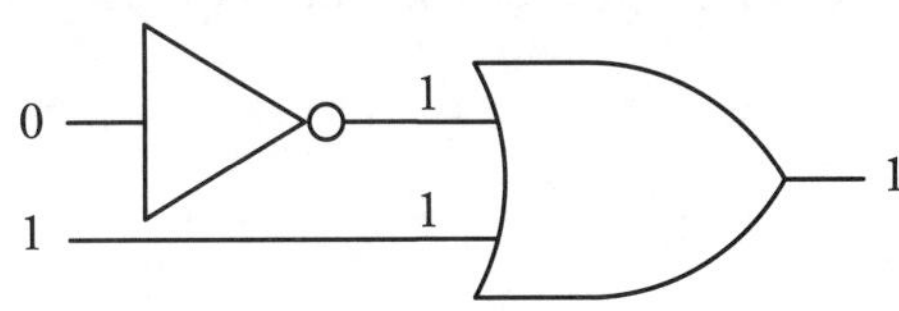

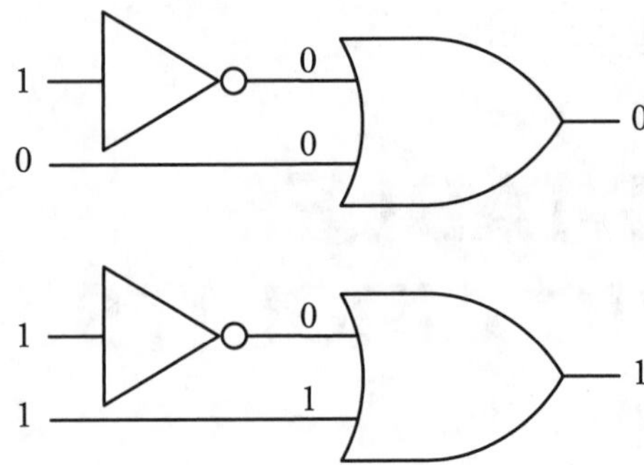

5. Have students look at the results. Make sure they can see that *X* (the final output) only equals 0 when *A = 1* and *B = 0.* Have students walk you through writing out the truth table for this circuit, beginning with 00. The completed truth table should look like this:

A	B	X
0	0	1
0	1	1
1	0	0
1	1	1

6. Remind students that they—smart cookies that they are—could have developed this truth table from the proposition *~A ∨ B* itself, without going through all the rigamarole of a circuit, because they know propositional logic.

7. Tell students that they're ready for something trickier (whether they think they are or not). Write on the board the proposition *(A ∨ B) • ~(A • B).* Have them walk you through setting up the circuit for this proposition. If they get stuck, remind them of the things they learned in the last lesson: *A* and *B* must be the two inputs; since they are the variables in both parts of the proposition, they will be the input for the two different gates and will therefore have to branch; the "two sets" of *A* and *B* must go through the disjunction and conjunction gates separately before their outputs are joined in the final conjunction gate, etc. The completed circuit should look like this, with *Y* symbolizing the final output:

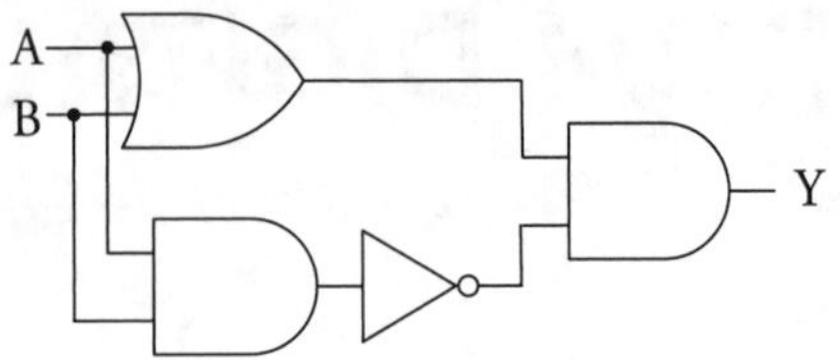

8. The next step is to determine what *Y* will be for every possible truth value of *A* and *B*. Once again, replace *A* and *B* with 0s, and have students walk you through determining the other truth values in the circuit. We know from the defining truth table for the OR gate that 0 and 0 disjoined give us 0, and we know from the defining truth table for the AND gate that 0 and 0 conjoined give us 0 as well. The output of the conjunction is negated, giving us 1. 0 and 1 conjoined at the end gives us another 0 as our final output.

9. Have students finish the truth table for this circuit (with or without your help). It should look like this:

A	B	Y
0	0	0
0	1	1
1	0	1
1	1	0

ASSIGNMENT

Have students complete Exercise 33, and go over it with them.

LESSON 33

FINDING TRUTH TABLES FROM DIGITAL LOGIC CIRCUITS

We have seen how to draw a circuit for a given proposition, and vice versa. We can now use the defining truth tables for the different gates to find the truth table for any digital logic circuit.

KEY POINT

You can find a truth table for a whole digital logic circuit using the defining truth tables for each gate.

The truth table for a logic circuit will give the truth value outputs for all the possible inputs. Consider the logic circuit for ~ A ∨ B:

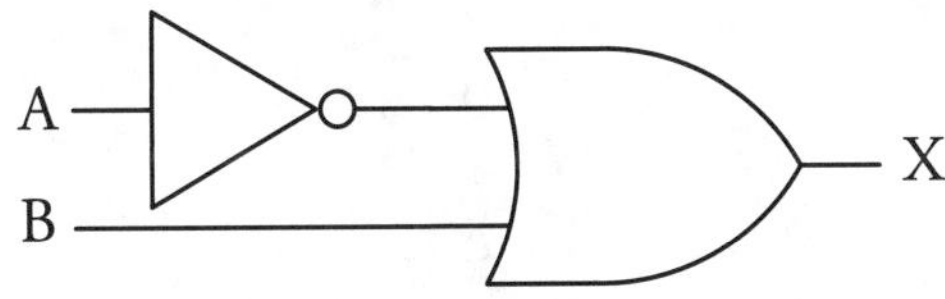

We call the output *X*. Let's determine what *X* would be for every possible input value.

First, the inputs *A* and *B* could both be false (*A* = 0, *B* = 0). If A is false (0), then the output from the NOT gate (~A) would be true (1). This true, along with the false from the input B, are the inputs for the OR gate.

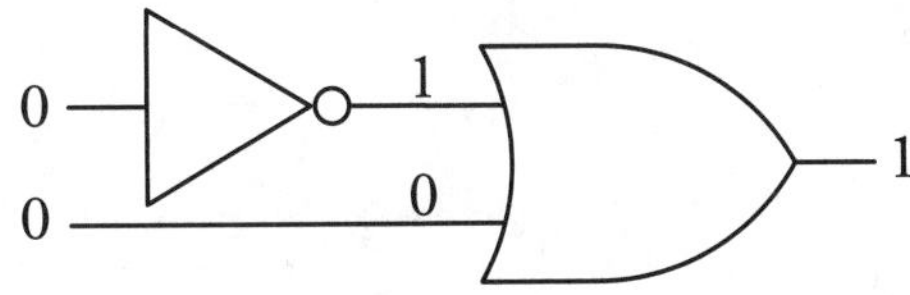

We know from the defining truth table for OR that "true OR false" is "true" (1 ∨ 0 = 1) So the output shown above is true (1).

This same procedure can be followed for the other possible input combinations 01, 10, 11 (note again that these count up in binary). The results would be as shown here:

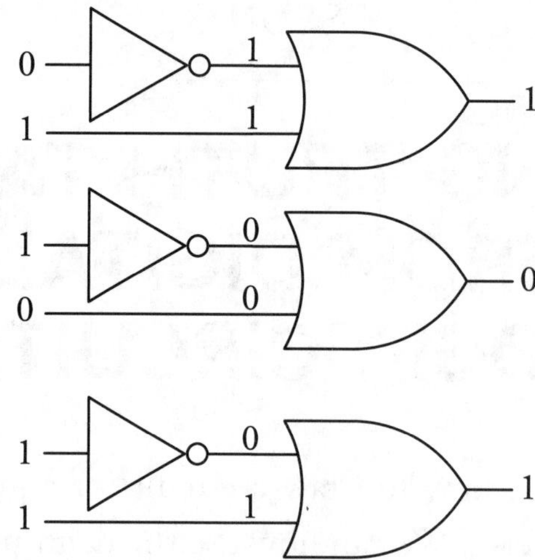

We can see that the output *X* = *0* only when *A* = *1* and *B* = *0.* We can thus write out the truth table as shown:

A	B	X
0	0	1
0	1	1
1	0	0
1	1	1

Of course, this truth table could have been developed from the proposition itself, rather than using the circuit.

Now consider the more complex circuit for the proposition *(A ∨ B) • ~ (A • B)*:

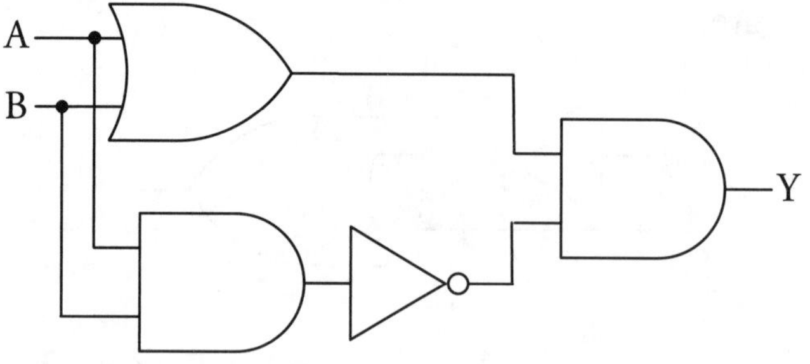

What would the output *Y* be for all every possible input? Again, consider the circuit when *A* and *B* are both false *(A* = *0, B* = *0).* That would give the following:

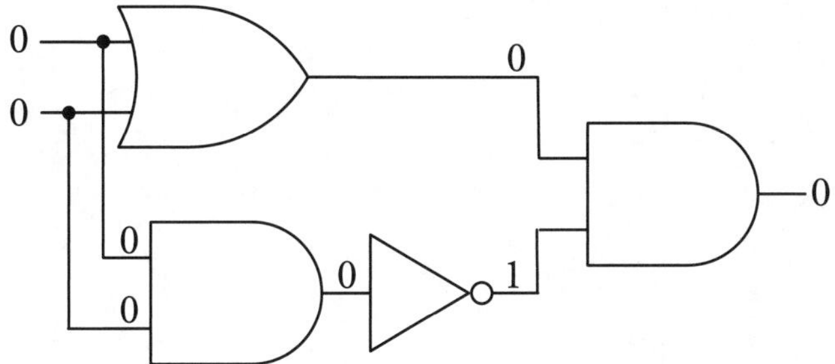

For those inputs, the output *Y* is *0*. So far, the truth table would look like this:

A	B	Y
0	0	0
0	1	
1	0	
1	0	

You should finish this truth table on your own. When you are done check your work by developing the truth table from the proposition itself.

SUMMARY

The truth table for a logic circuit gives the truth value output for all possible inputs, following the patterns of the defining truth table for each gate.

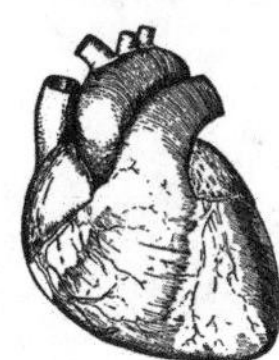

EXERCISE 33 (18 points)

Problems 1-2: Complete the truth table for the circuit. (4, 7, 7)

1. ~ (A • ~ B)

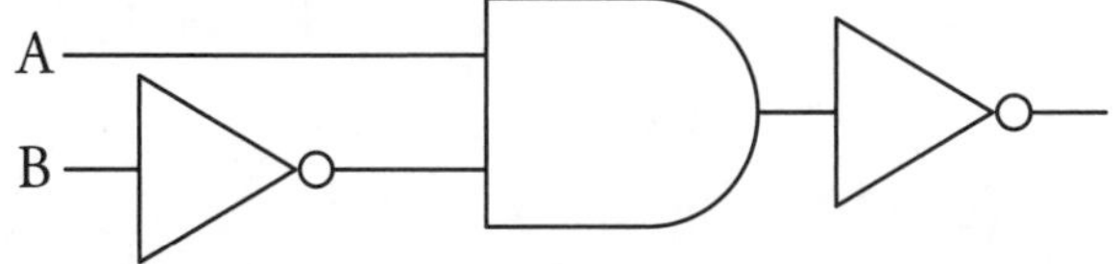

A	B	~ (A • ~ B)
0	0	1
0	1	1
1	0	0
1	1	1

2. (~ A • ~ B) ∨ C

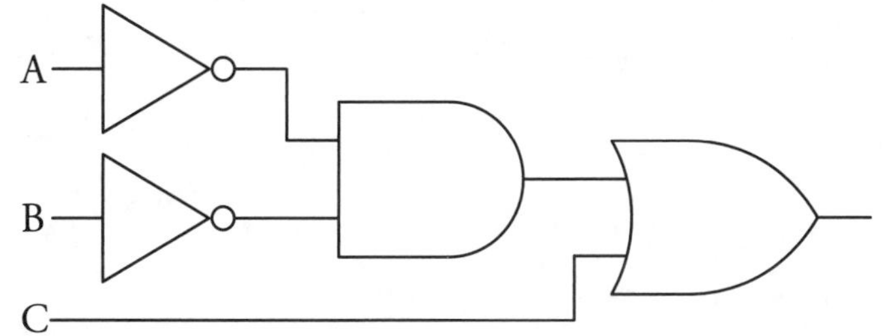

A	B	C	(~ A • ~ B) ∨ C
0	0	0	1
0	0	1	1
0	1	0	0
0	1	1	1
1	0	0	0
1	0	1	1
1	1	0	0
1	1	1	1

3. Draw the circuit and complete the truth table for the proposition A • (B ∨ ~ C).

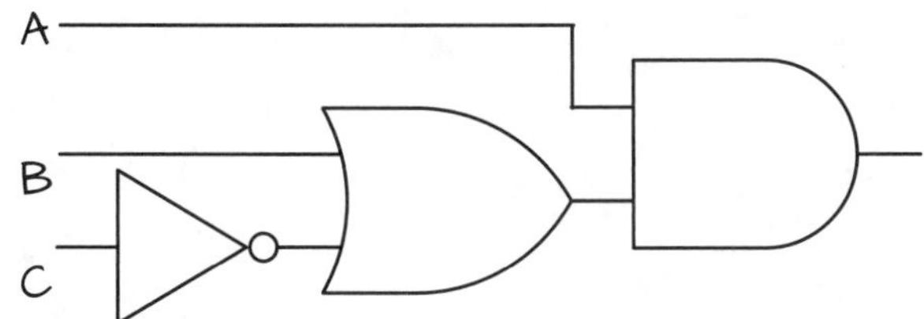

A	B	C	A • (B ∨ ~ C)
0	0	0	0
0	0	1	0
0	1	0	0
0	1	1	0
1	0	0	1
1	0	1	0
1	1	0	1
1	1	1	1

TEACHER'S NOTES on LESSON 34

CONVERTING TRUTH TABLES INTO DIGITAL LOGIC CIRCUITS

Intermediate Logic, pp. 277–279

STUDENT OBJECTIVES

1. Convert truth tables into propositions and digital logic circuits.
2. Complete Exercise 34.

TEACHING INSTRUCTIONS

1. Remind students that yesterday they learned how to turn propositions into logic circuits and then into truth tables. Explain that today they're simply going to learn how to do the opposite: turn truth tables into propositions, and then into logic circuits.
2. Write this truth table on the board:

A	B	X
0	0	1
0	1	0
1	0	1
1	1	0

Ask students how they think we can get from this truth table to the proposition that it expresses. They will probably be puzzled. Tell them that the way to do this might not make a lot of sense to them when you explain it, but that they just have to take your word for it that it's the right thing to do.

3. Tell them that the first step is to find all the rows that have an output of true (1). In this case, that's the first and third rows. These will be the rows that we use to form the proposition. Tell students that the next thing to do is to look at the inputs of these two rows, which will become part of the proposition. For each of these rows, if the input variable is true (1), then we will use that variable. If the input variable is false (0), then we will use that variable negated. In other words, saying "A is false (0)," is basically another way of saying *~A*. Finally, we join all the variables in the row, whether negated or unnegated, by conjunction. For example, our first input row of 00 should look like this: *~A* • *~B*. And the next (the 3rd) of 10 should look like this: *A* • *~B*.
4. Explain that another way of saying what you have just determined is that *X* is true when *A* and *B* are both false, or when *A* is true and *B* is false. But we can symbolize that statement with a proposition: write on the board *(~A* • *~B)* ∨ *(A* • *~B)*. Explain that this is the proposition which gives the output *X*. It is a complicated proposition, and can probably be very much simplified, but it is still a proposition that produces *X*.
5. Have students walk you through drawing the circuit for this proposition. The completed circuit should look like this:

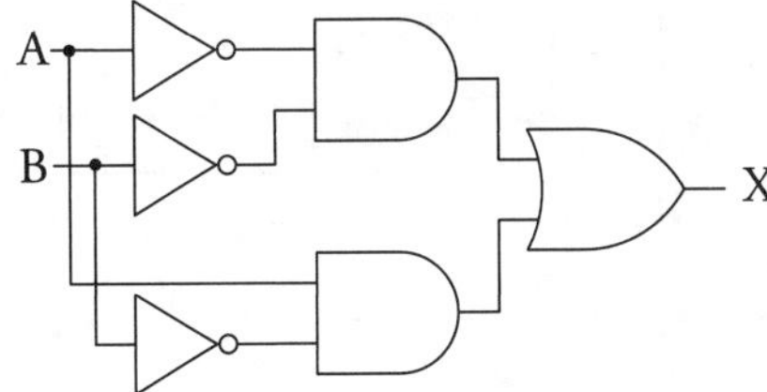

Have students go back and create a truth table for this circuit to check that it does indeed produce the same proposition and truth table as the ones we began with. Tell students that later they will learn how to simplify this proposition and circuit. For now, point out that the output from this truth table could be simplified from $(\sim A \bullet \sim B) \vee (A \bullet \sim B)$ to simply $\sim B$.

6. They thought it couldn't get more complicated than this. Tell students that you are going to work through an example with three variables this time. Write this truth table on the board:

A	B	C	Z
0	0	0	0
0	0	1	0
0	1	0	0
0	1	1	1
1	0	0	0
1	0	1	1
1	1	0	0
1	1	1	1

7. Remind students that the first thing to do is look for the rows with a true (1) output under the Z (rows 4, 6, and 8). The next step is to determine which variables are true and which false in each of these rows, negate the false ones, and connect the variables by conjunction. In row four, A is false and B and C are true, so the conjunction should look like this: $\sim A \bullet B \bullet C$. In row six, A is true, B is false, and C is true, so the conjunction should look like this: $A \bullet \sim B \bullet C$. In row eight, A, B and C are all true, so the conjunction should look like this: $A \bullet B \bullet C$.

8. Remind students that another way of saying this is that Z is true when A is false, and B and C are true; or when A is true, B is false, and C is true; or when A, B, and C are true. Have students walk you through symbolizing this proposition; it should look like this: $(\sim A \bullet B \bullet C) \vee (A \bullet \sim B \bullet C) \vee (A \bullet B \bullet C)$.

9. The massive circuit for this proposition appears below. Instead of having students create it themselves, draw it for them (it will probably take the whole board) and then work through it with them to make sure they see that it represents the given proposition.

(The input lines are drawn vertically to visualize the circuit more easily.)

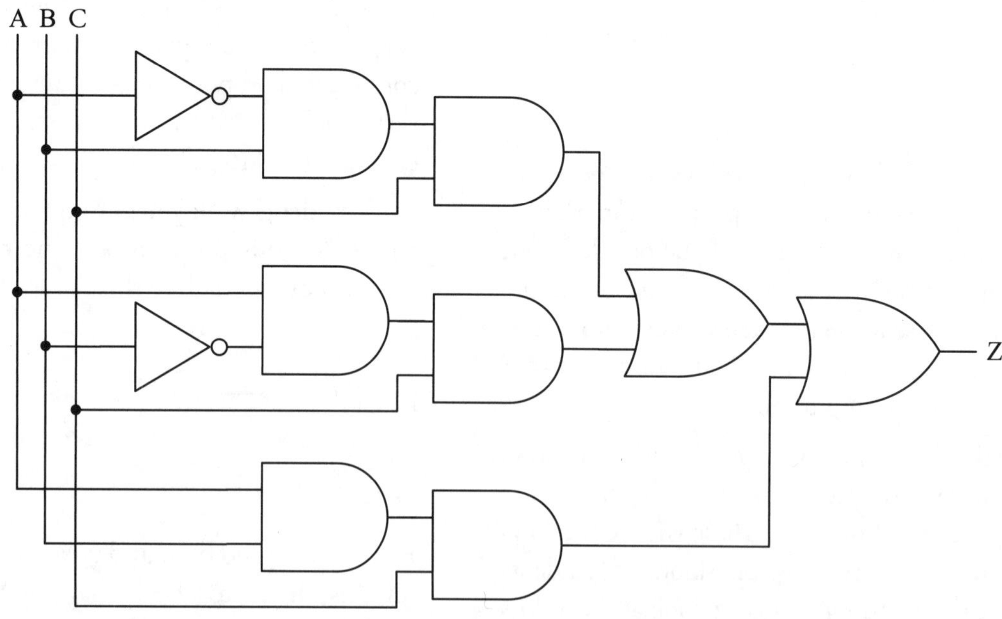

10. Tell students that this monstrosity of a proposition/circuit could be simplified into the proposition $(A \vee B) \bullet C$. Explain that in the next few lessons they will learn several tools for simplifying propositions and circuits.

ASSIGNMENT

Have students complete Exercise 34, and go over it with them.

LESSON 34

CONVERTING TRUTH TABLES INTO DIGITAL LOGIC CIRCUITS

We now need to learn how to convert truth tables directly into propositions, and then into logic circuits. To do this, we consider every row for which the truth table has an output of true (1). For each of these rows, when the input variable is false (0), that variable is negated. These are joined by conjunction to any variables in that row that are true (1). These propositions are then joined by disjunction in the completed proposition.

For example, consider this truth table:

A	B	X	
0	0	1	← X is true when A is false and B is false
0	1	0	OR
1	0	1	← X is true when A is true and B is false
1	1	0	

Note that the output *X* is true when *A* and *B* are both false, or *A* is true and *B* is false. Now consider that proposition: *A* is false and *B* is false, or *A* is true and *B* is false. Another way of saying this proposition is: (NOT *A* AND NOT *B*) OR (*A* AND NOT *B*). This can be symbolized in the proposition (~ A • ~ B) ∨ (A • ~ B) This is the proposition which gives the output *X*. We can then draw the circuit for this output:

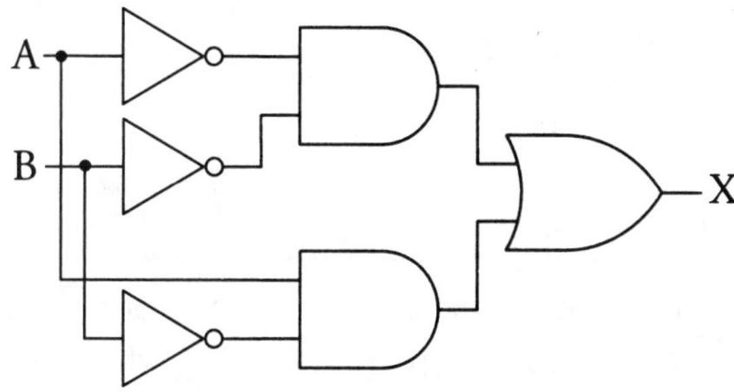

You should check to verify that this circuit does indeed produce the desired output. Later, we will consider how to simplify this proposition and circuit. For now, you might recognize the output from the truth table as being equivalent to simply *~B*.

Let's look at a more complicated example, with three variables this time. Consider the following truth table:

A	B	C	Z	Z is true when...
0	0	0	0	
0	0	1	0	
0	1	0	0	
0	1	1	1	← A is false and B and C are true (~ A • B • C)
1	0	0	0	OR
1	0	1	1	← A is true, B is false, and C is true (A• ~ B • C)
1	1	0	0	OR
1	1	1	1	← A and B and C are all true (A • B • C)

From the truth table we see the proposition Z is $(\sim A \bullet B \bullet C) \vee (A \bullet \sim B \bullet C) \vee (A \bullet B \bullet C)$. Here is a circuit for this proposition:

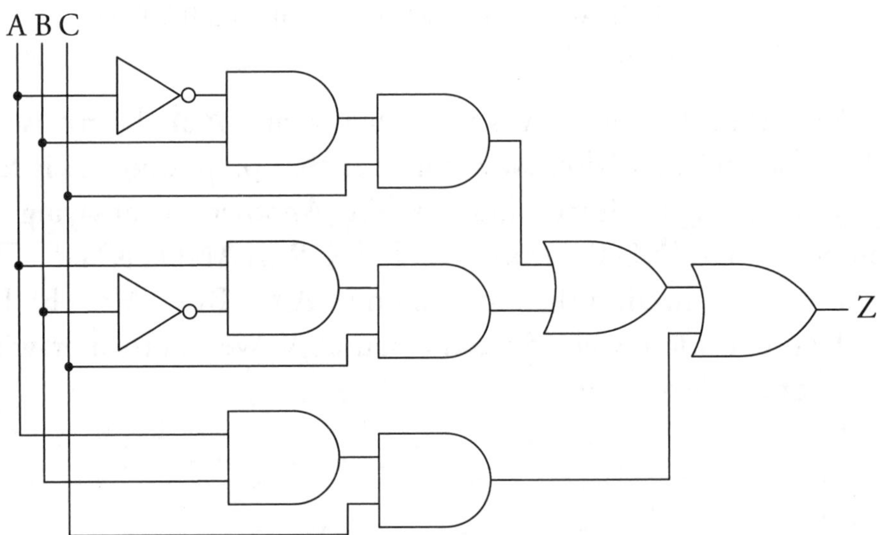

This is a fairly complicated circuit. You should work through it carefully to see that it represents the given proposition. Note how the input lines were drawn vertically to visualize the circuit more easily.

This proposition and circuit could be simplified to the proposition $(A \vee B) \bullet C$. We will examine several tools for simplifying propositions and circuits in the next few lessons.

SUMMARY

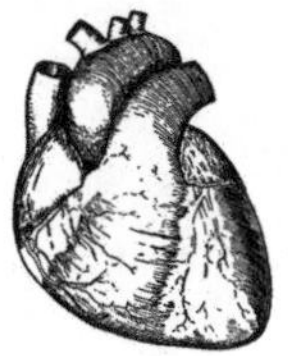

Follow these steps to convert truth tables directly into propositions:

- Consider every row for which the truth table has an output of true (1).
- In these rows, negate the input variable when it is false (0).
- Using conjunction, join these negated variables to any variables in the row that are true (1).
- Finally, using disjunction, join the propositions created by each row into a single completed proposition.

EXERCISE 34 (35 points)

For the given truth table, determine the propositions and draw the resulting logic circuit.

1.

A	B	W
0	0	0
0	1	1
1	0	0
1	1	0

Proposition: ~A•B (5)

Circuit:

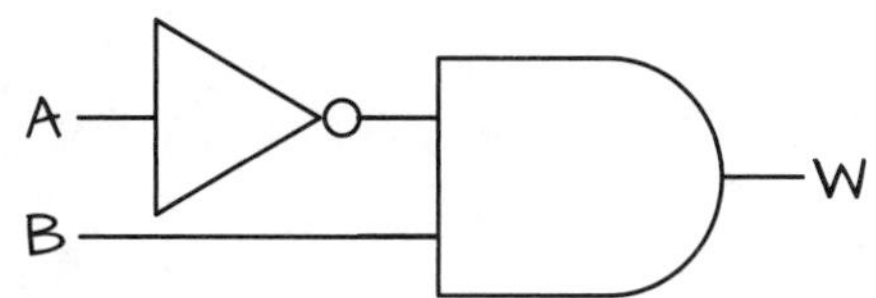

2.

A	B	X
0	0	0
0	1	1
1	0	1
1	1	0

Proposition: (~A•B)v(A•~B) (8)

Circuit:

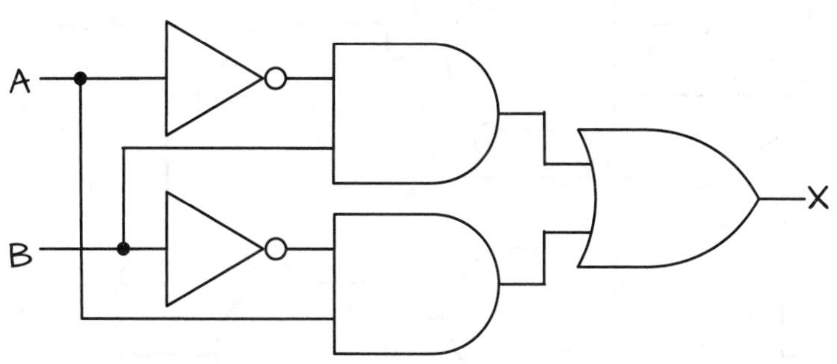

3.

A	B	C	Y
0	0	0	0
0	0	1	1
0	1	0	0
0	1	1	0
1	0	0	0
1	0	1	1
1	1	0	0
1	1	1	0

Proposition: (~A•~B•C)v(A•~B•C) (10)

Circuit:

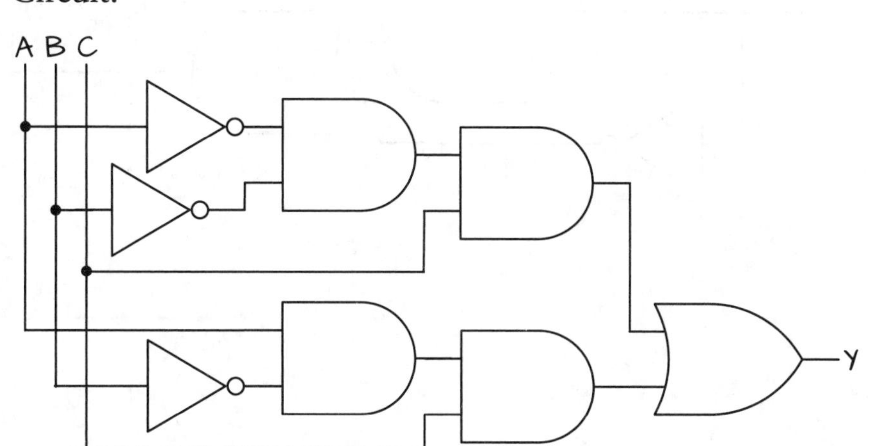

Continued on next page.

4.

A	B	C	Z
0	0	0	0
0	0	1	0
0	1	0	1
0	1	1	0
1	0	0	1
1	0	1	0
1	1	0	1
1	1	1	0

Proposition: (~A•B•~C)∨(A•~B•~C)∨(A•B•~C) (12)

Circuit:

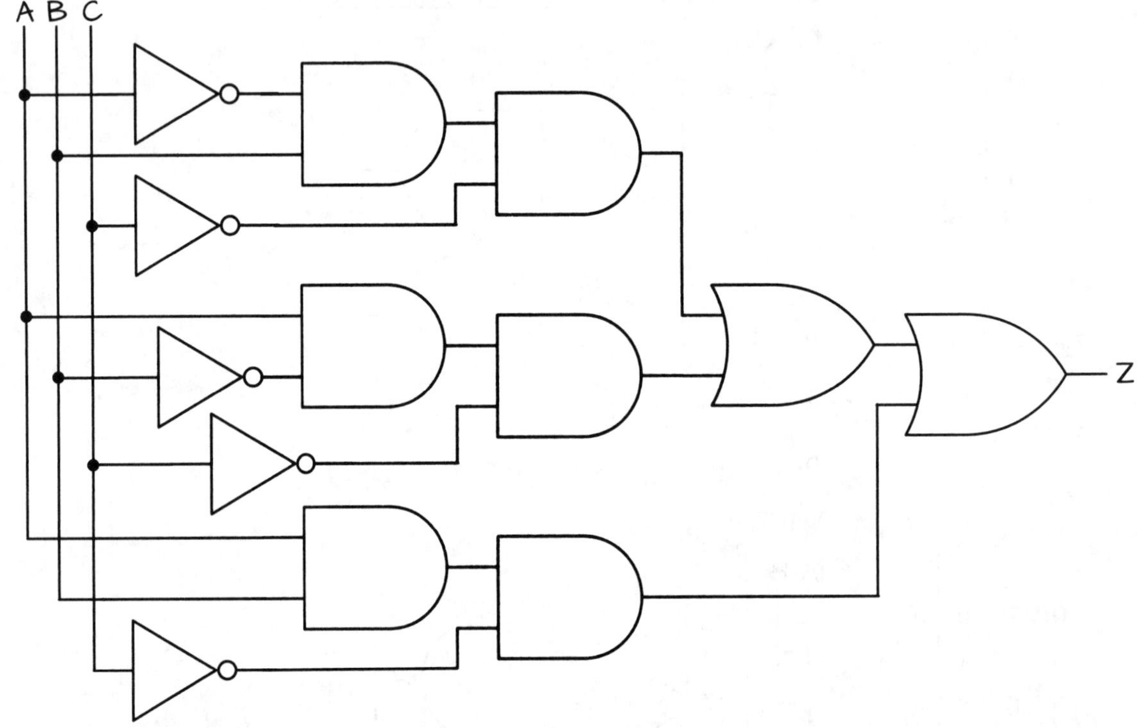

NAND GATES AND NOR GATES

Intermediate Logic, pp. 283–287

STUDENT OBJECTIVES

1. Draw and give the truth table for NAND and NOR gates.
2. Design circuits using these gates.
3. Demonstrate their truth-functional completeness
4. Complete Exercise 35.

TEACHING INSTRUCTIONS

1. Ask students what the three basic logic gates they have learned so far are (NOT, AND, and OR). Explain that today you will be teaching them how to combine these basic logic gates into more complex gates: two very useful gates called the NOR gate and the NAND gate.
2. Ask students to take a guess at what propositions these two gates do the job of. If they are clueless, point out that NAND and NOR look an awful lot like NOT squished together with and AND and OR. Explain that that is exactly what these gates are. **The NOR gate does the job of a negated disjunction**; have students tell you how to symbolize a negated disjunction and write $\sim(p \vee q)$ on the board. Have students walk you through creating the truth table for $\sim(p \vee q)$ in binary. It should look like this:

p	q	~(p ∨ q)
0	0	1
0	1	0
1	0	0
1	1	0

Make sure students see that the output for this gate is true if and only if both inputs are false. You might lead them to see this in a regular sentence, such as "A baby is neither a teenager NOR a student." This is true because "A baby is a teacher" and "A baby is a student" are both false.

3. Also have students take a guess at how we draw the NOR gate. Explain that since this gate is basically the equivalent of placing a NOT gate at the output of an OR gate, we abbreviate the NOT gate from a triangle and a gumball to just a gumball and put this gumball at the end of the OR gate, like so:

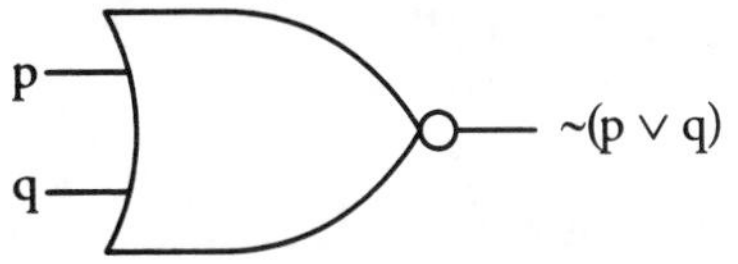

4. Explain that similarly **the NAND gate performs the job of a negated conjunction**. Have students tell you how to symbolize a negated conjunction: $\sim(p \bullet q)$. Again, have students tell you how to construct the truth table for this negated conjunction in binary. It should look like this:

p	q	~(p • q)
0	0	1
0	1	1
1	0	1
1	1	0

Make sure students see that the negated conjunction is almost the opposite of the negated disjunction: the output for this gate is false if and only if both inputs are true.

5. Have students take a stab at drawing the NAND gate. Explain that, similar to the NOR gate, this gate is equivalent to placing a NOT gate at the output of an AND gate; once again we simplify the NOT gate by taking away its triangle and putting its gumball or bubble (or whatever you'd like to think of it as) at the tip of the AND gate. It should look like this:

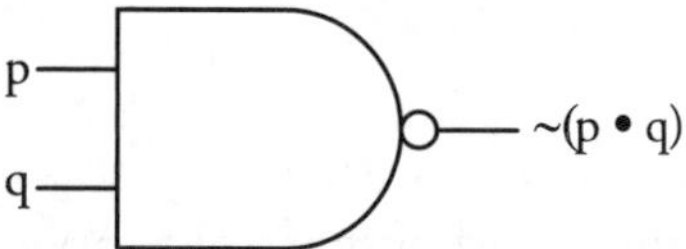

6. Tell students that one way we can use these NOR and NAND gates is to simplify circuits. For example, draw these two circuits on the board. Explain that they are equivalent, but that the second is a whole lot easier to draw than the first.

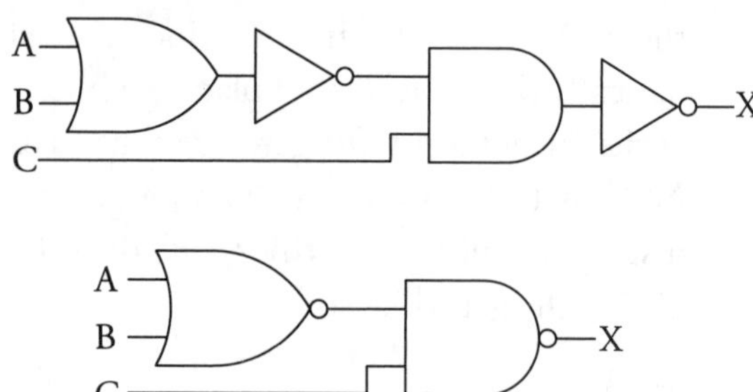

7. Tell students that another useful thing about these two gates is that they are **truth-functionally complete**. Have students remember back to when they learned about truth-functional completeness in Lesson 21. See if anyone can tell you what truth-functional completeness is. Explain that in propositional logic a logical operator (or operators) is truth-functionally complete if all possible combinations of true and false for two variables are derivable from it (or them). Explain that **in digital logic a gate is truth-functionally complete if any logic circuit can be designed using only that gate**. This is true of both NAND and NOR gates.

8. Explain that since the building blocks of more complex gates are the simple gates AND, OR, and NOT, the first step is to learn how to make the AND, OR, and NOT gates using only the NOR and NAND gates. Tell students that you're going to start with NOR.

9. Ask students if they have any ideas for how to make a NOR gate (a gate that does the work of the proposition $\sim(p \vee q)$) produce $\sim p$. If they're stumped (and who wouldn't be?), tell them they we do this by noting first that $\sim p$ if equivalent to $\sim(p \vee p)$. To get this output we just make p our input and split it, so that instead of sending p and q through the NOR gate, we send p through twice. This will result in the output $\sim(p \vee p)$, or simply $\sim p$. Draw this on the board like so:

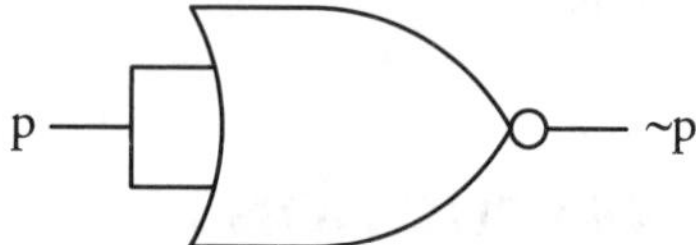

Make sure students see that this NOR gate has done exactly what a NOT gate does: negate something, turn p into $\sim p$. In fact, this *is* a NOT gate, just *made out of* a NOR gate.

10. Tell students that the next you will try to produce an OR gate $(p \vee q)$ out of a NOR gate $\sim(p \vee q)$. Explain that just as in the last example the key to making a NOR gate into a NOT gate was realizing that $\sim p$ was equivalent to $\sim(p \vee p)$, in this example the key is realizing that $p \vee q$ is equivalent to something else, something we can get from $\sim(p \vee q)$. If they have no ideas, write on the board that $p \vee q$ is equivalent to $\sim[\sim(p \vee q)]$. Make sure students see that $\sim[\sim(p \vee q)]$ is simply a negation of the NOR gate, and since we just learned how to use the NOR gate to do negation, we can produce a circuit that is equivalent to an OR gate by connecting a NOR gate to another split input NOR gate. The circuit should look like this:

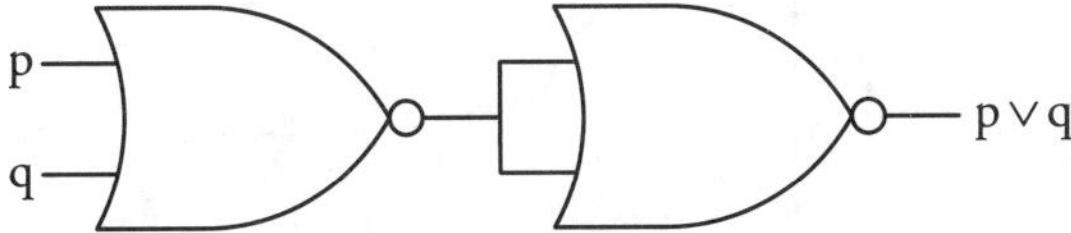

11. Walk students through the circuit. Make sure they see that p and q are the inputs of the first NOR gate, and that the (invisible) output is $\sim(p \vee q)$. Then we split that output into two identical inputs, $\sim(p\vee q)$ and $\sim(p\vee q)$, and send them through a second NOR gate which we know from the last example will result in the negation of the input: $\sim[\sim(p \vee q)]$.
12. Once students have (something) of a handle on that, tell them that the next thing to learn is how to make an AND gate $(p \bullet q)$ from a NOR gate $\sim(p\vee q)$, which is bit more complicated. Explain that to do this we need to use De Morgan's Theorem. (Give whoever can remember De Morgan's Theorem ice cream or something.) Remind students that De Morgan's Theorem says that $p \bullet q$ is equivalent to $\sim(\sim p \vee \sim q)$. Make sure students can see that $\sim(\sim p \vee \sim q)$ is the same as $\sim p$ NOR $\sim q$. So all we have to do is get our circuit to place where $\sim p$ and $\sim q$ can be our inputs into a NOR gate. We know already from the first example that we can produce negations by using split-input NOR gates, and then we just have to make those negations the input of our final NOR gate, like so:

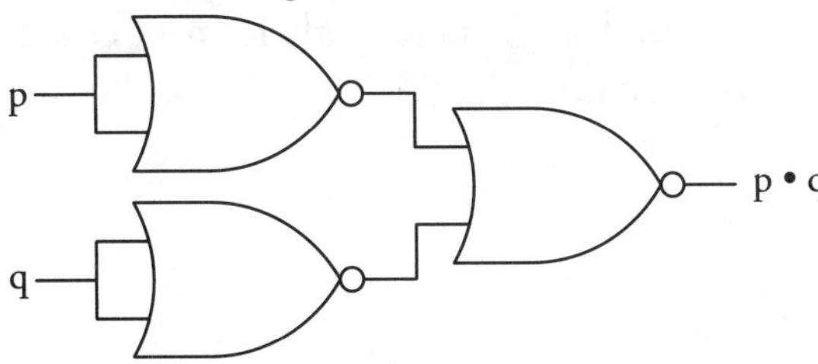

13. Tell students that they have to start treading water a bit faster now. Next they are going to design a circuit for the proposition $\sim p \vee q$. Ask students what this proposition is equivalent to (Hint: have students think back to the rules of replacement. Another hint: have them think back to Material Implication). Hopefully they will remember eventually that $\sim p \vee q$ is equivalent to $p \supset q$. Explain that really what they are about to do is use NOR gates to represent a conditional. Tell students that this time you are going to start by drawing the circuit for $\sim p \vee q$ not using NOR gates. Have them walk you through it; it should involve a NOT gate and an OR gate, like this:

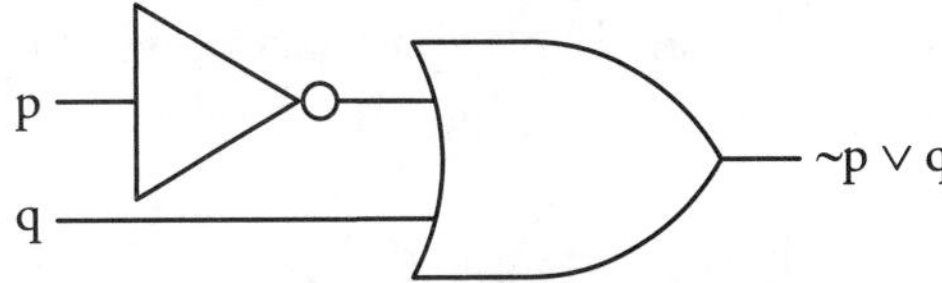

14. Explain that now what we have to do is figure out how to turn these gates into NOR gates. See if anyone has any ideas for how to proceed. Remind students that two negations in a row cancel each other out, so that if we were to add a negation bubble to the end of the OR gate—making it a NOR gate—we would just need to add an additional NOT gate to the circuit to get a circuit equivalent to the first one, like so:

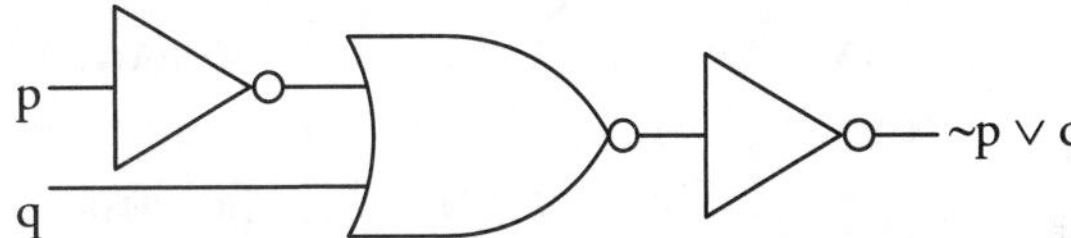

Make sure students see that propositionally, this was the same as turning $\sim p \vee q$ in $\sim\sim(\sim p \vee q)$.
15. Tell students that they know what to do next (whether they know they know or not): turn the NOT gates into split-input NOR gates, as the learned at the beginning of the lesson. The completed circuit should look like this:

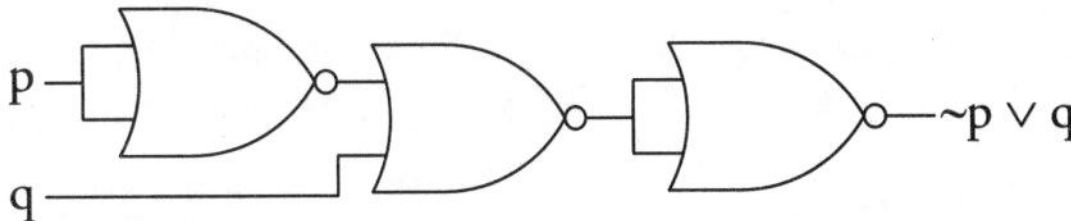

16. Tell students that they have just demonstrated the truth-functional completeness of NOR; next up: NAND. In case they can't remember back to several months ago when you began

this endless lesson, remind students that the NAND gate represents the proposition ~(*p* • *q*). The first thing to do is to learn how to do negation with the NAND gate, just as we did with NOR.

17. Point out that ~*p* is equivalent to ~(*p* • *p*). We can therefore do something very similar to what we did with the NOR gate. To get this output we once again split the input and send p through the NAND gate twice, which produces ~(*p* • *p*), or ~*p*, like so:

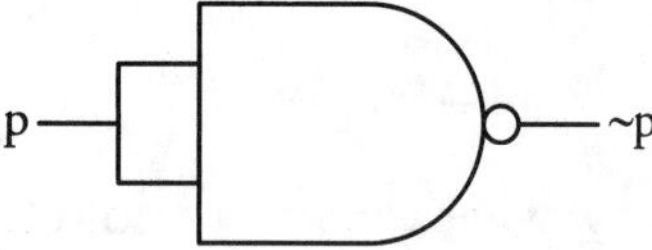

18. Explain that in order to produce an AND gate from NAND gates, we simply have to negate a NAND gate using the split-input NAND negation gate we just discovered, like this:

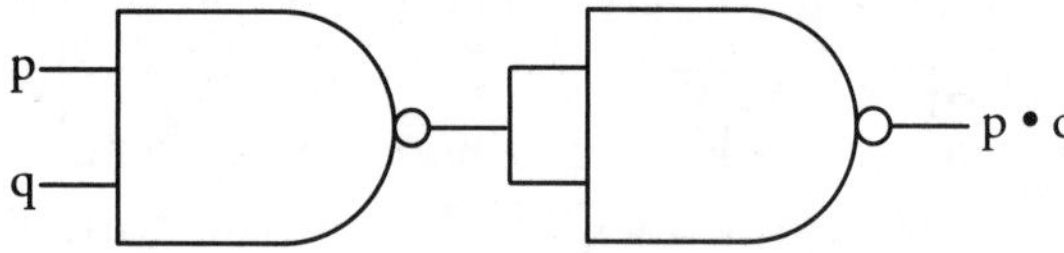

19. Explain that to make an OR gate from NAND gates we have to again use De Morgan's Theorem, which states that *p* ∨ *q* is equivalent to ~(~*p* • ~*q*). Since ~(~*p* • ~*q*) is the same as ~*p* NAND ~*q*, we simply have to create ~*p* and ~*q* using two separate split-input NAND gates as we learned above, and then put both of them through a final NAND gate, like this:

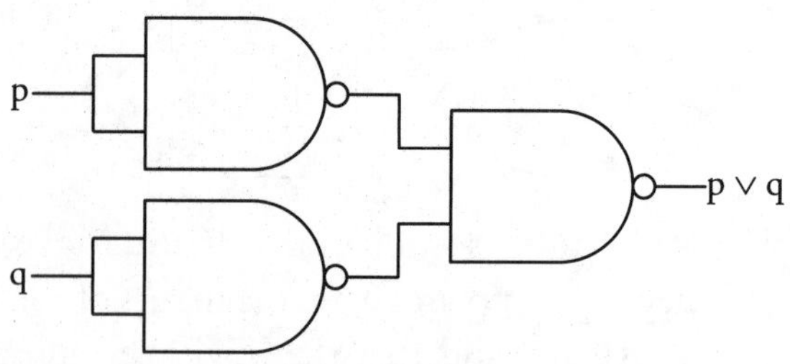

20. Tell students that you are going to look together at one more pretty complex circuit before you set them loose to work on some themselves. Say that you want to make a circuit for ~*p* ∨ *q* using only NAND gates. Above we learned to make the circuit *p* ∨ *q* from NAND gates; copy that circuit again. Explain that now we need to negate the variable p. Help students see that since the top split-input NAND gate negates *p*, another negation of *p* would just un-negate it, so we can simply send *p* right into the final NAND gate, like so:

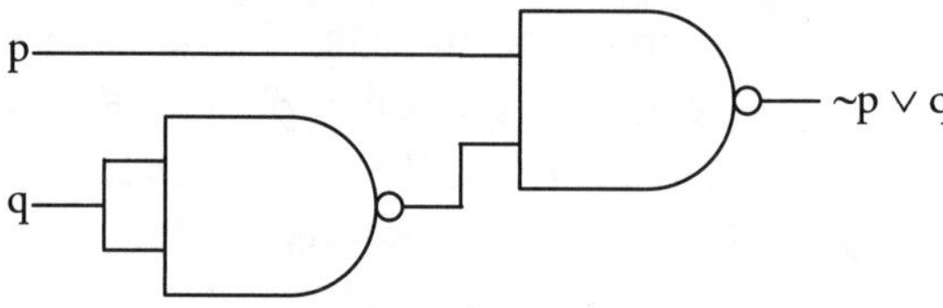

ASSIGNMENTS

1. Have students complete Exercise 35, and go over it with them.
2. Remind students to study for next class's quiz over Lessons 32–35.

LESSON 35

NAND GATES AND NOR GATES

Sometimes the basic logic gates are combined into more complex gates. Two such very useful gates are the NOR gate and the NAND gate.

KEY POINT

The NOR gate is a negated disjunction, and is true if and only if both inputs are false.

The NOR gate does the job of a negated disjunction $\sim(p \vee q)$. The output for this gate is true if and only if both inputs are false. This gate is equivalent to placing a NOT gate at the output of an OR gate, but in this case the NOT gate is simply represented by the bubble at the tip of the OR gate. The defining truth table and symbol for the NOR gate are:

p	q	~(p ∨ q)
0	0	1
0	1	0
1	0	0
1	1	0

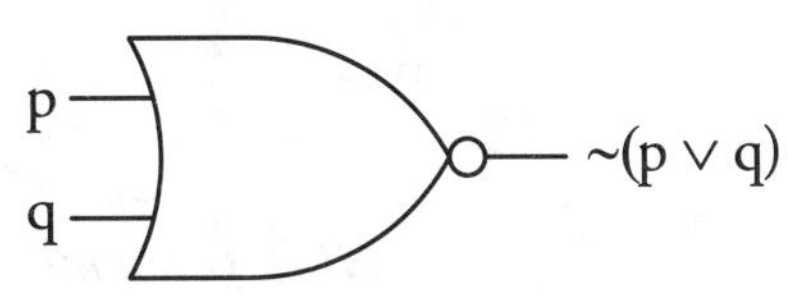

KEY POINT

The NAND gate is a negated conjunction, and is false if and only if both inputs are true.

The NAND gate does the job of a negated conjunction $\sim(p \bullet q)$. The output for this gate is false if and only if both inputs are true. This gate is equivalent to placing a NOT gate at the output of an AND gate. Again, the NOT is represented by placing a bubble at the tip of the AND gate. The defining truth table and symbol for NAND are:

p	q	~(p • q)
0	0	1
0	1	1
1	0	1
1	1	0

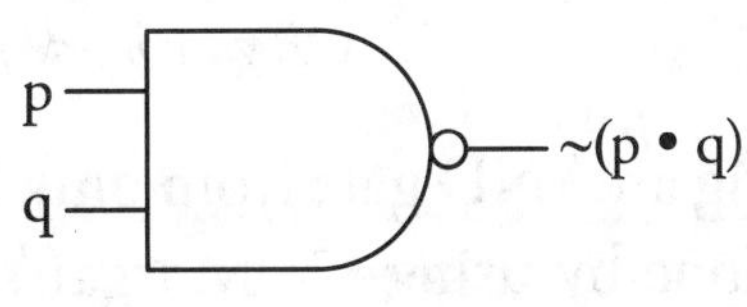

Because of the way these gates work, they can be used to simplify circuits by eliminating NOT gates. For example, the two circuits below are equivalent, but the second is simpler, with half the number of gates as the first.

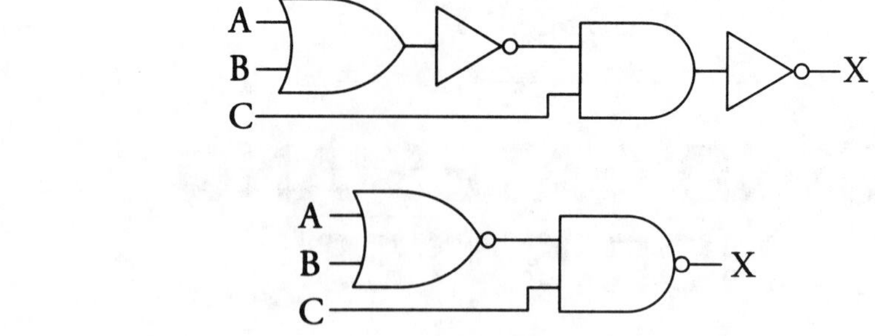

DEFINITION

A ***truth-functionally complete*** gate means that any basic digital logic circuit can be designed using that gate alone.

One of the benefits of NAND and NOR is that each of them has **truth-functionally completeness.** This means that any digital logic circuit can be designed using only NAND gates, or only NOR gates. Since the building blocks of more complex gates are the simple gates AND, OR, and NOT, let's consider how to make those basic gates using only the NOR gate.

The NOT gate can be produced out of a single NOR gate. This can be done by noting that *~p* is equivalent to *~(p ∨ p).* This is *p* NOR *p*, and can be drawn by splitting the input:

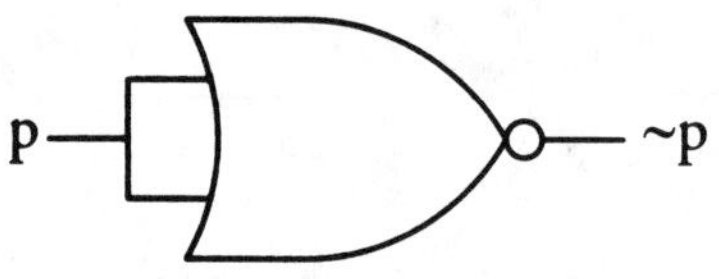

NOT gate made from NOR

The OR gate can be produced by noting that *p* ∨ *q* is equivalent to *~[~(p ∨ q)]*, that is, by negating *p* NOR *q*. Recalling that we can negate *p* NOR *q* by placing a split-input NOR on the output, we can produce the following circuit, equivalent to an OR gate:

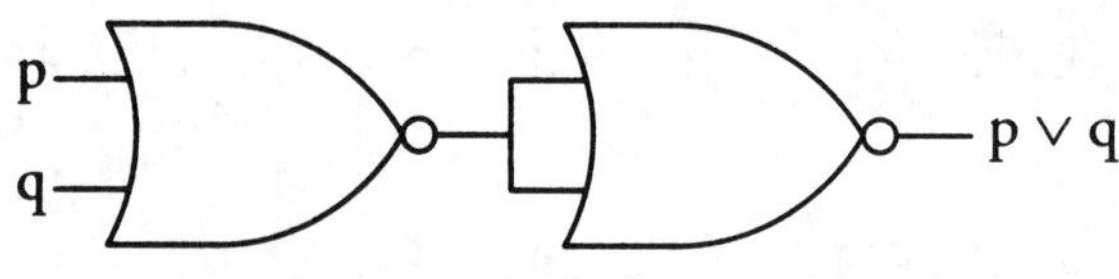

OR gate made from NOR

Making an AND gate from only NOR is more complicated. This can be done by using De Morgan's theorem and double negation, which together show that *p* • *q* is equivalent to *~(~p ∨ ~q).* You should see that this is *~p* NOR *~q*. Then, recalling that the negations can be produced by using split-input NOR, we can make an AND gate from three NOR gates, as shown:

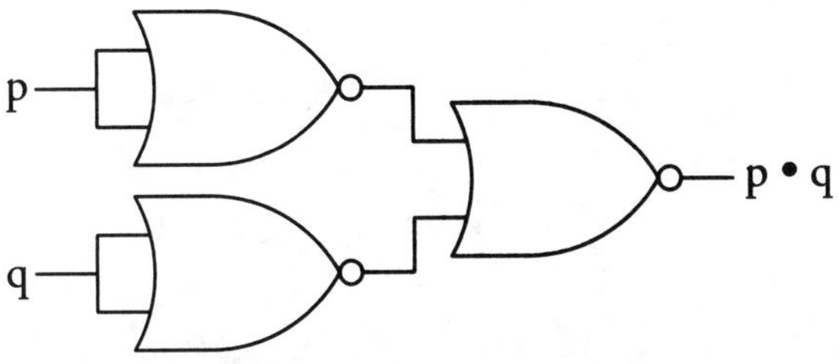

AND gate made from NOR

We will now design a circuit for the proposition $\sim p \vee q$ using only NOR gates (this is a *conditional* proposition). We can start by drawing a circuit for the given proposition:

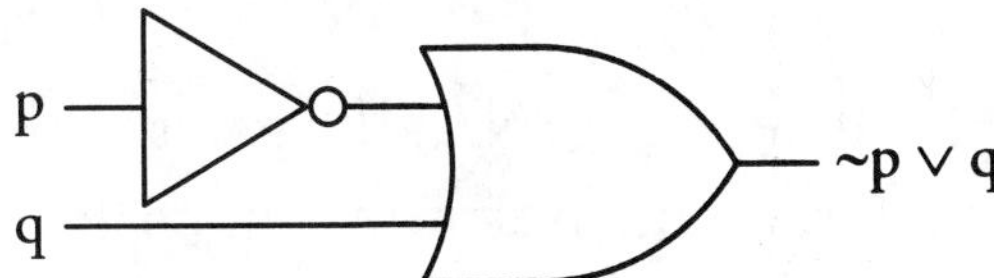

Next, note that two negations in a row will cancel each other. So we can add a negation bubble on the end of the OR gate, turning it into a NOR gate, then negate it again to get an equivalent circuit, as shown:

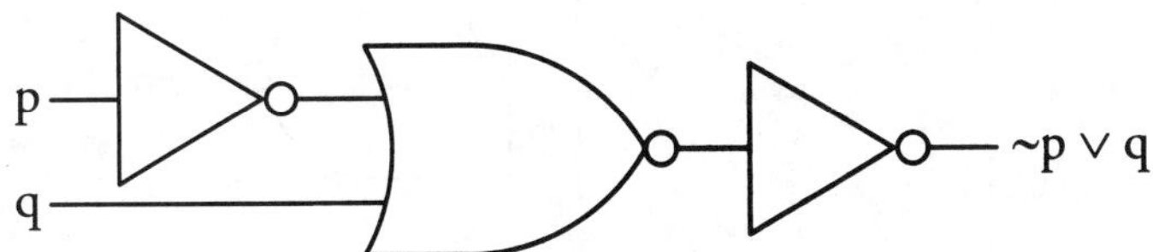

Propositionally, this is the same as turning $\sim p \vee q$ into $\sim\sim(\sim p \vee q)$. Finally, we can turn the NOT gates into split-input NOR gates, thus completing the transformation:

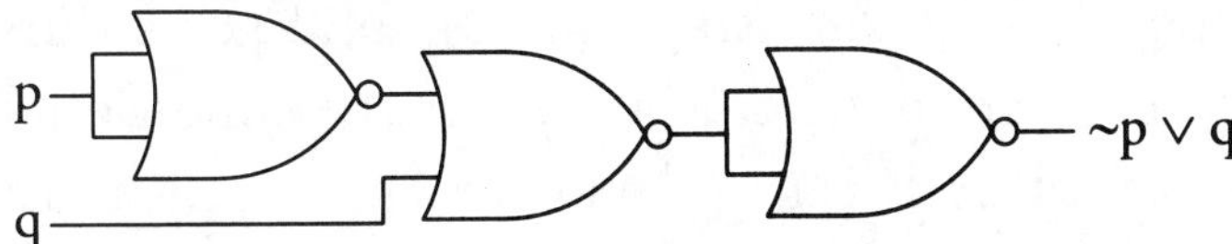

With practice, you should be able to do this quickly using the NOR-equivalents of the basic gates shown on the previous page.

Now we will consider the truth-functional completeness of NAND. First, since by the rule of Tautology $\sim p$ is equivalent to $\sim(p \bullet p)$, we can create negation from p NAND p, which is a split-input NAND.

FURTHER STUDY

Logic gates in actual electronic devices are usually made from components such as diodes or transistors. Basically, AND gates use these components in series while OR gates use them in parallel. Consider doing further research in your library or online to find out how these and other logic gates are constructed. You might even purchase an electronics kit that teaches you how to build a variety of interesting circuits that use logic gates.

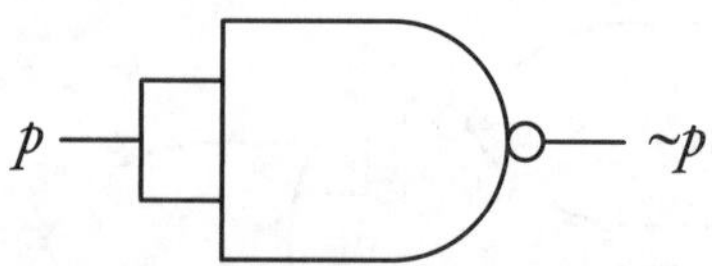

NOT gate made from NAND

Using this, we can produce an AND gate simply by negating a NAND gate with another split-input NAND, as shown:

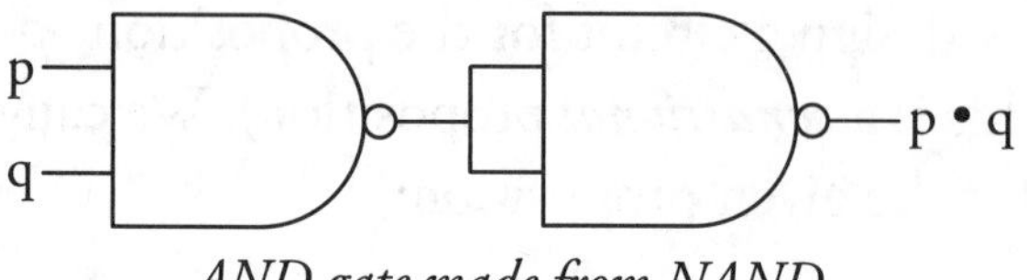

AND gate made from NAND

To make an OR gate using NAND gates, we again use De Morgan's theorem and double negation, which together state that $p \vee q$ is equivalent to $\sim(\sim p \bullet \sim q)$. This is $\sim p$ NAND $\sim q$. We can produce the $\sim p$ and $\sim q$ using split-input NAND gates, which results in the following circuit equivalent to OR:

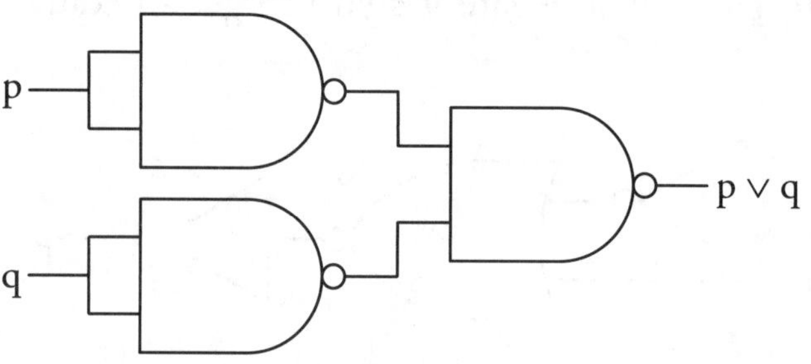

OR gate made from NAND

Other more complex gates can be produced using these basic gates. For example, let's see how to make a circuit for the conditional proposition $\sim p \vee q$ using only NAND gates. First, we see above how to make the circuit $p \vee q$. For the conditional we must negate the variable p. This negation would cancel the top split-input NAND, so we can negate p simply by dropping it, resulting in this conditional circuit:

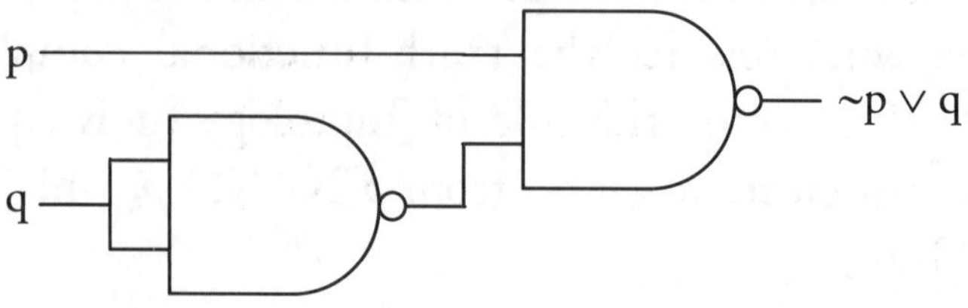

SUMMARY

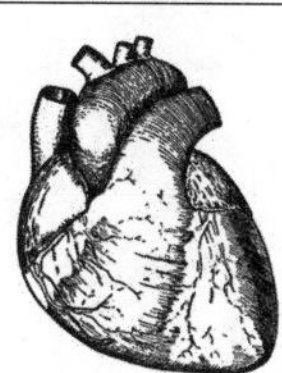

The NOR gate (negated disjunction) and the NAND gate (negated conjunction) can significantly simplify circuits by eliminating NOT gates. They are also truth-functionally complete, meaning that any basic digital logic circuit can be designed using only NAND gates, or only NOR gates.

EXERCISE 35 (27 points)

Problems 1-2: Write the proposition and determine the truth table for the circuit shown. (8, 10)

1. 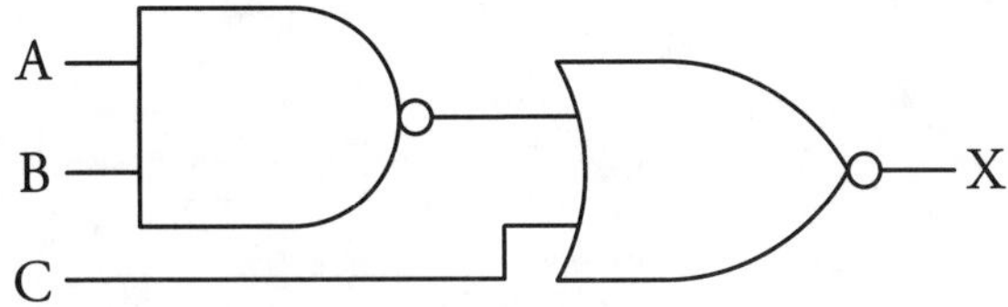

Proposition: ~[~(A•B)vC]

Truth table:

A	B	C	X
0	0	0	0
0	0	1	0
0	1	0	0
0	1	1	0
1	0	0	0
1	0	1	0
1	1	0	1
1	1	1	0

2. 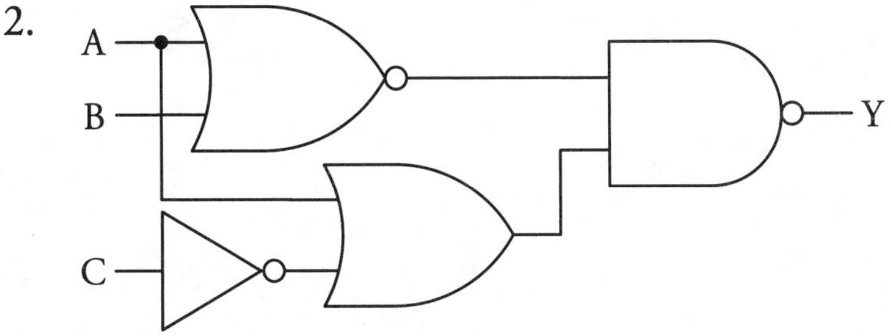

Proposition: ~[~(AvB)•(Av~C)]

Truth table:

A	B	C	Y
0	0	0	0
0	0	1	1
0	1	0	1
0	1	1	1
1	0	0	1
1	0	1	1
1	1	0	1
1	1	1	1

3. Using only NAND gates, design a circuit for the proposition $p \bullet \sim q$. (4)

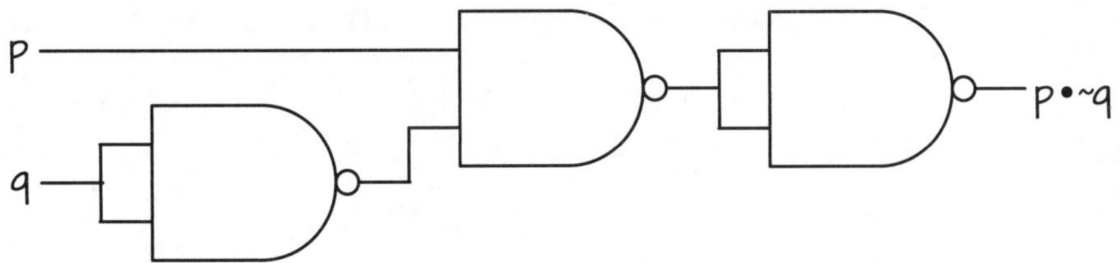

Continued on next page.

4. Using only NOR gates, produce a circuit equivalent to a NAND gate. (5)

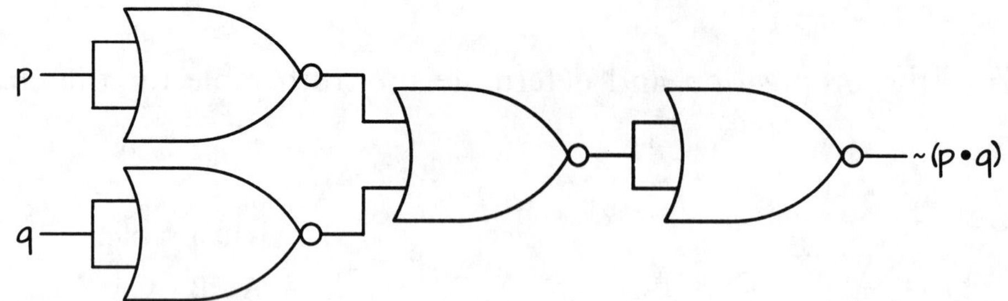

TEACHER'S NOTES

QUIZ 17 (LESSONS 32–35)

STUDENT OBJECTIVE

Complete Quiz 17.

TEACHING INSTRUCTIONS

1. Give Quiz 17. Allow 30 minutes. Grade quiz with students.
2. If you have extra time, introduce Lesson 36 to get a head start on next class's material.

INTERMEDIATE LOGIC | Quiz 17

Lessons 32–35 (22 points)

Name ________________________________

1. Draw the digital logic circuit for the proposition $\sim (A \bullet B) \vee C$ using only two gates. (3)

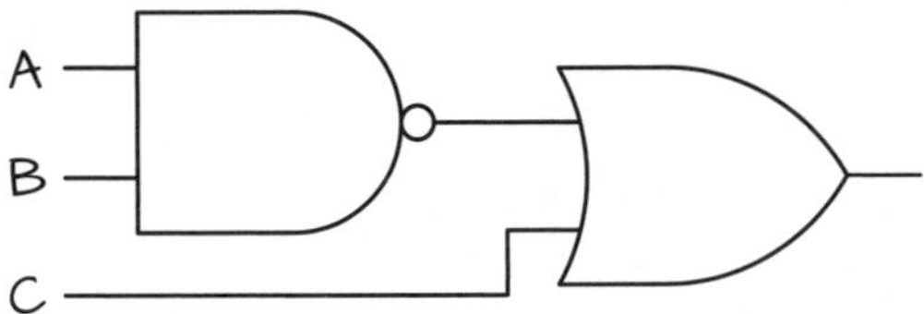

2. What is the proposition for the logic circuit shown below? (3) ~[(A ∨ B) • ~C]

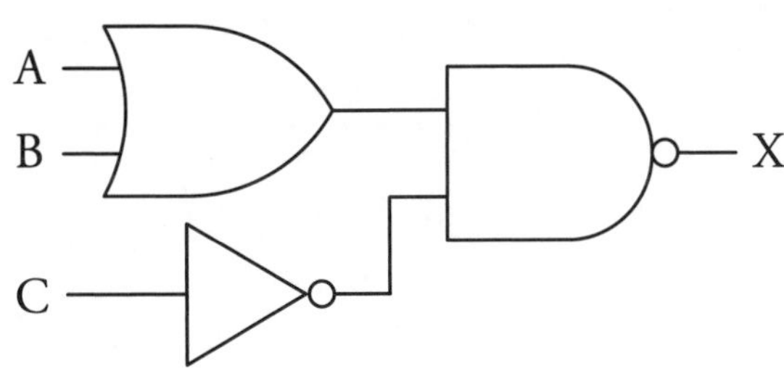

A	B	C	X
0	0	0	1
0	0	1	1
0	1	0	0
0	1	1	1
1	0	0	0
1	0	1	1
1	1	0	0
1	1	1	1

3. Complete the given truth table for this circuit. (5)

4. For the truth table below, determine the proposition. Draw the corresponding circuit using only two gates. (6)

A	B	C	Y
0	0	0	0
0	0	1	0
0	1	0	0
0	1	1	0
1	0	0	1
1	0	1	0
1	1	0	0
1	1	1	0

Proposition A • ~(B ∨ C)

Circuit:

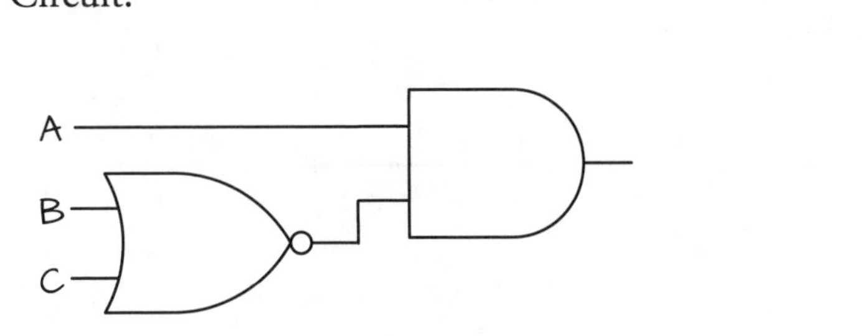

 |

5. Using only NOR gates, produce a circuit equivalent to the proposition p • ~ q. (5)

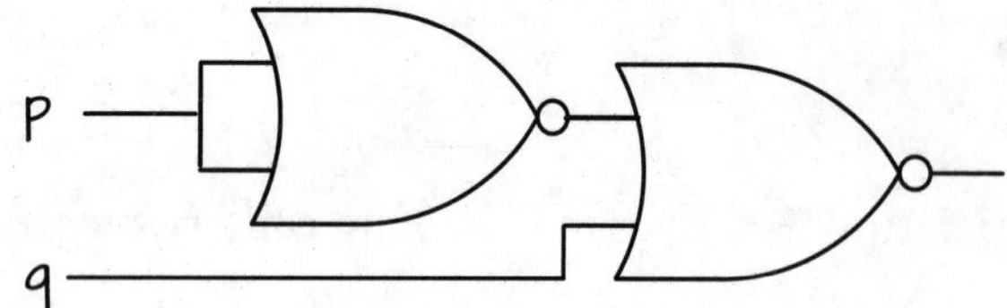

SIMPLIFICATION RULES

Intermediate Logic, pp. 291–293

STUDENT OBJECTIVES

1. Use tautology, self-contradiction, and algebraic identities to simplify digital logic circuits.
2. Complete Exercise 36.

TEACHING INSTRUCTIONS

1. Tell students that today you are going to teach them a few rules for simplifying circuits that might otherwise be murals that span several whiteboards. Explain that the simplification rules will use tautology, self-contradiction, and algebraic identities.
2. Have students remind you what a **tautology** is and give an example (a proposition that is true by logical structure, such as $p \vee {\sim}p$). Explain that because a tautology is always, always, always true, any proposition of the form $p \vee {\sim}p$ is equivalent to 1 in binary. Now how have students tell you what a **self-contradiction** is and give an example (a proposition that is a false by logical structure, such as $p \bullet {\sim}p$). Explain that since a self-contradiction is always false, a proposition of the form $p \bullet {\sim}p$ will always be equivalent to 0 in binary. Draw the following circuits on the board to demonstrate this, and make sure students see how they demonstrate this:

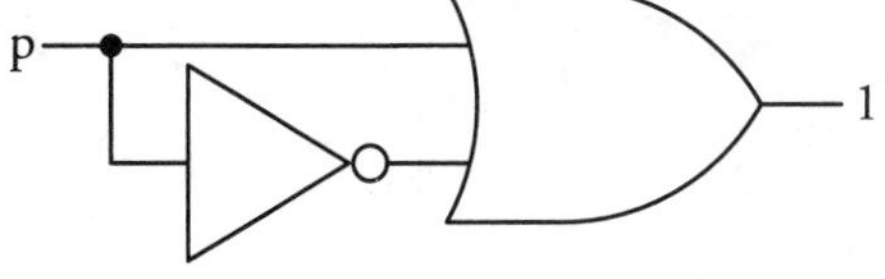

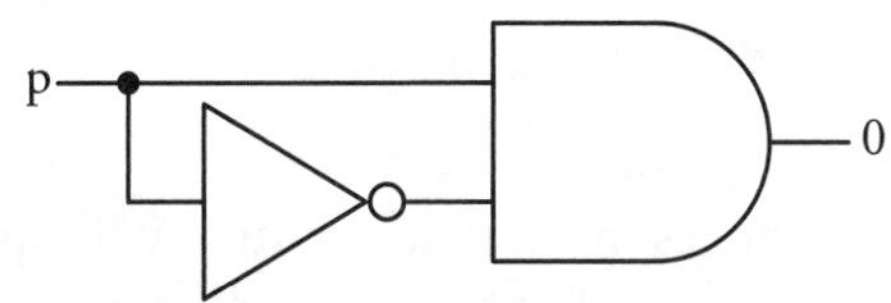

3. Explain to students that there are four basic algebraic identities that can also help simplify circuits. Tell students that these identities will probably look very similar to some rules they learned in algebra, just involving logic symbols and binary. Write them on the board:

   $p \vee 1 = 1$ $\quad$ $p \bullet 1 = p$
   $p \vee 0 = p$ $\quad$ $p \bullet 0 = 0$

   Tell students that these might look a little suspicious at first, but that they won't if we build truth tables for them. Remind students that 1 means true and 0 means false. Take $p \vee 1 = 1$, which is the same thing as saying "p or true is true. " Make the truth table for it:

p	1	$p \vee 1$
0	1	1
1	1	1

   Make sure students see that 1, being 1, must always be 1 (or true). And as long as one disjunct in a disjunction is true the whole disjunction is true: $0 \vee 1 = 1$ and $1 \vee 1 = 1$. Since both outputs are 1, $p \vee 1 = 1$.
4. Have students walk you through building truth tables for the other three identities.

p	∨ 0	= p
0	0	0
1	0	1

p	• 1	= p
0	1	0
1	1	1

p	• 0	= 0
0	0	0
1	0	0

5. Draw on the board the four circuits that represent the above identities.

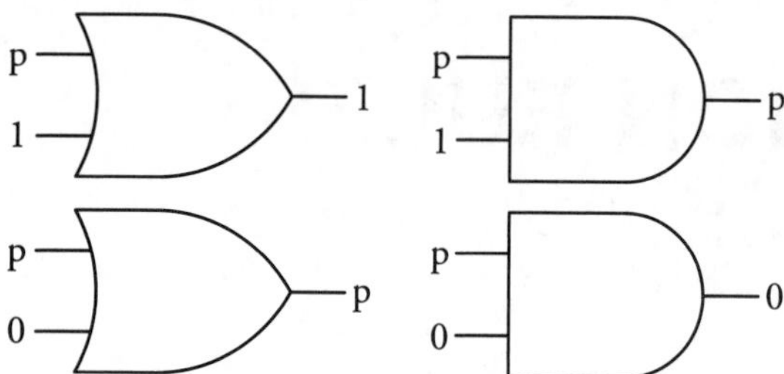

Tell students that all the simplification rules are summarized in Appendix D of their textbooks.

6. Tell students that we are now going to look at some examples in which these rules will make things a lot simpler. Write on the board the compound proposition *A ∨ [B • (C ∨ ~C)]*. Ask students what is the first thing they notice that can be simplified. They should see that *C ∨ ~C* is a tautology, and is therefore necessarily true and equivalent to 1. Explain that we can therefore simplify the proposition to *A ∨ (B • 1)*.

7. Ask students if they can see anything else in the proposition that can be simplified. Explain that *B • 1* has the form of one of the algebraic identities, and can therefore be simplified to B. The proposition is now simply *A ∨ B*.

8. Draw the circuit for the original proposition *A ∨ [B • (C ∨ ~C)]* below. Tell students that it is appropriate to grimace:

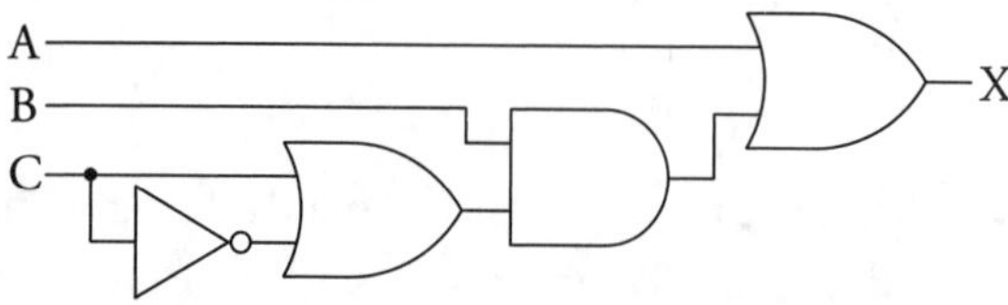

Now have students walk you through making the circuit for the simplified proposition *A ∨ B*, as given below. Make sure students understand that these are equivalent propositions:

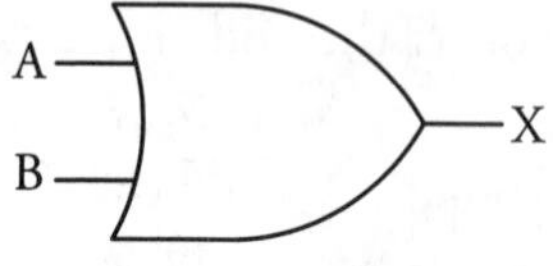

9. Now draw this circuit on the board:

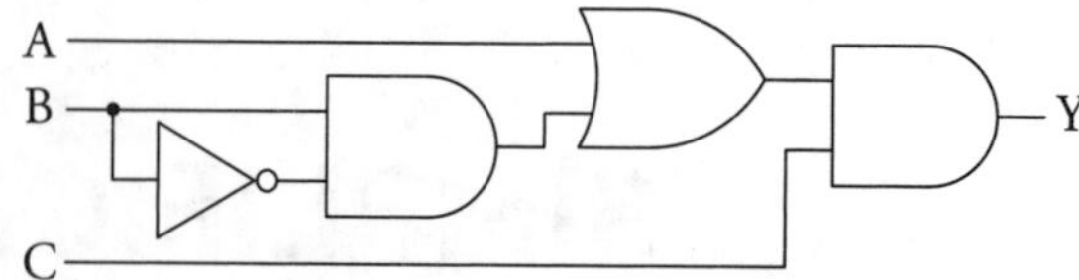

Tell students that using the rules they learned today we can simplify this circuit so that it uses only one logical gate.

10. Explain that the first thing we need to do is find the proposition for the above circuit. Walk students through this; they should come up with *[A ∨ (B • ~B)] • C*. Have students tell you what can be done to simplify this proposition; they should see first that *B • ~B* is equivalent to 0, leaving us with *(A ∨ 0) • C*; then, since one of the algebraic identities says that *p ∨ 0 = p*, we can simplify the proposition once again to *A • C*. Explain that we can write this simplification out step by step, and have students walk you through doing it on the board, like so:

1. [A ∨ (B • ~B)] • C	*Proposition from the circuit*
2. (A ∨ 0) • C	*Self-contradiction*
3. A • C	*Algebraic Identity*

11. Have students tell you how to build the circuit for this simplified proposition. As promised, all you need is the AND gate:

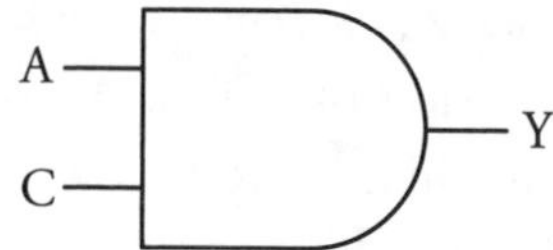

ASSIGNMENT

Have student complete Exercise 36, and go over it with them.

LESSON 36

SIMPLIFICATION RULES

A tautology is a proposition that is true by logical structure. A basic tautology takes the form $p \vee {\sim}p$. Because a tautology is always true, any proposition of the form $p \vee {\sim}p$ is equivalent to 1. Similarly, a self-contradiction is a proposition that is false by logical structure. A basic self-contradiction takes the form $p \bullet {\sim}p$. Propositions of this form are always false, and are thus equivalent to 0. These rules are shown in the following circuits:

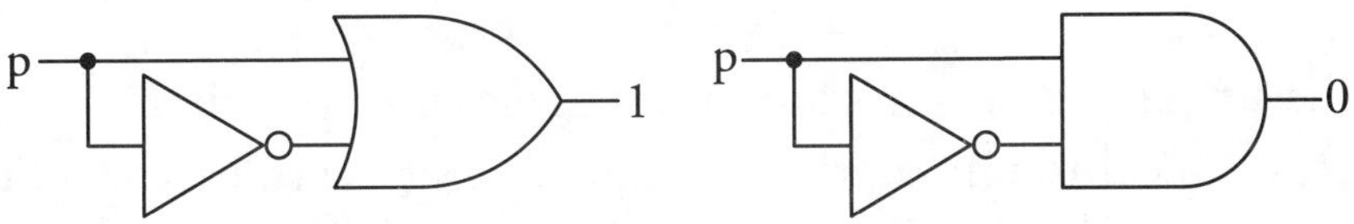

KEY POINT

Tautology, self-contradiction, and four algebraic identities can be used to simplify digital logic circuits.

There are four basic **algebraic identities** which will be helpful in simplifying propositions and their circuits. They are as follows:

$p \vee 1 = 1$ $\quad$ $p \bullet 1 = p$

$p \vee 0 = p$ $\quad$ $p \bullet 0 = 0$

These rules can be proven using truth tables. For example, consider the first: $p \vee 1 = 1$. It may help to read this as "*p* or true is true."

Since the rule has only one variable, the truth table is only two rows long. The first row shows that $0 \vee 1$ is *1*, the second that $1 \vee 1$ is *1*. Since both outputs are 1, then $p \vee 1$ is equivalent to *1*.

p	1	p∨1
0	1	1
1	1	1

We can represent the above identities with these circuits:

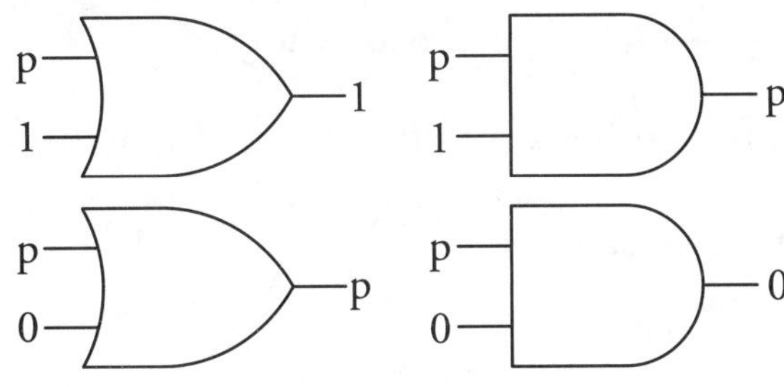

Now let's see how these rules can help us simplify things. Consider the compound proposition $A \vee [B \bullet (C \vee \sim C)]$. First, notice that the proposition $C \vee \sim C$ is a tautology, equivalent to *1*. This simplifies the proposition to $A \vee (B \bullet 1)$. By one of the algebraic identities, $B \bullet 1 = B$. This proposition is thus equivalent to $A \vee B$. Consequently, the following circuits are equivalent, the second being clearly simpler:

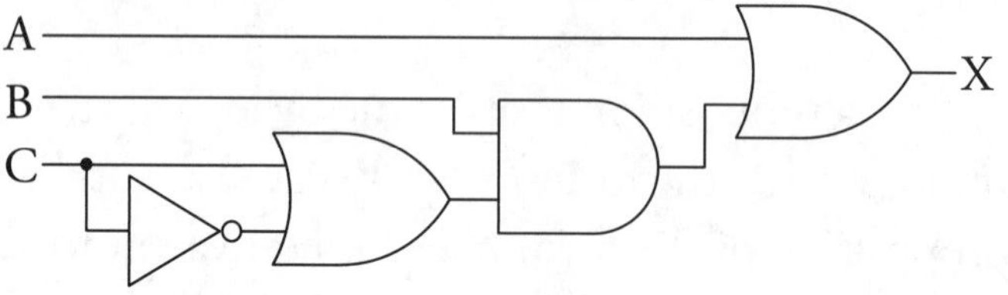

Equivalent to this circuit:

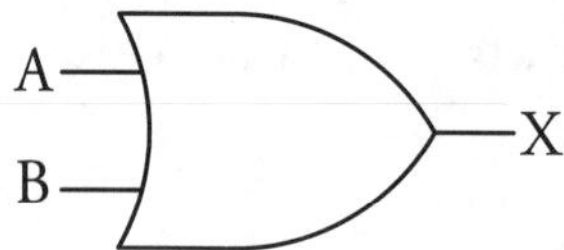

The simplification rules are summarized in Appendix D.

Let's work through another example. Using the rules, the following circuit can be simplified so that it uses a single logic gate:

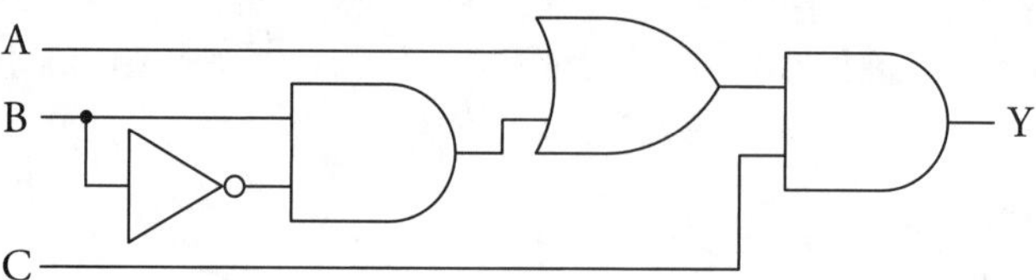

We should start by finding the proposition for the circuit. The proposition would be $[A \vee (B \bullet \sim B)] \bullet C$. Since $B \bullet \sim B$ is equivalent to 0, this can be simplified to $[A \vee 0] \bullet C$. Now, one of the algebraic identities says that $A \vee 0 = A$. Consequently, the proposition simplifies to $A \bullet C$. Here is this same simplification written out step by step:

1) $[A \vee (B \bullet \sim B)] \bullet C$	Proposition from the circuit
2) $(A \vee 0) \bullet C$	Self-contradiction
3) $A \bullet C$	Algebraic identity

Thus the circuit can be simplified to the following AND gate:

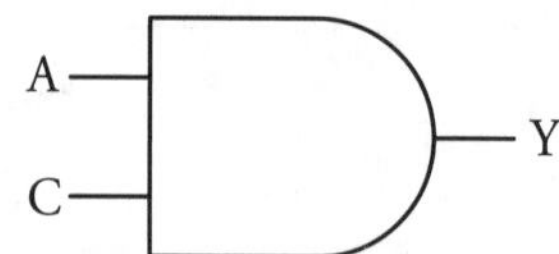

SUMMARY

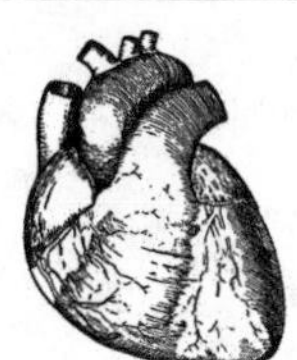

Digital logic circuits and the propositions they represent can be simplified by recognizing tautologies, which are always true (=1), and self-contradictions, which are always false (=0). These can be used along with these four basic algebraic identities: $p \vee 1 = 1$, $p \vee 0 = p$, $p \bullet 1 = p$, $p \bullet 0 = 0$.

EXERCISE 36 (18 points)

Problems 1-2: Simplify the proposition using the rules in this lesson, then draw the circuit for the simplified proposition. (4 each)

1. [(A ∨ ~ A) • B] ∨ C

   Simplified proposition:

   B∨C

   Circuit:

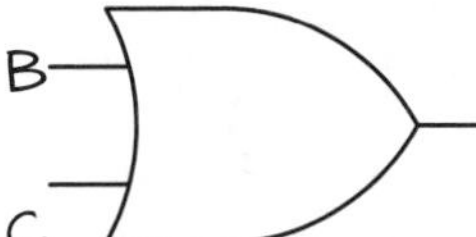

2. [A • (B ∨ ~ B)] • [(A • ~ A) ∨ B]

   Simplified proposition:

   A•B

   Circuit:

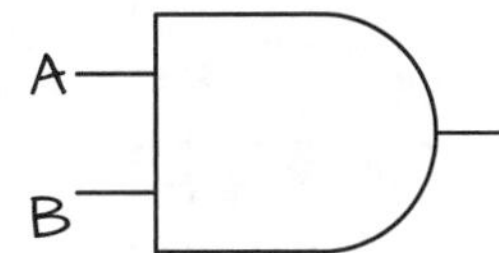

Problems 3-4: Simplify the following circuits. Draw the simplified circuit. (5 each)

3.

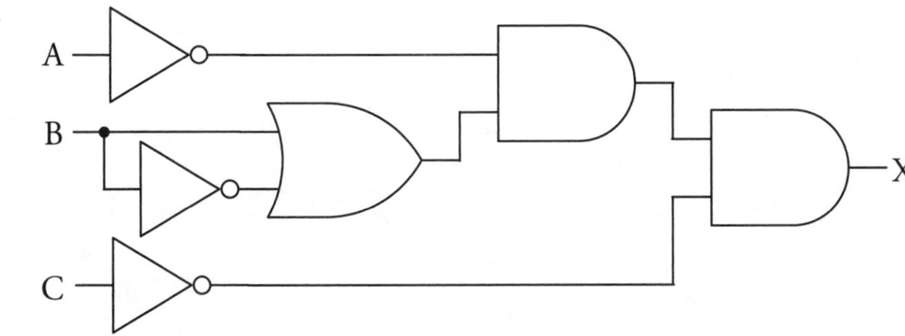

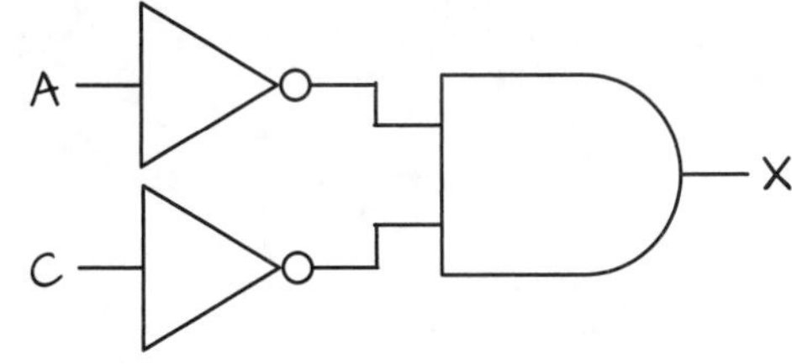

1) [~A•(B∨~B)]•~C
2) (~A•1)•~C
3) ~A•~C

4.

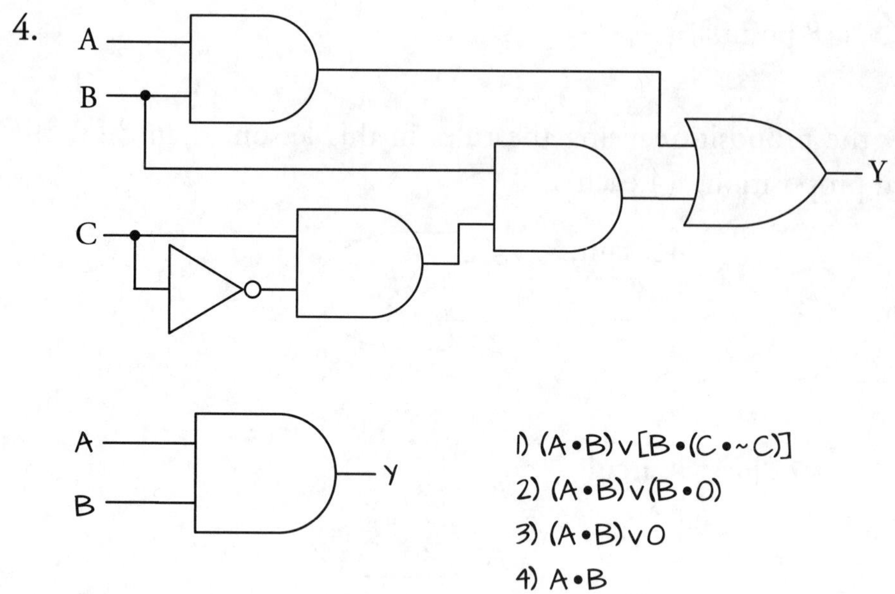

TEACHER'S NOTES on LESSON 37

RULES OF REPLACEMENT

Intermediate Logic, pp. 297–300

STUDENT OBJECTIVES

1. Use Double Negation, Distribution, and Commutation rules to simplify digital logic circuits.
2. Complete Exercise 37.

SPECIAL NOTES

Depending on which schedule you're following, you have two days to work through Lesson 37. Get through as much of the lesson as you can on the first day, and spend the second day tying up loose ends and working through Exercise 37 with students.

TEACHING INSTRUCTIONS

1. Have students remind you of the rules for simplifying circuits that they learned yesterday (tautology, self-contradiction, and algebraic identities). Explain that in this lesson you will be going over several rules of replacement that will also help to simplify circuits significantly.
2. Tell students that the first rule they should be on the lookout for is **double negation**. Remind students that since $\sim\sim p$ is equivalent to p, **when a negation is negated, both can be eliminated**. For example, draw this negated NAND gate on the board:

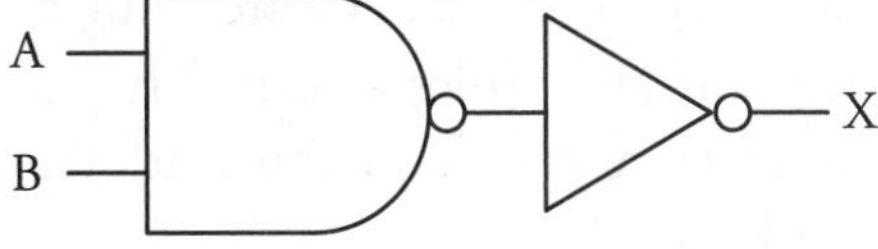

Ask students what this gate could be simplified to. They should see that the negated NAND gate can simply be replaced with an AND gate, like so:

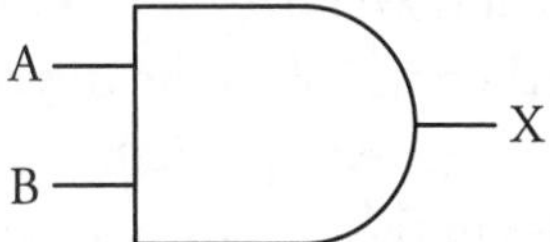

Explain that students can think of the NOT gate as canceling the bubble on the end of the NAND gate.

3. Tell students that the rule of **distribution** is very helpful in simplifying circuits. See if anyone can remember the rule of distribution, which is actually two rules. Write them on the board:

$(p \vee q) \bullet (p \vee r)$ is equivalent to $p \vee (q \bullet r)$
$(p \bullet q) \vee (p \bullet r)$ is equivalent to $p \bullet (q \vee r)$

4. Draw this circuit on the board, and have students figure out what the proposition is that it represents:

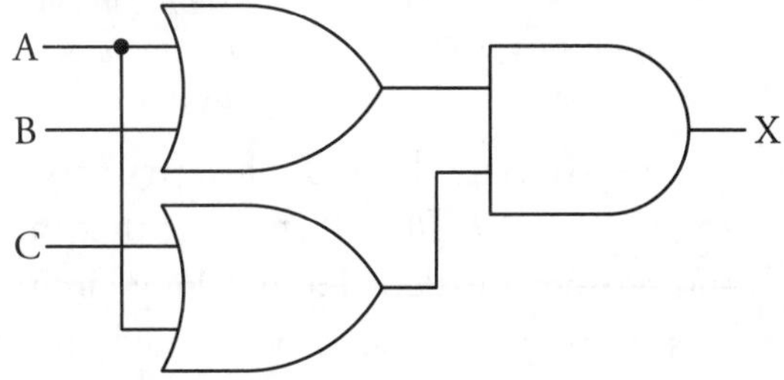

Make sure students understand that the proposition represented by the circuit is $(A \vee B) \bullet (A \vee C)$. Have them simplify this proposition using the distribution rules—they should come up with $A \vee (B \bullet C)$—and walk you through drawing the circuit for the simplified proposition, which only has two gates:

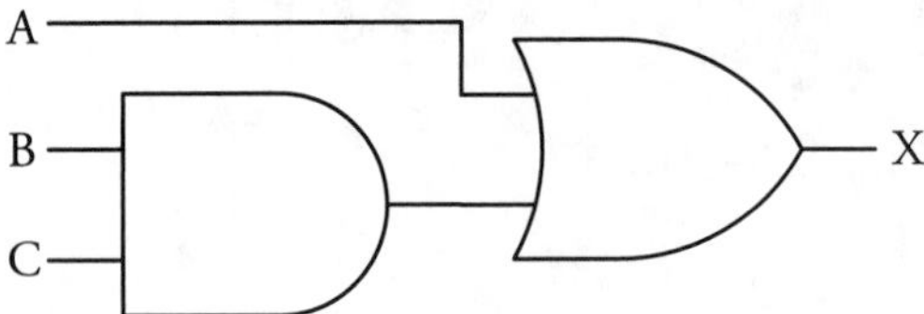

5. Now write this proposition on the board: $(A \bullet \sim B) \vee (C \bullet \sim B)$. Explain that the second distribution rule allows us to factor out the $\sim B$ and replace this proposition with the simpler proposition (write it) $(A \vee C) \bullet \sim B$. Right? But wait. See if students noticed how you "cheated" there. To be perfectly faithful to the distribution rule you should needed to switch around some of the variables in the proposition before simplifying it. Explain that it's fine to do that, as long as you know what rule you are using when you do it. Ask students what that rule is.

6. Remind students that the rule of **commutation** says that **$p \bullet q$ is equivalent to $q \bullet p$, and that $p \vee q$ is equivalent to $q \vee p$.** In other words, you are allowed to switch variables (or even entire propositions) around AND and OR. Have students walk you through making a proof for the above simplification, using the rules of distribution and commutation. It should look something like this:

1) (A • ~B) ∨ (C • ~B)	*Given proposition*
2) (~B • A) ∨ (~B • C)	*Commutation*
3) ~B • (A ∨ C)	*Distribution*
4) (A ∨ C) • ~B	*Commutation*

7. Write on the board the proposition $(\sim A \bullet \sim B) \vee (A \bullet \sim B)$. Tell students that in Lesson 34 they developed a nice long circuit for this proposition, and it was stated (but not proved) that this proposition could actually be simplified to $\sim B$, with a great relief of suffering for all. Tell students that with the rules from the last lesson and this one, they now have the tools to demonstrate this equivalence in a proof. Have them walk you through it. It should look something like this:

1) (~A • ~B) ∨ (A • ~B)	*Given proposition*
2) (~B • ~A) ∨ (~B • A)	*Commutation*
3) ~B • (~A ∨ A)	*Distribution*
4) ~B • 1	*Tautology*
5) ~B	*Algebraic Identity*

Have someone draw the $\sim B$ gate. Then have students flip back to Lesson 34 and find the circuit for the original proposition, which has six gates. Tell them that they should appreciate simplification rules.

8. Explain that we can also use the above rules to develop *more* simplification rules. Write on the board $p \vee (p \bullet q)$ and tells students that this proposition is equivalent to just plain old p. Have them walk you through a proof of this rule (or walk them through it, if necessary). Warn them that it's a bit tricky, because in the second step they are going to have to add something to the proposition before they can simplify it. The proof should look like this:

1) p ∨ (p • q)	*Given proposition*
2) (p • 1) ∨ (p • q)	*Algebraic identity*
3) p • (1 ∨ q)	*Distribution*
4) p • (q ∨ 1)	*Commutation*
5) p • 1	*Algebraic identity*
6) p	*Algebraic identity*

9. Now have them put together a proof that $p \vee (\sim p \bullet q)$ is equivalent to $p \vee q$. It should look like this:

1) p ∨ (~p • q)	*Given proposition*
2) (p ∨ ~p) • (p ∨ q)	*Distribution*
3) 1 • (p ∨ q)	*Tautology*
4) (p ∨ q) • 1	*Commutation*
5) p ∨ q	*Algebraic identity*

10. Have students work on their own to prove that $p \bullet (\sim p \vee q)$ is equivalent to $p \bullet q$.

11. Tell students that now that we are familiar with these simplification rules we can start applying them to real circuits. Write this truth table on the board:

A	B	C	X
0	0	0	1
0	0	1	0
0	1	0	1
0	1	1	0
1	0	0	0
1	0	1	0
1	1	0	0
1	1	1	0

Make sure students see that the output is 1 (or true) for only the first and third rows; that is, only when *A*, *B*, and *C* are all false, or when *A* and *C* are false and *B* is true.

12. Have students think way back to Lesson 32 where they learned how to convert truth tables into propositions. Remind them that to do this conversion from the truth table we look only at the rows on the truth table that have a 1 (or true) as the output. For each of these rows, we join all the input variables together into a proposition by conjunction, negating the input variables that are false (0) and leaving the input variables that are true (1) as they are. Have students do this with the above truth table (and help them out if they need it); they should come up with *(~A • ~B • ~C) ∨ (~A • B • ~C)*.

13. Tell students that if they were to leap right in and try to draw a circuit for this proposition, they would end up with about ten gates and a migraine. But if they first simplify the proposition, they will be able to replace it with a circuit that has only three gates. Work through the simplification proof together; it should look like this:

1) (~A • ~B • ~C) ∨ (~A • B • ~C)	*Given proposition*
2) [(~A • ~C) • ~B] ∨ [(~A • ~C) • B]	*Commutation*
3) (~A • ~C) • (~B ∨ B)	*Distribution*
4) (~A • ~C) • (B ∨ ~B)	*Commutation*
5) (~A • ~C) • 1	*Tautology*
6) ~A • ~C	*Algebraic identity*

14. Have students tell you how to draw the circuit for this new proposition. It should look like this:

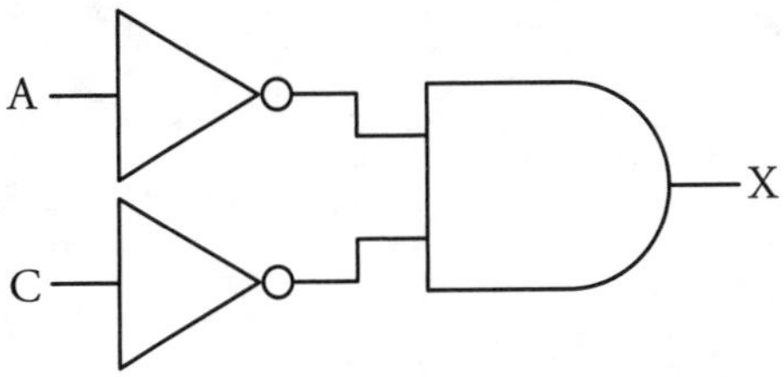

15. Have students work on their own to simplify the circuit in problem 3 of Exercise 32 to that it only has two gates. They should get the circuit for the proposition *(A ∨ C) • B*.

ASSIGNMENT

Have students complete Exercise 37, and go over it with them.

LESSON 37

RULES OF REPLACEMENT

When **double negation** occurs, both negations can be eliminated. This is true because the proposition $\sim\sim p$ is equivalent to p. This rule of double negation is used to simplify circuits, and was assumed in the section on truth-functional completeness in Lesson 35.

For example, the negated NAND shown here...

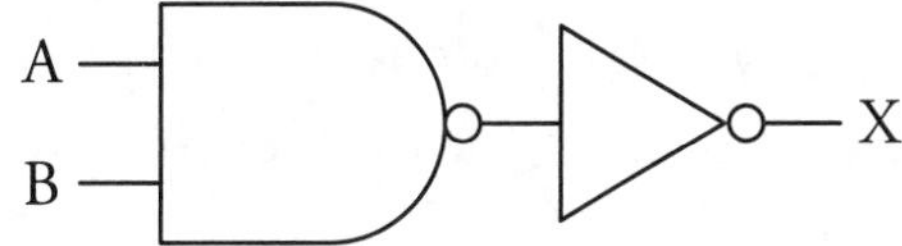

...can simply be replaced with this AND gate:

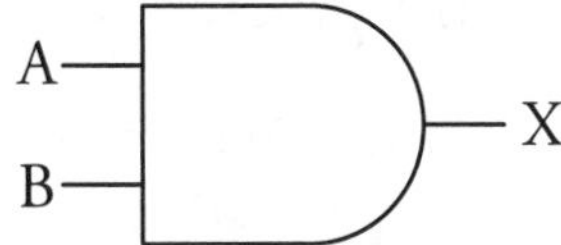

You can think of the NOT gate as canceling the bubble on the end of the NAND gate.

KEY POINT

The rules of double negation, distribution, and commutation can simplify logic circuits.

The rule of **distribution** is very helpful in simplifying circuits. It actually consists of two rules:

$(p \vee q) \bullet (p \vee r)$ is equivalent to $p \vee (q \bullet r)$
$(p \bullet q) \vee (p \bullet r)$ is equivalent to $p \bullet (q \vee r)$

The first rule now allows us to simplify this circuit, representing the proposition $(A \vee B) \bullet (A \vee C)$.

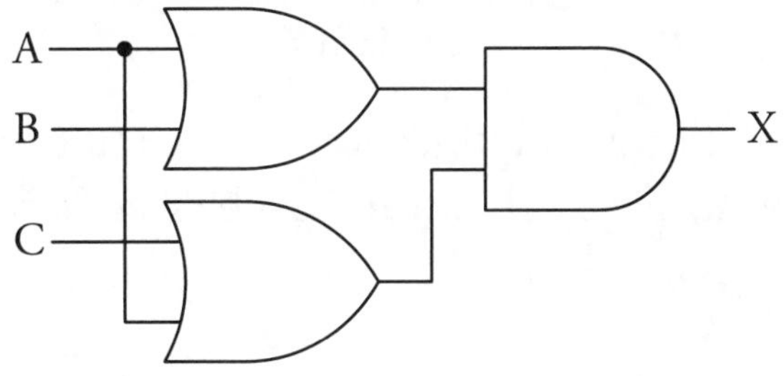

It could be replaced with this circuit, representing $A \vee (B \bullet C)$, which has only two gates:

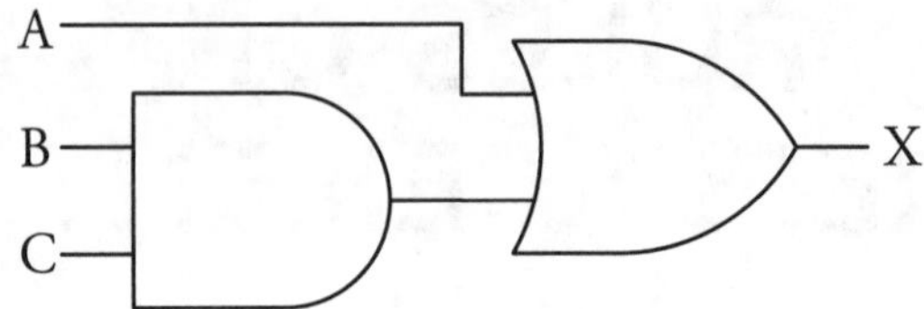

Now consider the proposition $(A \bullet {\sim} B) \vee (C \bullet {\sim} B)$. The second distribution rule would allow us to factor out the ${\sim} B$ and replace this proposition with the simpler proposition $(A \vee C) \bullet {\sim} B$. To see this more clearly, we must first consider another rule.

The rule of **commutation** says that $p \bullet q$ is equivalent to $q \bullet p$. This rule also says that $p \vee q$ is equivalent to $q \vee p$. This means that you are allowed to switch variables (or even entire propositions) around AND and OR.

With these rules, we can give each step for the above simplification. Follow these steps of the proof:

1) $(A \bullet {\sim} B) \vee (C \bullet {\sim} B)$	Given proposition
2) $({\sim} B \bullet A) \vee ({\sim} B \bullet C)$	Commutation
3) ${\sim} B \bullet (A \vee C)$	Distribution
4) $(A \vee C) \bullet {\sim} B$	Commutation

We will now return to a circuit that was developed in Lesson 34. In that lesson, it was stated (without proof) that the proposition $({\sim}A \bullet {\sim}B) \vee (A \bullet {\sim}B)$ is equivalent to ${\sim}B$. That equivalence can now be demonstrated in the following step-by-step proof:

1) (~A • ~B) ∨ (A • ~B)	Given proposition
2) (~B • ~A) ∨ (~B • A)	Commutation
3) ~B • (~A ∨ A)	Distribution
4) ~B • 1	Tautology
5) ~B	Algebraic identity

This is a significant simplification. The circuit for the original proposition had six gates. These can now be seen to be equivalent to a single gate for ${\sim}B$.

The rules of replacement are clearly helpful in simplifying compound propositions. The rules of Double Negation, Distribution, and Commutation are included in Appendix D.

We can use the above rules for **developing other helpful simplification rules**. For example, we can now prove that $p \vee (p \cdot q)$ is equivalent to p. Here is such a proof of this rule:

1) $p \vee (p \cdot q)$	Given proposition
2) $(p \cdot 1) \vee (p \cdot q)$	Algebraic identity
3) $p \cdot (1 \vee q)$	Distribution
4) $p \cdot (q \vee 1)$	Commutation
5) $p \cdot 1$	Algebraic identity
6) p	Algebraic identity

Here is a proof that $p \vee (\sim p \cdot q)$ is equivalent to $p \vee q$:

1) $p \vee (\sim p \cdot q)$	Given proposition
2) $(p \vee \sim p) \cdot (p \vee q)$	Distribution
3) $1 \cdot (p \vee q)$	Tautology
4) $(p \vee q) \cdot 1$	Commutation
5) $p \vee q$	Algebraic identity

We will now practice **applying the rules to cicuits**. Let's start with designing a simplified circuit using what we have learned in lessons 34, 36 and 37. We will start with the following truth table:

A	B	C	X
0	0	0	1
0	0	1	0
0	1	0	1
0	1	1	0
1	0	0	0
1	0	1	0
1	1	0	0
1	1	1	0

The output is 1 for the first and third rows. From lesson 34, we know that the proposition that produces this output would be $(\sim A \cdot \sim B \cdot \sim C) \vee (\sim A \cdot B \cdot \sim C)$. If the circuit were to be drawn for this proposition as is, it would have about ten gates.

We can simplify the proposition using the rules in this way (follow it carefully):

1) (~A • ~B • ~C) ∨ (~A • B • ~C)	Given proposition
2) [(~A • ~C) • ~B] ∨ [(~A • ~C) • B]	Commutation
3) (~A • ~C) • (~B ∨ B)	Distribution
4) (~A • ~C) • 1	Tautology
5) ~A • ~C	Algebraic identity

So the final circuit reduces to three gates, as shown:

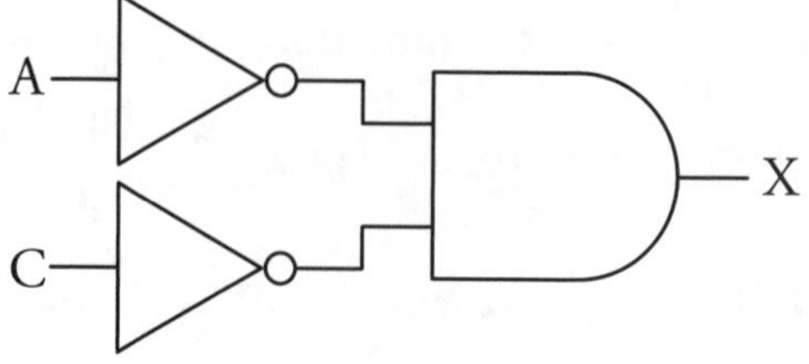

The next lesson will show how to reduce this to a single gate.

SUMMARY

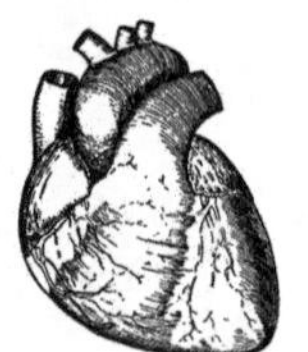

Another way to simplify a digital logic circuit is to find the proposition for the circuit and then use double negation, distribution, and commutation to simplify the proposition. You can derive other helpful simplification rules—for example, $p \vee (p \bullet q) = p$ and $p \vee (\sim p \bullet q) = p \vee q$—from the algebraic identities, distribution, and commutation. Using all these rules, you can drastically reduce the number of gates in a circuit.

EXERCISE 37 (34 points)

1. Prove that $(p \bullet q) \vee (p \bullet \sim q)$ is equivalent to p (a rule to be used later in this unit). (4)

1) $(p \bullet q) \vee (p \bullet \sim q)$	Given proposition
2) $p \bullet (q \vee \sim q)$	Distribution
3) $p \bullet 1$	Tautology
4) p	Algebraic identity

2. Simplify the proposition $(A \bullet \sim B \bullet \sim C) \vee (A \bullet B \bullet \sim C)$. (5)

1) $(A \bullet \sim B \bullet \sim C) \vee (A \bullet B \bullet \sim C)$	Given proposition
2) $[(A \bullet \sim C) \bullet \sim B] \vee [(A \bullet \sim C) \bullet B]$	Commutation
3) $(A \bullet \sim C) \bullet (\sim B \vee B)$	Distribution
4) $(A \bullet \sim C) \bullet 1$	Tautology
5) $A \bullet \sim C$	Algebraic identity

3. Simplify the circuit shown into an equivalent circuit using only two gates. Start by writing out the proposition for the circuit, then using the simplification rules. (7)

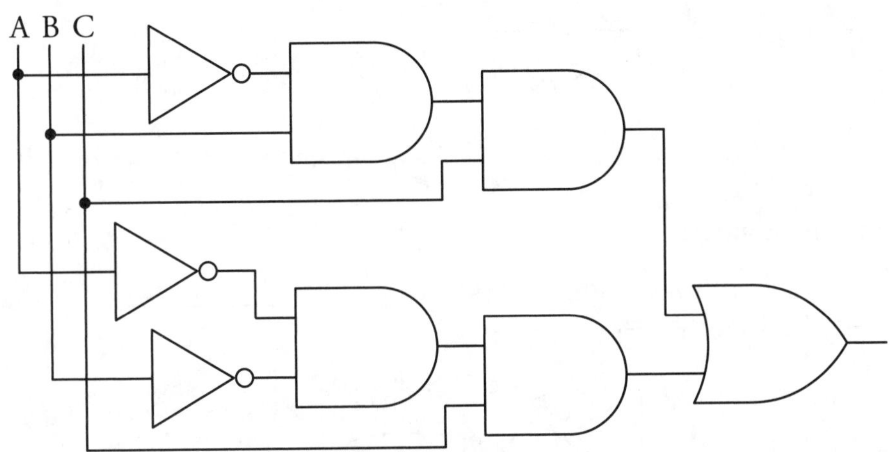

1) $(\sim A \bullet B \bullet C) \vee (\sim A \bullet \sim B \bullet C)$	Given proposition
2) $[(\sim A \bullet C) \bullet B] \vee [(\sim A \bullet C) \bullet \sim B]$	Commutation
3) $(\sim A \bullet C) \bullet (B \vee \sim B)$	Distribution
4) $(\sim A \bullet C) \bullet 1$	Tautology
5) $\sim A \bullet C$	Algebraic identity

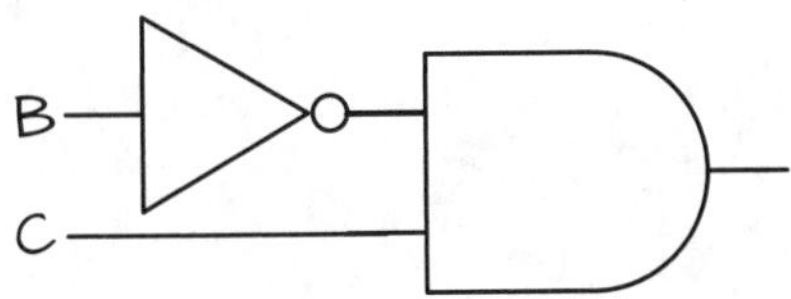

Continued on next page.

Problems 4-6: Determine the proposition for the given truth table. Then design the corresponding circuit, using simplification methods to reduce the circuit to the specified number of gates.

4. Reduce to one gate: (5)

A	B	X
0	0	1
0	1	1
1	0	0
1	1	0

Proposition: ~A

Circuit:

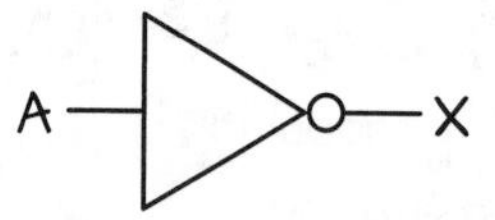

5. Reduce to two gates: (6)

A	B	Y
0	0	1
0	1	0
1	0	1
1	1	1

Proposition: A∨~B

Circuit:

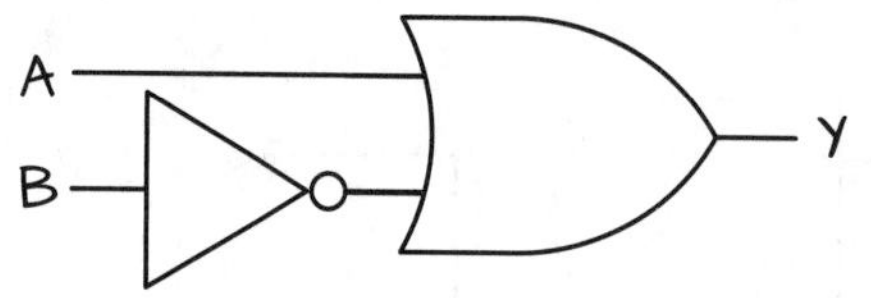

6. Reduce to three gates: (7)

A	B	C	Z
0	0	0	1
0	0	1	0
0	1	0	1
0	1	1	0
1	0	0	0
1	0	1	0
1	1	0	0
1	1	1	0

Proposition: ~A•~C

Circuit:

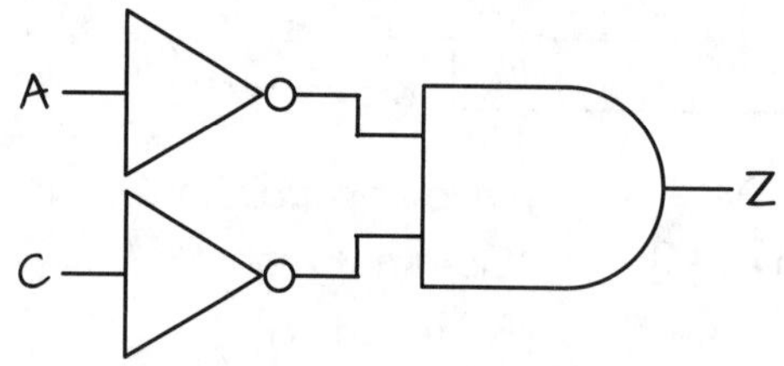

TEACHER'S NOTES on LESSON 38

DE MORGAN'S THEOREM

Intermediate Logic, pp. 303–304

STUDENT OBJECTIVES

1. Use De Morgan's Theorem and "bubble pushing" to simplify digital logic circuits.
2. Complete Exercise 38.

TEACHING INSTRUCTIONS

1. Have students remind you what three rules of replacement they recently learned could be used to simplify circuits (Double Negation, Distribution, and Commutation). Tell them that today they will add De Morgan's Theorem to this team.
2. See if anyone remembers De Morgan's theorem. If not, remind students De Morgan's theorem is actually two rules and write them on the board:

   ~p ∨ ~q is equivalent to ~(p • q)
   ~p • ~q is equivalent to ~(p ∨ q)

   Explain that De Morgan's theorem is similar to Distribution: we distribute the negation (~) to the variable *p* and *q* by changing OR to AND and vice versa.
3. Have students help you make circuits that represent these rules. They should look like this:

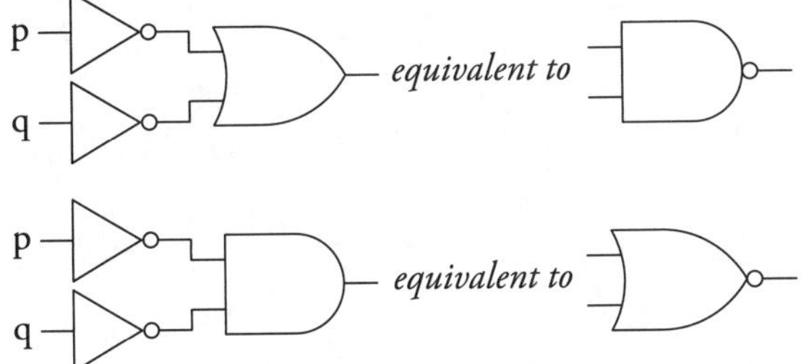

   Make sure students see that in both cases De Morgan's theorem reduces the number of gates from three to one.
4. Tell students that in digital logic one way to apply De Morgan's theorem is by using a technique called "bubble pushing." Explain that **bubble pushing involves exactly what the De Morgan's rule allows for: changing a gate in a circuit from AND to OR or vice versa, and negating or unnegating any lines running to or from the gates.** Have students look at the circuits you just drew on the board illustrating the theorem. Make sure they see that, in the first example, the OR was changed to an AND, and the negated input lines were unnegated and the unnegated output line was negated with a bubble, turning it from an AND gates into a NAND gate. In the same way in the second circuit the AND was changed to an OR, the input lines were unnegated, and the output line was negated with a bubble, turning it from an OR gate to a NOR gate.
5. Tell students that it gets a bit more complicated than this. Bubble pushing can also involve moving NOT gates from the input of a gate to the output of the gate that *precedes* it. Similarly an output bubble can be "pushed" forward to negate the input of the next gate. For example, draw this portion of a circuit (no variables) on the board:

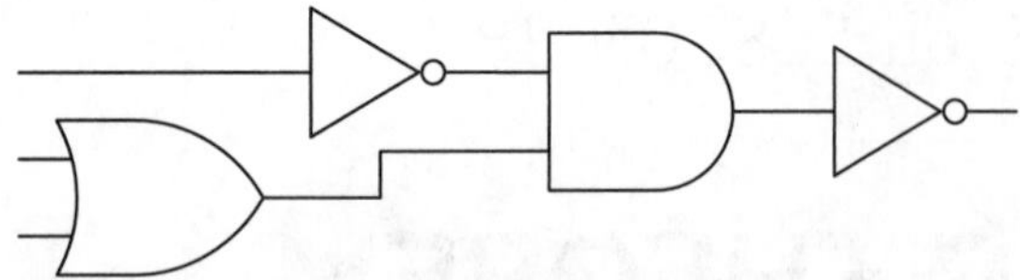

Explain that our first step is to ignore the first OR gate for a moment and apply De Morgan's to the AND gate. We changed it into an OR gate, negate the bottom input line, and unnegate the top input line and output line, like so:

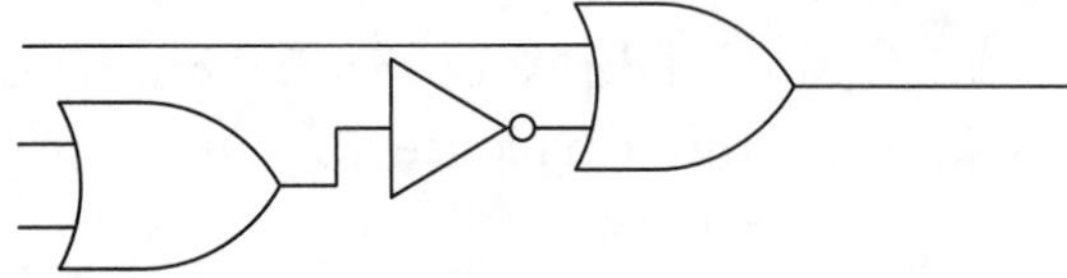

Now make sure students can see that this circuit can be simplified still further. We push the bubble of the NOT gate back onto the output of the OR, turning it into a NOR gate, like this:

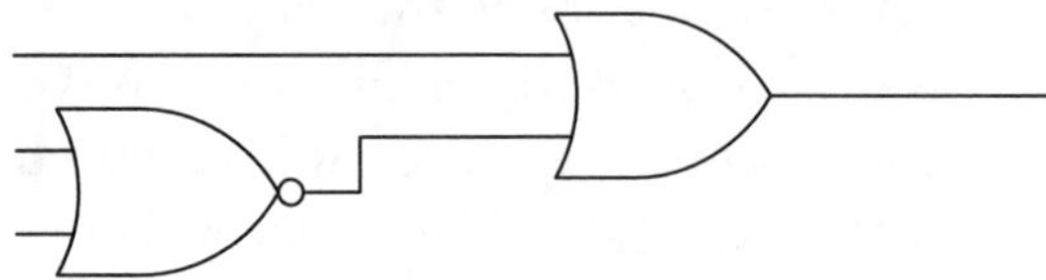

Point out that, using De Morgan's, we have managed to reduce the number of gates from four to two.

6. Work through this portion of a circuit with students, using bubble pushing to reduce the number of gates from four to two. (They should end with two AND gates.)

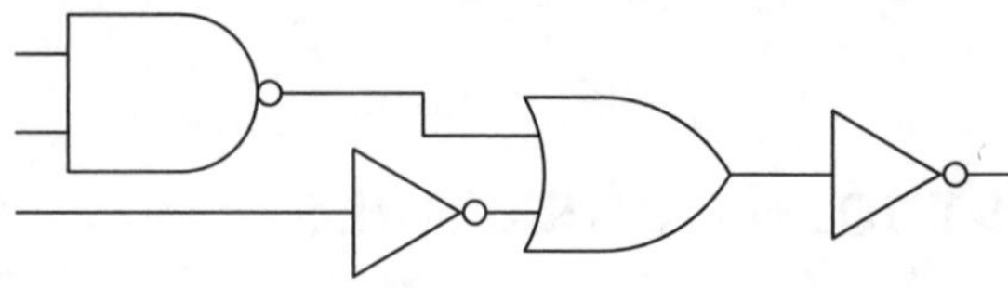

ASSIGNMENT

Have students complete Exercise 38, and go over it with them.

LESSON 38

DE MORGAN'S THEOREM

Another rule of replacement that will take some special consideration is De Morgan's theorem, which was briefly introduced earlier. De Morgan's theorem is actually the following two rules:

$\sim p \vee \sim q$ is equivalent to $\sim(p \bullet q)$
$\sim p \bullet \sim q$ is equivalent to $\sim(p \vee q)$

KEY POINT

De Morgan's theorem can be used to simplify logic circuits.

Written out in words, this allows the negation (~) to be distributed to the variables p and q simply by changing an OR to an AND, and vice versa.

These rules can by represented by the following circuits:

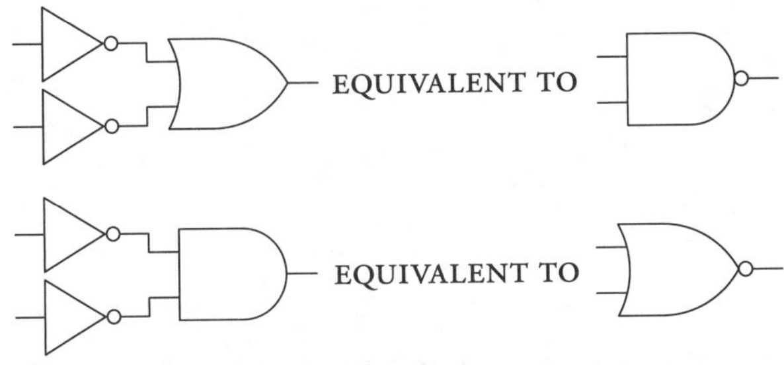

You see that De Morgan's theorem can reduce the number of gates from three to one. The rules of De Morgan's theorem are included in Appendix D.

KEY POINT

Bubble pushing applies De Morgan's theorem by changing a gate in a circuit from AND to OR or vice versa, and negating or un-negating any lines running to or from that gate.

In digital logic, the easiest way to apply De Morgan's theorem is by using a technique called **bubble pushing**. Bubble pushing involves changing a gate in a circuit from AND to OR, or vice versa, and negating or un-negating any lines running to or from that gate. You can see this in the diagrams illustrating De Morgan's theorem. For example, in the first equivalence above, the OR is changed to an AND, the input lines that were negated are un-negated, and the output line is negated with a bubble, turning the AND into a NAND.

Bubble pushing can also involve moving NOT gates from the input of a given gate to the output of the gate prior, adding (or

HISTORY

The rules we now know as De Morgan's Theorems had been informally observed by Aristotle and some medieval logicians such as William of Ockham, but it was British mathematician Augustus De Morgan (1806-1871) who introduced the formal versions of the laws in the language of modern logic.

removing) the bubble of a NAND or NOR. Similarly, an output bubble can be "pushed" forward to negate the input of the next gate.

Consider the following portion of a logic circuit:

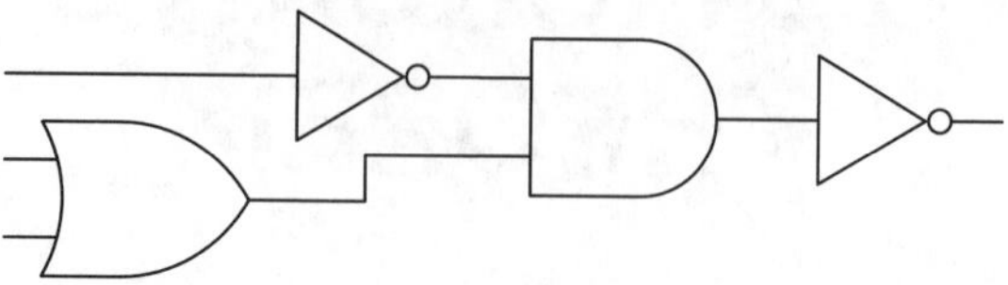

Applying De Morgan' theorem to the AND gate involves changing it into an OR gate, negating the input line on the bottom, and un-negating the top input line and output line, as shown:

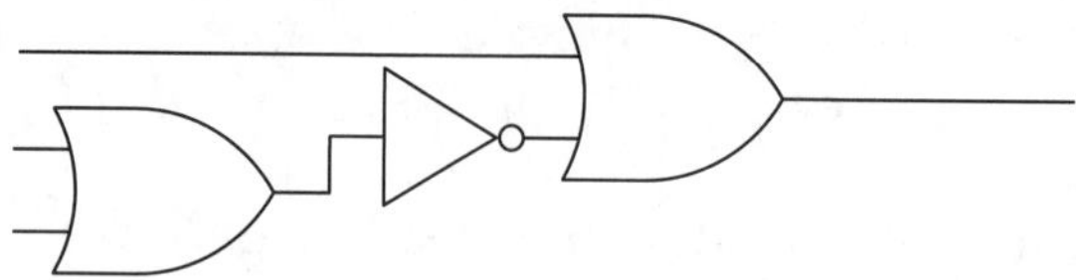

Notice that the original OR gate was left unchanged. Now the NOT gate can be pushed back onto the output of the OR, turning it into a NOR:

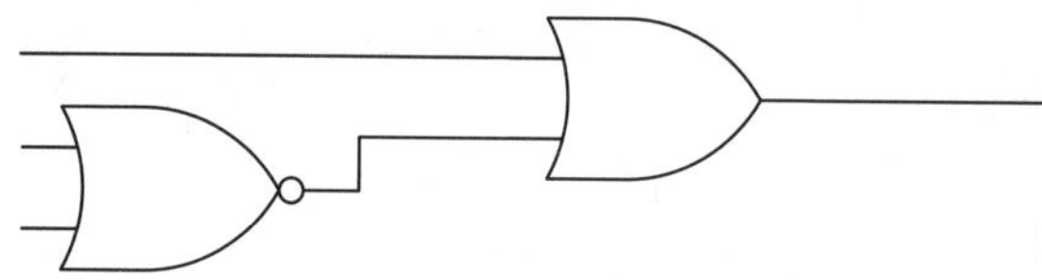

Thus the number of gates was reduced from four to two.

SUMMARY

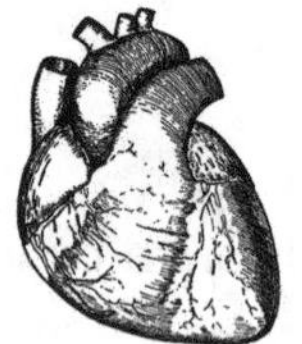

Yet another way to simplify a logical circuit uses bubble pushing, which is an application of De Morgan's Theorem to digital logic. Bubble pushing can involve moving NOT gates from the input of a given gate to the output of the gate prior, adding (or removing) the bubble of a NAND or NOR. Similarly, an output negation bubble can be "pushed" forward to negate the input of the next gate.

EXERCISE 38 (12 points)

Use bubble pushing to simplify each circuit so that it uses only two gates. (3, 4, 5)

1.

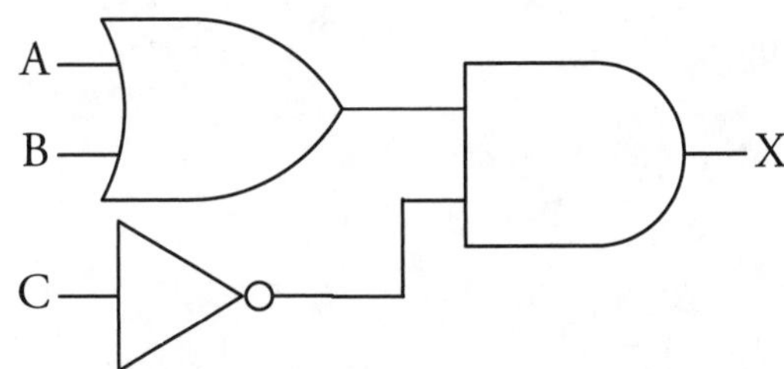

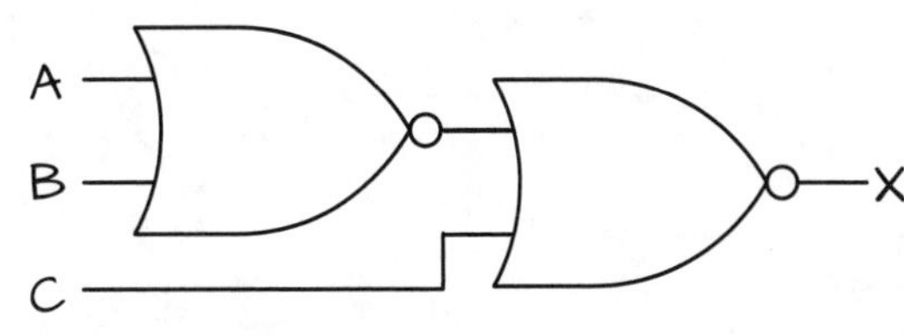

2.

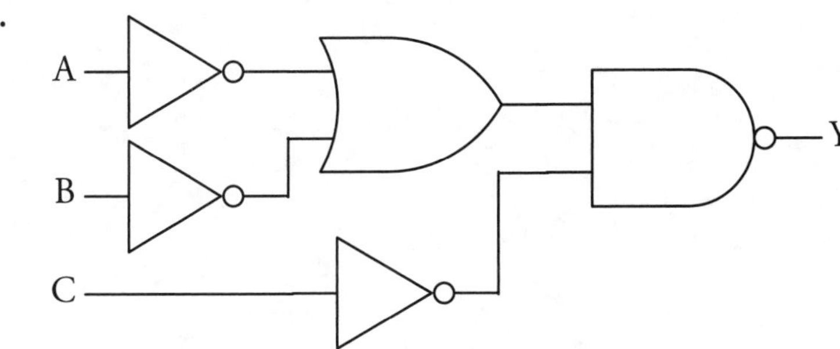

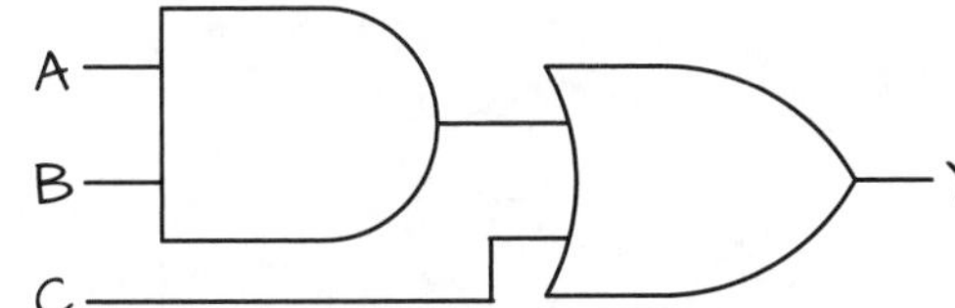

3.

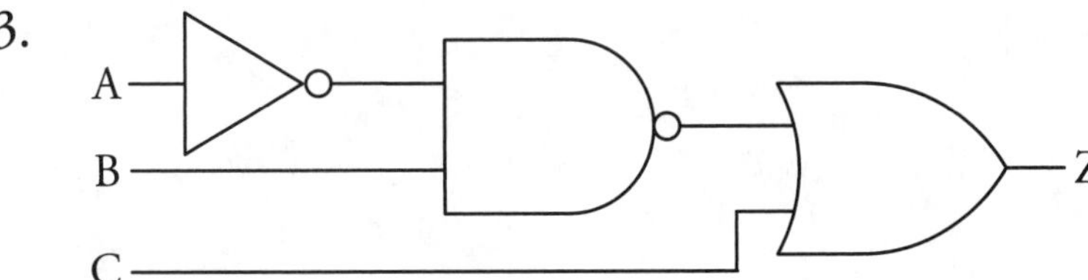

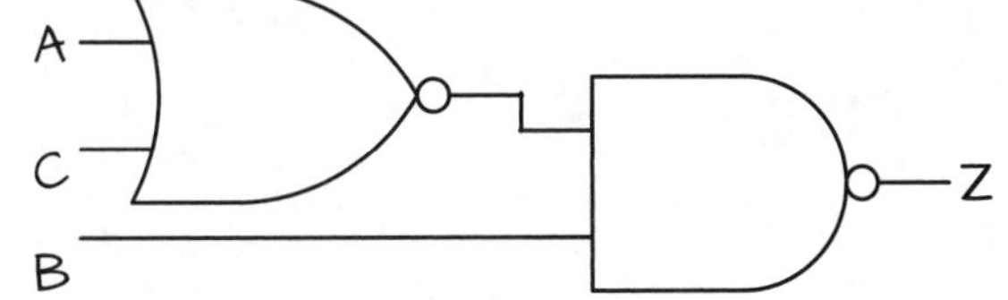

(Notice the order of inputs.)

QUIZ 18 (LESSONS 36–38)

STUDENT OBJECTIVE

Complete Quiz 18.

TEACHING INSTRUCTIONS

1. Give Quiz 18. Allow 30 minutes. Grade quiz with students.
2. If you have extra time, introduce Lesson 39 to get a head start on next class's material.

INTERMEDIATE LOGIC | Quiz 18

Lessons 36–38 (17 points)

Name ______________________________

1. What is the truth value of a tautology, such as $p \vee \sim p$? Give the answer as 0 or 1. (1) ___1___

2. In a step-by-step proof, show that the compound proposition $(p \vee q) \bullet (p \vee \sim q)$ is equivalent to the simple proposition p. Justify each step. (5)

1.	$(p \vee q) \bullet (p \vee \sim q)$	Given proposition
2.	$p \vee (q \bullet \sim q)$	Distribution
3.	$p \vee 0$	Self-contradiction
4.	p	Algebraic identity

3. Simplify the proposition $(\sim A \vee C) \bullet (\sim B \vee C)$ and draw the simplified circuit so that it uses only two gates. (5)

$\sim (A \vee B) \vee C$

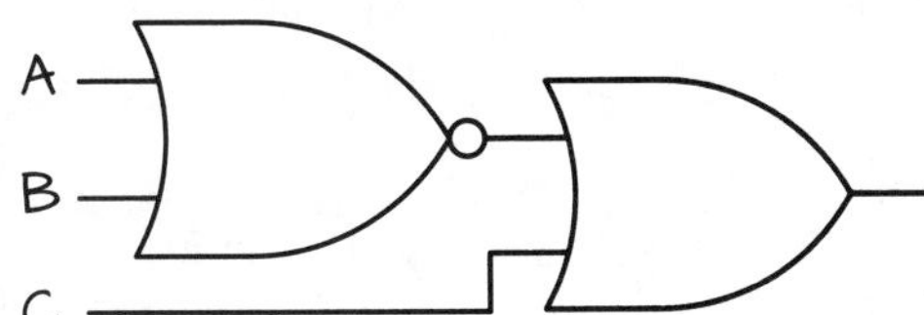

4. Determine the proposition for the given truth table. Then design the corresponding circuit, using simplification methods so that the final circuit has only two gates. (6)

A	B	X
0	0	1
0	1	1
1	0	0
1	1	1

$\sim A \vee B$

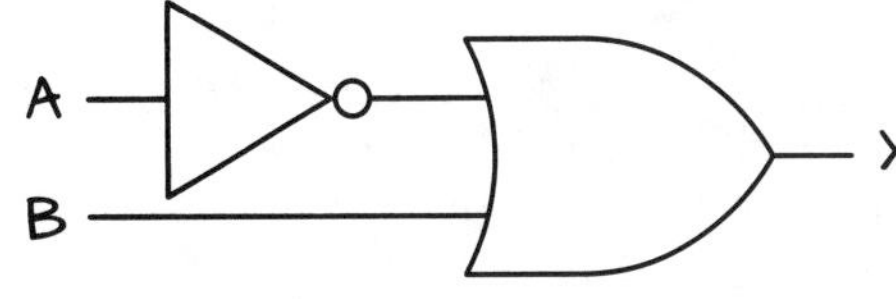

TEACHER'S NOTES on LESSON 39

TWO MORE LOGIC GATES

Intermediate Logic, pp. 307–309

STUDENT OBJECTIVES

1. Draw XOR and XNOR gates and write the symbols for them.
2. Give their defining truth tables.
3. Design circuits using these gates.
4. Complete Exercise 39.

TEACHING INSTRUCTIONS

1. Tell students that today you are going to teach them two new logic gates. See if they can remember back to learning about the logical operator $\vee$ in propositional logic (which is the OR gate in digital logic). Remind them that they learned that $\vee$ is an inclusive "or" rather than an exclusive "or." Ask students if they remember what the difference is. Explain that since $\vee$ is inclusive, $p \vee q$ means "either *p* or *q* or both *p* and *q*." We are using an inclusive "or" when we say something like, "The options are pumpkin pie or apple pie" (because of course any good hostess expects the men will ask for both). It is inclusive because it includes a greater number of truth values: *p* can be true and *q* false, or *p* can be false and *q* true, or *p* and *q* can both be true; the only combination excluded is for both *p* and *q* to be false. Explain that today we are going to learn about the other kind of "or," the exclusive "or."
2. Tell students that we call the exclusive "or" gate the XOR gate. Ask students how we might express the exclusive "or" gate using *p*'s and *q*'s. Explain that we would say "either *p* or *q*, but not both *p* and *q*." We are using an exclusive "or" when we say something like "The accused is either guilty or innocent," because he cannot be both innocent or guilty, and must be one or the other. Draw on the board the symbol for the XOR gate, which looks a bit like a rifle sight or a black widow without the legs: $\oplus$
3. Write the defining truth table for the XOR gate on the board:

p	q	p ⊕ q
0	0	0
0	1	1
1	0	1
1	1	0

Make sure students see that this truth table makes sense. If neither *p* nor *q* is true then the output is of course false. If *p* is true and *q* false or if *p* is false and *q* true, the output is true. But if both *p* and *q* are true, the output is false.

4. Draw the representation for the XOR gate on the board. It looks like an OR gate with an extra curved line after the inputs:

5. Write on the board $(p \vee q) \bullet {\sim}(p \bullet q)$. Have students walk you through creating a circuit for this rather complicated proposition. It should look like this:

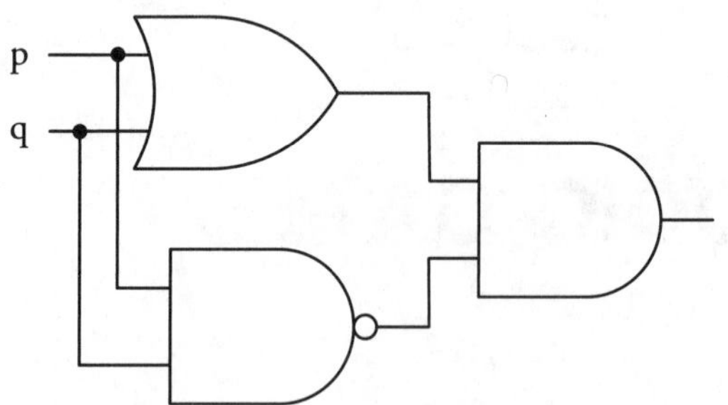

Remind students that since we just learned that $p \oplus q$ is equivalent to $(p \vee q) \bullet \sim(p \bullet q)$, we can replace this complicated circuit with the XOR gate, like so:

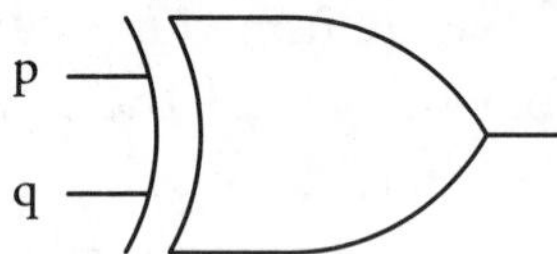

6. Have students look again at the truth table for XOR. Point out again that the output is true when p is true and q is false, or when p is false and q is true. Ask students if, given that, they can come up with another complicated proposition that is equivalent to $p \oplus q$. If they're stuck tell them that just by looking at the truth values in the truth table we know that $p \oplus q$ is logically equivalent to $(\sim p \bullet q) \vee (p \bullet \sim q)$.
7. Tell students that the XNOR ("exclusive NOR") gate is the same as the XOR gate with the output negated. Ask them what they think the defining truth table for this gate would look like. If they're clueless, remind them that since the XNOR gate is the XOR gate with negated output, the truth values of the output in the XNOR truth table will simply be the opposite of those in the XOR truth table. The truth table should look like this; draw it on the board, but don't include the $p \equiv q$ over the third column just yet:

p	q	p ≡ q
0	0	1
0	1	0
1	0	0
1	1	1

8. Make sure students see that the XNOR gate is true when both inputs are true or when both are false. In other words, XNOR is true whenever the inputs have the same truth value. Ask students if this reminds them of any other logical operator they have learned in the past. Remind them that biconditional (or logical equivalence) $(p \equiv q)$ has the same truth table. XNOR is therefore equivalent to logical equivalence (ha).
9. Have students tell you how to draw the XNOR gate. It should look like this:

p
q
p ≡ q

10. As with the XOR gate, have students consider the defining truth table for XNOR to find a more complicated proposition that $p \equiv q$ is equivalent to. They should come up with $(\sim p \bullet \sim q) \vee (p \bullet q)$. Make sure students see that by De Morgan's theorem and Commutation, this proposition is also equivalent to $(p \bullet q) \vee \sim(p \vee q)$. Have students tell you how to make the circuit for this latter proposition; it should look like this:

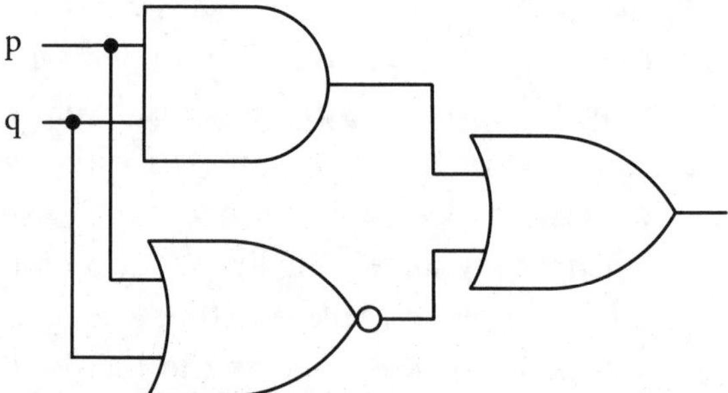

Make sure students understand that we can simply replace this circuit with the XNOR gate, now that we know that the propositions are equivalent. Tell students that the XOR and XNOR gates are particularly useful in digital logic for simplifying more complicated circuits.

11. Write this truth table on the board:

A	B	C	X
0	0	0	1
0	0	1	0
0	1	0	0
0	1	1	1
1	0	0	0
1	0	1	0
1	1	0	0
1	1	1	0

Have students use the technique they learned in Lesson 34 (making a disjunction out of the sets of truth values in the rows with true outputs) to come up with the proposition that produces this truth table. They should come up with *(~A • ~B • ~C) ∨ (~A • B • C)*.

12. Don't make them figure it out, but draw the circuit for this proposition on the board:

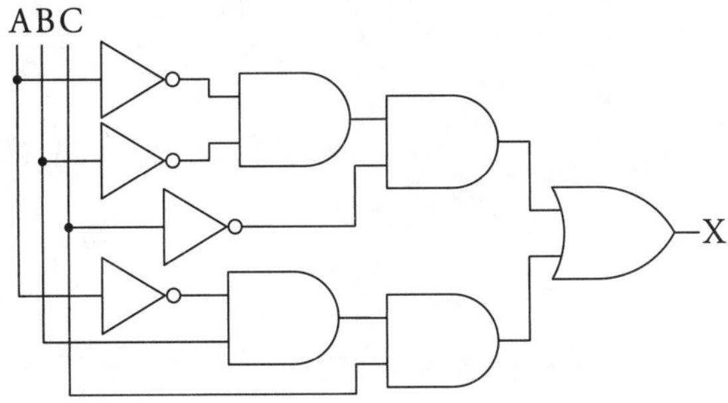

Which looks like a squadron of spaceships from Star Wars.

13. Tell students that we now have all the tools we need to simplify the proposition *(~A • ~B • ~C) ∨ (~A • B • C)* and make a much simpler circuit. Have students walk you through simplifying it on the board. Point out first of all that since both parts of the propositions include a *~A*, *~A* can be factored out using distribution, resulting in *~A • [(~B • ~C) ∨ (B • C)]*. Now have students look at the portion of the proposition in brackets. They should recognize it as one of the forms of XNOR. This means that we can simplify the proposition all the way down to *~A • (B ≡ C)*. Have students make the circuit for this new proposition, which should look like this:

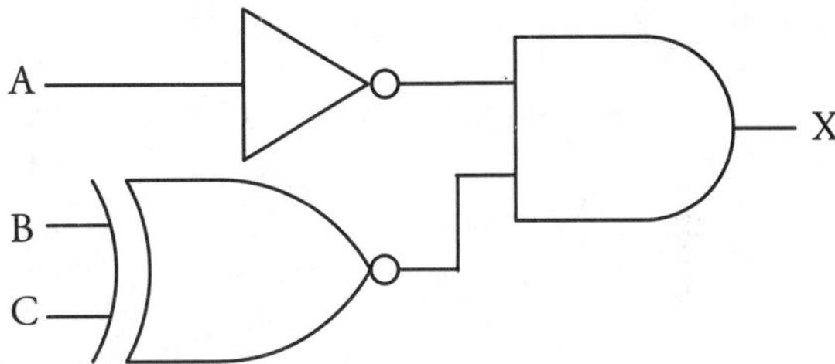

Just a small spaceship squadron.

14. Now have students use bubble pushing to reduce the above circuit to only *two* gates, *~[A ∨ (B ⊕ C)]*.

ASSIGNMENT

Have students complete Exercise 39, and go over it with them.

LESSON 39

TWO MORE LOGIC GATES

The **XOR ("exclusive or") gate** represents the operation of "either this or that, but not both." The output of this gate is true when either input is true, but not when both inputs are true at the same time. The symbol for this gate is "⊕". The defining truth table and representation for the gate are given here:

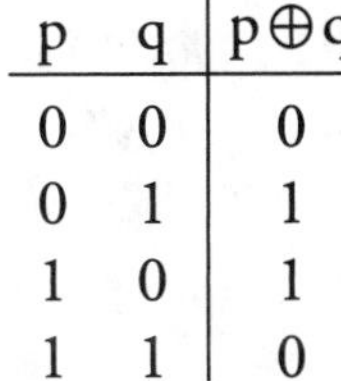

p	q	p⊕q
0	0	0
0	1	1
1	0	1
1	1	0

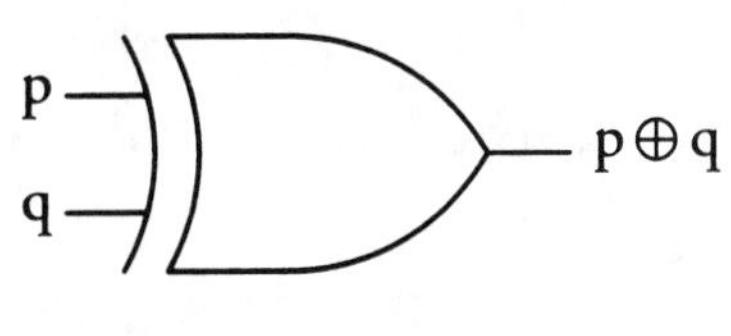

KEY POINT

The XOR gate is an exclusive or (⊕), and is true when either input is true, but not when both inputs are true at the same time.

Given that this logical operator means "either p or q, but not both p and q," you can see why this operation is equivalent to the more complex $(p \vee q) \bullet \sim(p \bullet q)$. This means that this circuit...

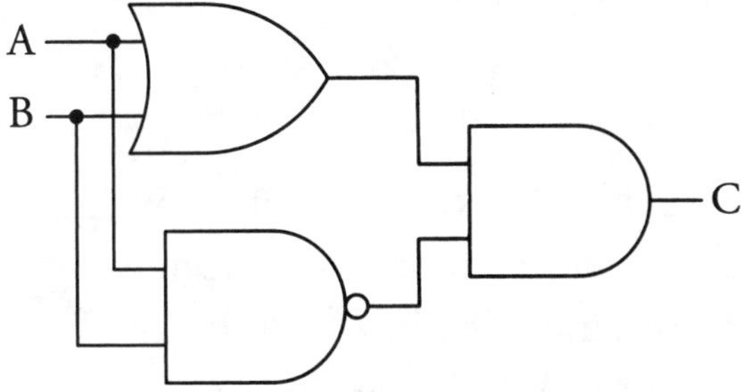

...can be replaced by this much simpler circuit:

A
B
C

Look back at the truth table for XOR. The output is true when p is false and q is true, or when p is true and q is false. Consequently, another complex proposition that is logically equivalent to $p \oplus q$ is $(\sim p \bullet q) \vee (p \bullet \sim q)$.

KEY POINT

The XNOR gate is an exclusive nor (≡), and is true when both inputs are true or when both inputs are false.

The XNOR ("exclusive NOR") gate is the same as the XOR gate with the output negated. The XNOR gate is true when both inputs are true or when both inputs are false. In other words, XNOR is true whenever the inputs have the same truth value. This implies that XNOR means the same as logical equivalence, which has the symbol ≡.

The defining truth table and representation for the gate are given here:

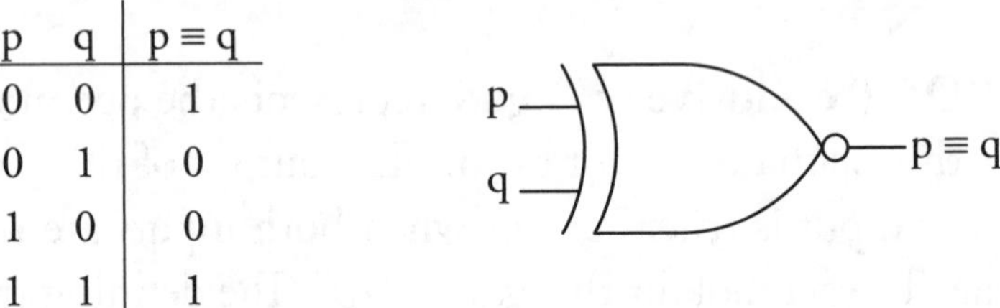

p	q	p ≡ q
0	0	1
0	1	0
1	0	0
1	1	1

Consider the defining truth table. You should see here that $p \equiv q$ is logically equivalent to $(\sim p \bullet \sim q) \vee (p \bullet q)$, which is also equivalent to $(p \bullet q) \vee \sim(p \vee q)$. Thus, the circuit shown below can be replaced by the XNOR gate A ≡ B:

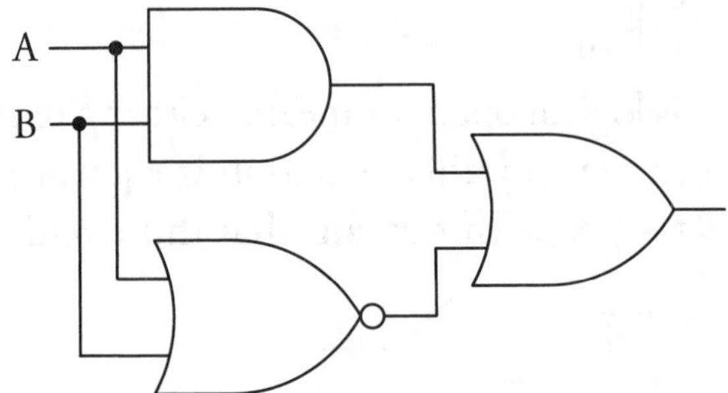

The XOR and XNOR gates are useful in digital logic, and can clearly be used to simplify more complicated logic circuits. Their equivalence rules are included in Appendix D.

Consider the truth table below. You should see (following the procedure from Lesson 34) that the proposition that produces this truth table is the one given to the right.

A	B	C	X
0	0	0	1
0	0	1	0
0	1	0	0
0	1	1	1
1	0	0	0
1	0	1	0
1	1	0	0
1	1	1	0

(~A • ~B • ~C) ∨ (~A • B • C)

The circuit for the proposition would be as shown:

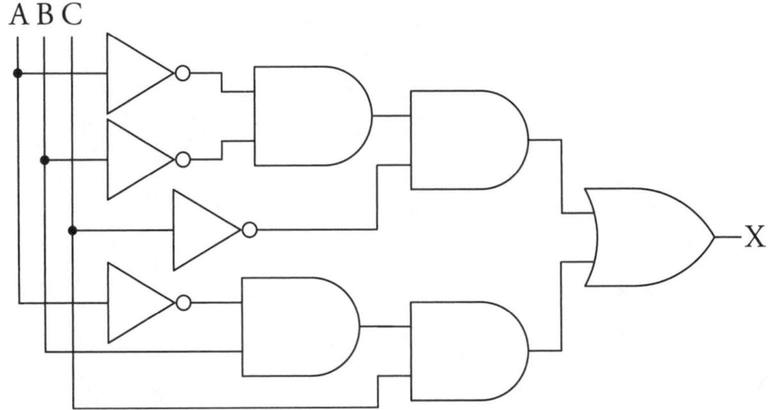

We can now simplify the proposition $(\sim A \bullet \sim B \bullet \sim C) \vee (\sim A \bullet B \bullet C)$. Start by factoring out the ~A using distribution, to get $\sim A \bullet [(\sim B \bullet \sim C) \vee (B \bullet C)]$. Look at the part of this proposition in brackets. You should see that this is one of the forms of XNOR. That means we can simplify this proposition to $\sim A \bullet (B \equiv C)$. Thus the complicated circuit above can be replaced with this circuit:

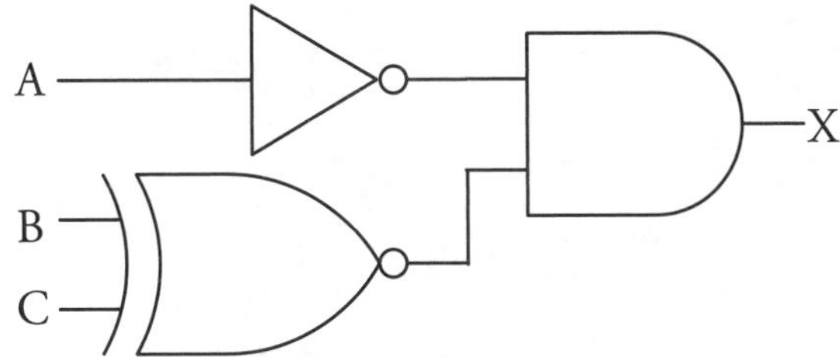

Can you use bubble pushing to reduce the above circuit to only two gates?

FURTHER STUDY

The symbols used in this text for logic gates are only one way of representing them. This is called the "distinctive shape" set. Do some research in your library or online to discover other commonly used methods of representing logic gates.

SUMMARY

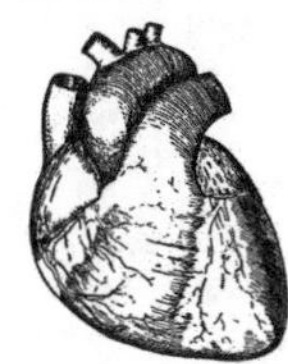

The last two gates in this text are the XOR gate (⊕) and the XNOR gate (≡). XOR (exclusive OR) is true when one or the other input (but not both) is true. XNOR (exclusive NOR) is the biconditional, which is true when the inputs have the same truth value. XOR and XNOR allow you to further simplify even more complicated circuits.

EXERCISE 39 (25 points)

Problems 1-2: Use the rules to simplify the proposition and design the circuit for the specified number of gates.

1. ~ [(A • ~ B) ∨ (~ A • B)] — One gate. (4)

1) $\sim(A \oplus B)$
2) $A \equiv B$

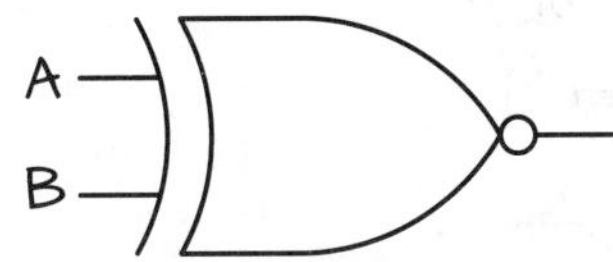

2. ~ A ∨ [(B • C) ∨ (~ B • ~ C)] — Two gates. (5)

1) $\sim A \vee (B \equiv C)$
2) $\sim[A \bullet \sim (B \equiv C)]$
3) $\sim[A \bullet (B \oplus C)]$

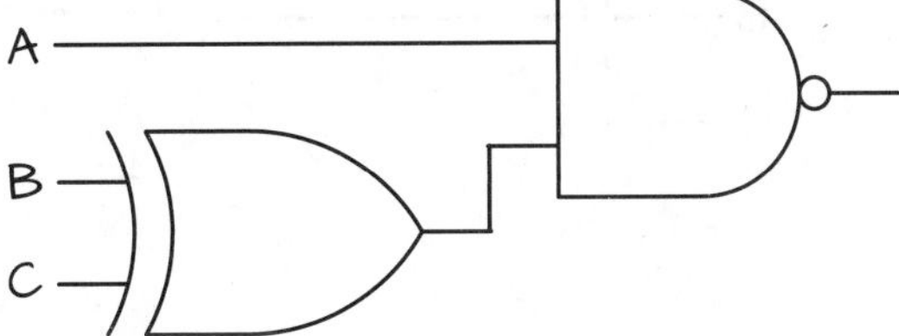

3. Reduce the given circuit to only two gates. (7)

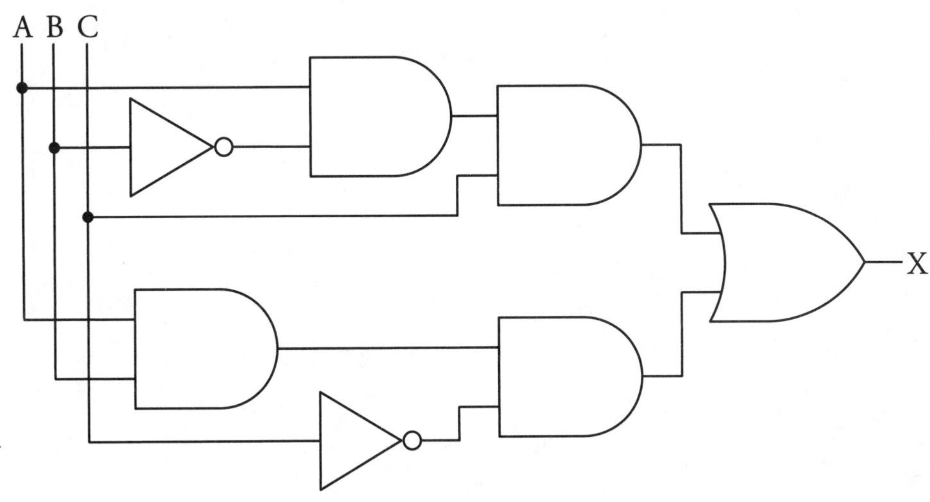

1) $[(A \bullet \sim B) \bullet C] \vee [(A \bullet B) \bullet \sim C]$
2) $[A \bullet (\sim B \bullet C)] \vee [A \bullet (B \bullet \sim C)]$
3) $A \bullet [(\sim B \bullet C) \vee (B \bullet \sim C)]$
4) $A \bullet (B \oplus C)$

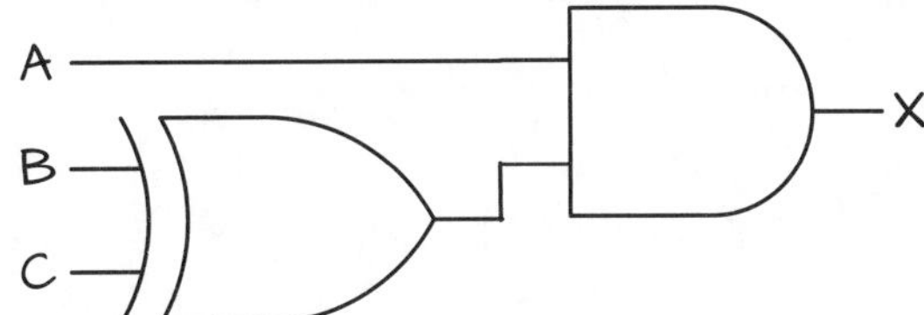

Continued on next page.

4. Design the simplest possible circuit that produces the given truth table. (9)

A	B	C	Y
0	0	0	0
0	0	1	1
0	1	0	0
0	1	1	0
1	0	0	1
1	0	1	0
1	1	0	0
1	1	1	0

1) (~A•~B•C) v (A•~B•~C)
2) (~B•~A•C) v (~B•A•~C)
3) ~B•[(~A•C) v (A•~C)]
4) ~B•(A⊕C)
5) ~[B v ~(A⊕C)]
6). ~[B v (A≡C)]

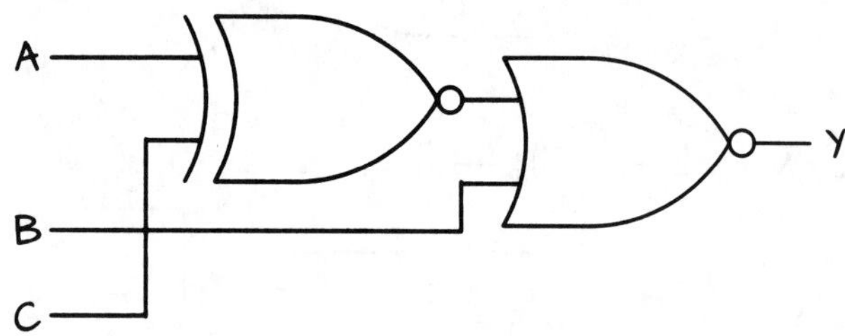

TEACHER'S NOTES on LESSON 40

KARNAUGH MAPPING

Intermediate Logic, pp. 313–320

STUDENT OBJECTIVES

1. Use K-mapping to design digital logic circuits from truth tables.
2. Use K-maps to simplify propositions for logic circuits.
3. Complete Exercise 40a.

SPECIAL NOTE

Exercise 40b is a special project to be completed after the quiz on Lessons 38–40.

TEACHING INSTRUCTIONS

1. Tell students that they have probably noticed that the process of generating a simplified circuit from a truth table is far from simple; in fact it can be quite difficult and time-consuming. Explain that today students are going to learn a new method for simplifying the simplifying process, called Karnaugh mapping. The process uses a tool called a Karnaugh map (or K-map) to represent all the different possibilities of inputs and outputs for the circuit, enabling us to determine a proposition for the truth table.
2. Tell students that you are going to start with a very simple truth table; draw it on the board:

p	q	x
0	0	0
0	1	0
1	0	1
1	1	0

Make sure students see that this is a truth table for two input variables, p and q; we don't know yet what proposition or circuit the truth table represents, but we do know that it has only one true (1) for the output variable x.

3. Now draw this K-map on the board:

	p	~p
q	0	0
~q	(1)	0

Make sure students can see how this K-map represents the truth table. The four boxes represent the four rows of the truth table. The upper left box containing 0 represents the very bottom row of the truth table, where *p* and q are both true and the output is 0 (which the 0 in the box represents). The upper right box containing 0 represents the second row of the truth table, where *p* is false (or not *~p* is true), *q* is true, and the output is again false (0). The lower right box of the K-map also containing 0 represents the first row of the truth table, where *p* and *q* are both false (or rather *~p* and *~q* are both true) and the output is false (0). Finally the lower left box with the 1 in it represents the third row of the truth table, where *p* is true, *q* is false (or ~*q* is true) and the output is true (1). Explain that we circle the box containing the 1, because that is the box (and the row) that will give us our proposition. Remind students that the proposition only depends on the row with the true (1) output, so we can ignore the boxes with the 0s in them. Explain that the circled 1 represents the proposition *p* • ~*q* (the conjunction of its inputs), and that this is the proposition for the truth table.

4. Now write on the board this proposition from problem 1 of Exercise 37: *(p • q)* ∨ *(p • ~q)*. Remind students that they were asked to show that this proposition is equivalent to p. Have students walk you through a quick proof for this equivalence; it should look like this:

1) (p • q) ∨ (p • ~q)	*Given*
2) p • (q ∨ ~q)	*Distribution*
3) p • 1	*Tautology*
4) p	*Algebraic Identity*

Explain that we could also have proved this equivalence by making a truth table. We know from the proposition that to get a true output either *p* and *q* are both true or 1 (the first disjunct in the disjunction) or p is true or 1 and *q* is false or 0 (the second disjunct). Make sure students see that given this information we can draw this truth table:

p	q	y
0	0	0
0	1	0
1	0	1
1	1	1

5. Ask students how we can know from this patterns of 1s and 0s that *(p • q)* ∨ *(p • ~q)* is equivalent to *p*. Make sure they see that the proposition *(p • q)* ∨ *(p • ~q)* is true when *p* is true and when *q* is *either true or false*. In other words, the truth value of *q* has no effect on the truth value of the whole proposition; *q* doesn't matter, so we can ignore it.

6. Draw the K-map for this proposition on the board:

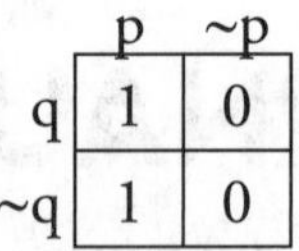

Have students compare the K-map to the truth table. Make sure they see that the 0s and 1s in the boxes correspond to the output values in the truth table, and that they were placed in each cell corresponding to the truth values of the input. Just as in the fourth row of the truth table, when *p* and *q* are both true (1), their box (top left) is also true (1); just as in the third row of the truth table, when *p* is true and *q* is false (or ~*q* is true), their box (bottom left) is true (1).

7. Tell students that the next step is to draw a circle around the 1s when they appear in a row or column, in groupings of two or powers of two, like so:

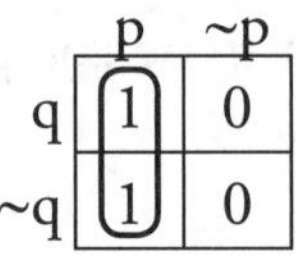

Make sure students see that the circled 1s are located in the cells *p* and *q* and *p* and ~*q*. Tell them that once we have determined that, we look for what changes between the two cells: *p* is unchanged, but *q* changes from *q* to ~*q*. Drive home to students that in K-mapping *we are only interested in what doesn't change.* Since *q* changes we can ignore it until the final proposition and only consider what remains unchanged. That is how we know that the proposition for this K-map is simply p: because in the cells with the two 1s circled the *p* does not change.

8. Write this truth table on the board:

p	q	z
0	0	1
0	1	1
1	0	0
1	1	1

Have students walk you through making the K-map for this truth table. It should look like this:

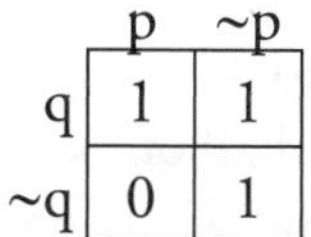

	p	~p
q	1	1
~q	0	1

9. Have students tell you what should be circled in this K-map. Remind them that we are looking for groups of 1s, and make sure they see that in this K-map we have two circles, one vertical (on the right) and one horizontal (on the top). Explain that it is fine for these circles to overlap. Beginning with the vertical circle, ask students which input variable changes and which doesn't. They should see that while *q* changes to *~q*, *~p* remains constant. Since we are only concerned with the unchanging variable, we know that this vertical circle represents *~p*. But we're not done; have students look at the horizontal circle and determined which input variable is changed and which unchanged. In this case the *q* is constant, while the *p* changes to *~p*. The horizontal circle thus represents q. Tell students that we know the propositions for the two circles, but we don't yet know the proposition for the entire K-map. Explain that we find that by connecting the two circle propositions with an OR: $\sim p \vee q$. Have students stare at the K-map and the proposition for a minute until the understand how the two are related. Then have students check on their own to make sure that this proposition gives us the truth table we started with.

10. Tell students that the craziness of K-maps is far from over; we have only scratched the surface. Now we will consider how to make a K-map for a three-variable truth table. Write this truth table on the board:

p	q	r	x
0	0	0	1
0	0	1	1
0	1	0	1
0	1	1	0
1	0	0	1
1	0	1	0
1	1	0	1
1	1	1	1

11. Tell students that since our truth table now has eight rows, our K-map must have (have them say it) eight corresponding cells. Explain that we will do this by making a map with two rows and four columns of boxes. Draw this K-map on the board:

	pq	$p\bar{q}$	$\bar{p}\bar{q}$	$\bar{p}q$
r	1	0	1	0
$\bar{r}$	1	1	1	1

Explain that we label the two rows of the K-map with r and ~r respectively and the four columns with two variables each, with the values of the variables changing from affirmative to negative one at a time. Explain that in order to save space, we use the alternative notation for negation and conjunction that we learned a few lessons ago: for example, $p \bullet \sim q$ is written as $p\bar{q}$.

12. Also have students notice where the 0s and 1s are placed in the K-map. Make sure they understand that the 0 in the upper right corner cell is the output for $\bar{p}qr$, that is, for $\sim p \bullet q \bullet r$, which corresponds to the fourth row of the truth table. Ask students what the other 0 in the map is the output for ($p\bar{q}r$ or $p \bullet \sim q \bullet r$, which corresponds to the sixth row of the truth table).

13. Now have students walk you through circling the 1s in the K-map as they appear in groups. Remind students that the groups must be groupings of powers of two, i.e., 1, 2, 4, or 8; we can't have a group of three ones. Also tell them that we are looking for the minimum number of circles

of maximum size: so bigger circles and fewer. Repeat these very important points about circles in K-maps. Tell the students to write them down. The circled map should look like this:

	pq	$p\bar{q}$	$\bar{p}\bar{q}$	$\bar{p}q$
r	1	0	1	0
$\bar{r}$	1	1	1	1

14. Tell students that we now have all we need to determine the proposition that this map represents. In the circle around the first column on the left, *p* and *q* remain unchanged but *r* changes to ~*r*; the proposition for that circle is therefore $p \bullet q$. In the circles around the third column ~*p* and ~*q* remain unchanged, but once again r changes to ~*r*; so the proposition for this circle is $\sim p \bullet \sim q$. In the circle along the bottom row, *p* and *q* change several times, but ~*r* remains unchanged; so the circle around the bottom row represents the proposition ~*r*. Ask students what we do next with these three propositions; remind them that we connect them with disjunctions to get the proposition for the entire map. Have them do the connecting: they should get the proposition $(p \bullet q) \vee (\sim p \bullet \sim q) \vee \sim r$. Tell students that we could now draw a circuit from this proposition, but that the proposition can still be further reduced to only two with some creative simplification. Tell them that you will give anyone who figures it out extra credit. (It is $\sim[(p \oplus q) \bullet r]$).

15. Write this truth table on the board:

p	q	r	y
0	0	0	0
0	0	1	0
0	1	0	0
0	1	1	1
1	0	0	1
1	0	1	1
1	1	0	1
1	1	1	1

Have students walk you through making the K-map for this truth table. It should look like this:

	pq	$p\bar{q}$	$\bar{p}\bar{q}$	$\bar{p}q$
r	1	1	0	1
$\bar{r}$	1	1	0	0

16. On to circling. Students should immediately see that the four 1s in the left half of the K-map should be circled together. But what about the lonely 1 in the right-hand corner? Tell students that in fact this 1 can be connected to the 1 in the upper leftmost square; a neat feature of K-maps is that the K-mapping circle *wraps around*. The circling for this K-map should look like this:

	pq	$p\bar{q}$	$\bar{p}\bar{q}$	$\bar{p}q$
r	1	1	0	1
$\bar{r}$	1	1	0	0

Ask students what proposition the circle around the four left 1s represents. They should see that in this chunk the only variable that doesn't change (and therefore the only one that we care about) is *p*. So this circle represents *p*. Ask students what proposition the circle wrapping around the two ones on opposite ends represents. They should see that neither q nor r change, so the proposition represented is $q \bullet r$. Have students puts these propositions together to get the proposition represented by the whole K-map: $p \vee (q \bullet r)$.

17. Tell students that you are now going to show them one example of a four-variable K-map (gasp!) and introduce one more new idea. Explain that sometimes when using K-maps we come across certain variables that don't have a value at all; they are neither 1 nor 0. These variables are called "don't cares," and when we are analyzing them in a K-map we can use them as either a 1 or a 0, depending on which choice simplifies the proposition the most (convenient, huh?). Explain that the letter "X" is used to represents "don't cares" in the truth table and K-map.

18. Tell students that you are going to show them a real-world example. Have them remember

back to the decimal displays they saw in an earlier lesson, and write 0 to 9 out on the board, like so:

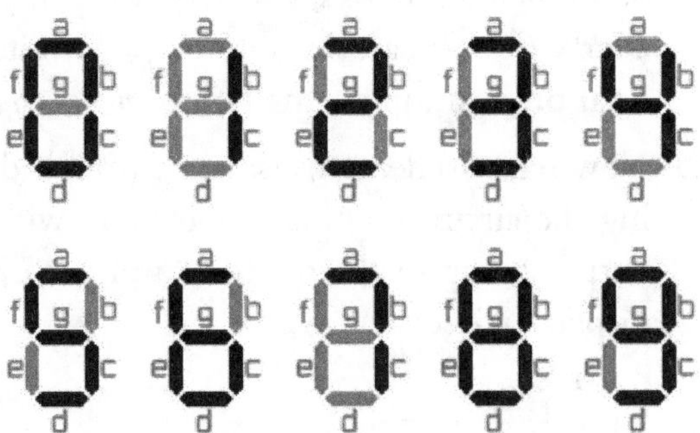

Tell students that for this example we are going to design a circuit that will control the top segment, *a*. Explain that when the segment is "on" the output of the circuit will be 1 and when it is "off" the output will be 0. Ask students in which numbers you have just written on the board the segment a is off (1 and 4).

19. Write this truth table on the board and explain that each row is a number in binary from 0 on up (0000, 0001, 0010, 0011, etc.) and that the output of each row corresponds to whether the segment a in the digital display is on or off.

p	q	r	s	a
0	0	0	0	1
0	0	0	1	0
0	0	1	0	1
0	0	1	1	1
0	1	0	0	0
0	1	0	1	1
0	1	1	0	1
0	1	1	1	1
1	0	0	0	1
1	0	0	1	1
1	0	1	0	X
1	0	1	1	X
1	1	0	0	X
1	1	0	1	X
1	1	1	0	X
1	1	1	1	X

Make sure students see that the only rows where the output is 0 are rows 1 and 4, since 1 and 4 are the numbers in which the segment a in the digital display is off. Also point out that output values are given for the binary inputs 0 to 9; everything after that (10 and up) is a "don't care," because the decimal display is only a single digit.

20. Have students walk you through making a K-map for this table. Tell them that the map will need to have 16 boxes since there are 16 rows in the table, and that both the columns and the rows will need to be labeled with two variables each: pq and its variations along the top and rs and its variation along the side. The map should look like this:

	pq	$p\bar{q}$	$\bar{p}\bar{q}$	$\bar{p}q$
rs	X	X	1	1
$r\bar{s}$	X	X	1	1
$\bar{r}\bar{s}$	X	1	1	0
$\bar{r}s$	X	1	0	1

21. Tell students that the next step is tricky: figuring out how to circle the values to include all the 1s with the minimum number of circles and avoiding redundant circles as much as possible. Remind students that the circles must include cells in rectangular groups of powers of two (1, 2, 4, or 8). Also tell them to keep in mind that the larger the circle the better, because the proposition will end up being simpler.

22. Make sure students see that we can circle the entire top half of the map at once, since we can use the "don't cares" as 1s. This whole chunk represents the proposition r, since r is the only value that stays the same for all eight of the cells in the circle. Next, make sure students see that we can also circle the entire left half of the map, including the two 1s in the bottom of the second column with all the "don't cares." The proposition represented by this circle is p, since p is the only variable that doesn't change.

23. Tell students that we only have two 1s left to circle. Make sure students can see that the 1 in the third row of the third column can be included in the circle of four cells right in the middle of the K-map, which would represent the proposition $\sim q \bullet \sim s$. The final reclusive 1 off by itself in the bottom rightmost corner is the most interesting. Explain that because the K-map values can wrap around—both left-right and up-down, a "circle" can include the four corners of a K-map. Explain that this would be the largest circle that could include our final 1. It might take them a little brain-racking and turning upside-down, but have students figure out what proposition this final circle represents $q \bullet s$. The final circled K-map should look like this:

	pq	$p\bar{q}$	$\bar{p}\bar{q}$	$\bar{p}q$
rs	X	X	1	1
$r\bar{s}$	X	X	1	1
$\bar{r}\bar{s}$	X	1	1	0
$\bar{r}s$	X	1	0	1

24. Explain that we can now use this K-map to come up with the total proposition and draw the circuit. Have students connect all the propositions for all the circles with disjuncts to get the total proposition: $p \vee r \vee (q \bullet s) \vee (\sim q \bullet \sim s)$. Now have them look very hard at this proposition. Ask if they recognize anything in it that can be significantly simplified. If they are mystified, have them flip back to Lesson 38 in their textbooks, where they learned that $(q \bullet s) \vee (\sim q \bullet \sim s)$ can simplify to $q \equiv s$. Write the final proposition on the board: $p \vee r \vee (q \equiv s)$.

25. Now have students walk you through drawing the circuit for this proposition, with the output going to the segment a of the digital display, like so:

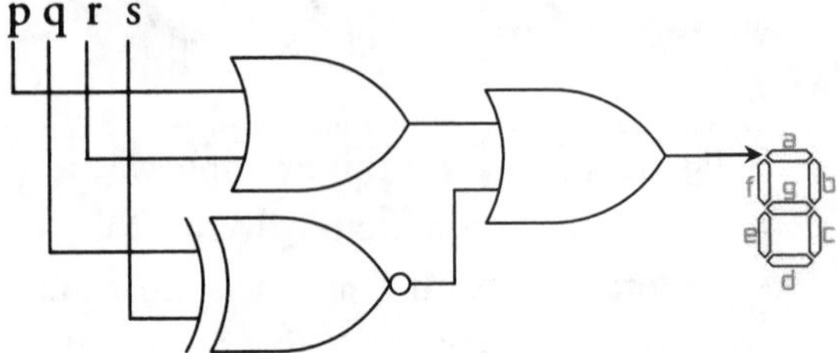

26. Before you finish up the lesson, have students flip to the list of Karnaugh Mapping Steps at the end of the lesson in their textbooks; go through it with them and make sure they understand the process.

ASSIGNMENTS

1. Have students complete Exercise 40a, and go over it with them.
2. Remind students to study for Quiz 19 over Lessons 38–40.

KARNAUGH MAPPING

As you have seen, generating a simplified circuit from a truth table can be quite difficult and time consuming, with a large possibility for error. One method for simplifying the process is called Karnaugh mapping. This process uses a tool called a Karnaugh map (or K-map) to represent all the different possibilities of inputs and outputs for the circuit in order to determine a proposition for the truth table. Let's see how this works.

DEFINITION

A ***Karnaugh map*** (or ***K-map***) is a diagram that displays a truth table for a proposition in such a way as to simplify the proposition quickly.

We'll start with **two-variable K-maps.** Consider the following truth table for variables *p* and *q*, having a single true (1) for the output variable *x*. To the right is a K-map representing the truth table.

p	q	x
0	0	0
0	1	0
1	0	1
1	1	0

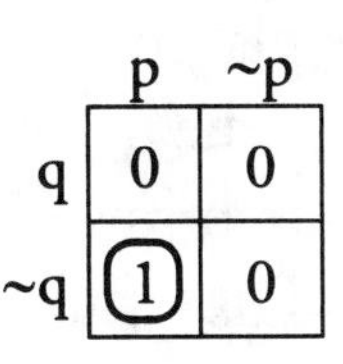

The upper left 0 in the K-map represents the bottom 0 in the truth table, next to the true *p* and *q*. The upper right 0 in the K-map represents the 0 in the second row of the truth table, next to the false *p* and true *q*. The lower right 0 in the K-map represents the 0 in the first row of the truth table, where *p* and *q* are both false. Finally, the circled 1 represents the 1 in the third row of the truth table, where *p* is true and *q* is false. Thus the circled 1 represents the proposition $p \bullet {\sim}q$, which is in fact the proposition for the truth table. Since the proposition only depends on the single 1, the 0s can be ignored.

KEY POINT

In a K-map, the proposition is determined by considering only where the output is 1.

Now, consider the symbolic proposition from Exercise 37, problem 1: $(p \bullet q) \vee (p \bullet {\sim} q)$. At that time you were asked to show that this is equivalent to *p*. One proof of this equivalence is shown here:

1) $(p \bullet q) \vee (p \bullet {\sim} q)$	Given
2) $p \bullet (q \vee {\sim} q)$	Distribution
3) $p \bullet 1$	Tautology
4) p	Algebraic identity

You could also have seen this equivalence by considering a truth table. The proposition $(p \bullet q) \vee (p \bullet {\sim} q)$ is true when p and q are both true (1), or when p is true (1) and q is false (0), as in this truth table:

p	q	y	
0	0	0	
0	1	0	
1	0	1	← *p* is true and *q* is false
1	1	1	← *p* is true and *q* is true

You can see from the pattern of 1s and 0s that this proposition is equivalent to *p*. Consider why this is so: the proposition $(p \bullet q) \vee (p \bullet {\sim} q)$ is true when *p* is true and when *q* is either true or false. This means that the truth value of *q* has no effect on the truth value of the whole proposition, and so it can be ignored.

The K-map for this proposition looks like this.

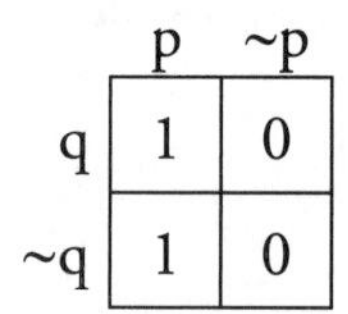

	p	~p
q	1	0
~q	1	0

Look back at the truth table. The output truth values, 0 or 1, were placed in each cell corresponding to the truth values of the input. A 1 occurs when *p* and *q* both are true (fourth row of the truth table), or when *p* is true and *q* is false (third row of the truth table).

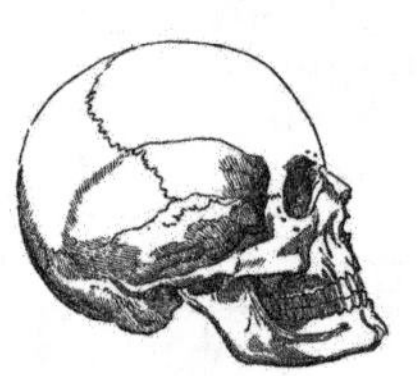

CAUTION

In a K-map, the 1s are only circled in groupings of powers of two (1, 2, 4, 8, or 16).

Now we draw a circle around the 1s when they appear in the column (in groupings of two or powers of two, which we will consider later), as shown.

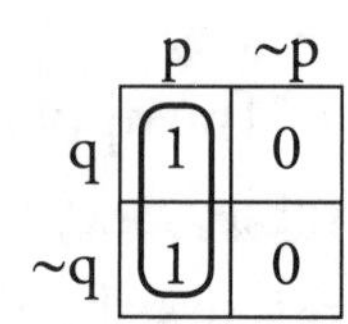

	p	~p
q	1	0
~q	1	0

The 1s circled are located in the cells *p* and *q*, and *p* and *~q*. So the *p* is unchanged, but *q* changes from *q* to *~q*. Since *q* changes we ignore it in the final proposition, and only consider what remains unchanged. So the proposition for this K-map is simply *p*.

KEY POINT

The proposition is determined by looking at the circled 1s and seeing what is unchanged for that grouping.

Again, the proposition for this K-map is *p* because for the cells with the two 1s circled, the *p* does not change.

Let's look at another truth table, and draw the K-map to determine the corresponding proposition. Here is the truth table, with its corresponding K-map.

p	q	z
0	0	1
0	1	1
1	0	0
1	1	1

	p	~p
q	1	1
~q	0	1

Now we circle the 1s in the K-map as they appear in groups. In the right (vertical) circle, what is the unchanged input variable? It is *~p*. The *q* changes from *q* to *~q* as you look from the top 1 to the bottom 1. This circle thus represents *~p*. In the top (horizontal) circle, what is the unchanged input variable? It is *q*. The *p* changes from *p* to *~p* as you go from the left 1 to the right 1. So this circle represents the proposition *q*. We connect these propositions with an OR to obtain the entire proposition for the K-map of $\sim p \vee q$. Look again at this proposition and at the circles in the K-map. Try to understand how this proposition is represented by that K-map. You should also check that this proposition gives the truth table that we started with.

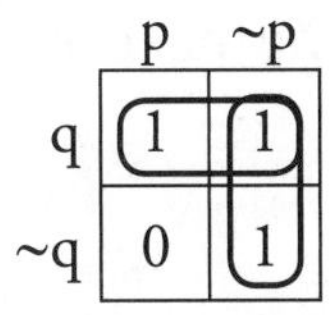

KEY POINT

When a K-map has more than one circled group of 1s, their corresponding propositions are connected with an OR.

Now let's consider how to make and use a **three-variable K-map**. We will start with the truth table given here.

p	q	r	x
0	0	0	1
0	0	1	1
0	1	0	1
0	1	1	0
1	0	0	1
1	0	1	0
1	1	0	1
1	1	1	1

	pq	$p\bar{q}$	$\bar{p}\bar{q}$	$\bar{p}q$
r	1	0	1	0
$\bar{r}$	1	1	1	1

Since the truth table has eight rows, the K-map must have eight corresponding cells. This works by making a table with two rows and four columns. The columns are labeled with two variables each, with the values of the variables changing from affirmative to negative, one at a time. In order to save space, we use the alternate notation for negation and conjunction, so that $p \bullet \sim q$ (for example) is written as $p\bar{q}$.

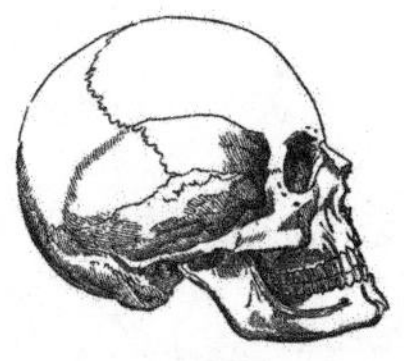

CAUTION

Three-variable K-maps use the alternate notation for negation to save space.

KEY POINT

The simplest proposition is found by grouping the 1s with a minimum number of circles of maximum size.

Notice where the 0s and 1s are placed. The 0 in the upper right corner cell is the output for $\bar{p}qr$ (that is, $\sim p \bullet q \bullet r$), which is output for the fourth row in the truth table. The other 0 is the output for $p\bar{q}r$ (that is, $p \bullet \sim q \bullet r$), the sixth row in the truth table.

Circle the 1s in the K-map as they appear in groups. The groups must be groupings of powers of two, i.e., 1, 2, 4, or 8. We want a minimum number of circles of maximum size. Thus we should circle as shown.

	pq	$p\bar{q}$	$\bar{p}\bar{q}$	$\bar{p}q$
r	1	0	1	0
$\bar{r}$	1	1	1	1

We can now determine the proposition. The circle around the first column (on the left) represents the proposition $p \bullet q$. The circle around the third column represents $\sim p \bullet \sim q$. The circle around the bottom row represents simply $\sim r$. These three propositions are connected with a disjunction.

Consequently, the entire proposition for this K-map is $(p \bullet q) \vee (\sim p \bullet \sim q) \vee \sim r$. The circuit could now be drawn for this proposition. (Note: this can be reduced to only two gates, with some creative simplification.)

We will do one more three-variable K-map to demonstrate another important concept. Consider this truth table and its corresponding K-map:

p	q	r	y
0	0	0	0
0	0	1	0
0	1	0	0
0	1	1	1
1	0	0	1
1	0	1	1
1	1	0	1
1	1	1	1

	pq	$p\bar{q}$	$\bar{p}\bar{q}$	$\bar{p}q$
r	1	1	0	1
$\bar{r}$	1	1	0	0

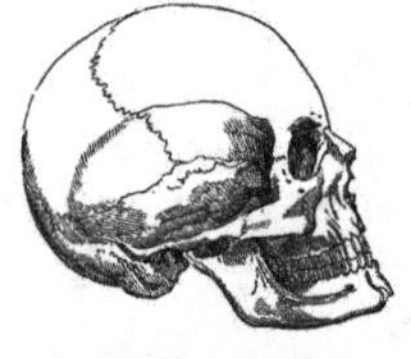

CAUTION

A K-mapping circle can wrap around from one side of the K-map to the other.

You should immediately see that the four 1s in the left half of the K-map should be circled together. But what about the single 1 in the upper right? In fact, this 1 can be connected to the 1 in the upper left square, that is, the K-mapping circle *wraps around.* This is one reason for the given pattern of p and q, in which only one value changes at a time. Thus the circling for this K-map would give this.

	pq	$p\bar{q}$	$\bar{p}\bar{q}$	$\bar{p}q$
r	1	1	0	1
$\bar{r}$	1	1	0	0

The circle around the four left 1s represents the proposition p. The circle wrapping around the two 1s on opposite ends represents the proposition $q \bullet r$ (again, because those are the values that do not change for the cells in this circle).

Thus the entire proposition for this truth table is $p \vee (q \bullet r)$.

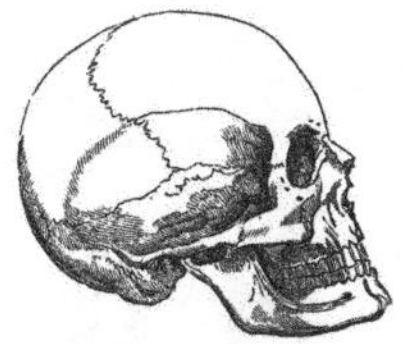

CAUTION

"Don't cares" (variables represented by X) can be used either as a 1 or a 0.

We will look at one example of a **four-variable K-map**, and at the same time introduce one more new idea. Sometimes when using K-maps, you will come across certain variables that are not given a value. These are called "don't cares." When analyzing them in the K-map, they can be used either as a 1 or a 0, depending which choice helps simplify the proposition the most. The letter "X" is used to represent "don't cares" in the truth table and K-map.

Let's consider a real-world example. Recall the decimal displays that we saw in an earlier lesson. You want to design a circuit that will take a binary input, from zero to nine, and produce the decimal value on the display, as shown again here:

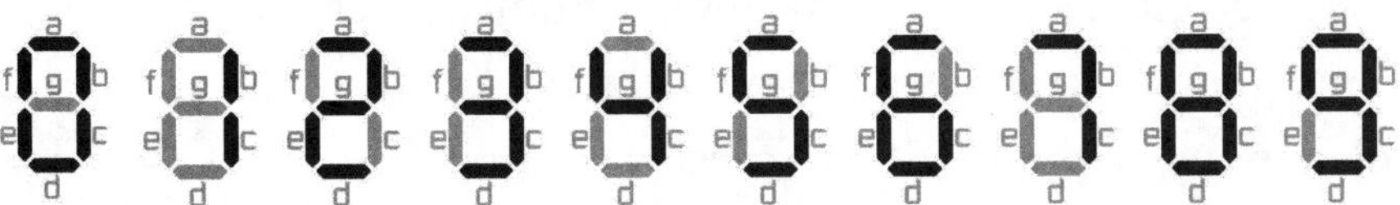

For this example, we will design a circuit that will control the top segment, segment "a." When the segment is "on" the output of the circuit will be 1, when it is "off" it is 0. You can see that the segment "a" is off for the numerals 1 and 4.

The truth table shown below takes the binary input (remember that the truth table counts up in binary) and gives a single output, in this case an output corresponding to whether the segment "a" in the digital display is on or off. Segment "a" is off for the binary one and four, so the output for these are 0. Output values are given for the binary inputs zero to nine; everything else is a "don't care" because the decimal display is only a single digit.

p	q	r	s	a
0	0	0	0	1
0	0	0	1	0
0	0	1	0	1
0	0	1	1	1
0	1	0	0	0
0	1	0	1	1
0	1	1	0	1
0	1	1	1	1
1	0	0	0	1
1	0	0	1	1
1	0	1	0	X
1	0	1	1	X
1	1	0	0	X
1	1	0	1	X
1	1	1	0	X
1	1	1	1	X

	pq	$p\overline{q}$	$\overline{p}\overline{q}$	$\overline{p}q$
rs	X	X	1	1
$r\overline{s}$	X	X	1	1
$\overline{r}\overline{s}$	X	1	1	0
$\overline{r}s$	X	1	0	1

We must now consider how to circle the values to include all of the 1s, with the minimum number of circles (avoiding redundant circles). Remember that the circles must include the number of cells in rectangular groups of powers of two (1, 2, 4, or 8). Also, keep in mind that the larger the circle, the simpler the proposition, even if those large circles include a number of don't cares.

The group of four 1s in the top right can be circled along with the don't cares in the top two rows, as shown. This represents the proposition r, since that is the only value that stays the same for all eight of the cells in this circle.

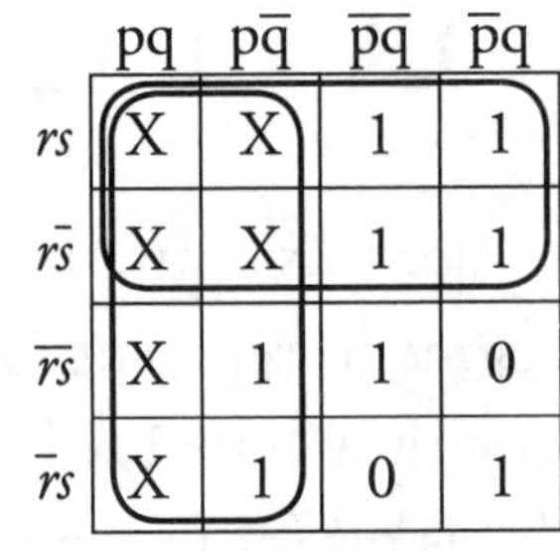

	pq	$p\overline{q}$	$\overline{p}\overline{q}$	$\overline{p}q$
rs	X	X	1	1
$r\overline{s}$	X	X	1	1
$\overline{r}\overline{s}$	X	1	1	0
$\overline{r}s$	X	1	0	1

Next, the two 1s in the bottom of the second column can be circled along with the six don't cares (remember, the larger the circle the better). The proposition represented by that circle is p.

With this done, we have two 1s left to circle. The 1 in the cell for $\overline{p}\overline{q}\overline{r}\overline{s}$ can be included in a circle of four cells right in the middle of the K-map. This would represent the proposition $\sim q \bullet \sim s$. The final 1 in the bottom right cell is most interesting. Remembering the K-map values wrap around, both left-right and up-down, you should realize that a "circle"

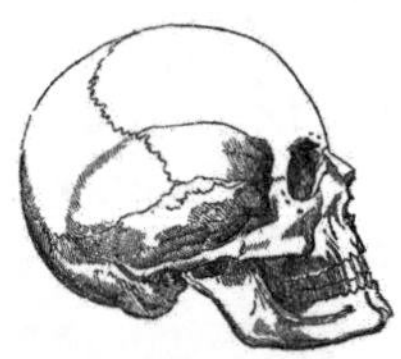

CAUTION

A K-mapping circle can include the four corners of a K-map.

can include the four corners of a K-map. This would be the largest circle to include our final 1, and would represent the proposition $q \bullet s$.

Thus the final circled K-map for our truth table would be as shown here:

	pq	$p\bar{q}$	$\bar{p}\bar{q}$	$\bar{p}q$
rs	X	X	1	1
$r\bar{s}$	X	X	1	1
$\bar{r}\bar{s}$	X	1	1	0
$\bar{r}s$	X	1	0	1

The total proposition would be $p \vee r \vee (q \bullet s) \vee (\sim q \bullet \sim s)$. Now, from Lesson 36, you may recall that $(q \bullet s) \vee (\sim q \bullet \sim s)$ can simplify to $q \equiv s$, thus giving the final proposition as $(p \vee r) \vee (q \equiv s)$.

We draw the circuit for this proposition here, with the output going to the segment *a* of the digital display.

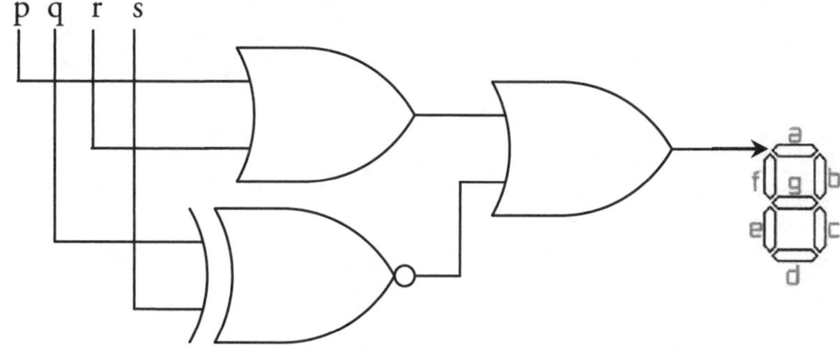

SUMMARY

Karnaugh Mapping Steps

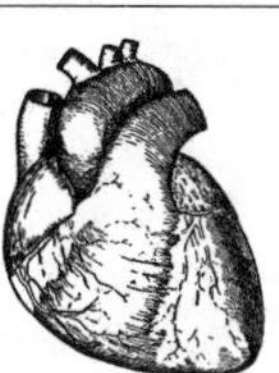

- STEP 1. Draw a table with the number of cells equal to the number of rows in the truth table. Label the axes with the proper combination of variables and negated variables, changing one bit at a time, as in the examples.
- STEP 2. Fill in each cell that has a value of 1 as it is found in the truth table, then fill in all of the remaining cells with 0s.

- Step 3. Circle the 1s in rectangular groups of one, two, four, eight, etc. Use the largest possible circle, and the least number of circles to include all of the 1s.
- Step 4. Identify the common, unchanging elements in the circled groups and "AND" them together.
- Step 5. "OR" together the groups of elements from step 4 into a final proposition.
- Step 6. Draw the logic circuit corresponding to the proposition from Step 5.

Follow the six Karnaugh Mapping steps to quickly and accurately determine a proposition from a truth table. Don't forget that K-mapping circles can wrap around from one side of the K-map to the other and also can include the four corners of a K-map. Use "don't cares" as 1s or 0s to help simplify the proposition as much as possible.

EXERCISE 40a (30 points)

1. Design a "majority detector" circuit. When the majority of the inputs *p*, *q*, and *r* are 0, the output *m* is a 0. When the majority of the inputs are 1, the output is a 1. From the truth table, fill in the K-map, determine the proposition, and draw the circuit. (12)

p	q	r	m
0	0	0	0
0	0	1	0
0	1	0	0
0	1	1	1
1	0	0	0
1	0	1	1
1	1	0	1
1	1	1	1

	pq	$p\bar{q}$	$\bar{p}\bar{q}$	$\bar{p}q$
r	1	1	0	1
$\bar{r}$	1	0	0	0

Proposition: (P•Q) v (P•R) v (Q•R)

Circuit:

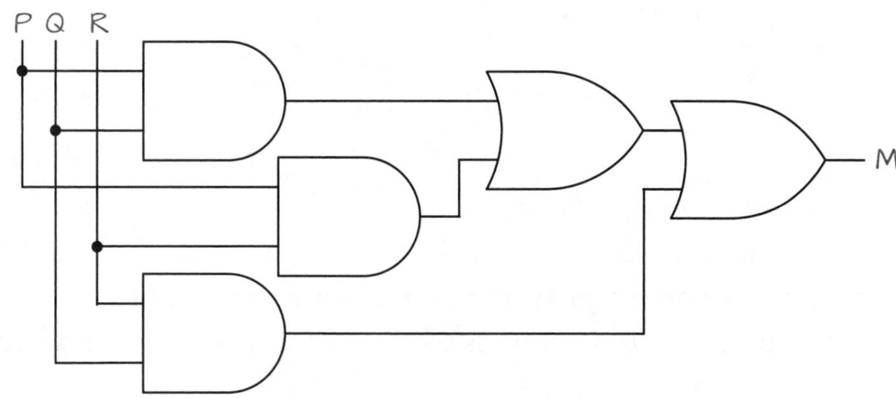

Continued on next page.

2. Design a "half-adder" circuit. The truth table will have two inputs, A and B. It will also have two outputs. The first output will be the value of the sum S. The second will be the "carry" value C. For each output, complete the K-map, and determine the proposition. Draw the circuits to produce the two outputs, with the gates coming from the same input lines. (8)

A	B	S	C
0	0	0	0
0	1	1	0
1	0	1	0
1	1	0	1

OUTPUT S

	A	$\bar{A}$
B	0	1
$\bar{B}$	1	0

OUTPUT C

	A	$\bar{A}$
B	1	0
$\bar{B}$	0	0

Proposition S A⊕B

Proposition C A•B

Circuits:

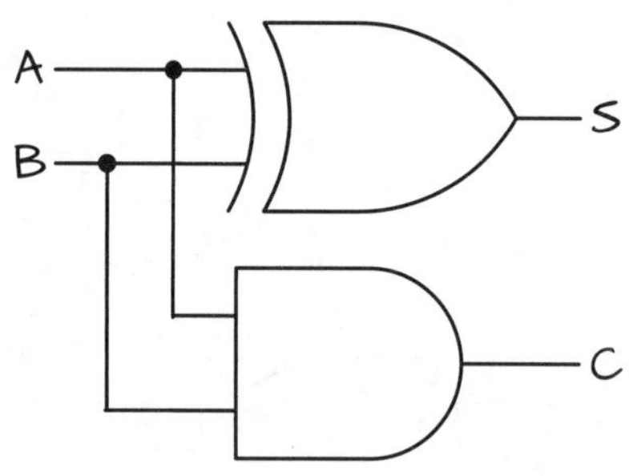

3. Design a "symmetrical" detector circuit. When the inputs *P*, *Q*, and *R* produce a symmetrical pattern of 0s and 1s, the output is a 1. If the input values are not symmetrical, the output is a 0. Complete the K-map, proposition, and circuit. (10)

P	Q	R	S
0	0	0	1
0	0	1	0
0	1	0	1
0	1	1	0
1	0	0	0
1	0	1	1
1	1	0	0
1	1	1	1

	PQ	$P\bar{Q}$	$\bar{P}\bar{Q}$	$\bar{P}Q$
R	1	1	0	0
$\bar{R}$	0	0	1	1

Proposition: P≡R

Circuit:

QUIZ 19 (LESSONS 38–40)

STUDENT OBJECTIVE

Complete Quiz 19.

TEACHING INSTRUCTIONS

1. Give Quiz 19. Allow 30 minutes. Grade quiz with students.
2. If you have extra time, introduce Exercise 40b to get a head start on next class's material.

INTERMEDIATE LOGIC | Quiz 19

Lessons 38–40 (19 points)

Name ______________________________

1. Simplify the following circuit so that it only uses two gates. Draw the simplified circuit to the right. (3)

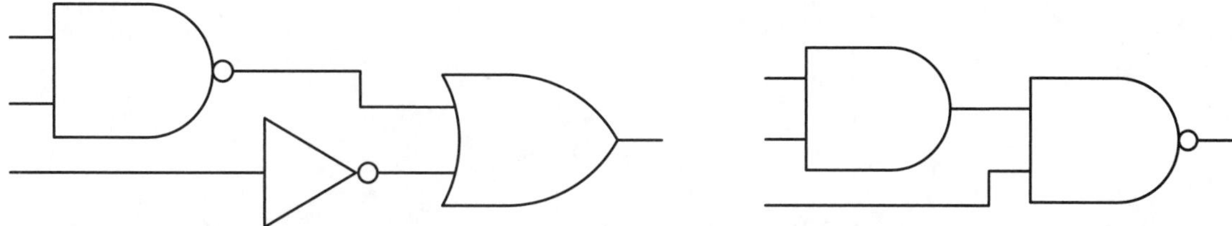

2. Complete the defining truth tables for XOR and XNOR: (4)

p	q	$p \oplus q$	$p \equiv q$
0	0	0	1
0	1	1	0
1	0	1	0
1	1	0	1

3. Complete the K-map for the given truth table. Write a simplified proposition to produce that output, and draw the corresponding digital logic circuit with the minimum number of gates. (12)

p	q	r	x
0	0	0	1
0	0	1	1
0	1	0	1
0	1	1	0
1	0	0	1
1	0	1	1
1	1	0	0
1	1	1	1

	pq	$p\bar{q}$	$\bar{p}\bar{q}$	$\bar{p}q$
r	1	1	1	0
$\bar{r}$	0	1	1	1

Proposition: $\sim [Q \bullet (P \oplus R)]$

Circuit:

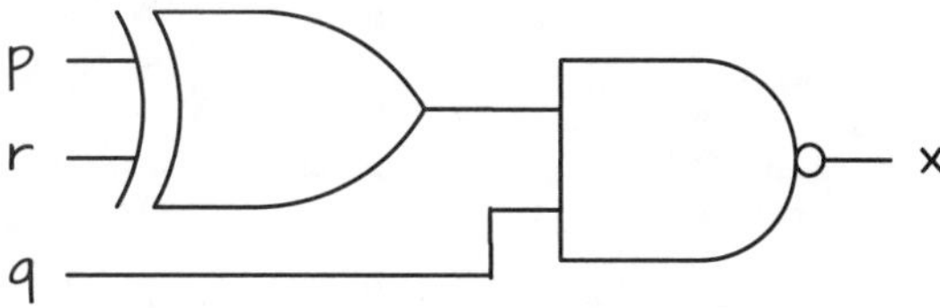

DIGITAL LOGIC PROJECT

Intermediate Logic, pp. 323–325

STUDENT OBJECTIVE

Design a binary to decimal converter logic circuit.

SPECIAL NOTE

Depending on which schedule you're following, you have several days to work through the digital logic project with students. It's up to you how hands-on or hands-off you want to be with the project, or whether you want to students to work together on the whole project or portion out different parts to different students. Assess your students' abilities and do whatever would be most beneficial but also most enjoyable for them.

TEACHING INSTRUCTION

Help students work through Exercise 40b.

ASSIGNMENT

Have students complete Exercise 40b, and go over it with them.

EXERCISE 40b — DIGITAL LOGIC PROJECT (100 points)

Goal

Design the logic circuits necessary to convert binary numbers into decimal numbers.

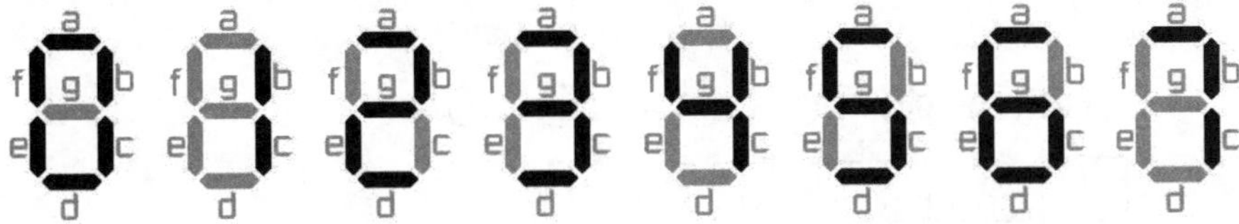

Directions

For this project, design the circuits necessary to produce the displays shown above. You will have three inputs—*P*, *Q* and *R*—and seven outputs, corresponding to the seven segments of a digital display, a-g. Use the following procedure:

1. Complete the truth tables below for the display outputs that correspond to the binary inputs. Each output letter designates one of the seven segments on the display. If a segment on the display is "on" the output is 1. If the segment is "off" the output is 0. (7)
2. On the next page, use the truth tables to fill in the K-maps for each lettered output, a through g. (28)
3. Use the K-maps to determine the propositions that produce the seven outputs. Write the proposition for each output next to its K-map. Simplify the propositions as much as possible. (35)
4. On the last page, draw the circuits for the propositions. Connect the input lines for each circuit to the input lines drawn to combine these into one total circuit with three inputs and seven outputs. Show each output going to the proper segment of the display. (30)

INPUTS				OUTPUTS						
Decimal	P	Q	R	a	b	c	d	e	f	g
0	0	0	0	1	1	1	1	1	1	0
1	0	0	1	0	1	1	0	0	0	0
2	0	1	0	1	1	0	1	1	0	1
3	0	1	1	1	1	1	1	0	0	1
4	1	0	0	0	1	1	0	0	1	1
5	1	0	1	1	0	1	1	0	1	1
6	1	1	0	1	0	1	1	1	1	1
7	1	1	1	1	1	1	0	0	0	0

Continued on next page.

PROPOSITIONS

SEGMENT a

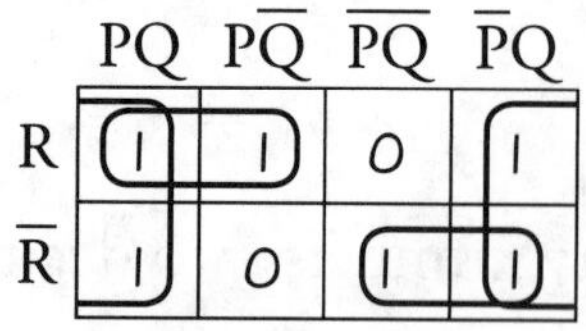

	PQ	$P\overline{Q}$	$\overline{P}\,\overline{Q}$	$\overline{P}Q$
R	1	1	0	1
$\overline{R}$	1	0	1	1

$(P \equiv R) \vee Q$

(Answers may vary, but must be equivalent.)

SEGMENT b

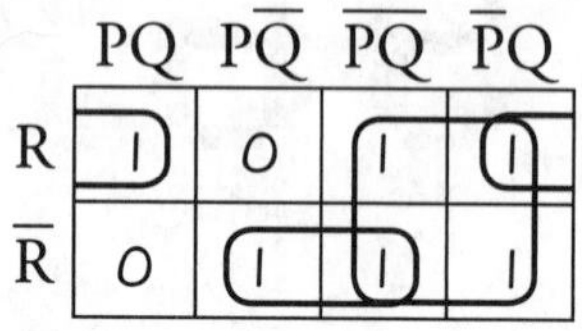

	PQ	$P\overline{Q}$	$\overline{P}\,\overline{Q}$	$\overline{P}Q$
R	1	0	1	1
$\overline{R}$	0	1	1	1

$\sim[P \bullet (Q \oplus R)]$

SEGMENT c

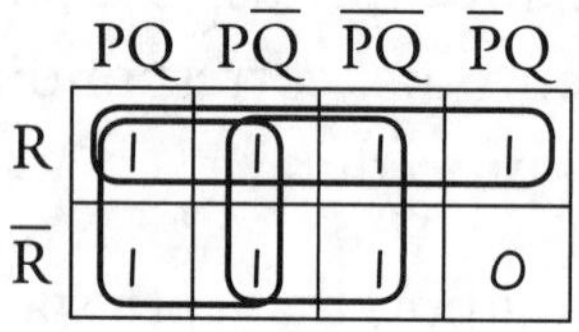

	PQ	$P\overline{Q}$	$\overline{P}\,\overline{Q}$	$\overline{P}Q$
R	1	1	1	1
$\overline{R}$	1	1	1	0

$\sim[\sim(P \vee R) \bullet Q]$

SEGMENT d

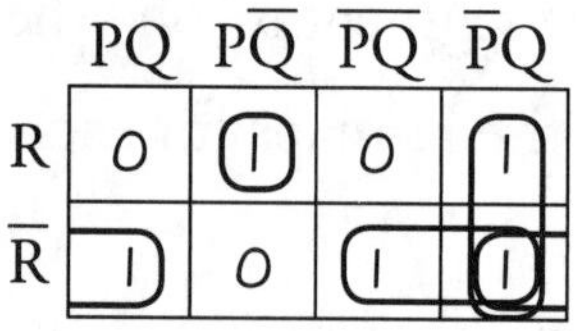

	PQ	$P\overline{Q}$	$\overline{P}\,\overline{Q}$	$\overline{P}Q$
R	0	1	0	1
$\overline{R}$	1	0	1	1

$\sim(P \vee R) \vee [Q \oplus (P \bullet R)]$

SEGMENT e

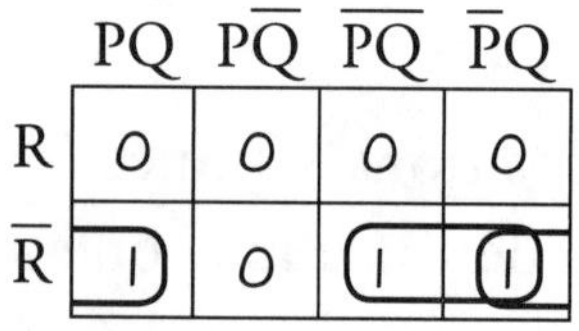

	PQ	$P\overline{Q}$	$\overline{P}\,\overline{Q}$	$\overline{P}Q$
R	0	0	0	0
$\overline{R}$	1	0	1	1

$\sim[(P \bullet \sim Q) \vee R]$

SEGMENT f

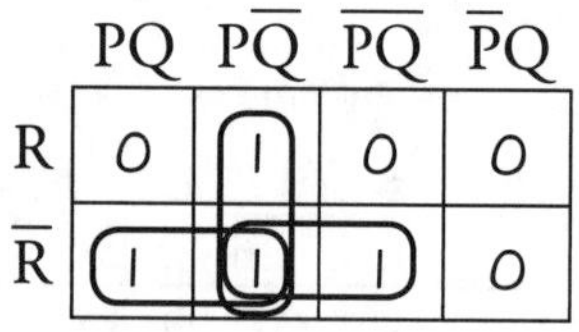

	PQ	$P\overline{Q}$	$\overline{P}\,\overline{Q}$	$\overline{P}Q$
R	0	1	0	0
$\overline{R}$	1	1	1	0

$[P \bullet \sim(Q \bullet R)] \vee \sim(Q \vee R)$

SEGMENT g

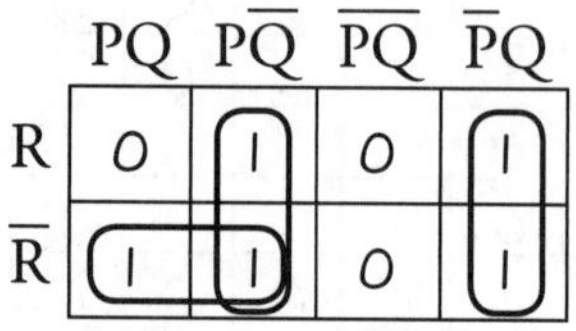

	PQ	$P\overline{Q}$	$\overline{P}\,\overline{Q}$	$\overline{P}Q$
R	0	1	0	1
$\overline{R}$	1	1	0	1

$(P \oplus Q) \vee (P \bullet \sim R)$

Continued on next page.

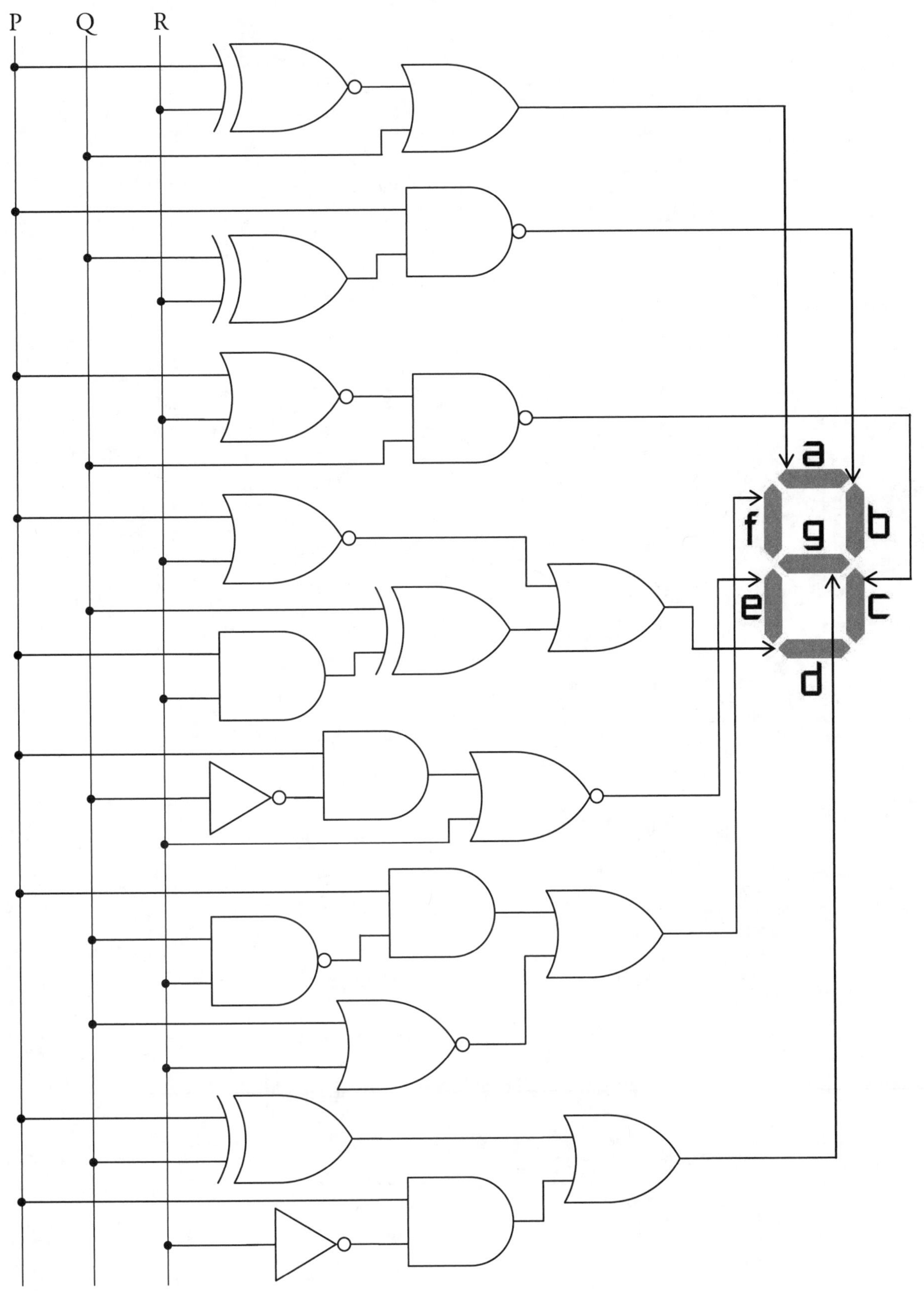

P
Q
R
a
b
c
d
e
f
g

REVIEW FOR TEST 8 (LESSONS 29–40)

STUDENT OBJECTIVES

Complete the objectives from Lessons 29–40. Objectives are listed at the beginning of each lesson's teacher's notes.

TEACHING INSTRUCTIONS

1. To review for the test, choose problems from the Review Questions for Lessons 29–40 on pp. 327–329 and from the Review Exercises for Lessons 29–40 on pp. 331–350 of the student text for students to work through.
2. If you'd like, give students "Test 8: Form A" from the *Intermediate Logic Test and Quiz Packet* as a practice exam. Go over the answers together.

ASSIGNMENT

Have students study for Test 8.

TEST 8 (LESSONS 29–40)

STUDENT OBJECTIVE

Complete Test 8.

TEACHING INSTRUCTIONS

1. Give students Test 8: Form B from the *Intermediate Logic Test and Quiz Packet.* Allow one hour to complete it.
2. Grade tests. Have them ready to hand back to students within a week.

INTERMEDIATE LOGIC | Test 8, Form A

Lessons 29–40 (53 points)

Name ______________________

1. What is digital logic? (2) Digital logic is a branch of formal logic used in electronic devices.

2. In the digital display, fill in the segments that would be on for the numeral 7. Then complete the binary representation by writing 1s and 0s beneath the segment letters. (3)

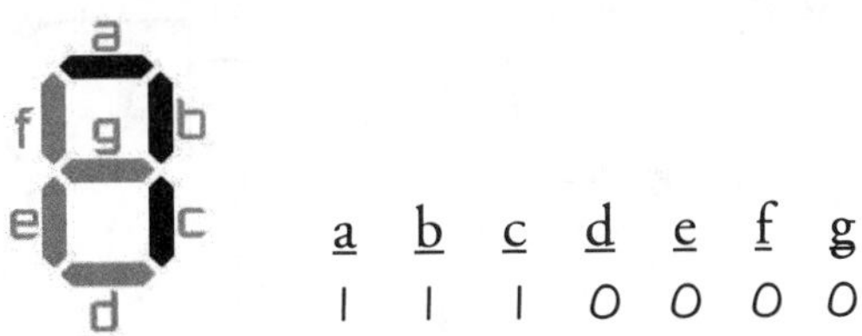

a	b	c	d	e	f	g
1	1	1	0	0	0	0

3. Complete the binary counting table. (6)

Decimal	Binary
6	110
7	111
8	1000
9	1001
10	1010
11	1011
12	1100

4. Convert the binary number 11010 into a regular decimal number (3): 26

5. Convert the regular decimal number 79 into binary (3): 1001111

Problems 6-7: Complete the binary arithmetic. (3, 5)

6.
```
  11100
 + 1101
 ------
 101001
```

7.
```
    1101
  × 1001
 -------
 1110101
```

8. What is the proposition for the digital logic circuit shown? (3) (P ∨ Q)•~(Q•R)

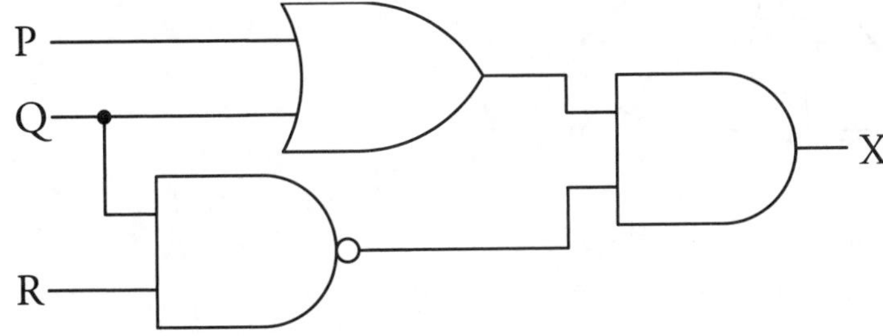

P	Q	R	X
0	0	0	0
0	0	1	0
0	1	0	1
0	1	1	0
1	0	0	1
1	0	1	1
1	1	0	1
1	1	1	0

9. Complete the given truth table for this circuit. (5)

10. Using only NAND gates, design a circuit equivalent to $P \vee Q$. (4)

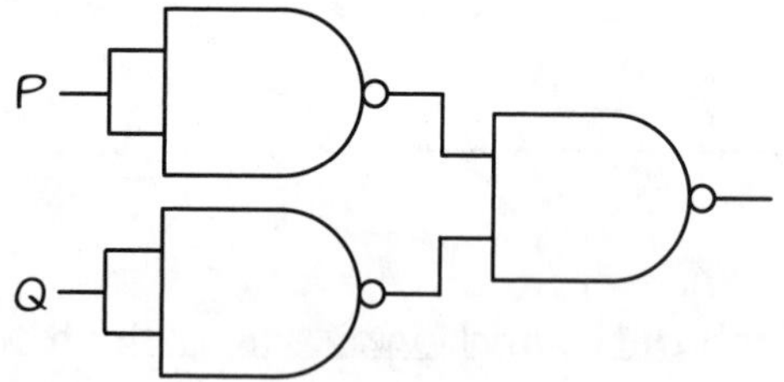

11. Use bubble pushing to reduce the circuit below to only two gates. Draw the final circuit in the space to the right. (4)

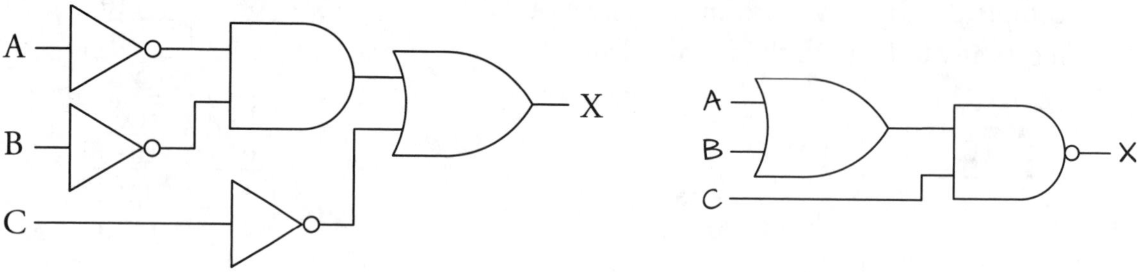

12. Complete the K-map for the given truth table. Write a simplified proposition to produce that output, and draw the corresponding digital logic circuit with the minimum number of gates. (12)

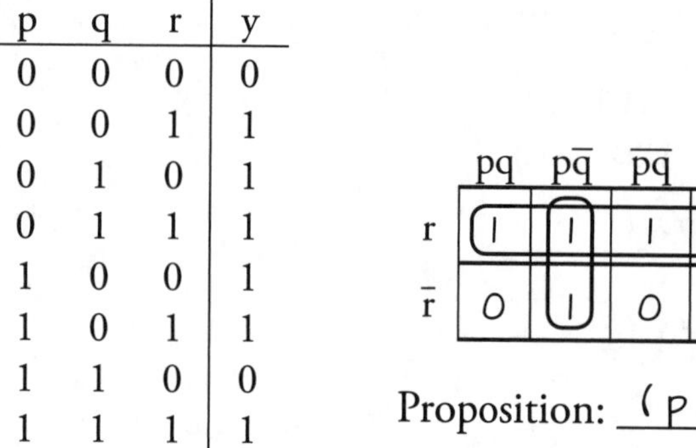

p	q	r	y
0	0	0	0
0	0	1	1
0	1	0	1
0	1	1	1
1	0	0	1
1	0	1	1
1	1	0	0
1	1	1	1

	pq	$p\bar{q}$	$\bar{p}\bar{q}$	$\bar{p}q$
r	1	1	1	1
$\bar{r}$	0	1	0	1

Proposition: $(p \oplus q) \vee r$

Circuit:

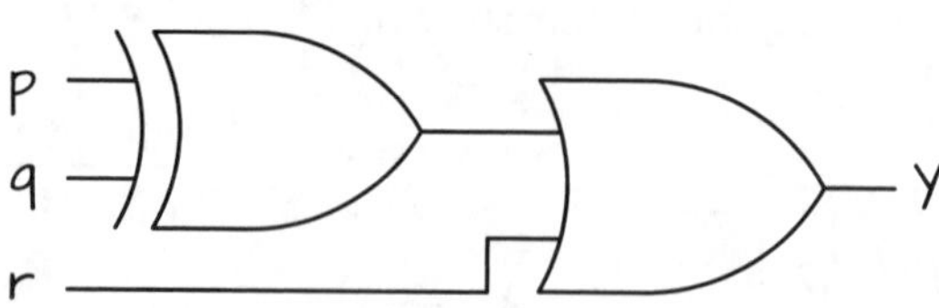

INTERMEDIATE LOGIC | Test 8, Form B

Lessons 29–40 (51 points)

Name ______________________________

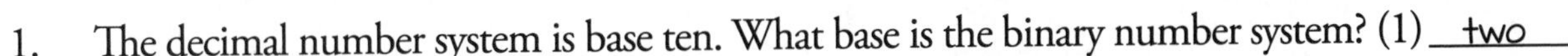

1. The decimal number system is base ten. What base is the binary number system? (1) two

2. In the digital display, fill in the segments that would be on for the numeral 4. Then complete the binary representation by writing 1s and 0s beneath the segment letters. (3)

3. If the binary representation in the answer to question 2 is a binary number, what is its equivalent decimal number? (3)

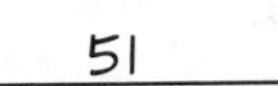

51

a	b	c	d	e	f	g
0	1	1	0	0	1	1

4. What is the decimal equivalent to the binary number 101010? (3) 42

5. What is the binary equivalent to the decimal number 129? (4) 10000001

Problems 6-7: Complete the binary arithmetic. (3, 5)

6.
```
  1110
- 1001
------
   101
```

7.
```
   1101
  × 101
-------
1000001
```

8. What is the proposition for the digital logic circuit shown? (3) ~[(P•Q) v R]

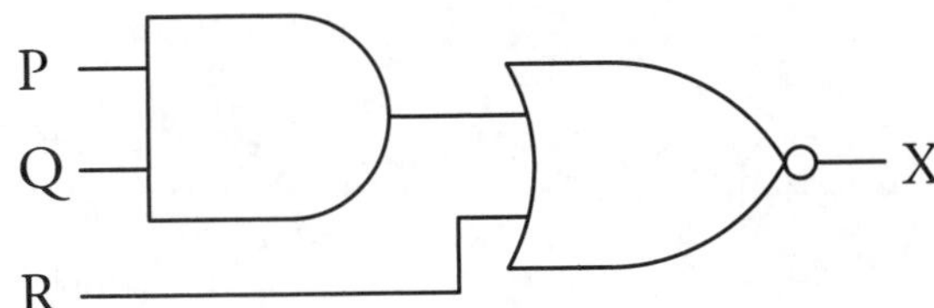

P	Q	R	X
0	0	0	1
0	0	1	0
0	1	0	1
0	1	1	0
1	0	0	1
1	0	1	0
1	1	0	0
1	1	1	0

9. Complete the given truth table for this circuit. (5)

 |

10. Using only NOR gates, design a circuit for the proposition p • ~ q. (5)

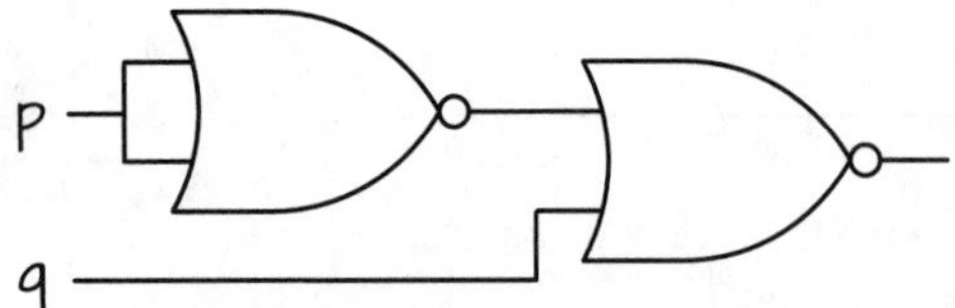

11. Use bubble pushing to reduce the circuit below to only two gates. Draw the final circuit in the space to the right. (4)

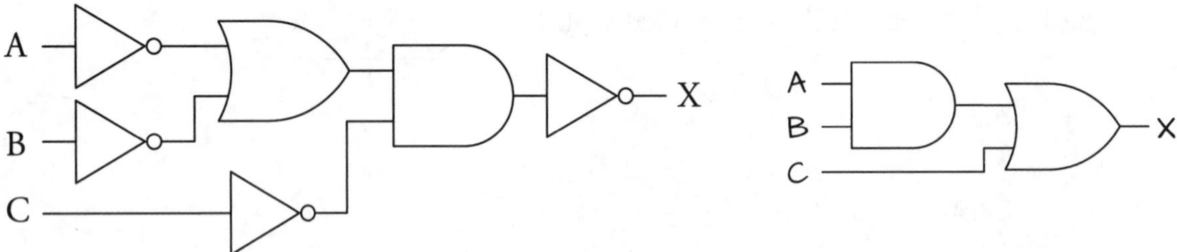

12. Complete the K-map for the truth table. Write a simplified proposition to produce that output, and draw the corresponding digital logic circuit with the minimum number of gates. (12)

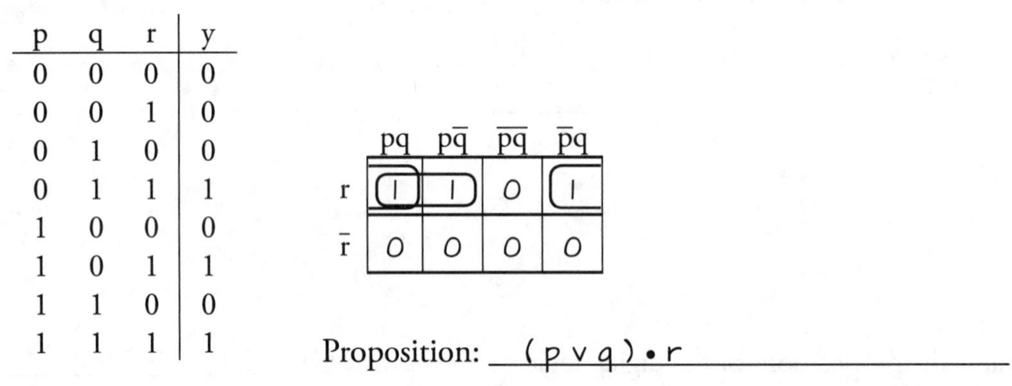

p	q	r	y
0	0	0	0
0	0	1	0
0	1	0	0
0	1	1	1
1	0	0	0
1	0	1	1
1	1	0	0
1	1	1	1

	pq	$p\bar{q}$	$\bar{p}\bar{q}$	$\bar{p}q$
r	1	1	0	1
$\bar{r}$	0	0	0	0

Proposition: (p ∨ q) • r

Circuit:

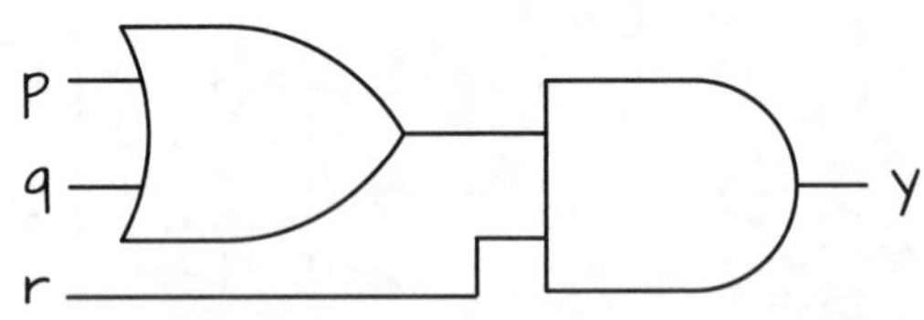

UNIT 5

REVIEW QUESTIONS

Answers can be found in the lesson under which the questions are listed.

Lesson 29

What is digital logic? In digital logic, what is a bit? What is a byte? What do digital logic and ordinary propositional logic have in common? How do they differ? What is a digital display? What number is used to represent the lettered segments of a digital display as "on"? As "off"?

Lesson 30

What base is used in the decimal number system? What base is used in the binary number system? How do place values work in a number? What two numerals are used to make every other number in binary? How are binary numbers converted into decimal numbers, and vice versa?

Lesson 31

What are the basic operations of arithmetic? How is the number two written in binary? How is the number three written in binary? What is the procedure for adding binary numbers? What is the procedure for subtracting binary numbers? How is multiplication in binary identical to multiplication in decimal, and how is it different? How is a binary number doubled?

Lesson 32

What is a logic gate? How many outputs does a logic gate have? In digital logic, what number represents true? What number represents false? How many inputs does a NOT gate have? What is another name for a NOT gate? When is the output for a NOT gate false? How many inputs does an AND gate have? When is the output for an AND gate true? How many inputs does an OR gate have? When is the output for an OR gate true? How does an OR gate differ in appearance from an AND gate? How are logic gates connected to form logic circuits?

Lesson 33

How can a logic circuit be used to find the truth table for a compound proposition? What other method can be used to find the truth table for a compound proposition?

Lesson 34

When determining the proposition for a given truth table, what rows in the truth table are considered? How is a proposition for a given row of a truth table produced? What logical operator is used to combine these propositions from each row to make the final compound proposition?

Lesson 35

What compound proposition does a NOR gate represent? When is the output for a NOR gate true? How does a NOR gate differ in appearance from an OR gate? What compound proposition does a NAND gate represent? When is the output for a NAND gate false? How does a NAND gate differ in appearance from an AND gate? How can NAND and NOR gates be used to simplify circuits? What does it mean that NOR (or NAND) is truth-functionally complete? How is a NOT gate produced out of a single NOR gate or NAND gate? How many NOR gates are needed to produce an OR gate? How many NOR gates are needed to produce an AND gate?

Lesson 36

What is the output of a logic circuit that represents a tautology? What is the output of a logic circuit that represents a self-contradiction? What are the four basic algebraic identities? How are these rules beneficial in the design of digital logic circuits?

Lesson 37

How does the rule of double negation help to simplify logic circuits? What are the two rules of distribution? What are the two rules of commutation? How can these rules be used to simplify logic circuits? Can other rules of simplification be developed?

Lesson 38

What are the two rules of De Morgan's Theorem? How many NOT gates can be eliminated by one use of De Morgan's Theorem? What is bubble pushing, and how does it work? In bubble pushing, what is a 'bubble' equivalent to?

Lesson 39

What compound proposition does an XOR gate represent? When is the output for an XOR gate true? How does an XOR gate differ in appearance from an OR gate? What symbol is used for the XOR logical operation? What compound proposition does an XNOR gate represent? How does a XNOR gate differ in appearance from an XOR gate? When is the output for an XNOR gate true? What symbol is used for the XNOR logical operation?

Lesson 40

What process is made easier by Karnaugh mapping? How many rows and columns in a two-variable K-map? a three-variable K-map? a four-variable K-map? What is the proper pattern of the variables and their negations for the columns of a three-variable K-map? for the columns and rows of a four-variable K-map? Once a K-map is filled out from a truth table, what truth values are circled? What rules must be followed when circling them? What does it mean that circles in a K-map 'wrap around'? What is a 'don't care'? How do we determine whether a given 'don't care' should be a one or zero? What are the steps for translating a truth table into a logic circuit using a Karnaugh Map?

UNIT 5

REVIEW EXERCISES

Students may do these exercises for further review of this unit.

ADDITIONAL EXERCISES FOR LESSON 29

1. Using the following digital display for the numeral 7, write out the binary representation:

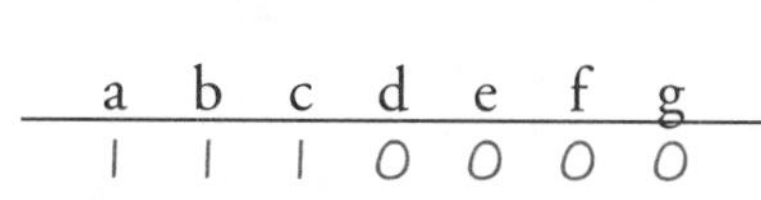

a	b	c	d	e	f	g
1	1	1	0	0	0	0

2. In a digital display, what numeral is shown when all the segments are on?

   The numeral 8.

3. Given the binary representation below, what numeral would appear on a digital display?

a	b	c	d	e	f	g
1	1	0	1	1	0	1

   The numeral 2.

4. Since there are two states ("on" or "off") for each of the seven segments on a digital display, how many total possible patterns can be created? Which patterns are recognizable symbols?

   There are 2^7, or 128, total patterns. Many are recognizable (e.g., the ten numerals and several capital letters).

ADDITIONAL EXERCISES FOR LESSON 30

1. In binary, what is the final digit in any even number? In any odd number?

   The final digit in any even number is 0, in any odd number is 1.

2. How is a binary number modified when it is multiplied by two? By four? By 2^n?

   To multiply by two, put 0 on the end. To multiply by four, put 00 on the end. To multiply by 2^n, place n zeroes on the end.

3. Using the provided table, write out the number 1,728 according to the different places.

Place:	Fifth	Fourth	Third	Second	First
Can hold	10,000s	1000s	100s	10s	1s
Power	10^4	10^3	10^2	10^1	10^0
Example		1	7	2	8

   $\underline{0} \times 10^4 + \underline{1} \times 10^3 + \underline{7} \times 10^2 + \underline{2} \times 10^1 + \underline{8} \times 10^0 = \underline{1{,}728}$

4. Complete the table counting from 16 to 20 in binary.

Decimal Number	Binary Number
16	10000
17	10001
18	10010
19	10011
20	10100

5. Convert the binary number 10101 into decimal. 21
6. Convert the binary number 100001 into decimal. 33
7. Convert the decimal number 42 into binary. 101010
8. Convert the following decimal numbers into binary:

   15 1111   31 11111   63 111111

   127 1111111   255 11111111

9. What do you notice about all binary numbers that are one less than a power of 2 (i.e., the numbers 2^n-1)?

   They are made up entirely of 1s.

ADDITIONAL EXERCISES FOR LESSON 31

Problems 1–3: Perform the binary addition. Check your work by converting the numbers to decimal.

1.
```
  101100
+ 111010
--------
 1100110
```
(44 + 58 = 102)

2.
```
  11111
+     1
-------
 100000
```
(31 + 1 = 32)

3.
```
  110100
+  11101
--------
 1010001
```
(52 + 29 = 81)

Problems 4–9: Perform the binary subtraction. Check your answers either by addition or by converting the numbers to decimal.

4.
```
  1001
- 1000
------
     1
```
(9 - 8 = 1)

5.
```
  1111
-  110
------
  1001
```
(15 - 6 = 9)

6.
```
  101
-  10
-----
   11
```
(5 - 2 = 3)

7.
```
  1101
- 1011
------
    10
```
(13 - 11 = 2)

8.
```
  10001
-  1011
-------
    110
```
(17 - 11 = 6)

9.
```
  10100
- 10110
-------
INVALID
```

Problems 10–13: Perform the binary multiplication. Convert the binary numbers to decimal and multiply to check your work.

10.
```
  100
×  10
-----
 1000
```
(4 x 2 = 8)

11.
```
  101
×  11
-----
 1111
```
(5 x 3 = 15)

12.
```
  1001
×  101
------
101101
```
(9 x 5 = 45)

13.
```
   111
×  111
------
110001
```
(7 x 7 = 49)

ADDITIONAL EXERCISES FOR LESSON 32

Draw the digital logic circuit for the given propositions.

1. ~(A ∨ B)

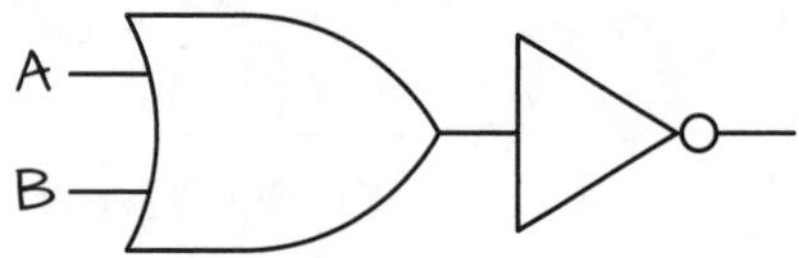

2. ~A ∨ (A • B)

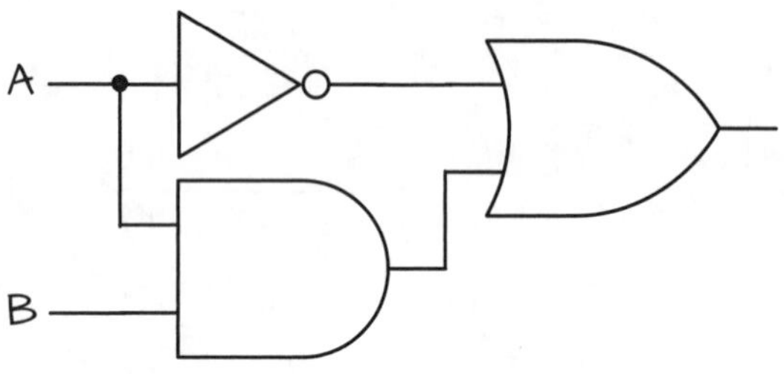

3. (A • ~B) ∨ (~A • B)

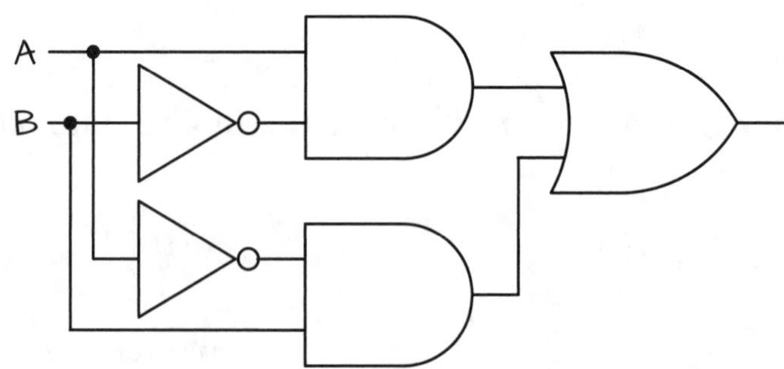

Write the proposition for the given digital logic circuit.

4.

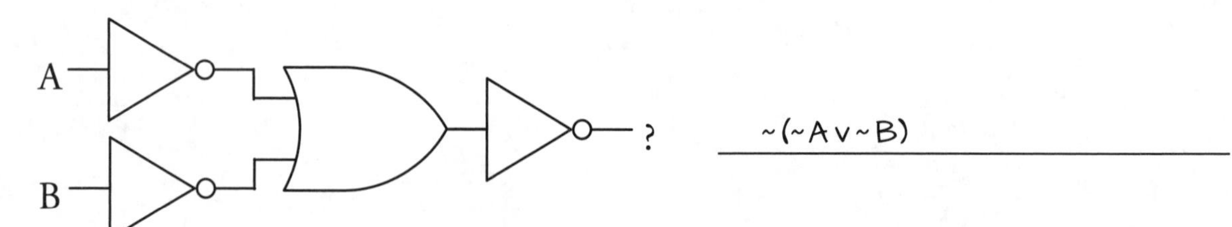

5.

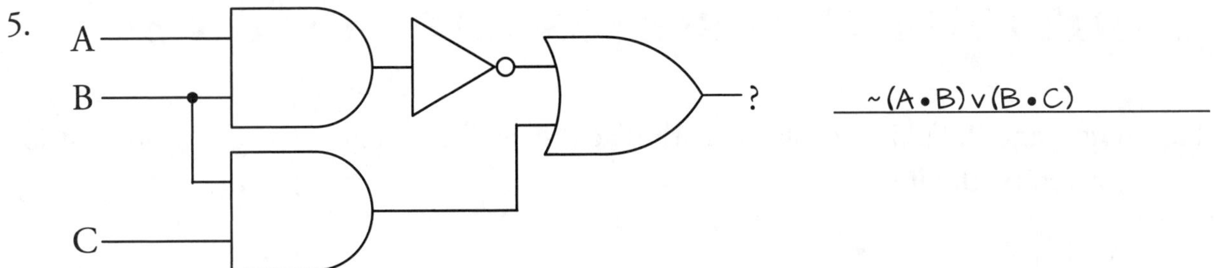

~(A•B)v(B•C)

ADDITIONAL EXERCISES FOR LESSON 33

Complete the truth table for the given circuit.

1. ~(~A ∨ B)

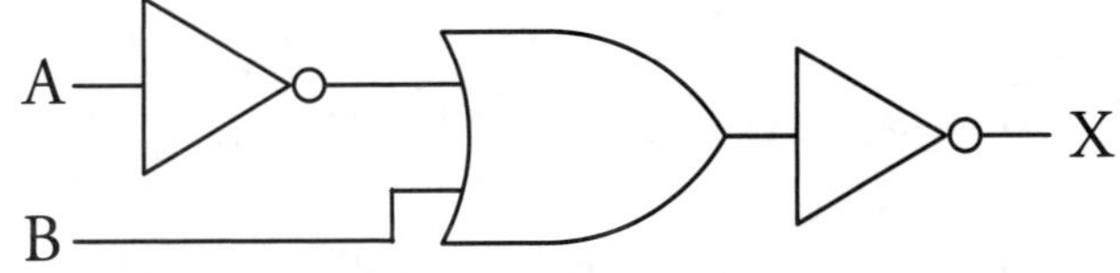

A	B	X
0	0	0
0	1	0
1	0	1
1	1	0

2. (A • B) ∨ (B • C)

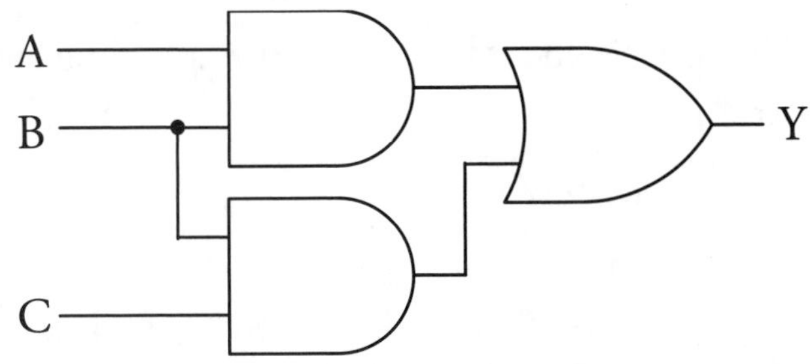

A	B	C	Y
0	0	0	0
0	0	1	0
0	1	0	0
0	1	1	1
1	0	0	0
1	0	1	0
1	1	0	1
1	1	1	1

3. Draw the circuit and complete the truth table for the proposition (~A • B) ∨ (A • ~B).

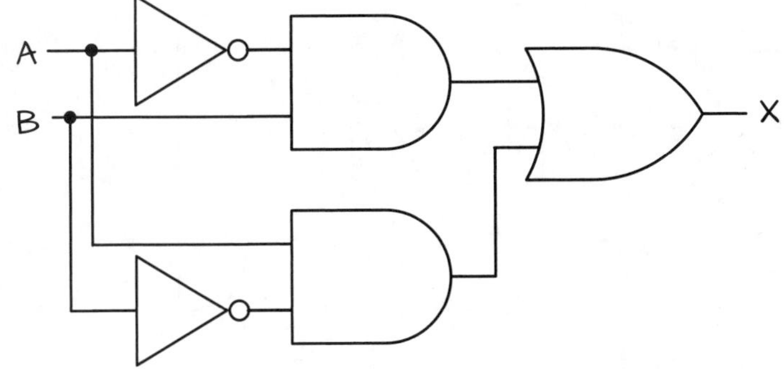

A	B	X
0	0	0
0	1	1
1	0	1
1	1	0

ADDITIONAL EXERCISES FOR LESSON 34

Problems 1 and 2: Fill in the blanks with true or false, and then determine a proposition for the given truth table.

1.

A	B	X
0	0	0
0	1	0
1	0	1
1	1	0

A•~B

← X is true when A is true and B is false.

2.

A	B	C	Y
0	0	0	0
0	0	1	0
0	1	0	0
0	1	1	1
1	0	0	0
1	0	1	1
1	1	0	0
1	1	1	1

(~A•B•C) v (A•~B•C) v (A•B•C)

Y is true when

← A is false and B is true and C is true

OR

← A is true and B is false and C is true

OR

← A is true and B is true and C is true.

3. For the given truth table, determine the proposition and draw the corresponding circuit. Use a separate sheet of paper if necessary.

A	B	C	Z
0	0	0	1
0	0	1	0
0	1	0	0
0	1	1	0
1	0	0	1
1	0	1	0
1	1	0	0
1	1	1	1

(~A•~B•~C) v (A•~B•~C) v (A•B•C)

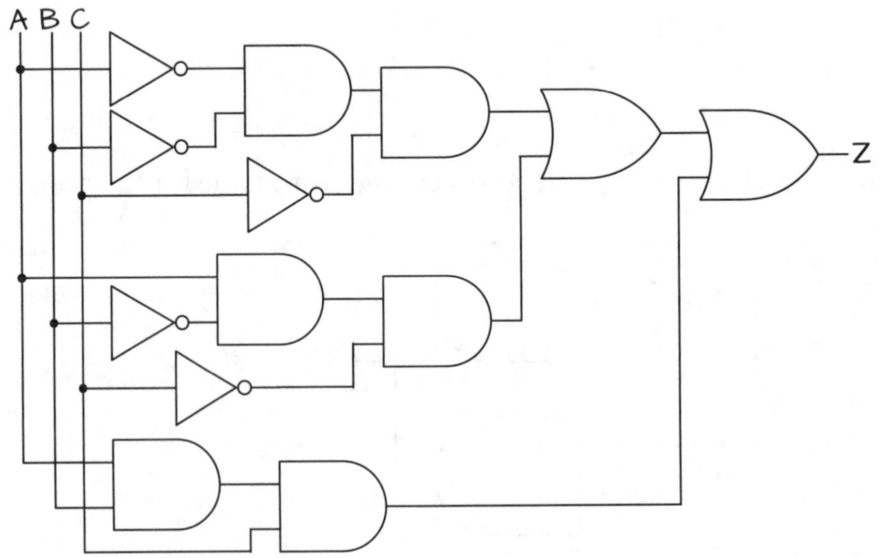

A B C

Z

ADDITIONAL EXERCISES FOR LESSON 35

Problems 1 and 2: Write the propositions and determine the truth tables for the circuits shown.

1.

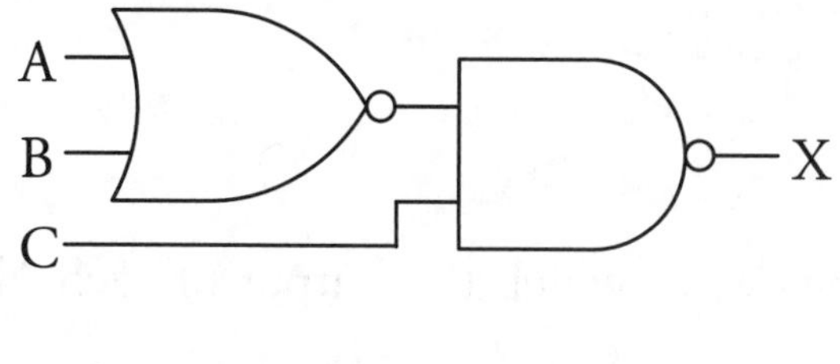

$\sim[\sim(A \vee B) \bullet C]$

A	B	C	X
0	0	0	1
0	0	1	0
0	1	0	1
0	1	1	1
1	0	0	1
1	0	1	1
1	1	0	1
1	1	1	1

2.

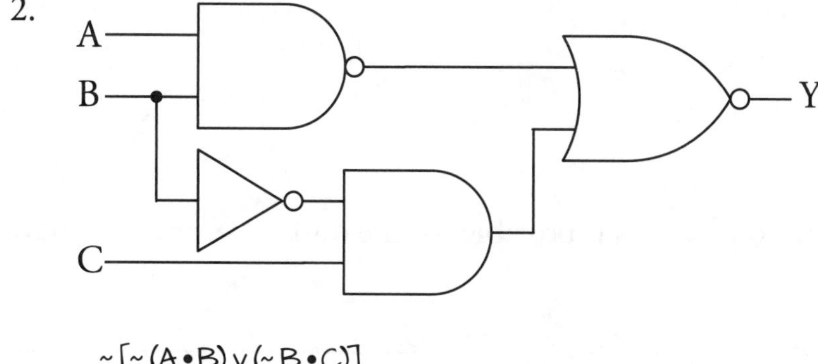

$\sim[\sim(A \bullet B) \vee (\sim B \bullet C)]$

A	B	C	Y
0	0	0	0
0	0	1	0
0	1	0	0
0	1	1	0
1	0	0	0
1	0	1	0
1	1	0	1
1	1	1	1

3. Using only NOR gates, produce a circuit equivalent to the proposition $p \vee \sim q$.

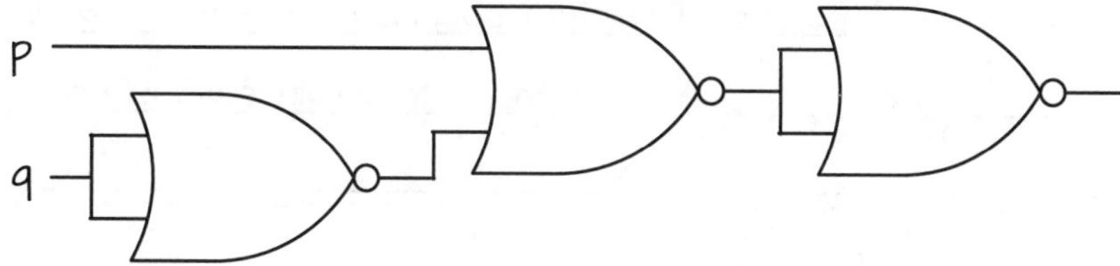

4. Using only NAND gates, produce a circuit equivalent to a NOR gate.

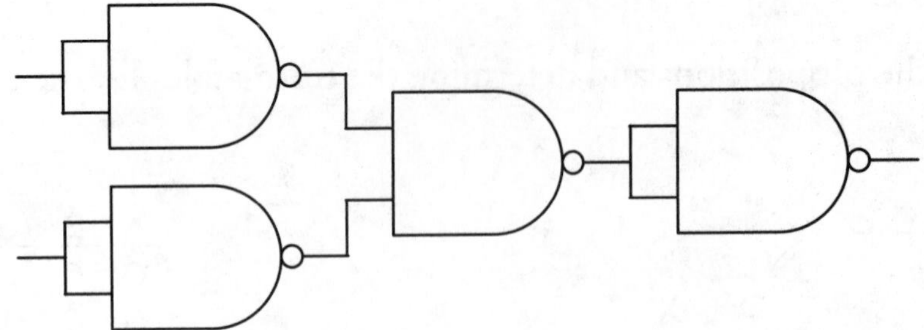

Problems 5–8: Consider the circuit shown below, in which the output of each NOR gate is an input of the other.

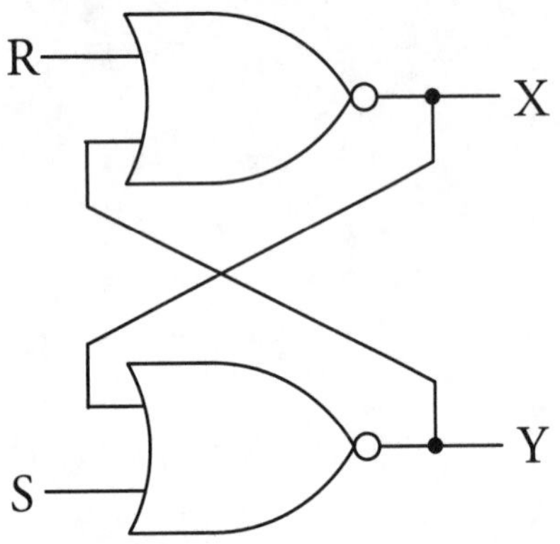

5. If the inputs S and R are both 0 (false), is it possible for the outputs X and Y to have the same truth value?

No, one must be true (1) and the other must be false (0).

6. Imagine that the inputs S and R were both 0, the output X was 0 and Y was 1. If the input S was given the truth value 1, how would that affect the output values? Would the output values change if the input S was again given the value 0?

If S were given the truth value 1, the output values would reverse: X would be 1, Y would be 0. If S was again given the value of 0, the output values would not change.

7. Now imagine that the inputs S and R were both 0, the output X was 1 and Y was 0. If the input R was given the truth value 1, how would that affect the output values? Would the output values change if the input R was again given the value 0?

   If R were given the truth value 1, the output values would again reverse: X would be 0, Y would be 1. If R was again given the value 0, the output values would not change.

8. In electronics, such a circuit is called a *flip flop*. Research flip flop circuits to see how they are used.

   Flip flop circuits have two stable states and can be used as memory devices to store state information. The inputs S and R can be thought of as set and reset, and the outputs X and Y have stable but opposite truth values. As seen in the previous questions, changing one input value can cause the output values to reverse. They maintain these new values until the other input value is changed.

ADDITIONAL EXERCISES FOR LESSON 36

1. Design a tautology circuit using only NAND gates.

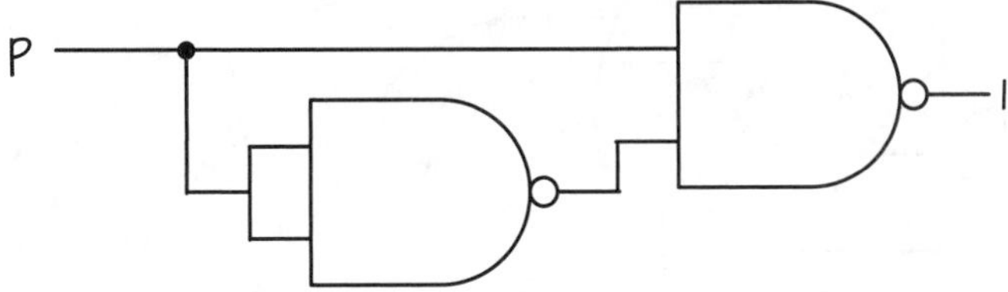

2. In the lesson a truth table was used to show that $p \vee 1 = 1$. Use truth tables to prove the other three identities.

p	0	p∨0
0	0	0
1	0	1

p∨0=p

p	1	p•1
0	1	0
1	1	1

p•1=p

p	0	p•0
0	0	0
1	0	0

p•0=0

Problems 3–4: Simplify the proposition, then draw the circuit for the simplified proposition.

3. [(A • ~A) ∨ B] ∨ C

Simplifies to B ∨ C

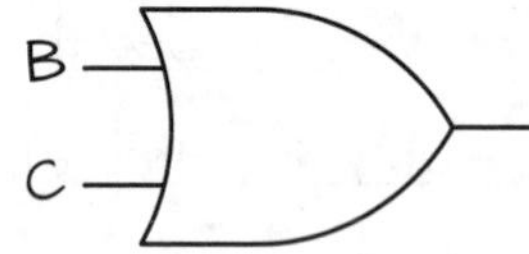

4. ~[A • (B ∨ ~B)] ∨ [C • ~(D • ~D)]

Simplifies to ~A ∨ C

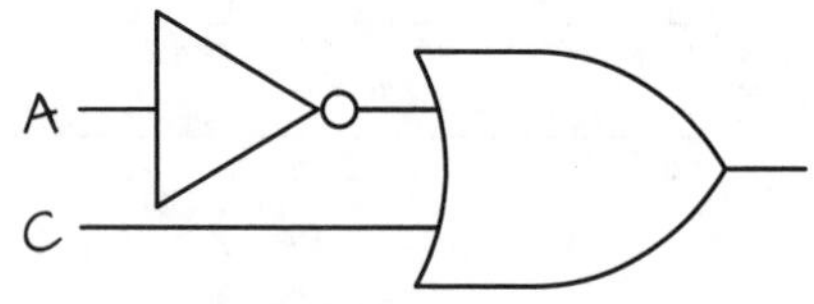

5. Simplify the following circuit.

Simplifies to B ∨ C

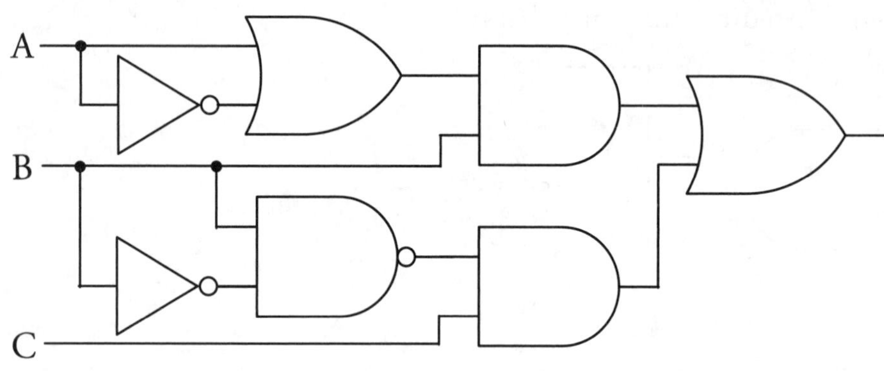

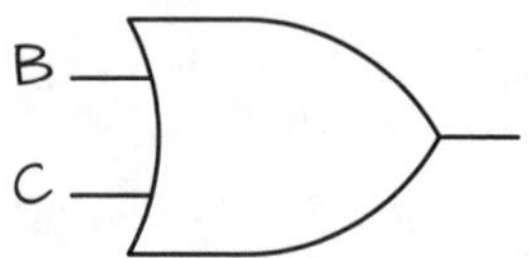

ADDITIONAL EXERCISES FOR LESSON 37

1. Write a proof to show that p • (~p ∨ q) is equivalent to p • q.

1) p • (~p ∨ q)	Given proposition
2) (p • ~p) ∨ (p • q)	Distribution
3) 0 ∨ (p • q)	Self-contradiction
4) (p • q) ∨ 0	Commutation
5) p • q	Algebraic identity

2. Simplify the proposition (A • ~B • C) ∨ (~A • ~B • C).

~B • C

3. Simplify the circuit shown into an equivalent circuit using only one gate.

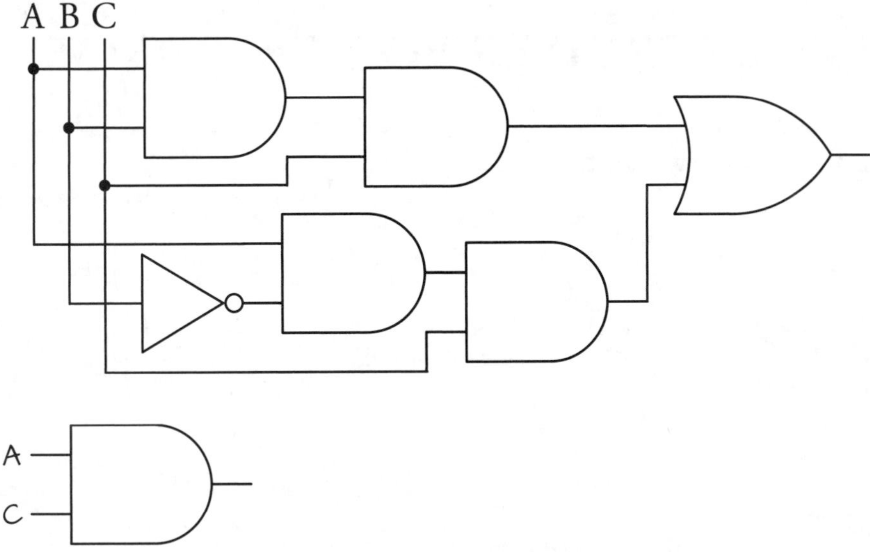

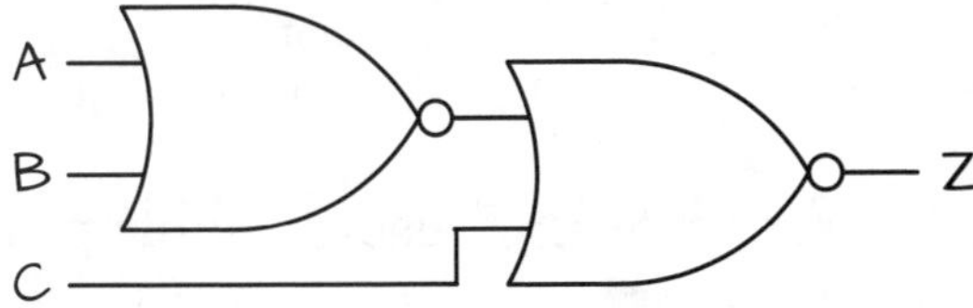

4. Simplify the circuit in Exercise 34, problem 4 so that it uses only two gates.

A
B
C
Z

5. Determine a simplified proposition for the given truth table, then design a circuit for it that uses only four gates.

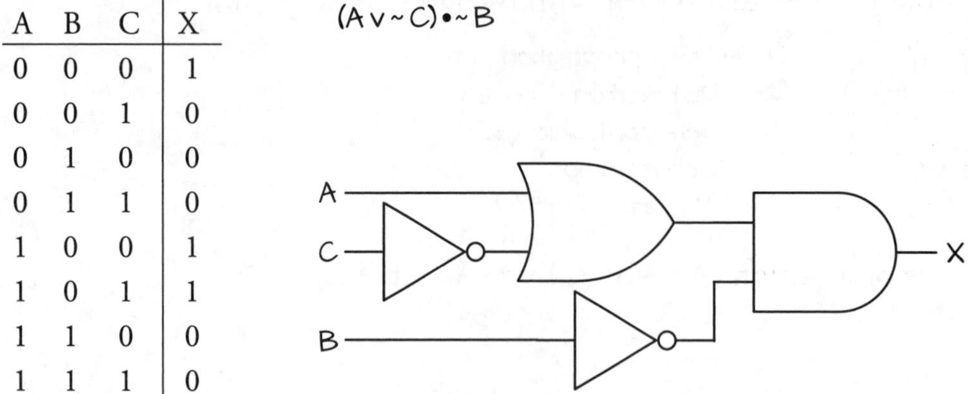

A	B	C	X
0	0	0	1
0	0	1	0
0	1	0	0
0	1	1	0
1	0	0	1
1	0	1	1
1	1	0	0
1	1	1	0

ADDITIONAL EXERCISES FOR LESSON 38

1. Reduce this circuit to only two gates.

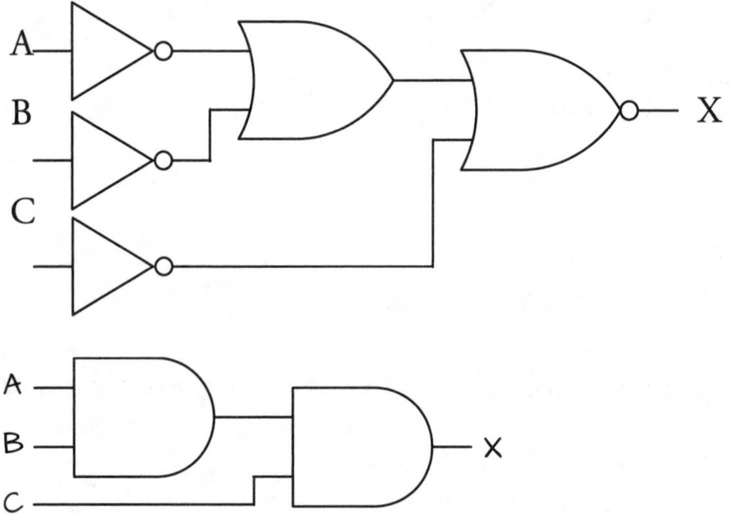

2. Re-do problem 5 of the Additional Exercises for Lesson 37, using bubble pushing to reduce the circuit to only three gates.

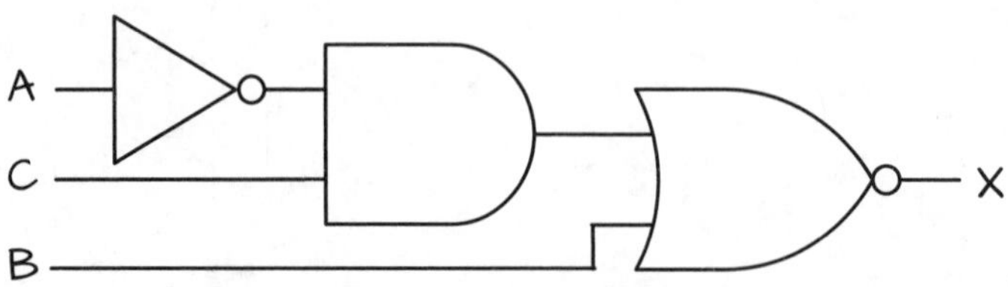

3. Use bubble pushing and other simplification rules to reduce this circuit to only two gates.

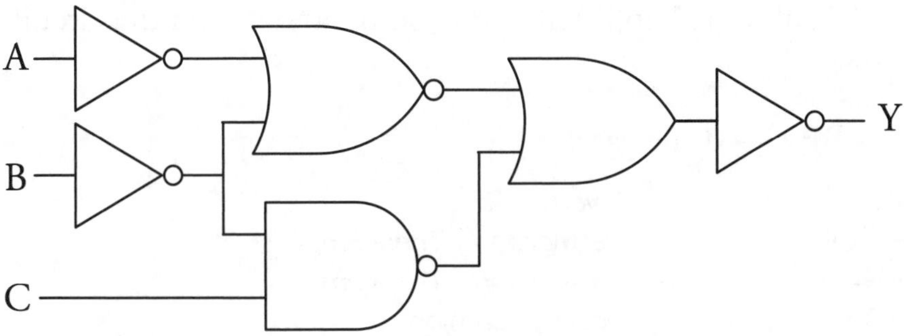

Bubble-push to this point:

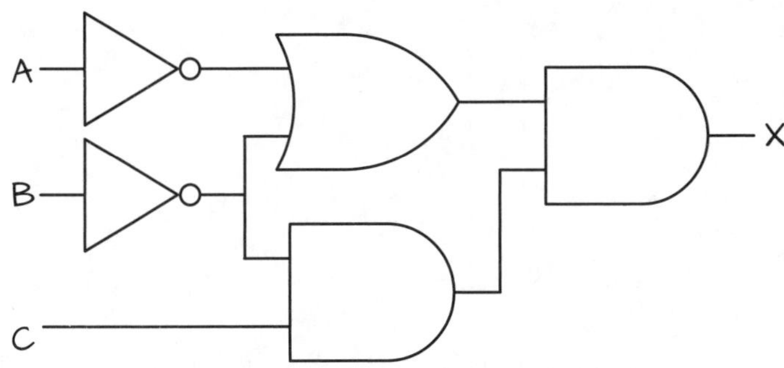

Then these steps could be followed:

1) (~ A v ~B) • (~ B • C)	Given
2) [(~ A v ~ B) • ~ B] • C	Association
3) [(~ A v ~ B) • (~ B v 0)] • C	Algebraic identity
4). [(~ B v ~ A) • (~ B v 0)] • C	Commutation
5) [~ B v (~ A • 0)] • C	Distribution
6) (~ B v 0) • C	Algebraic identity
7) ~ B • C	Algebraic identity

So the final circuit is

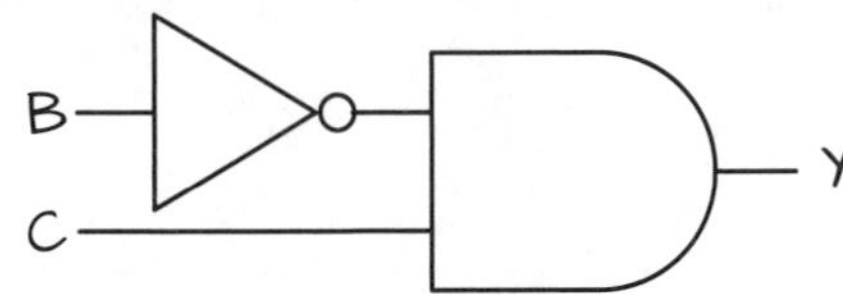

ADDITIONAL EXERCISES FOR LESSON 39

Problems 1 and 2: Use the rules to simplify the proposition and design the circuit with the given number of gates.

1. ~[(A ∨ ~B) • (~A ∨ B)] — One gate.

1) ~[(A ∨ ~B) • (~A ∨ B)]	Given
2) ~(A ∨ ~B) ∨ ~(~A ∨ B)	De Morgan's Theorem
3) (~A • ~~B) ∨ (~~A • ~B)	De Morgan's Theorem
4) (~A • B) ∨ (A • ~B)	Double negation
5) A ⊕ B	Definition of XOR

So the final circuit is

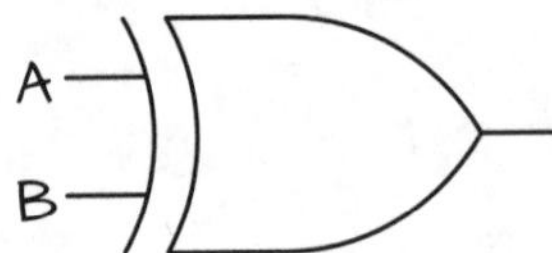

2. (A • B • C) ∨ (~A • B • ~C) — Two gates.

1) (A • B • C) ∨ (~A • B • ~C)	Given
2) (B • A • C) ∨ (B • ~A • ~C)	Commutation
3) B • [(A • C) ∨ (~A • ~C)]	Distribution
4) B • (A ≡ C)	Definition of XNOR

So the final circuit is

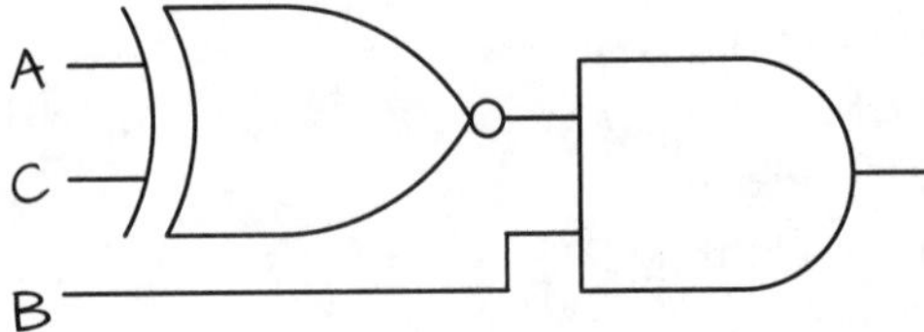

3. Reduce the circuit below to only two gates.

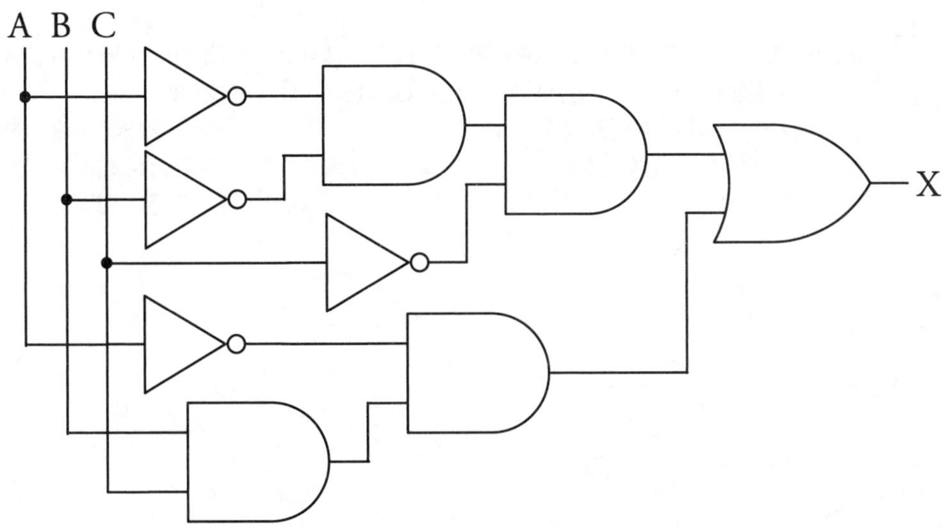

1) (~A•~B•~C) v (~A•B•C) Proposition from the given circuit
2) ~A•[(~B•~C) v (B•C)] Distribution
3) ~A•(B≡C) Definition of XNOR
4) ~A•~(B⊕C) Definition of XNOR
5) ~[A v (B⊕C)] De Morgan's Theorem

So the final circuit is

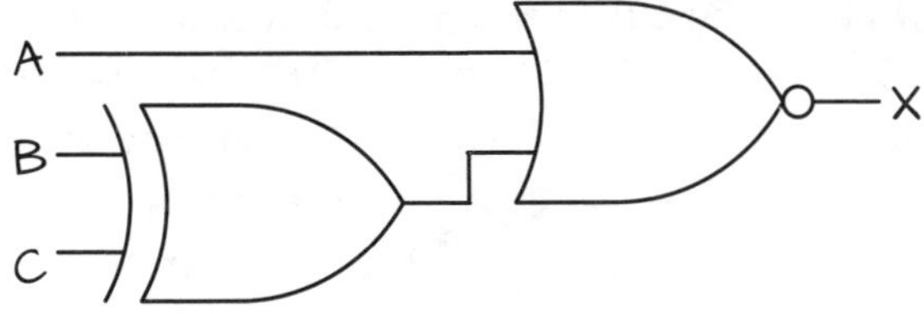

Problems 4 and 5: Design the simplest circuit to produce the given output.

4.

A	B	C	Y
0	0	0	0
0	0	1	1
0	1	0	1
0	1	1	0
1	0	0	1
1	0	1	0
1	1	0	0
1	1	1	1

1) (~A•~B•C)v(~A•B•~C)v(A•~B•~C)v(A•B•C)	Proposition from table
2) {~A•[(~B•C)v(B•~C)]}v{A•[(~B•~C)v(B•C)]}	Distribution
3) [~A•(B⊕C)]v[A•(B≡C)]	Def. XOR and XNOR
4) [~A•~(B≡C)]v[A•(B≡C)]	Def. of XNOR
5) A≡(B≡C)	Def. of XNOR

So the final circuit is

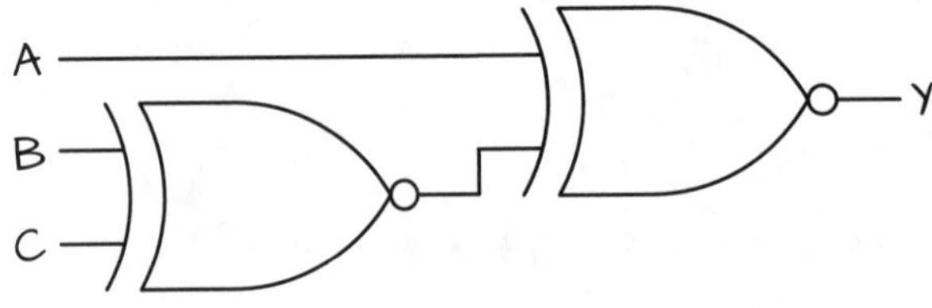

5.

A	B	C	Z
0	0	0	0
0	0	1	1
0	1	0	1
0	1	1	0
1	0	0	0
1	0	1	1
1	1	0	1
1	1	1	0

1) (~A•~B•C)v(~A•B•~C)v(A•~B•C)v(A•B•~C)	Proposition from table
2) {~A•[(~B•C)v(B•~C)]}v{A•[(~B•C)v(B•~C)]}	Distribution
3) [~A•(B⊕C)]v[A•(B⊕C)]	Definition of XOR
4) [(B⊕C)•~A]v[(B⊕C)•A]	Commutation
5) (B⊕C)•(~AvA)	Distribution
6) (B⊕C)•1	Tautology
7) B⊕C	Algebraic identity

So the final circuit is:

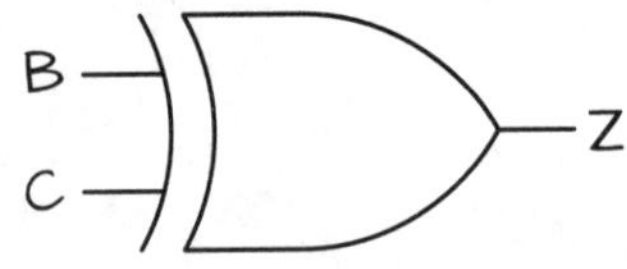

ADDITIONAL EXERCISES FOR LESSON 40

1. Create a random output truth table for three inputs (you could do this by flipping a coin eight times, counting "heads" as ones and "tails" as zeroes), and then use K-mapping to design the simplest digital logic circuit to produce that output.

(Answers will vary, but should follow this general format.)

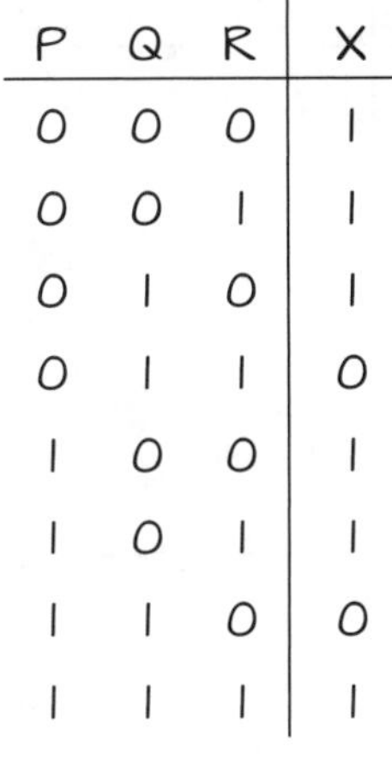

P	Q	R	X
0	0	0	1
0	0	1	1
0	1	0	1
0	1	1	0
1	0	0	1
1	0	1	1
1	1	0	0
1	1	1	1

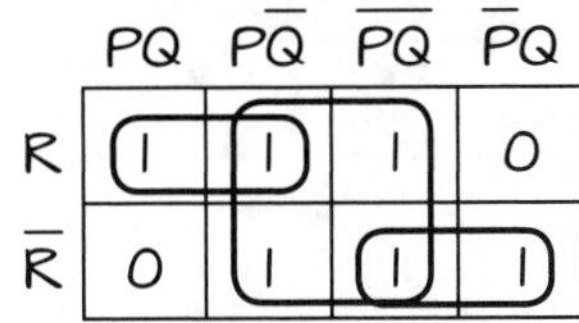

	PQ	$P\overline{Q}$	$\overline{P}\overline{Q}$	$\overline{P}Q$
R	1	1	1	0
$\overline{R}$	0	1	1	1

The proposition is ~Q v (P • R) v (~P • ~R), which simplifies to ~[Q • (P ⊕ R)].

The circuit would be as shown here:

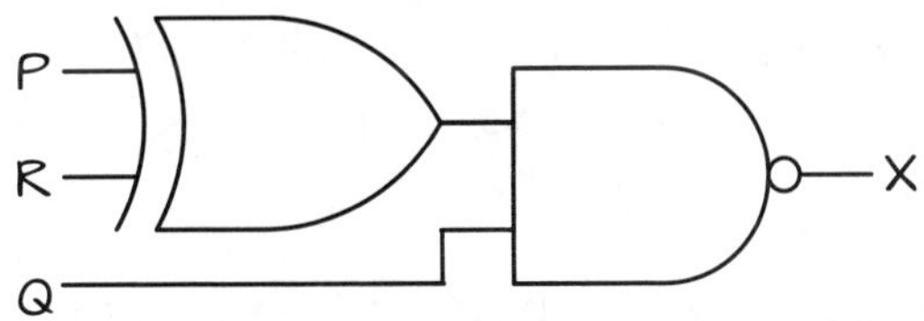

2. In Lesson 34 the compound proposition *(~A • B • C)* ∨ *(A • ~B • C)* ∨ *(A • B • C)* was developed from a truth table. It was said at that time that this is equivalent to the simpler proposition *(A* ∨ *B)* • *C*. Use a K-map to develop this simpler proposition from that truth table (shown again here).

A	B	C	Z
0	0	0	0
0	0	1	0
0	1	0	0
0	1	1	1
1	0	0	0
1	0	1	1
1	1	0	0
1	1	1	1

	AB	$A\overline{B}$	$\overline{A}\overline{B}$	$\overline{A}B$
C	1	1	0	1
$\overline{C}$	0	1	0	0

The proposition is (A • C) v (B • C), which simplifies to (A v B) • C.

3. Design a "full adder" circuit, similar to Exercise 40a, problem #2, but with three inputs, *P*, *Q* and *R*, and two outputs, *S* and *C*.

The truth table and corresponding K-maps would be as follows:

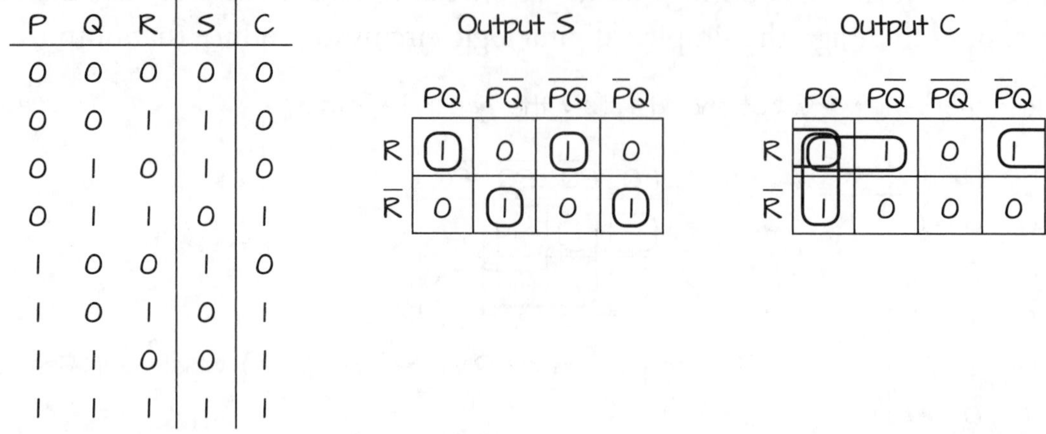

P	Q	R	S	C
0	0	0	0	0
0	0	1	1	0
0	1	0	1	0
0	1	1	0	1
1	0	0	1	0
1	0	1	0	1
1	1	0	0	1
1	1	1	1	1

Output S

	PQ	$P\overline{Q}$	$\overline{P}\overline{Q}$	$\overline{P}Q$
R	1	0	1	0
$\overline{R}$	0	1	0	1

Output C

	PQ	$P\overline{Q}$	$\overline{P}\overline{Q}$	$\overline{P}Q$
R	1	1	0	1
$\overline{R}$	1	0	0	0

The proposition for S would be (P • Q • R) v (P • ~Q • ~R) v (~P • ~Q • R) v (~P • Q • ~R)

This simplifies as follows: {P • [(Q • R) v (~Q • ~R)]} v {~P • [(~Q • R) v (Q • ~R)]}
[P • (Q ≡ R)] v [~P • ~(Q ≡ R)]
P ≡ (Q ≡ R)

The proposition for C would be (P • Q) v (P • R) v (Q • R)

The circuit would be as shown here::

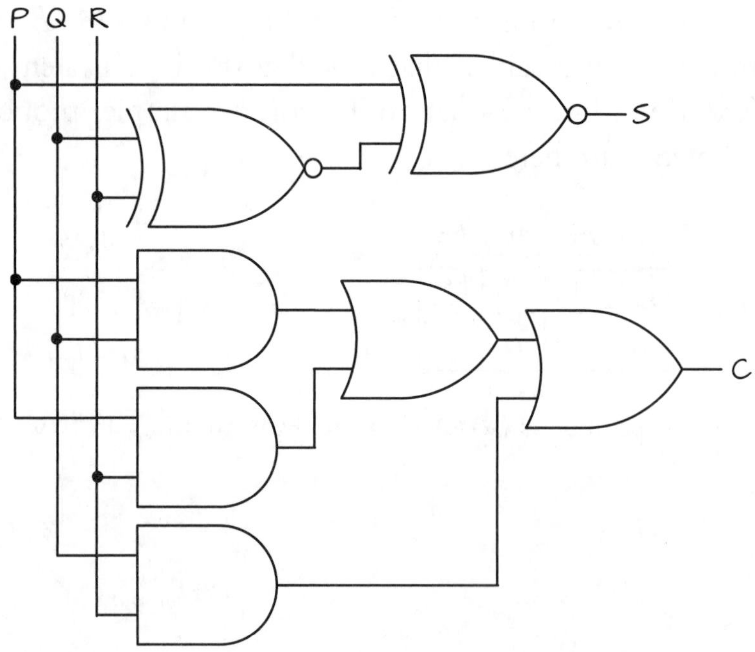

4. Expand Exercise 40b by designing digital logic circuits to display all ten numerals, 0 through 9, on the digital display. You will need to use four input variables, and the K-maps will use "don't cares" (as was already done for the segment *a* in the lesson). Continue on next page if additional space is needed.

The truth table (with don't cares as X):

Dec	P	Q	R	S	A	B	C	D	E	F	G
0	0	0	0	0	1	1	1	1	1	1	0
1	0	0	0	1	0	1	1	0	0	0	0
2	0	0	1	0	1	1	0	1	1	0	1
3	0	0	1	1	1	1	1	1	0	0	1
4	0	1	0	0	0	1	1	0	0	1	1
5	0	1	0	1	1	0	1	1	0	1	1
6	0	1	1	0	1	0	1	1	1	1	1
7	0	1	1	1	1	1	1	0	0	0	0
8	1	0	0	0	1	1	1	1	1	1	1
9	1	0	0	1	1	1	1	1	0	1	1
	1	0	1	0	X	X	X	X	X	X	X
	1	0	1	1	X	X	X	X	X	X	X
	1	1	0	0	X	X	X	X	X	X	X
	1	1	0	1	X	X	X	X	X	X	X
	1	1	1	0	X	X	X	X	X	X	X
	1	1	1	1	X	X	X	X	X	X	X

The K-maps are as follows (the K-map for output A is done in the text):

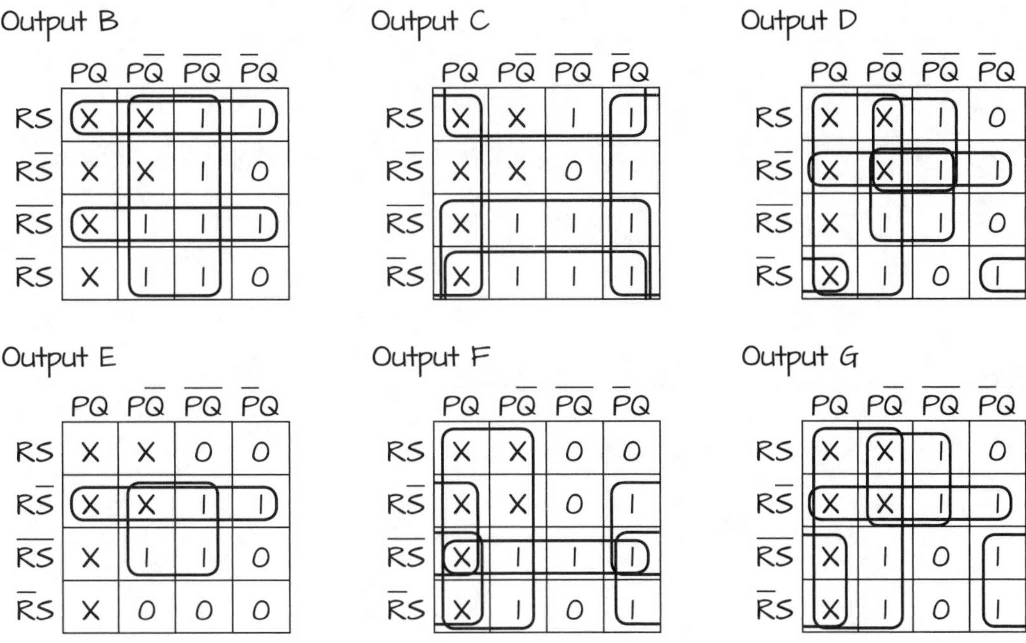

The propositions for these K-maps could be as follows:

B: $\sim Q \vee (R \equiv S)$
C: $(Q \vee S) \vee \sim R$
D: $P \vee \sim(Q \vee S) \vee [R \oplus (Q \bullet S)]$
E: $(\sim Q \vee R) \bullet \sim S$
F: $P \vee \sim(R \vee S) \vee [Q \bullet \sim(R \bullet S)]$
G: $P \vee (R \bullet \sim S) \vee (Q \oplus R)$

The circuits for these propositions could be simplified further using bubble pushing.
We leave it up to the student to draw the final circuit

REVIEW FOR COMPREHENSIVE TEST (LESSONS 1–40)

STUDENT OBJECTIVES

Complete the objectives from Lessons 1–40. Objectives are listed at the beginning of each lesson's teacher's notes.

SPECIAL NOTES

1. If you chose not to cover Unit 5, do not use this review. Instead, see page T-cxlvii.
2. You have two days to review for the Comprehensive Test.

TEACHING INSTRUCTIONS

1. To review for the test, choose problems from the Review Questions and Review Exercises in the student text for students to work through.
2. If you'd like, give students "Comprehensive Test: Form A" from the *Intermediate Logic Test and Quiz Packet* as a practice exam. Go over the answers together.

ASSIGNMENT

Have students study for Comprehensive Test.

COMPREHENSIVE TEST (LESSONS 1–40)

STUDENT OBJECTIVE

Complete Comprehensive Test.

TEACHING INSTRUCTION

1. Give students Comprehensive Test: Form B from the *Intermediate Logic Test and Quiz Packet.* Allow one hour to complete it.
2. Grade tests. Have them ready to hand back to students within a week.

INTERMEDIATE LOGIC | Comprehensive Exam, Form A

Units 1–4 (Problems 1–17, 88 points) OR *Units 1–5 (Problems 1–19, 100 points)*

Name ______________________________

1. What is a *proposition*? (1) A statement.

2. What is a *tautology*? (2) A proposition that is true due to its logical structure, such as p ∨ ~ p.

3. Give an example of a compound proposition that is *not* truth functional. (2)
   Hobbes is a tiger and Hobbes is not a tiger. (Any tautology, self-contradiction, or self-report.)

4. What does it mean that an argument is *valid*? (2) The premises imply the conclusion; if the premises are true the conclusion must also be true.

5. What does it mean that a set of propositions is *consistent*? (2) The propositions can all be true at the same time; there is no logical conflict between them.

6. Complete the truth tables for the fundamental logical operators. (5)

p	q	~ p	p • q	p ∨ q	p ⊃ q	p ≡ q
T	T	F	T	T	T	T
T	F	F	F	T	F	F
F	T	T	F	T	T	F
F	F	T	F	F	T	T

7. Use either the longer or shorter truth-table method to determine if the propositions below are logically equivalent (7):

~ p ∨ (q • r)	≡	(p ⊃ q) • (p ⊃ r)
F T T T T T	T	T T T
F T F T F F	T	T F F
F T F F F T	T	F F T
F T F F F F	T	F F F
T F T T T T	T	T T T
T F T T F F	T	T T T
T F T F F T	T	T T T
T F T F F F	T	T T T

Are they equivalent? **(YES)** NO

(Note: A shorter truth table requires three rows, each of which will show a contradiction).

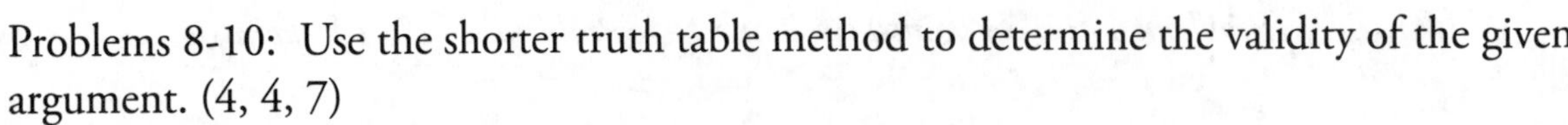

Problems 8-10: Use the shorter truth table method to determine the validity of the given argument. (4, 4, 7)

8. $\sim p \supset (q \vee r) \quad p \quad \therefore\ q \supset \sim r$

F T T T T T   T   T F F T

Is it valid? YES **(NO)**

9. $p \bullet \sim r \quad q \vee r \quad \therefore\ \sim(p \supset \sim q)$

T T T F   T T F   F T [T/F] F T

Is it valid? **(YES)** NO

10. If the government spies on suspected terrorists, then the rights of some innocent people will be violated. If the government does not spy on suspected terrorists, then innocent people's lives will be endangered. The government either spies on suspected terrorists or not. Thus, innocent people will either have their rights violated or their lives endangered. (7)

$S \supset R \quad \sim S \supset L \quad S \vee \sim S \quad \therefore\ R \vee L$

T [T/F] F   F T T F   T   F F F

Is it valid? **(YES)** NO

11. The argument in problem 10 is a dilemma. List the three methods of answering a dilemma, and use one of those methods to answer the dilemma. Circle the method you use. (6)

1) Go between the horns 2) Grasp the horns 3) Rebut the horns

Go between the horns: They could spy on only the most suspicious terrorists.

Grasp the horns: Innocent people's lives may not be endangered if they are protected another way.

Rebut the horns: If the government spies on suspected terrorists, then innocent lives will be protected. If the government does not spy on suspected terrorists, then innocent people's rights will not be violated, etc.

12. Use the shorter truth-table method to determine if the propositions below are consistent. (4)

$(p \vee q) \bullet \sim(p \vee r) \quad (q \supset p) \vee r$

F T T T T F F F   T F F [T/F] F

Are they consistent? YES **(NO)**

Problems 13-16: Write a formal proof of validity for the given argument. (4, 6, 10, 10)

13.

1.	$A \vee B$	
2.	$B \supset C$	
3.	$\sim A \quad / \therefore C$	
4.	B	1, 3 D.S.
5.	C	2, 4 M.P.

14.

1.	$(D \bullet E) \supset F$	
2.	$\sim(\sim E \vee F) \quad / \therefore \sim D$	
3.	$D \supset (E \supset F)$	1 Exp.
4.	$\sim(E \supset F)$	2 Impl.
5.	$\sim D$	3, 4 M.T.

15.

1.	$G \supset H$	
2.	$J \supset \sim H \quad / \therefore \sim(G \bullet J)$	
3.	$\sim\sim H \supset \sim J$	2 Trans.
4.	$H \supset \sim J$	3 D.N.
5.	$G \supset \sim J$	1, 4 H.S.
6.	$\sim G \vee \sim J$	5 Impl.
7.	$\sim(G \bullet J)$	6 De M.

16.

1.	$K \bullet L$	
2.	$\sim K \vee M \quad / \therefore K \bullet (L \bullet M)$	
3.	K	1 Simp.
4.	$\sim\sim K$	3 D.N.
5.	M	2, 4 D.S.
6.	$(K \bullet L) \bullet M$	1, 5 Conj.
7.	$K \bullet (L \bullet M)$	6 Assoc.

17. Demonstrate the validity of the argument in problem 14 using a truth tree. Include line numbers and justifications. Remember to justify the premises as P and the negated conclusion as NC. (12)

1.	$(D \bullet E) \supset F$ ✓		P
2.	$\sim(\sim E \vee F)$ ✓		P
3.	$\sim\sim D$ ✓		NC
4.	D		3 $\sim\sim$D
5.	$\sim\sim E$ ✓		2 $\sim\vee$D
6.	$\sim F$		2 $\sim\vee$D
7.	E		5 $\sim\sim$D
	/	\	
8.	$\sim(D \bullet E)$ ✓	F	1 $\supset$D
	/ \	6x8	
9.	$\sim D$ $\sim E$		8 $\sim\bullet$D
	4x9 7x9		

Unit Five Questions: Skip if you only covered units 1–4.

Problems 18-19: Consider the given truth table.

p	q	r	x
0	0	0	1
0	0	1	1
0	1	0	1
0	1	1	1
1	0	0	1
1	0	1	0
1	1	0	0
1	1	1	1

18. Construct a K-map to determine the proposition to produce the output x. (9)

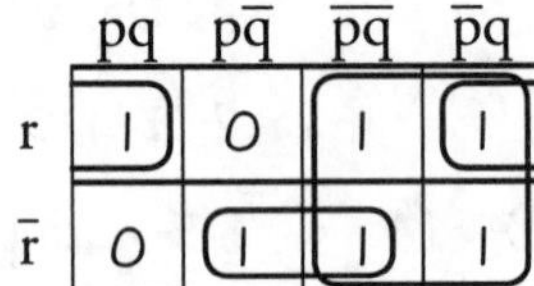

Proposition? ~[P • (Q ⊕ R)]

19. Draw the circuit to produce the output x using a minimum number of gates. (3)

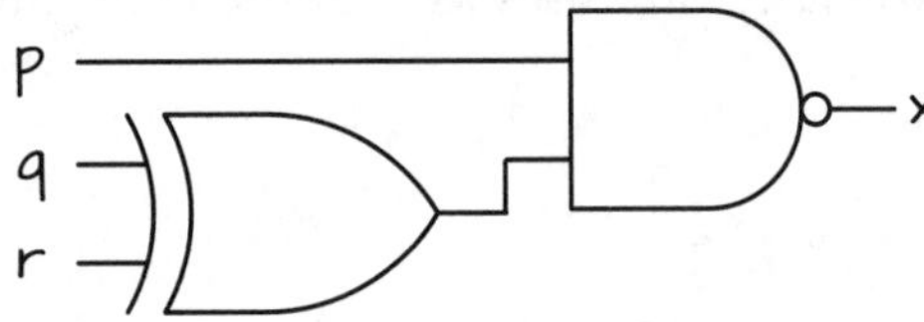

INTERMEDIATE LOGIC | Comprehensive Exam, Form B

Units 1–4 (Problems 1–17, 94 points) OR *Units 1–5 (Problems 1–20, 106 points)*

Name ____________________

Problems 1-4: Definitions and short answers.

1. What is a *proposition*? (1) A statement.

2. What does it mean that a proposition is *truth-functional*? (2) The truth value of the proposition depends on the truth value of its component parts.

3. What is a *logical operator*? (2) A word or phrase that modifies or combines simple propositions, making them compound.

4. How does a shorter truth table show an argument to be invalid? (3) The argument is assumed to be invalid, with true premises and a false conclusion. If this is possible without contradiction, the argument is invalid.

Problems 5-8: Consider the compound propositions ~ (p • q) and ~ p • ~ q.

5. Use a longer truth table to show that the two propositions are NOT equivalent. (5)

~ (p • q)	~ p • ~ q
F	F
T	F
T	F
T	T

6. Write a simple proposition in normal English for each variable p and q such that the compound proposition ~ (p • q) is *true*, and the compound proposition ~ p • ~ q is *false*. (2)

p The prince is a chess piece. q The queen is a chess piece.

(Answers may vary)

7. Using your simple propositions from problem 6, translate each compound proposition. (4)

~ (p • q) The prince and the queen are not both chess pieces.

~ p • ~ q Both the prince and the queen are not chess pieces. (Answers may vary)

8. Use a shorter truth table to determine if the two propositions are consistent. (3)

$\sim(p \bullet q)$	$\sim p \bullet \sim q$
T FFF	T TT

Are they consistent? (YES) NO

Problems 9-10: Use the shorter truth table method to determine the validity of the given argument. (4, 6)

9.

$p \equiv (q \bullet r)$	$s \supset (q \bullet \sim r)$	$\therefore\ s \supset \sim p$
T[T] TFF [F]	TT TTT	TFF

Is it valid? (YES) NO

10.

$p \vee q$	$\sim(p \bullet q)$	$\therefore\ p \equiv \sim q$
TTT	T T[F]T [T]	TFF
F[T]F [F]	T FFF	FFT

Is it valid? (YES) NO

Problems 11-12: Translate the argument into symbolic form using the given constants, then use a shorter truth table to determine the validity.

11. A sentence is a categorical statement if and only if it predicates something of a subject. If it predicates something of a subject then it must have a truth value. Therefore, a sentence is a categorical statement if and only if it has a truth value. (**C**, **P**, **T**) (6)

$C \equiv P$	$P \supset T$	$\therefore\ C \equiv T$
FTF	FTT	FFT

Is it valid? YES (NO)

12. If I join the mock trial team then I won't have time to exercise. But if I join the basketball team then I won't develop my rhetorical skills. I join the mock trial team or the basketball team. Therefore, I either won't have time to exercise or I won't develop my rhetorical skills. (**M**, **E**, **B**, **R**) (7)

$M \supset \sim E$	$B \supset \sim R$	$M \vee B$	$\therefore\ \sim E \vee \sim R$
FTF	FTF	F[T]F [F]	F FF

Is it valid? (YES) NO

13. Refute the dilemma in problem 12 by rebutting the horns with a counter-dilemma. (3)

If I join the Mock Trial team, I will develop my rhetorical skills, and if I join the basketball team then I will get lots of exercise. I will either join the Mock Trial team or the basketball team. Thus, I will either develop my rhetoric skills, or I will get exercise.

Problems 14-15: Write a formal proof of validity for the given argument. (8 each)

14.

1.	$\sim(A \bullet B)$	
2.	B / $\therefore \sim A$	
3.	$\sim A \vee \sim B$	1 De M.
4.	$\sim B \vee \sim A$	3 Com.
5.	$\sim\sim B$	2 D.N.
6.	$\sim A$	4, 5 D.S.

15.

1.	$C \equiv D$	
2.	$C \bullet E$ / $\therefore D$	
3.	$(C \supset D) \bullet (D \supset C)$	1 Equiv.
4.	$C \supset D$	3 Simp.
5.	C	2 Simp.
6.	D	4, 5 M.P

Problems 16-17: Write a formal proof of validity for the given argument. Use conditional proof on #16, and *reductio ad absurdum* on #17. (9 each)

16.

1.	$F \supset G$	
2.	$\sim F \supset H$ / $\therefore \sim H \supset G$	
3.	$\sim H$	C.P.A.
4.	$\sim\sim F$	2, 3 M.T.
5.	F	4 D.N.
6.	G	1, 5 M.P.
7.	$\sim H \supset G$	3-6 C.P.

17.

1.	$J \supset (J \supset K)$	
2.	$\sim K$ / $\therefore \sim J$	
3.	J	R.A.A.
4.	$J \supset K$	1, 3 M.P.
5.	K	4, 3 M.P.
6.	$K \bullet \sim K$	5, 2 Conj.
7.	$\sim J$	3-6 R.A.

18. Determine the consistency of the set of propositions by truth tree. Number and justify each step. Write CONSISTENT or INCONSISTENT. Recover the truth values if the set is consistent. (12)

$$\{ P \equiv (Q \vee R), \sim (Q \bullet R), \sim (Q \supset \sim P) \}$$

1.	$P \equiv (Q \vee R)$ ✓	SM
2.	$\sim (Q \bullet R)$ ✓	SM
3.	$\sim (Q \supset \sim P)$ ✓	SM
4.	Q	$3 \sim \supset D$
5.	$\sim\sim P$ ✓	$3 \sim \supset D$
6.	P	$5 \sim\sim D$
7.	$\sim Q$ / $\sim R$	$2 \sim \bullet D$
	4x7 (under $\sim Q$)	
8.	P / $\sim P$ (under $\sim R$)	$1 \equiv D$
9.	$Q \vee R$ ✓ / $\sim (Q \vee R)$	$1 \equiv D$
	6x8 (under $\sim P$)	
10.	Q / R (under $Q \vee R$)	$9 \vee D$
	O (under Q); 7x10 (under R)	

CONSISTENT

P	Q	R
T	T	F

Unit Five Questions: Skip if you only covered units 1–4.

Problems 19-20: Consider the given truth table.

p	q	r	x
0	0	0	1
0	0	1	1
0	1	0	1
0	1	1	0
1	0	0	1
1	0	1	1
1	1	0	0
1	1	1	0

19. Construct a K-map to determine the proposition to produce the output x. (9)

	pq	$p\bar{q}$	$\bar{p}\bar{q}$	$\bar{p}q$
r	0	1	1	0
$\bar{r}$	0	1	1	1

Proposition? $\sim [q \bullet (p \vee r)]$

20. Draw the circuit using a minimum number of gates. (3)

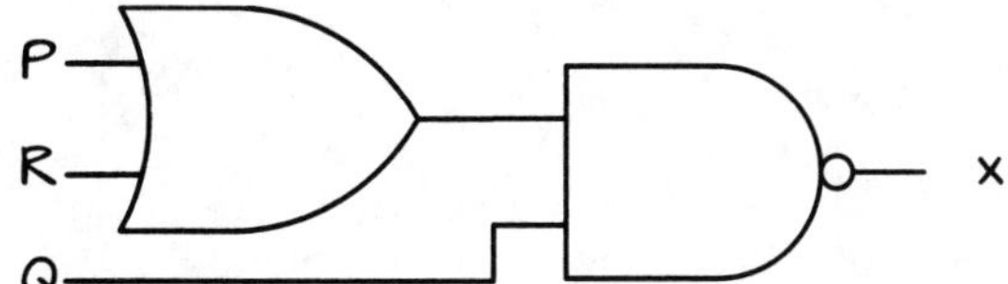

APPENDIX A

DEFINING TRUTH TABLES FOR THE FIVE LOGICAL OPERATORS

Negation

p	~p
T	F
F	T

Conjunction

p	q	p • q
T	T	T
T	F	F
F	T	F
F	F	F

Disjunction

p	q	p ∨ q
T	T	T
T	F	T
F	T	T
F	F	F

Conditional

p	q	p ⊃ q
T	T	T
T	F	F
F	T	T
F	F	T

Biconditional

p	q	p ≡ q
T	T	T
T	F	F
F	T	F
F	F	T

APPENDIX B

RULES OF INFERENCE AND REPLACEMENT

1. Modus Ponens (M.P.)
   $p \supset q$
   p
   $\therefore q$

2. Modus Tollens (M.T.)
   $p \supset q$
   $\sim q$
   $\therefore \sim p$

3. Hypothetical Syllogism (H.S.)
   $p \supset q$
   $q \supset r$
   $\therefore p \supset r$

4. Disjunctive Syllogism (D.S.)
   $p \vee q$
   $\sim p$
   $\therefore q$

5. Conjunction (Conj.)
   p
   q
   $\therefore p \bullet q$

6. Constructive Dilemma (C.D.)
   $(p \supset q) \bullet (r \supset s)$
   $p \vee r$
   $\therefore q \vee s$

7. Simplification (Simp.)
   $p \bullet q$
   $\therefore p$

8. Absorption (Abs.)
   $p \supset q$
   $\therefore p \supset (p \bullet q)$

9. Addition (Add.)
   p
   $\therefore p \vee q$

The following sets of logically equivalent expressions can replace each other wherever they occur:

10. De Morgan's Theorems (De M.)	$\sim(p \bullet q) \equiv (\sim p \vee \sim q)$ $\sim(p \vee q) \equiv (\sim p \bullet \sim q)$
11. Commutation (Com.)	$(p \vee q) \equiv (q \vee p)$ $(p \bullet q) \equiv (q \bullet p)$
12. Association (Assoc.)	$[p \vee (q \vee r)] \equiv [(p \vee q) \vee r]$ $[p \bullet (q \bullet r)] \equiv [(p \bullet q) \bullet r]$
13. Distribution (Dist.)	$[p \bullet (q \vee r)] \equiv [(p \bullet q) \vee (p \bullet r)]$ $[p \vee (q \bullet r)] \equiv [(p \vee q) \bullet (p \vee r)]$
14. Double Negation (D.N.)	$p \equiv \sim\sim p$
15. Transposition (Trans.)	$(p \supset q) \equiv (\sim q \supset \sim p)$
16. Material Implication (Impl.)	$(p \supset q) \equiv (\sim p \vee q)$
17. Material Equivalence (Equiv.)	$(p \equiv q) \equiv [(p \supset q) \bullet (q \supset p)]$ $(p \equiv q) \equiv [(p \bullet q) \vee (\sim p \bullet \sim q)]$
18. Exportation (Exp.)	$[(p \bullet q) \supset r] \equiv [p \supset (q \supset r)]$
19. Tautology (Taut.)	$p \equiv (p \vee p)$ $p \equiv (p \bullet p)$

APPENDIX C

TRUTH TREE DECOMPOSITION RULES

Double negation

~~p ✓

p

Conjunction

p • q ✓

p

q

Disjunction

p ∨ q ✓

/\

p q

Conditional

p ⊃ q ✓

/\

~p q

Negated Conjunction

~(p • q) ✓

/\

~p ~q

Negated Disjunction

~(p ∨ q) ✓

~p

~q

Negated Conditional

~(p ⊃ q) ✓

p

~q

Biconditional

p ≡ q ✓

/ \

p ~p

q ~q

Negated Biconditional

~(p ≡ q) ✓

/ \

p ~p

~q q

APPENDIX D

DIGITAL LOGIC SIMPLIFICATION RULES

Tautology and Self-contradiction

$p \vee \sim p = 1$	$p \bullet \sim p = 0$

Algebraic Identities

$p \vee 1 = 1$	$p \vee 0 = p$
$p \bullet 1 = p$	$p \bullet 0 = 0$

Rules of Replacement

Double Negation	$\sim\sim p \equiv p$
Distribution	$(p \vee q) \bullet (p \vee r) \equiv p \vee (q \bullet r)$
	$(p \bullet q) \vee (p \bullet r) \equiv p \bullet (q \vee r)$
Commutation	$p \bullet q \equiv q \bullet p$
	$p \vee q \equiv q \vee p$
De Morgan's Theorem	$\sim p \bullet \sim q \equiv \sim(p \vee q)$
	$\sim p \vee \sim q \equiv \sim(p \bullet q)$

Exclusive OR

$p \oplus q$ is equivalent to	$(p \vee q) \bullet \sim (p \bullet q)$
	$(\sim p \bullet q) \vee (p \bullet \sim q)$

Exclusive NOR

$p \equiv q$ is equivalent to	$\sim(p \oplus q)$
	$(p \bullet q) \vee \sim (p \vee q)$
	$(p \vee \sim q) \bullet (\sim p \vee q)$